Merged With
ARLIS
ANCHORAGE, ALASKA
Est. 1997

D1096261

Harper's Geoscience Series

Carey Croneis, Editor

STRUCTURAL METHODS

AND A SERIES OF PROBLEMS

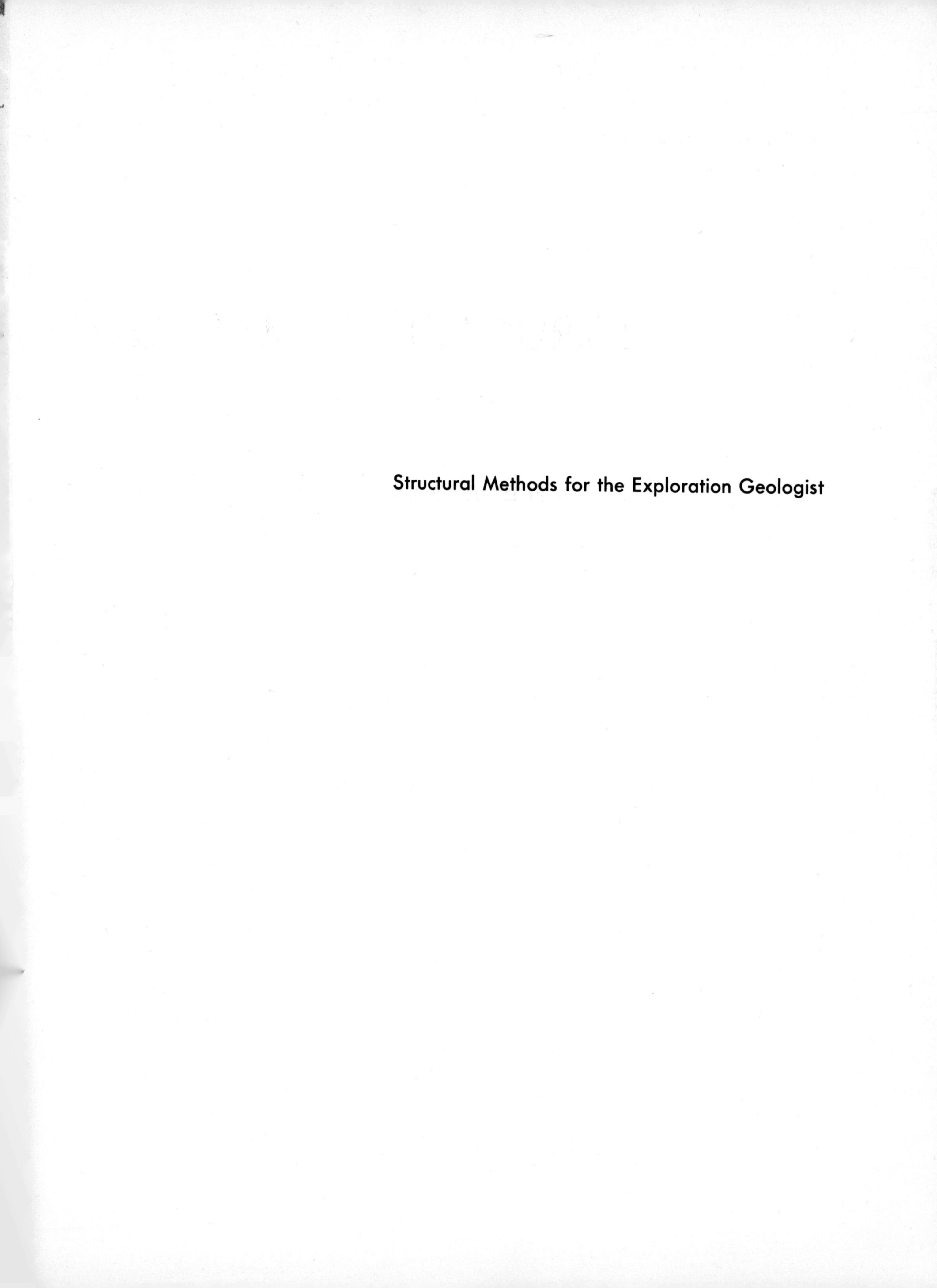

Structural Methods for the Exploration Geologist

FOR THE EXPLORATION GEOLOGIST

FOR STRUCTURAL GEOLOGY STUDENTS

PETER C. BADGLEY
Colorado School of Mines

HARPER & BROTHERS, PUBLISHERS, NEW YORK

STRUCTURAL PROBLEMS FOR THE EXPLORATION GEOLOGIST

Printed in the United States of America

Library of Congress catalog card number: 59–11039

Contents

List of Problems

A brief description of the problem, indicating its degree of complexity and estimated solution time, is given for the benefit of instructors and students. The solution time is only an estimate and will vary considerably depending upon the experience of the student. Problems described as elementary or intermediate should be handled by well-prepared, junior-level undergraduate students without difficulty. Those classed as intermediate require more thought and ingenuity. Problems classed as advanced are for seniors, graduate students, or professional geologists.

Editor's Introduction

Peter Badgley's *Structural Methods for the Exploration Geologist* is a purposefully practical book as the title succinctly implies. It is not, however, lacking in academic precision or, indeed, in theoretical overtones. Perhaps it will be regarded by some as a field and office manual on geological structures rather than as an orthodox textbook in structural geology. Nevertheless, one may safely predict that *Structural Methods* will be widely and successfully used in the classrooms precisely because it is a text which not only reviews the fundamental principles of structural geology, but relates them realistically to a great variety of actual field situations.

The book includes a clear-cut explanation of practically every method in structural geology now in vogue. Moreover, the writer attempts to show that there may be a rather wide range of interpretation possible for each kind of structural situation ordinarily encountered by the exploration geologist. The author then demonstrates the importance of taking especial care in the selection of the one most suitable method of structural analysis and interpretation in the light of the particular kind of local structural situation being studied. Higher mathematics are kept at a minimum, but there are numerous diagrams and simple mathematical procedures relating to descriptive geometry. These have been emphasized in order that the reader may improve his three-dimensional thinking and sharpen his spatial perceptions.

Structural Methods is a book built around the solution of 41 problems. These range from simple exercises, such as the determination of strike and dip from three points on the same stratum, to complex problems such as "The Tectonic Analysis of the Yellowknife District of the Northwest Territories, Canada." Other problems deal with such practical geological procedures as the isometric projection of the Flin Flon ore body, a study of the structural fabric of the Flin Flon region, and a determination of the relation between folding and jointing by statistical analysis. Still other exercises involve structural interpretations of the Laurentian Shield and structural contouring from subsurface information. Important oil fields, as well as significant ore bodies, are brought directly to the student's attention by incorporating their actual structural features into the various directed studies. For example, Problem 22 has to do with the use of isochore and structure contour maps in the delineation of the Golden Spike biohermal reef mass, and Problem 18 is concerned with the structure of the famous Leduc oil field and the Stettler reefs.

Dr. Badgley has brought to the preparation of *Structural Methods* an unusually rich and varied background. He was graduated from McGill University, which awarded him First

Class Honors in Geology and the Sir William Logan Gold Medal. He received his A.M. and Ph.D. degrees from Princeton where his major subject was Economic Geology.

After serving some time as a pilot in the Royal Canadian Air Force, Peter Badgley began, in 1945, the first of a long series of detailed geological and geophysical field investigations which have taken him from the Yukon to the Middle East. In his work he has been associated with the Geological Survey of Canada, with several of the larger corporations dealing with metal mining and smelting, and with a number of major oil companies. He has interspersed his field work with research and teaching assignments, and presently is Associate Professor of Structural Geology at the Colorado School of Mines.

It is perhaps inevitable that Dr. Badgley presents his courses in a fashion which draws heavily on structural actualities as he has seen them and has interpreted them in the field. Mine development and drilling programs have been based on his interpretations, and thus Dr. Badgley has had an understandable urge to be correct rather than theoretical. Rewarding theory, however, commonly stems from successful practice—and students will gain some appreciation of both from *Structural Methods.*

The Rice Institute
July, 1959

CAREY CRONEIS

Preface

This book is designed to give a comprehensive coverage of structural geology methods and to demonstrate their application in exploration. The work was initially compiled to meet the laboratory requirements of undergraduate and graduate structural courses at the Colorado School of Mines. It was later expanded to be valuable for professional geologists also.

Many individual aspects of this book have been treated well by other authors, but there is nothing currently available which brings the whole subject into one volume. The bibliographies have been made extensive to permit deeper investigation by those interested. These references will also serve to give credit to those authors and publications which may not have been acknowledged specifically in the text.

The book began as a group of structural problems drawn largely from the writer's own exploration experience. The author believes that actual field problems stimulate greater interest than abstract ones. Slight modifications have been made in many cases to adjust the actual field conditions for use in the classroom.

Each chapter begins with a review of principles, illustrated by case histories. A group of problems follows. Directions are kept to a minimum within the problems to stimulate ingenuity and thought. Some of the problems may be solved by several methods, and the student may select that method which seems most suitable to him. This demands a familiarity with most of the methods even though only a portion of the problems is selected during any one-semester course. The range of problems is flexible enough for use by geologists, geophysicists, and mining and petroleum engineers. Each chapter is more or less independent; the student need not start with the first chapter.

Several points are stressed throughout the book:

1. Simplicity of presentation. The student does not read a course to refresh his knowledge of mathematical principles, as most of the drawings have been redrafted in simplified form. It would have been desirable to have some of the problem maps larger but space made this impossible.
2. Regional structural thinking to emphasize the importance of tectonic framework.
3. Ingenuity, judgment, and imaginative thinking.
4. An organized approach in exploration.
5. A sense of economic values.

The final chapter on tectonic analysis shows one way to investigate entire exploration provinces. This approach would be modified in petroleum exploration by also using isopach and lithofacies maps in combination with the methods described in Chapter 9.

In addition to those acknowledgments listed elsewhere, the writer wishes to thank Dr. L. W. LeRoy of the Colorado School of Mines, who read many parts of the original manuscript, and Dr. Carey Croneis of Rice Institute, who read the final manuscript in his capacity as editor of Harper's Geoscience Series. Dr. Robert Carpenter kindly read Chapter 6, and Dr. M. A. Klugman read Chapter 9. All presented valuable suggestions. The facilities of the Colorado School of Mines were much appreciated also. Gary Melickian, Phillip Howell, and James Trimble are almost entirely responsible for the drafting. Greta Melickian typed the manuscript.

The following organizations and authors have given me permission to reproduce portions of their publications, and their kindness is gratefully acknowledged.

The American Association of Petroleum Geologists
The American Institute of Mining, Metallurgical, and Petroleum Engineers
Jack Ammann Photogrammetric Engineers, Inc.
The Australian Institute of Mining and Metallurgy
California State Division of Mines
Cambridge University Press
The Canadian Institute of Mining and Metallurgy
Chemical Engineering and Mining Review
Colorado School of Mines
Commission Geologique (Finland)
Economic Geology
The Geologists Association
The Geological Society of America
The Geological Association of Canada
The Geological Survey of Canada
The Society of Exploration Geophysicists
McGraw-Hill Book Company, Inc.
Oliver & Boyd, Ltd.
Oxford University Press
Professor R. D. Parks, Massachusetts Institute of Technology
Princeton University Press
Johns Hopkins Press
Royal Canadian Air Force
The United States Geological Survey, Department of the Interior
University of Texas Publications
John Wiley & Sons, Inc., and Chapman & Hall, Ltd.
World Oil

All figures and tables with no credit designation are from original drawings or compilations by the present author.

MATERIALS REQUIRED

The following materials will be used for most of the problems:

Pencils (3H-5H).
Colored pencils (five or six common colors).
Eraser.

Drafting tape (masking variety).
Protractor.
Drawing triangles (45°, 60°).
Engineer's triangular scale (10, 20, 30, 40, 50, 60).
Compass of drafting-set quality.
Ruling pen of drafting-set quality.
A slide rule will be useful occasionally.
Pad of good quality $8\frac{1}{2}'' \times 11''$ tracing paper.
One dozen sheets of $8\frac{1}{2}'' \times 11''$ thin acetate overlay paper.
Lens-type stereoscope (pocket size). This may be supplied by the instructor.

GENERAL INSTRUCTIONS FOR INSTRUCTORS AND STUDENTS

Many of the problems in this book are drawn from actual case histories and consequently are comprehensive and thought-provoking in nature. In the author's experience this type of problem is more valuable and more stimulating than a series of briefer exercises. For beginning students each problem may be greatly simplified if it is solved by a series of steps. Fault problems 27, 28, 29, and 35 will illustrate this point. If all steps are attempted on the same sheet of paper, a confusing mass of lines results. The picture becomes clear if each step is performed on a separate sheet of transparent paper and if different colored pencils are used for separate steps. None of the problems requires previous descriptive geometry training if this simple approach is adopted. After completing each laboratory problem it will be desirable for the student to summarize the steps involved in the solution. This will greatly facilitate future reference to the problem.

Many of the problems are designed to occupy a full laboratory period subsequent to a reading assignment on the method. The most advanced problems require more than one laboratory session. The instructor may shorten many of the problems by terminating them after the initial or intermediate steps have been completed. Problem 11 could be shortened by eliminating the cross section construction work below the thrust fault, while problem 27 could be simplified by eliminating the results of the later thrust faulting (solving for normal fault displacement only). Similarily, problem 35 could be shortened by terminating it after the pole of rotation and amount of rotation have been determined. The instructor may thus adjust the problems to the academic level of his students.

A determined effort has been made to remove all "busy work" from the problems. This situation can be improved further by having students work in pairs or groups of three when it comes to cases, such as problems 17 and 18, which involve a series of structure contour maps.

The author discusses most of the methods with his students but requires each student to complete only a portion of the problems during a semester course. The particular problems are selected by consultation between instructor and individual student.

PETER C. BADGLEY

Golden, Colorado
July, 1959

CHAPTER 1

Introduction to Descriptive Geometry as Applied to Structural Geology

Terminology and Principles Involved

Descriptive geometry is concerned with the representation on a plane of two dimensions of the form and position of objects which have three dimensions. The ability to visualize objects in three dimensions is probably the most fundamental principle which the structural geologist must grasp, and consequently it is well to review this subject before dealing with more specialized approaches to the solution of structural problems. The objects to be represented may be points, lines or planes, or the combination of all three. The representation is accomplished by means of *projections*. There are two principle planes of projection, known as the horizontal and vertical planes (Figs. 1, 2), and these are at right angles to each other. The method of projection may be either perspective (Fig. 1) or orthographic (Fig. 2). In *orthographic projections,* projected objects have the same size as the originals from which they were projected. In other words, orthographic projection is the art of drawing objects as if they were seen from an infinite distance (Fig. 3). Should the eye of an observer be moved to an infinite distance, the light rays from the object will be parallel to each other, and consequently will be perpendicular to the plane to which the object is being projected. The *direction of projection* is the direction in which a point is projected into the plane of projection. The term *normal projection* is also used for those projections in which the direction of projection is perpendicular to the plane of projection.

The projection of a point onto a plane is a point (Fig. 1). The projection of a line onto a plane is a line (Figs. 1, 2), and both lines will have the same length in orthographic projections. In contrast, distance enters the picture in *perspective projections* (Fig. 1). The reduction in size with distance is caused by the fact that edges of the object which are actually parallel do not appear parallel (Fig. 1). Vertical lines are drawn vertical, but horizontal parallel lines converge in such a way that they eventually meet in a point (Fig. 4).

The line of intersection of two planes is the *trace* of one plane upon the other plane (Figs. 1, 2). The trace of one plane upon a second plane of projection is called a *folding line* (Figs. 1, 2). To represent a plan view (map view) and a vertical section on one plane (the plane of the paper), it is necessary to rotate the section into the plane of the map around the folding line as an axis of rotation.

General Usage

Descriptive geometry may be used to solve many types of structural problems, such as the determination of net slip and movement direction in faulting and the pattern of outcrops for formations in mountainous areas. It can also be used to determine the attitude of beds or other planar features. The concept of attitude (strike and dip) determination is of fundamental importance in structural and field geology, and consequently we shall illustrate the application and usage of descriptive geometry as used in attitude determination.

It is very important to understand precisely what is meant by the terms which contribute to attitude. *Strike* is the direction of a line formed by the intersection of the bedding planes of strata or foliation planes with the horizontal. *True dip* of a bed is the angle between the bedding plane and the horizontal plane, as measured in a vertical section at right angles to the strike. *Apparent dip* is the angle measured between the bedding or foliation plane and the horizontal plane in a vertical section not at

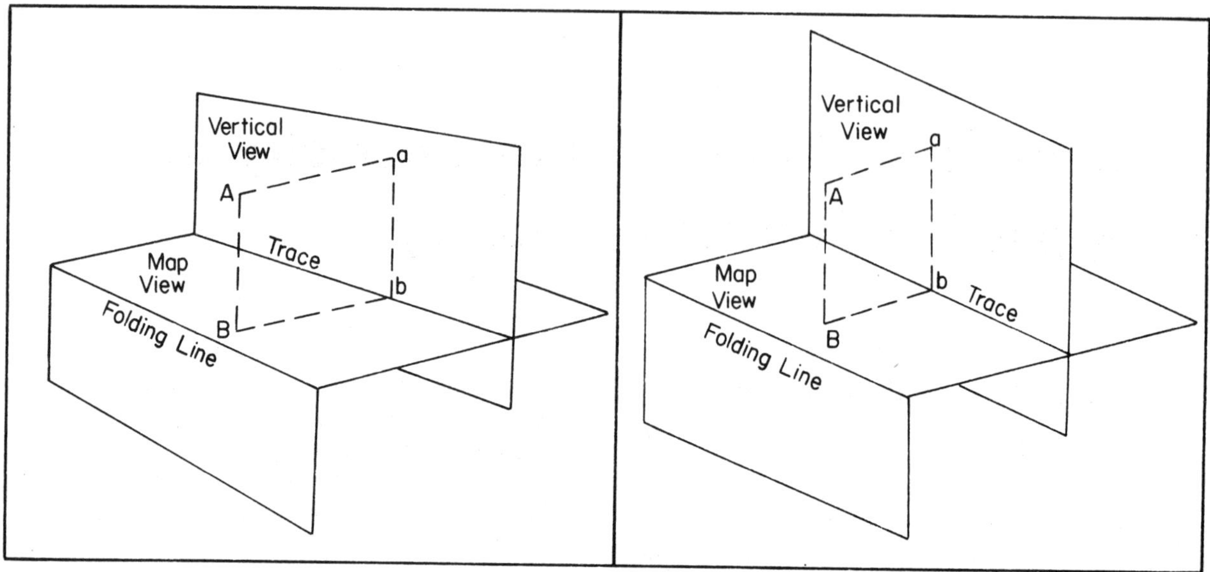

FIGURE 1. Projection of lines and points as seen in perspective view.

FIGURE 2. Projection of lines and points as seen in orthographic projection.

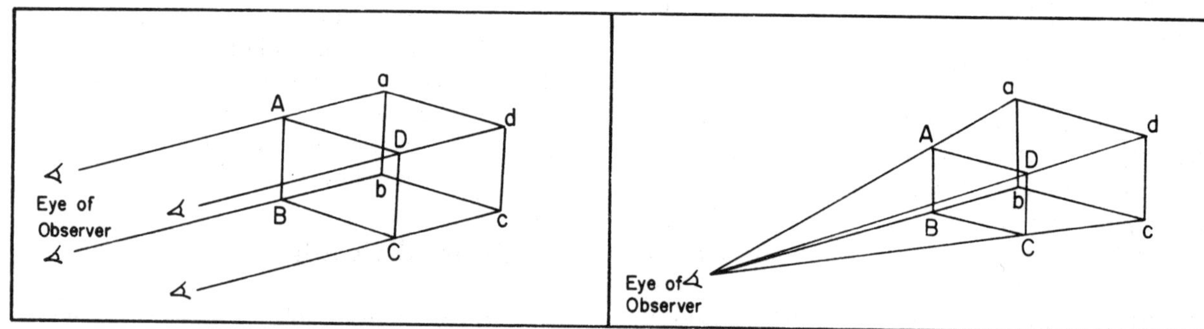

FIGURE 3. Orthographic projection. The eye of the observer is at an infinite distance from the object. (Modified from G. W. Salzer and J. M. Coke, *Descriptive Geometry with Practical Applications,* Colorado School of Mines.)

FIGURE 4. Perspective projection. The eye of the observer is at a limited distance from the object. (Modified from G. W. Salzer and J. M. Coke, *Descriptive Geometry with Practical Applications,* Colorado School of Mines.)

right angles to the strike. Apparent dip is always less than true dip. Dip may be expressed in degrees and minutes of arc, in feet per mile, and in per cent of grade. The *per cent grade* of an inclined surface is the number of feet of rise or fall which occurs in 100 feet of horizontal distance. For example, if a stratum rises 100 feet in a horizontal distance of 500 feet, in a direction normal to the strike of the strata, then the grade is 20 per cent. A *dip component* is the dip measured in a vertical plane which is not perpendicular to the strike. The direction of the vertical plane in which the dip component is measured is known as the *bearing* of the dip component line. The dip of the dip component line is known as the *inclination* of the line. Thus the terms *dip* and *strike* together determine the position or attitude of a planar surface with respect to horizontality and compass direction, whereas the terms *bearing* and *inclination* determine the attitude or position of a line, or of the intersection of two planes (which is a line), with horizontality and compass direction.

Attitude may be obtained directly through actual contact with bedding planes, using a Brunton compass, or it may be obtained indirectly by sighting methods, using either a Brunton compass, plane table and alidade, transit and alidade, or a compass and a hand level. The actual use of these instruments is described ably by Forrester (1947), Lahee (1941), and Low (1957). When the attitude cannot be obtained directly by the contact method using the Brunton compass, then the information obtained must be projected into the horizontal and vertical planes by descriptive geometry. There are several ways to obtain the attitude of planes or lines through descriptive geometry:

1. Apparent dip method.
2. Three-point method.
3. Dip Component method.
4. Intersecting plane method.
5. Combination of topographic and geologic maps.

The following section describes these methods in detail. The combination of topographic and geological maps is described in a separate chapter.

Application of Descriptive Geometry to Attitude Determination

DETERMINATION OF STRIKE AND DIP BY DESCRIPTIVE GEOMETRY, GIVEN TWO APPARENT DIPS

Applications and Limitations: Commonly sections at right angles to the strike are not exposed, but if two vertical sections are available in which the apparent dip can be measured, then the true strike and dip can be obtained by the method used in the following example. It is of course assumed that the same bed is measured at each outcrop and that the bed is not folded, warped, or faulted between outcrops.

Data Provided: Two apparent dips exposed in vertical sections whose strikes are known. The elevations at the outcrops where the apparent dips are obtained are also known:

Vertical section striking 045°, apparent dip = 27°, elevation = 5000 feet.

Vertical section striking 150° (S30°E), apparent dip = 42.5°, elevation = 5000 feet.

Determine: The attitude of the bed exposed at the two outcrops.

Method: With A as center (Fig. 5), draw in lines at 045° (N45°E) and at 150° (S30°E). About AB

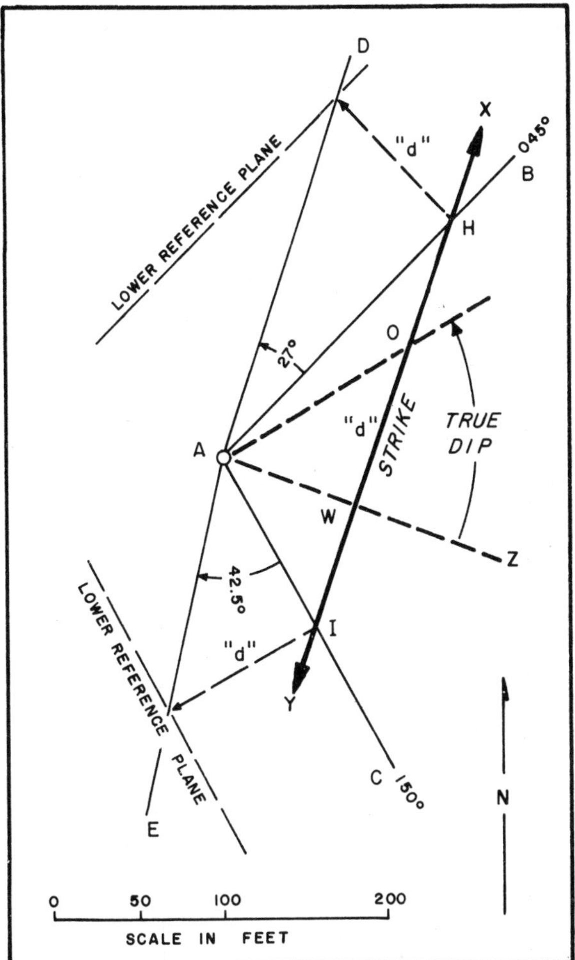

FIGURE 5. Determination of strike and true dip, given two apparent dips.

and AC as folding lines, draw vertical sections showing the apparent dips BAD (27°) and EAC (42.5°). With a scale and triangle, lay off the depth "d" (say, 100 feet) on both of the vertical sections. This gives us points H and I. By joining H and I we immediately obtain the *strike* as we have joined two points on the same bed and at the same elevation. Now draw AZ perpendicular to XY so as to intersect the horizontal surface projection of HI at W. Then, using AZ as a folding line, draw WO perpendicular to AZ and equal to "d" in length. Thus, O being "d" distance below AZ, it must fall directly on line HI, as HI is exactly 100 feet below the surface. We now have two points A and O both on the same bedding plane and in the vertical section perpendicular to the strike. Thus the angle

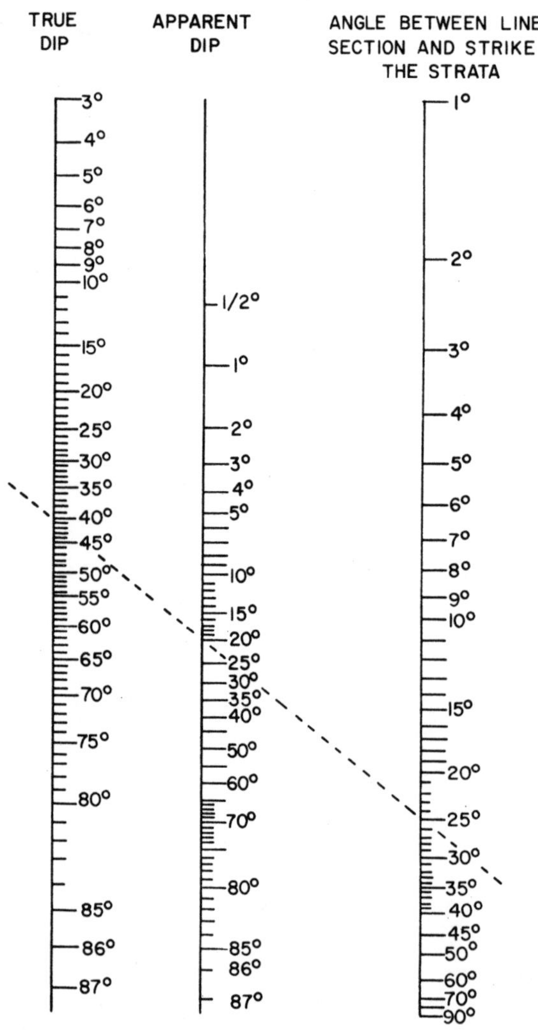

FIGURE 6. Alignment nomograph for converting apparent dip into true dip or true dip to apparent dip. (From H. S. Palmer [1918], *U.S. Geol. Surv.*, Prof. Paper 120-G.)

ZAO must = the *true dip* by definition. In this case the attitude is: strike = 020° (N20° E) and the dip = 50°. The strike can be expressed either as an azimuth (020°) or as a quadrant bearing (N20° E). *Azimuths* are clockwise bearings measured from true north.

True dip can be determined from apparent dip by using tables or nomographs (Fig. 6, Table 1) if the angle between the strike of the bedding and the strike of the vertical section exposing the apparent dip is known. This method is preferable to descriptive geometry when a large number of conversions must be made, as in drawing up vertical cross sections for an area. In such situations the true dip and strike are often known and the desired vertical section line is known, and it is necessary to compute the apparent dip which would be observed in the line of section. Descriptive geometry is one method which can be used when the strike of the bedding is unknown.

DETERMINATION OF STRIKE AND DIP FROM THREE POINTS ON THE SAME BED

Applications and Limitations: Attitude can be determined by plotting the positions and elevations of three points on the same stratigraphic horizon, provided the three points are not on the same straight line and provided the bed is not folded or warped between the three outcrops. The method is handicapped by the fact that areas not suitable for direct attitude determination are usually too poorly exposed to give assurance of nonwarping between outcrop. The method involved is illustrated by the following example:

Data Provided: Three points *X, Y,* and *Z* (Fig. 7) with known positions and elevations. The three points are all on the same stratigraphic horizon.

Determine: Attitude of the bed.

Method: Select any east-west line *FG* below the triangle formed by joining points *X, Y,* and *Z.* Project points *X, Y,* and *Z* perpendicular to *FG,* intersecting *FG* at *X′, Y′,* and *Z′.* Using FG as a folding line, drop lines vertically below *X′, Y′,* and *Z′,* and on these vertical lines plot the auxiliary points *X″, Y″,* and *Z″* at the respective elevations of *X, Y,* and Z. Now join points *X″, Y″,* and *Z″* so as to form a triangle as seen in vertical view. Now draw in line *Z″W″* parallel to the datum line *FG.* Project vertically a line from *W″* so as to intersect *XY* at *W.* We now have two points *Z* and *W* both on the same bed and at the same elevation. The line *ZW* is the *strike.* Now project *ZW* outward to the northwest quadrant of the diagram, and draw in the new datum line *LK* perpendicular to *ZW.* Now plot the auxiliary points *X‴, Z‴,* and *Y‴* at their respective elevations below the datum line *LK.* The angle *RY‴ X‴* is the *dip.*

Note: The line *FG* does not have to be an east-west line. It is best to place the first datum (*FG*) on that side of the original triangle (triangle *XYZ*) opposite the highest of the three original points (point *Y*) so that the highest point (*Y″*) will be flanked by a lower point on each side.

TABLE 1. Conversion of True Dip to Component in the Line of Section

Angle Between Line of Section and Strike of Strata (Degrees)	Apparent Dips in the Line of Section																
5	0.5	1.0	1.5	2.0	2.5	3.0	3.5	4.0	5.0	6.0	7.0	8.5	10.0	13.0	18.0	26.0	44.0
10	1.0	2.0	3.0	4.0	5.0	6.0	7.0	8.5	10.0	12.0	14.0	16.5	20.0	25.0	32.0	44.0	62.0
15	1.5	3.0	4.0	5.5	7.0	8.5	10.5	12.0	15.0	17.5	20.0	24.0	29.5	35.0	43.0	55.0	70.0
20	1.5	3.5	5.5	7.0	9.0	11.0	13.5	16.0	19.0	22.5	26.0	31.0	36.0	42.5	51.0	62.0	75.0
25	2.0	4.5	6.5	9.0	11.0	13.5	17.0	19.5	22.5	27.0	31.0	36.5	42.0	48.5	57.0	67.0	78.0
30	2.5	5.0	8.0	10.5	13.0	16.0	19.0	23.0	26.0	31.0	35.5	41.0	46.5	53.0	61.0	70.5	80.0
35	3.0	6.0	9.0	12.0	15.0	18.0	23.0	26.0	29.0	34.5	39.9	45.0	50.5	57.5	65.0	73.0	82.0
40	3.0	6.5	10.0	13.5	16.5	20.5	24.0	28.0	32.0	37.5	43.0	48.0	54.0	61.0	67.0	75.0	83.0
45	3.5	7.0	11.0	14.5	18.0	22.0	26.5	31.0	35.5	40.0	45.5	51.0	56.5	63.0	69.0	76.5	83.5
50	3.5	7.5	11.5	16.0	19.5	24.0	28.0	33.0	37.5	42.5	47.5	53.0	59.0	65.0	71.0	77.5	84.0
55	4.0	8.0	12.0	17.0	21.0	25.0	30.0	35.0	39.5	44.5	49.5	55.0	60.5	66.5	72.0	78.0	84.0
60	4.5	9.0	13.0	18.0	22.0	27.0	31.5	36.5	41.0	46.0	51.0	56.5	61.5	67.5	73.0	79.0	84.0
65	4.5	9.0	13.5	18.5	23.0	28.0	32.5	37.5	42.0	47.0	52.0	57.5	62.5	68.5	73.5	79.5	84.5
70	4.5	9.0	14.0	19.0	23.5	28.5	33.5	38.0	43.0	48.0	53.0	58.5	63.5	69.0	74.0	79.5	85.0
75	5.0	9.5	14.5	19.5	24.0	29.0	34.0	39.0	44.0	49.0	54.0	59.0	64.0	69.5	74.5	80.0	85.0
80	5.0	10.0	15.0	20.0	24.5	29.5	34.5	39.5	44.5	49.5	54.5	59.5	64.5	69.5	74.5	80.0	85.0
85	5.0	10.0	15.0	20.0	25.0	30.0	35.0	40.0	44.5	49.5	54.5	59.5	64.5	69.5	75.0	80.0	85.0
Degrees	5	10	15	20	25	30	35	40	45	50	55	60	65	70	75	80	85
	True Dips at 90° to the Strike																

Example 1: Strike N 10° E, Dip 30° SE, line of section N 50° E. Find apparent dip along line of section. Angle between strike and line of section 50° − 10° = 40°. Find 40° in left column, 30° on bottom row; dip component in line of section is 20.5°.

Example 2: Strike of strata N 15° E, component of dip along a line bearing N 40° E is 20°. Find true dip. Angle between strike and line of component is 40° − 15° = 25°. From left column at 25°. Find 20° to the right (19.5 is nearest point). From 19.5 read true dip at bottom: 40°, approximate.

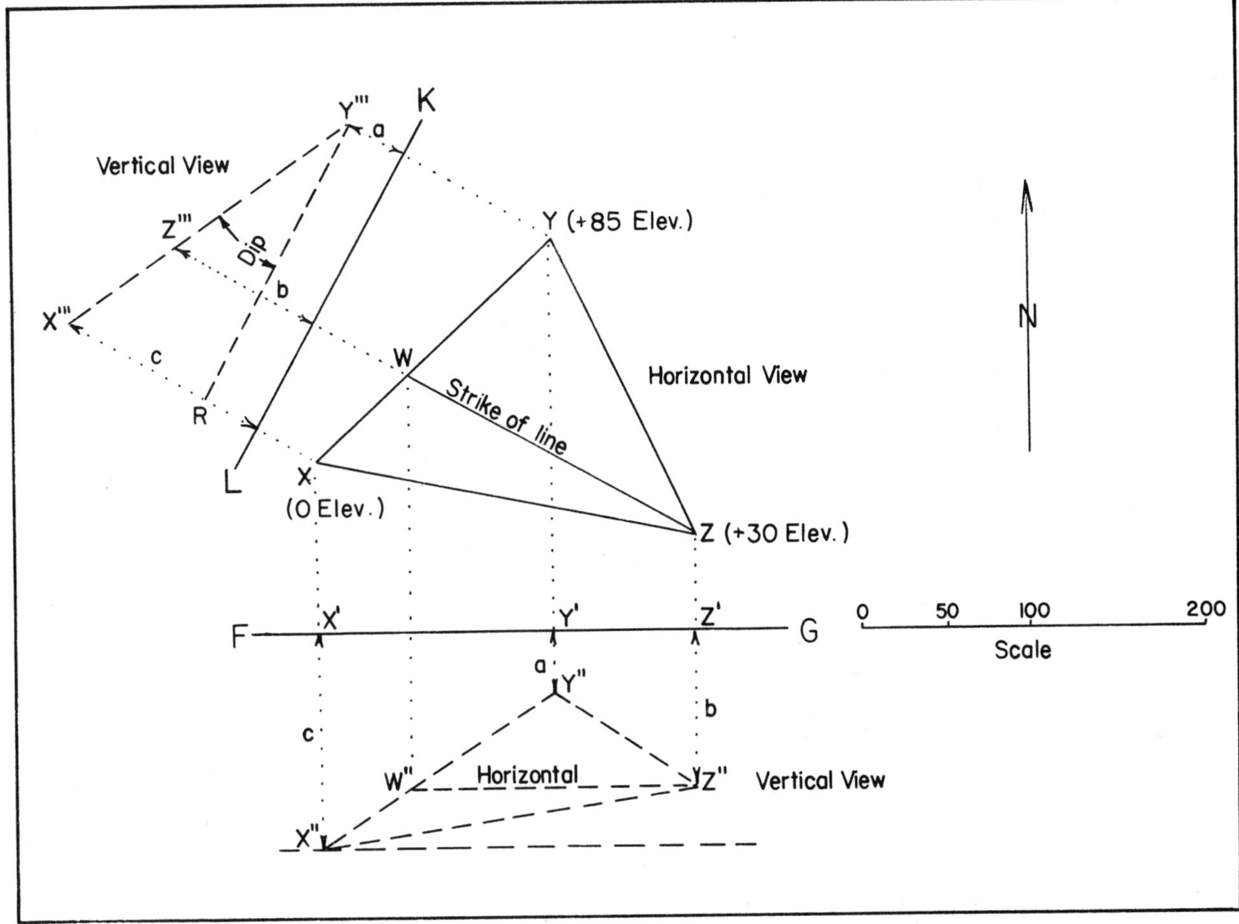

FIGURE 7. Strike and dip determination by three points on a plane.

DETERMINATION OF ATTITUDE BY THE DIP COMPONENT METHOD

Applications and Limitations: This method is used in regions where the strike and dip cannot be obtained directly either because of poor exposure (inability to trace individual beds from outcrop to outcrop) or because the dip is too low to measure accurately with a Brunton compass. In these instances the dip component is usually expressed in terms of *per cent grade,* although expression in terms of degrees can be used. The information is easier to obtain, however, as per cent grade. The method has the advantage of not requiring recognition of the same bed at different outcrops. The only limitation is that there should be no warping between outcrops.

Data Provided: Bedding is inclined downward 1 foot in 100 feet of horizontal distance on a bearing of 320° (N40°W), and it is inclined downward 1 foot in 175 feet on a bearing of 025° (N25°E). See Figure 8.

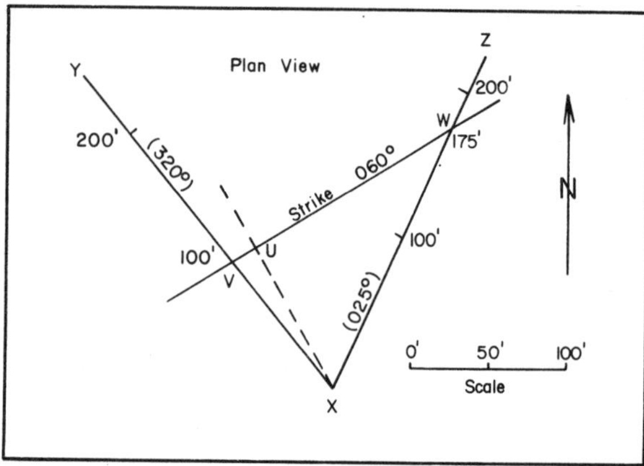

FIGURE 8. Determination of attitude by the dip component method.

Determine: Attitude of the bedding in this region.

Method: Draw in lines *XY* and *XZ* on bearings of 320° and 025°. Scale off distances of 100 feet and 175 feet on *XY* and *XZ* respectively, so as to give points *V* and *W*. Now join *VW* to give the *strike* of the bed. If we now lay off *XU* perpendicular to *VW,* the line *XU* is the dip direction, and the length of the line *XU* will give the per cent grade for the true dip direction (1 foot down in 98 feet or 1.2 per cent grade.

Note: When the inclination is given in degrees rather than in per cent grade, then the apparent dip method can be used if the dips are not too low to introduce graphical errors.

DETERMINATION OF ATTITUDE FOR THE INTERSECTION OF TWO PLANES

Applications and Limitations: It is commonly desirable to know the inclination and bearing of linear structures. One of the most common types of linear structure is produced by the intersection of two planar structures. Many such intersections, for example the intersection of two fractures, are important economically as channelways or hosts for ore deposits. Thus it is commonly important to be able to determine the inclination of such linear features. The method has one serious limitation—the two planar structures cannot be warped in the area of determination. Areas containing intersecting structures frequently are folded also.

Data Provided: One fracture which strikes 050° (N50°E) and dips 45° NW (Fig. 9). The second fracture strikes 320° and dips 60° NE. In this case both of these attitudes were obtained on the 500-foot level underground in a mine.

Determine: The attitude of intersection of the two fractures.

Method: Draw in strike lines *XY* (050°) and *WZ* (320°) through outcrop points *L* and *M* where the attitudes of those two fractures were obtained. Construct folding lines *CE* and *AB* through the points *L* and *M*. Draw in the dips *CLF* (45°) and *BMN* (60°) so as to intersect a lower reference plane 100 feet below the 500-foot mine level at *F′* and *N′*. Then project lines *F′Q* and *N′P* on to *H* and *K,* respectively, making lines *F′H* and *N′K* parallel to lines *XY* and *WZ,* respectively. It will be noted that *XY* and *WZ* intersect at *S* and that *F′H* and *N′K* also intersect. This latter intersection is 100 feet below the 500-foot mine level. The position of this latter intersection will be *S′* on the 500-foot level as the vertical upward projection of a point appears directly above that intersection point. The line *SS′* is thus the *bearing* as it joins two points on the same line at the same elevation. Now draw in *S′D′* and *SS‴* perpendicular to *SS′*. Lay off *S″D* (at any convenient position) parallel to *SS′*. Now draw in a lower reference horizon 100 feet below *S″D*. The point *D′* is thus situated ex-

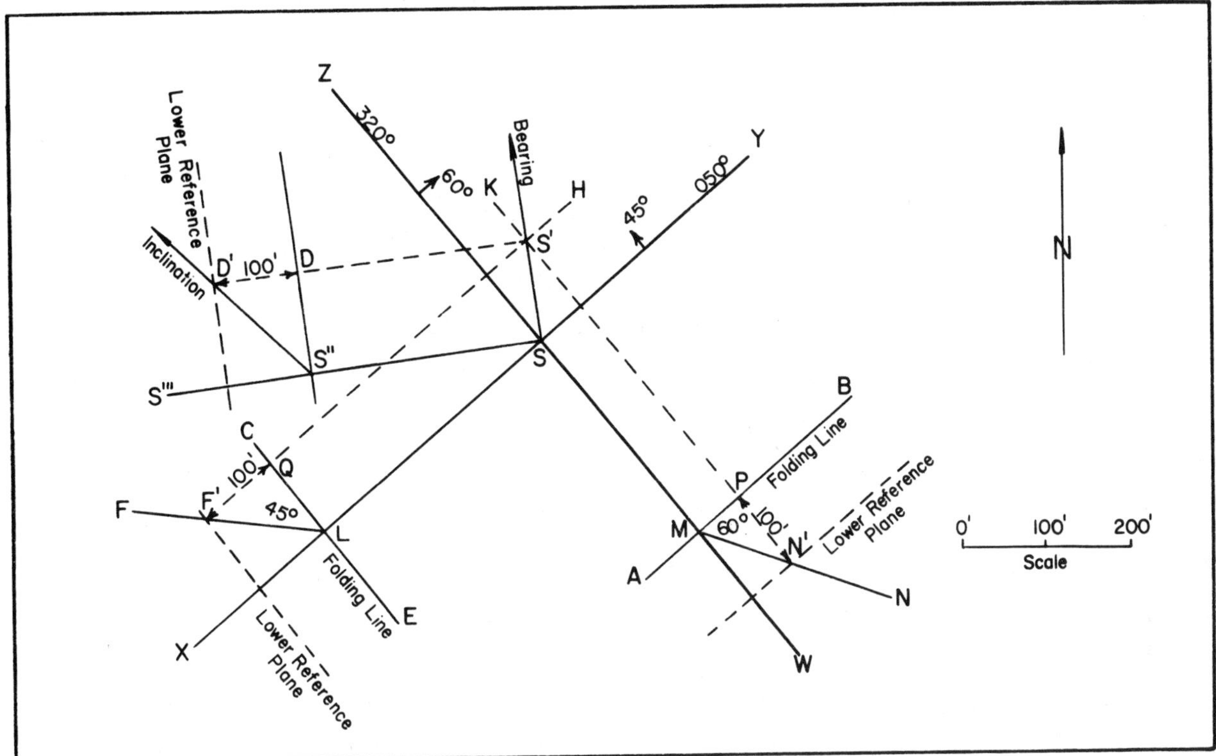

FIGURE 9. Determination of the attitude of intersection of two planes by descriptive geometry.

actly 100 feet below point *D*. The angle *DS″D′* is the inclination of the line *SS′*.

Note: The inclination is obtained in a vertical plane which is parallel to the bearing, whereas dip is obtained in a vertical plane which is perpendicular to the strike.

DETERMINATION OF APPARENT THICKNESS, OUTCROP WIDTH, AND APPARENT DIP GIVEN TRUE DIP

Applications and Limitations: This method, although not used for obtaining true attitude, does demonstrate how true attitude and formation thickness, and so forth, can be converted into apparent attitude, apparent thickness, and apparent outcrop width. In mining work particularly, one is often required to lay out vertical sections through an ore body to illustrate its shape. This usually requires the projection of information obtained in the underground workings into vertical cross sections which are related to the co-ordinate system being used in the region. The direction of the underground workings (where the geology has to be observed) usually does not have the same bearing as the desired cross sections. The method again requires no warping of beds as in the other methods just discussed. The term *true width* as used here means the width of a formation as it would appear along a horizontal line at right angles to the strike of the formation.

Data Provided: Strike (060°) and dip (−45° SE); thickness of bed = 100 feet (Fig. 10).

Determine: Apparent dip, apparent thickness, and outcrop width in an east-west vertical section on the −500-foot level in a mine.

Method: Draw in strike line *AB* (060°) and east-west line *SR* at any convenient spot on the paper. Draw folding line *EM* perpendicular to strike and draw in true dip (−45°) on this section. Lay off true thickness *FG* (100 feet) perpendicular to *OP*. Project *HF* parallel to *AB* so as to intersect *RS* at *K*. Draw in *WK* perpendicular to *RS* so that *KW* has the same length as *HF* (depth "d"). Join *LW*. Then the angle *KLW* is the *apparent dip,* the line *KI* is the *apparent thickness,* and *LK* is the *apparent width.*

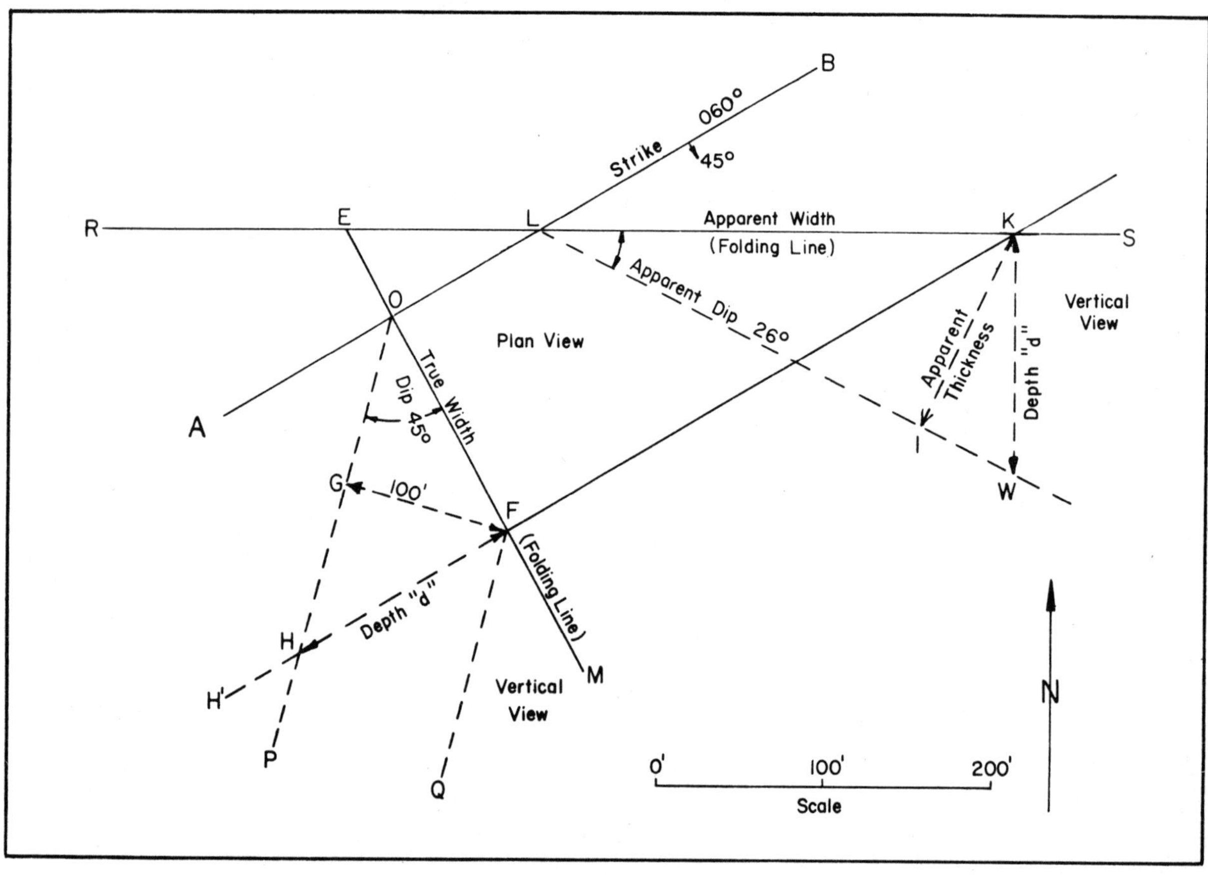

FIGURE 10. Determination of apparent thickness by descriptive geometry.

Questions Based on Attitude Determination Methods

1. Would the three-point method work if two of the points were at the same surface elevation? Would it work if all three points were at the same elevation and not on the same line? Explain.
2. If three inclined drill holes, all at different elevations, and all drilled on different bearings and inclinations, intersected the same formation top at different drilling depths (inclined distances), how would you go about using this data to determine the strike and dip of the formation? Explain, giving the steps involved.
3. Given two dip component lines for the same formation top, whose bearings and inclinations are known from two separate outcrops at *different* known elevations, explain, with a diagram, how to determine the attitude of the formation *if the two dip component lines are parallel?* What is the relationship between the amount of dip of the formation and the inclination of the two lines?
4. What would be the position of the line of intersection of two fractures if the strikes were parallel but the dips were not? Can the inclination of the line of intersection exceed the dip of either of the two veins if the veins are not parallel? Of both veins? Explain.
5. Suppose an ore shoot was controlled by the intersection of a fault with a limestone bed, neither of which cropped out at the surface. How would you go about determining the position of the ore shoot if you had a diamond drill at your disposal? Explain, outlining the steps involved.
6. If the attitude of two intersecting plane surfaces were at different elevations, how would you modify the procedure used above in determining the attitude of the vein intersections? Explain, outlining the steps involved and illustrating your answer with a diagram.
7. What is the relationship between (use nonmathematical terms):
   a. The apparent dip and the true dip?
   b. The apparent thickness and the true thickness?
   c. The apparent outcrop width and the true outcrop width (if true outcrop width is measured at right angles to the strike)?
8. What factors determine the width of the outcrop of a formation as seen in a horizontal outcrop (assuming constant thickness)?

PROBLEM 1

DETERMINATION OF DIP AND STRIKE FROM THREE POINTS IN A PLANE

Data Provided: Three points *A, B,* and *C* all on the same plane surface, with elevations of 75 feet, 175 feet, and 100 feet, respectively.
Determine: Strike and dip of the plane surface. Use a red pencil for lines in plan view and a green pencil for lines in vertical view. Label all lines and answers clearly, and list the steps used to determine your answers.
Scale: 1 inch = 100 feet.

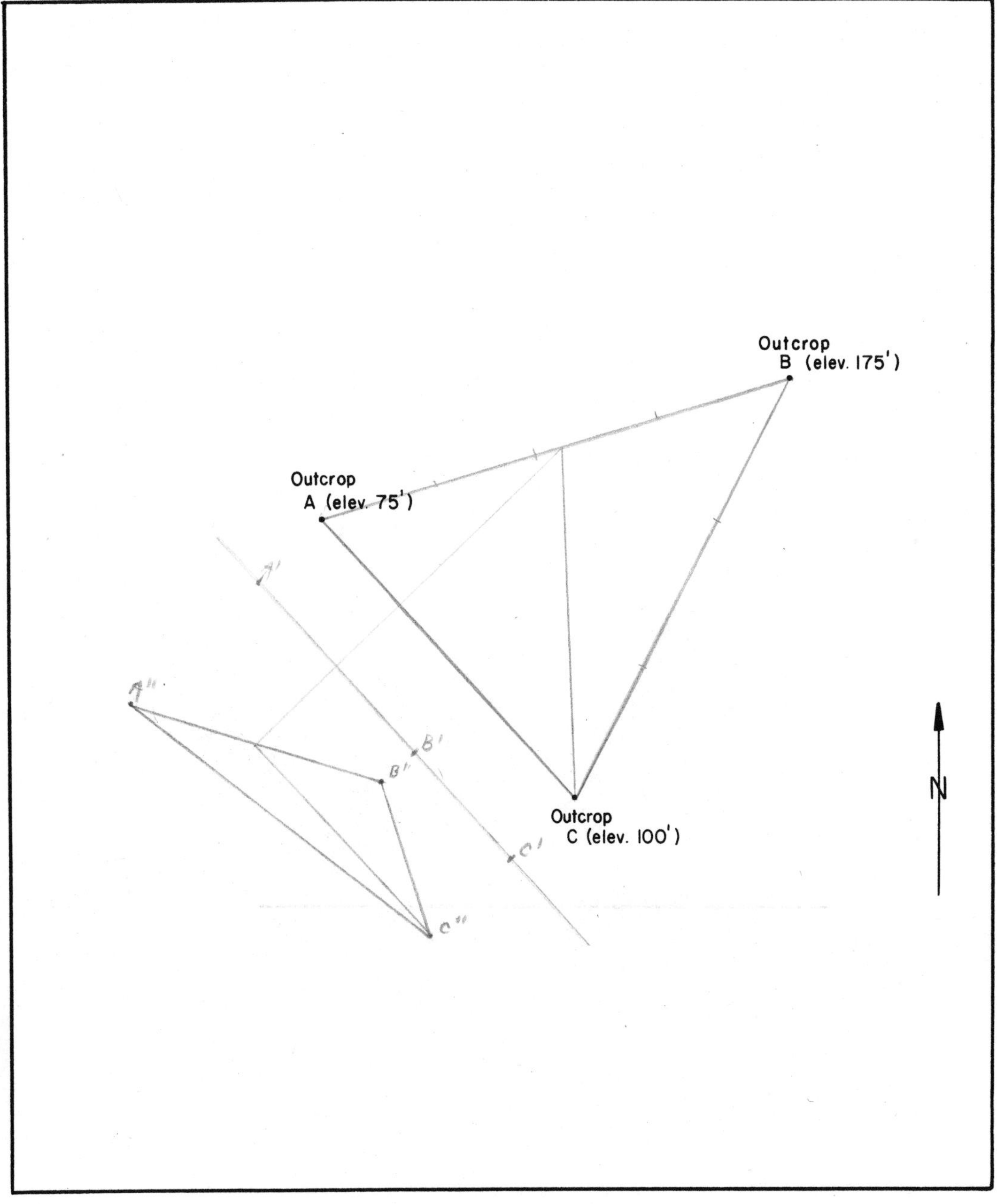

PROBLEM 2

DETERMINATION OF APPARENT DIP, APPARENT THICKNESS, AND APPARENT WIDTH IN A SECTION NOT PARALLEL TO THE DIP OF THE BED

Data Provided: The top of a formation, 60 feet thick crops out at point *A* at an elevation of 200 feet. The strike of the formation is 334° and the dip is 35° to the northeast.

Determine: The true outcrop width, the apparent outcrop width, the apparent formation thickness, and the apparent dip, in a north-south vertical section passing through point *B*, whose elevation is 150 feet. Use a red pencil for lines in plan view and a green pencil for lines in vertical view. Show the position of all the required features as they would appear on the 150-foot level in the north-south section. Label all lines and answers clearly, and list the steps used to determine the answers.

Scale: 1 inch = 100 feet.

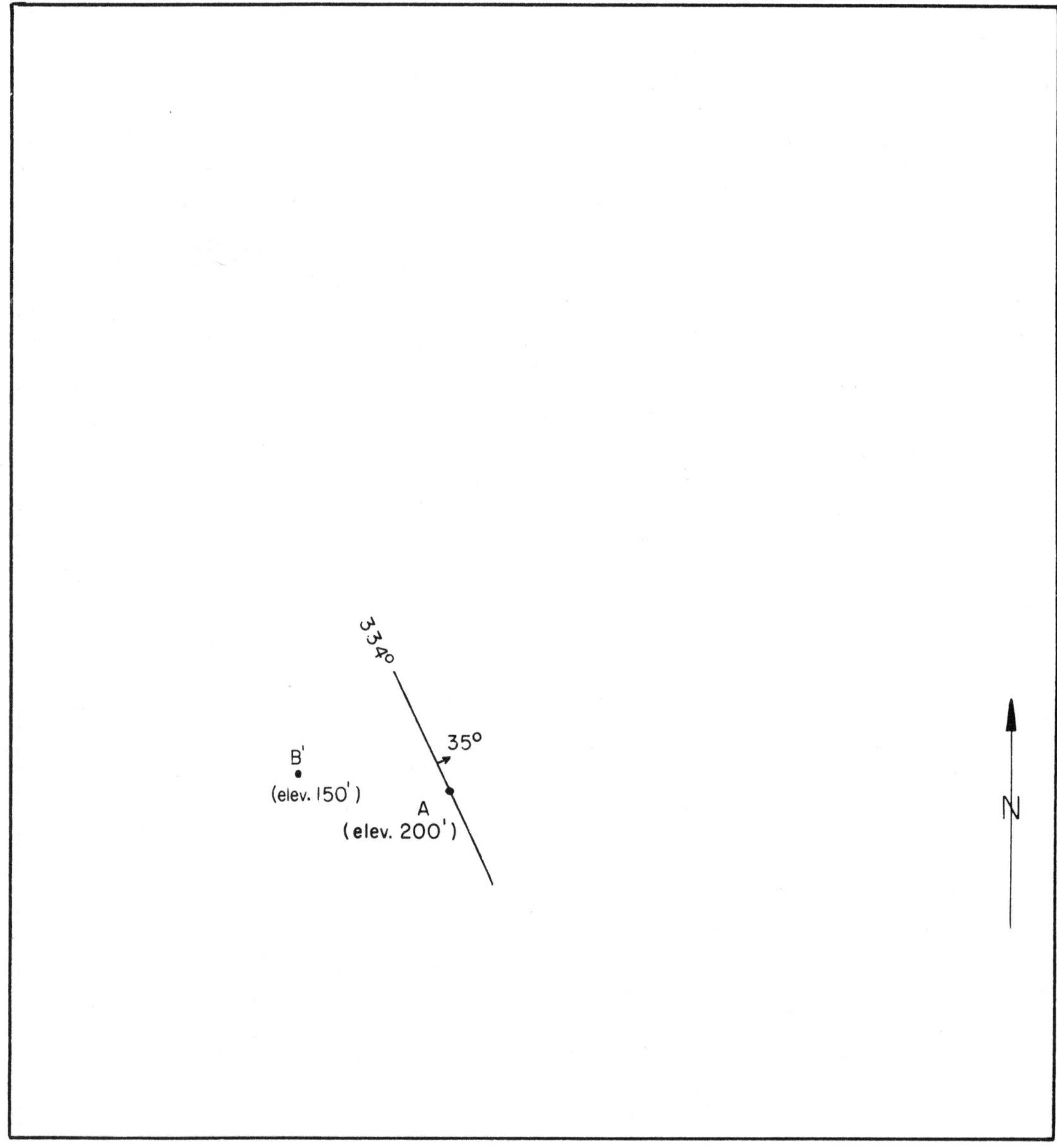

PROBLEM 3

DETERMINATION OF ATTITUDE BY MEANS OF TWO COMPONENT LINES IN THE SAME PLANE

Data Provided: A dip component line bearing 336° and plunging 39° passes through outcrop *A,* whose elevation is 50 feet. A second dip component line bearing 050° and plunging 20° passes through outcrop *B,* whose elevation is 150 feet. *Both dip component lines are in the same plane.* Bear in mind that dip components are lines in space and can pass through only one point on any horizontal line in the diagram.

Determine: Strike and dip of the plane. *At what elevation do the two dip component lines intersect?* Draw plan view lines in red and vertical section lines in green. Label all lines and answers clearly. List the steps used to determine the answers.

Scale: 1 inch = 100 feet.

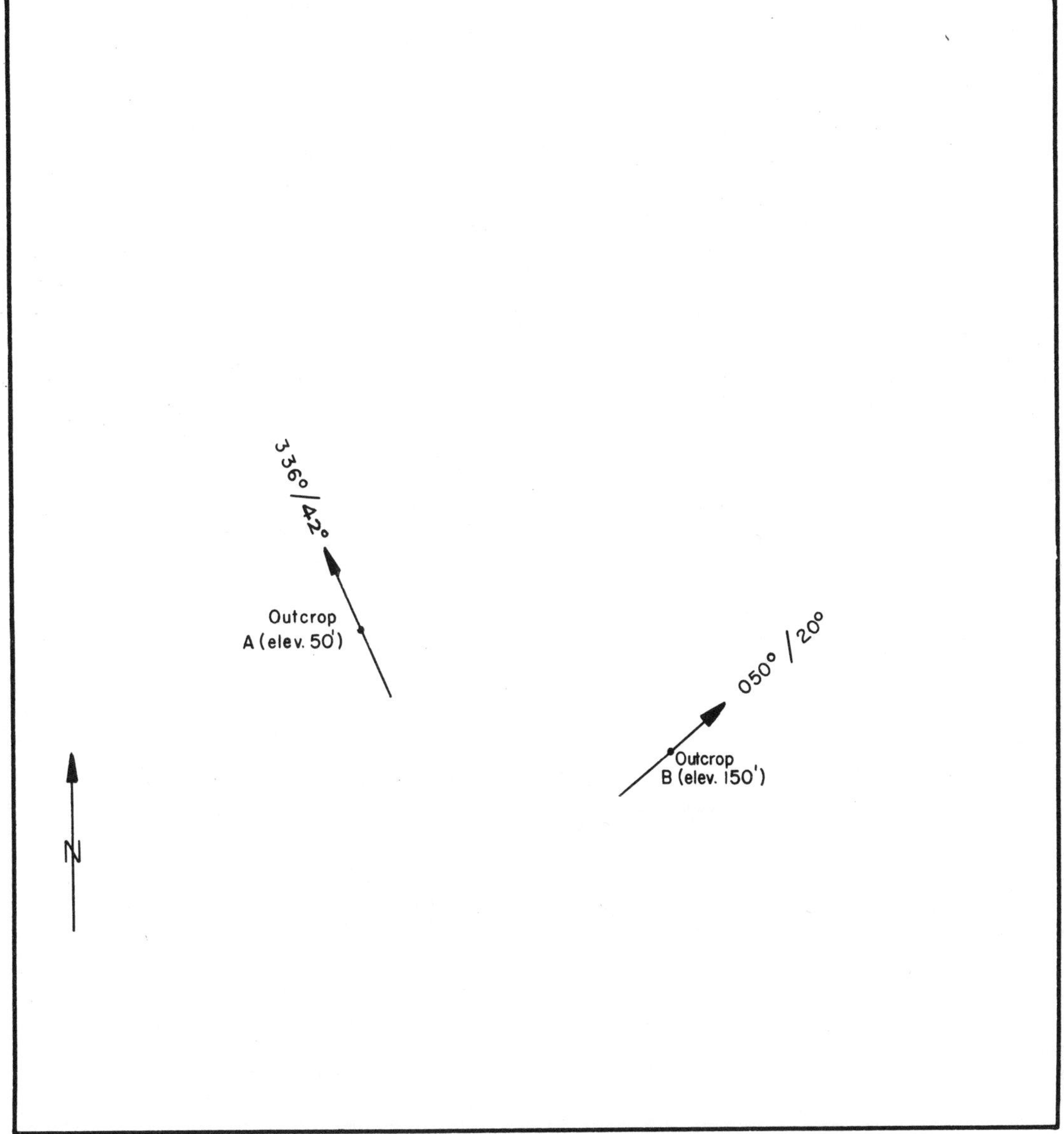

PROBLEM 4

DETERMINATION OF THE BEARING AND INCLINATION OF THE LINE OF INTERSECTION OF TWO PLANES

Data Provided: Limestone bed striking 150° through point *B* (elevation, 100 feet), and dipping 45° SW. Shear zone striking 074° through point *A* (elevation, 200 feet), and dipping 65° NNW. An ore shoot is believed to occur at the intersection of these two plane surfaces.

Determine: The bearing and inclination of the ore shoot and the point where it will occur at the 100-foot level. Use a red pencil for lines appearing in plan view. Use a green pencil for lines appearing in vertical view. Label all lines and answers clearly. List the steps used to determine the answers.

Scale: 1 inch = 100 feet.

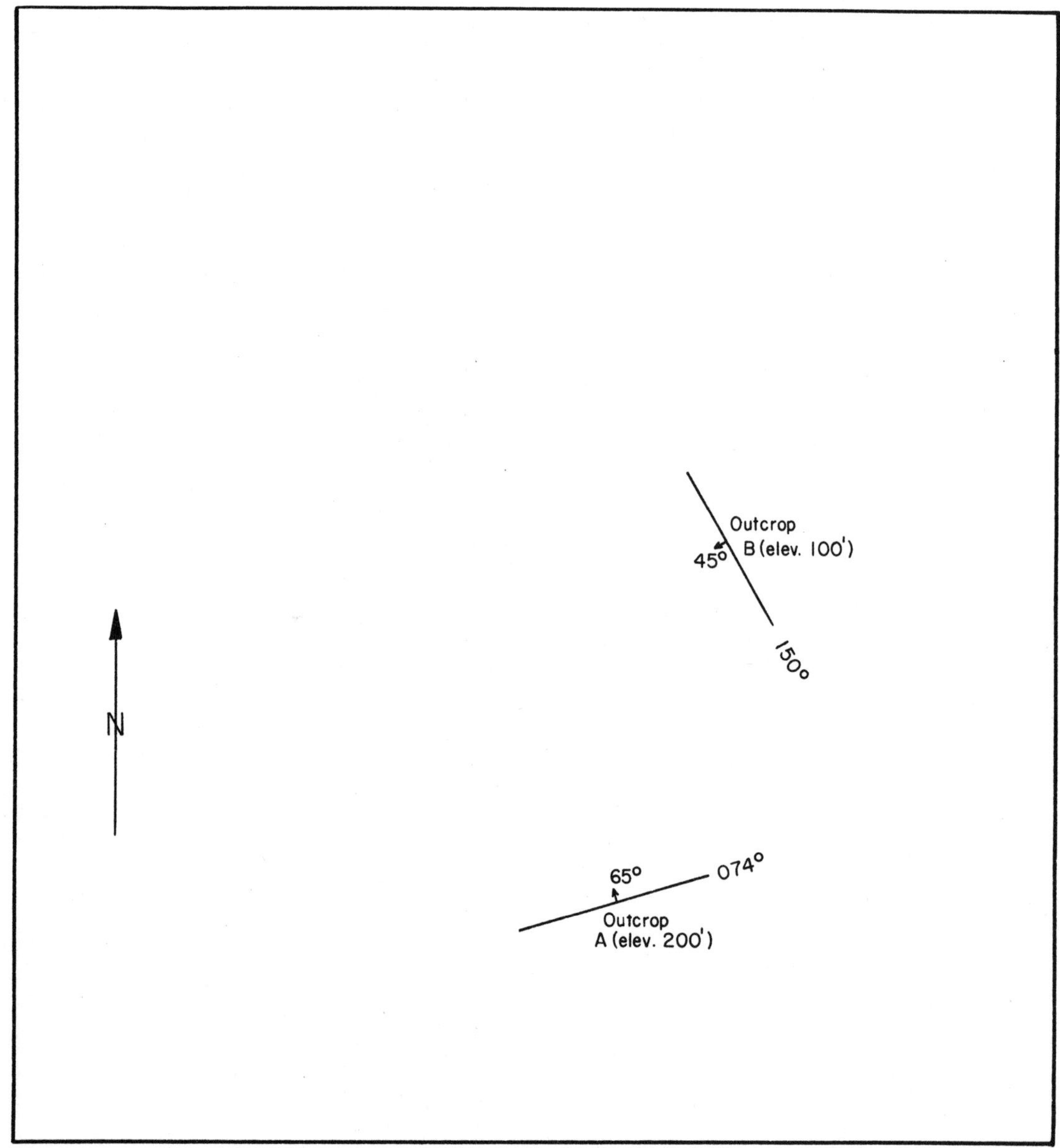

References

Billings, M. P., (1954), *Structural Geology,* 2nd ed., Prentice-Hall, Inc., 514 pp.

Earle, K. W. (1934), *Dip and Strike Problems,* Murby & Co., 126 pp.

Forrester, J. D. (1946), *Principles of Field and Mining Geology,* John Wiley & Sons, Inc., 647 pp.

Haddock, M. H. (1929), *Disrupted Strata,* Crosby Lockwood & Son, 100 pp.

Hobson, G. D. (1942), Calculating the True Thickness of a Folded Bed, *Bull. Am. Assoc. Petrol. Geol.,* vol. 26, pp. 1827–1831.

Hubbert M. K. (1931), Graphic Solution of Strike and Dip from Two Angular Components, *Bull. Am. Assoc. Petrol. Geol.,* vol. 15, pp. 283–286.

Kitson, H. W. (1929), Graphic Solutions of Strike and Dip from Two Angular Components, *Bull. Am. Assoc. Petrol. Geol.,* vol. 13, pp. 1211–1213.

Lahee, F. H. (1941), *Field Geology,* 4th ed., McGraw-Hill Book Co. Inc., 853 pp.

Low, Julian W. (1957), *Geologic Field Methods,* Harper & Brothers, 489 pp.

Mead, W. J. (1921), Determination of Atttitude of Concealed Bedding Formations by Diamond Drilling, *Econ. Geol.,* vol. 21, pp. 37–47.

Miller, F. S. (1944), Graphs for Obtaining True Thickness of a Vein or Bed, *Am. Inst. Min. Eng.,* Contrib. no. 136, 6 pp.

Nettleton, L. L. (1931), Graphic Solution of Strike and Dip from Two Angular Components, *Bull. Am. Assoc. Petrol. Geol.,* vol. 15, pp. 79–82.

Nevin, C. M. (1953), *Principles of Structural Geology,* 4th ed., John Wiley & Sons, Inc., 410 pp.

Palmer, H. S. (1916), Nomographic Solutions of Certain Stratigraphic Measurements, *Econ. Geol.,* vol. 11, pp. 14–29.

Palmer, H. S. (1918), New Graphic Method for Determining the Depth and Thickness of Strata and the Projection of Dip, *U. S. Geol. Surv.,* Prof. Paper 120–G, pp. 123–128.

Rich, J. L. (1932), Simple Graphical Methods for Determining True Dip from Two Components and for Constructing Maps from Dip Observations, *Bull. Am. Assoc. Petrol. Geol.,* vol. 16, pp. 92–95.

Salzer, G. W. and Coke, J. W. (no date), *Descriptive Geometry with Practical Applications,* Colorado School of Mines Publication

Stein, H. A. (1941), A Trigonometric Solution of the Two-Drillhole Problem, *Econ. Geol.,* vol. 36, pp. 84–94.

Tanner, W. F. (1953), Use of Apparent Dip in Measuring Thickness, *Bull Am. Assoc. Petrol. Geol.,* vol. 37, pp. 566–567.

Tolman, C. F., Jr. (1911), *Graphical Solution of Fault Problems,* Mining and Scientific Press, San Francisco, California.

Warner, F. M. (1938), *Applied Descriptive Geometry,* 2nd ed., McGraw-Hill Book Co. Inc., 229 pp.

Wellman, B. L. (1948), *Technical Descriptive Geometry,* McGraw-Hill Book Co. Inc., 508 pp.

CHAPTER 2

Outcrop Patterns

Principles Involved

Geologists always face the problem of drawing in outcrop patterns during field mapping. There is no particular difficulty involved in areas of continuous or almost continuous outcrop, but numerous difficulties arise in areas of poor exposure. Several aspects of the problem should be considered:

1. The effect of topography.
2. The effect of dip (planar structures).
3. The effect of folding.

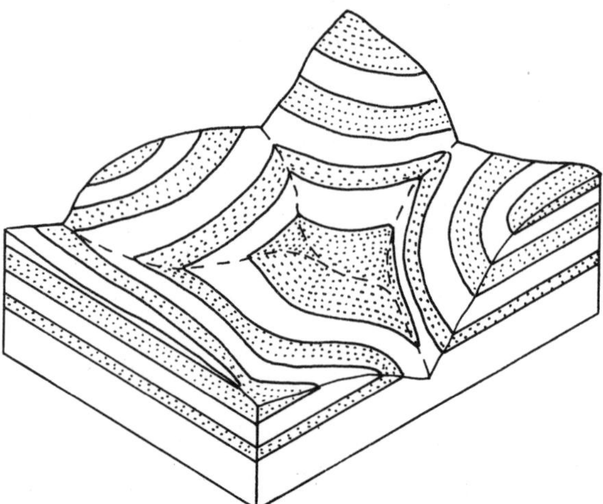

FIGURE 11. Effects of topography on horizontal strata.

In completely flat areas of no dip, the surface formation is continuously at the surface. In areas with an uneven land surface, the contacts of horizontal formations follow topographic contours. Where such beds cross valleys, their outcrop pattern forms a "V" or "U" which points upstream (Fig. 11).

Where the bedding dips upstream crossing valleys on an uneven land surface, then the outcrop pattern will form a "V" or "U" pointing upstream also (Fig. 12), but the "V" or "U" will not be as acute as in Figure 11.

Where the bedding dips downstream at a steeper angle that the stream gradient (Fig. 13), then a "V" or "U" is formed pointing downstream.

Where the bedding dips downstream at a lesser angle than the stream gradient, a "V" or "U" is formed which points upstream (Fig. 14).

Where the bedding is vertical, topography has no effect on the outcrop pattern (Fig. 15).

The outcrop patterns discussed above concern planar structures, beds which are tilted but not

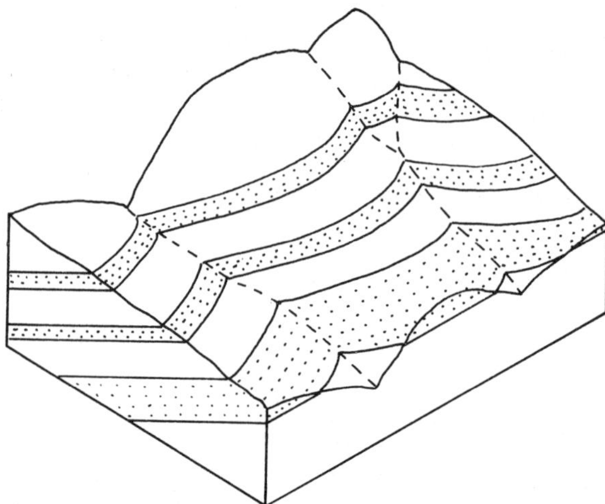

FIGURE 12. Effects of topography on beds which dip upstream.

folded. The outcrop patterns for nonplunging folds are similar to those for dipping strata (Figs. 12–14) except in the area of dip reversal along the axis of the fold (Fig. 16).

The outcrop patterns for plunging folds (Fig. 17) are more complicated than those for nonplunging folds. A zigzag pattern of ridges is formed in areas of vertical relief, as well as in peneplaned areas. Anticlines form "noses" or "U's" whose apexes

FIGURE 13. Effects of topography on beds which dip downstream at an angle greater than the stream gradient.

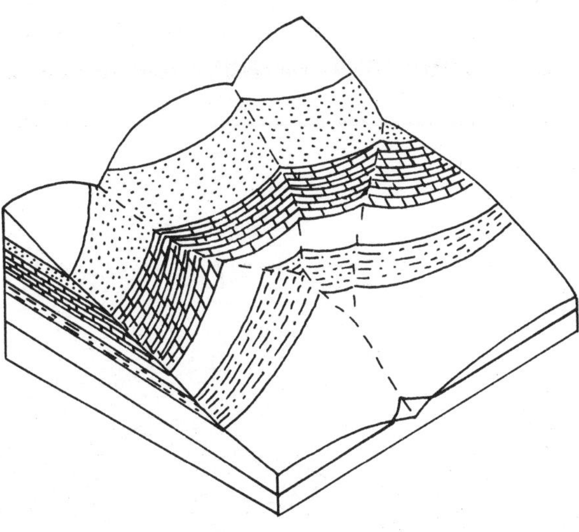

FIGURE 14. Effects of topography on beds which dip downstream at an angle less than the stream gradient.

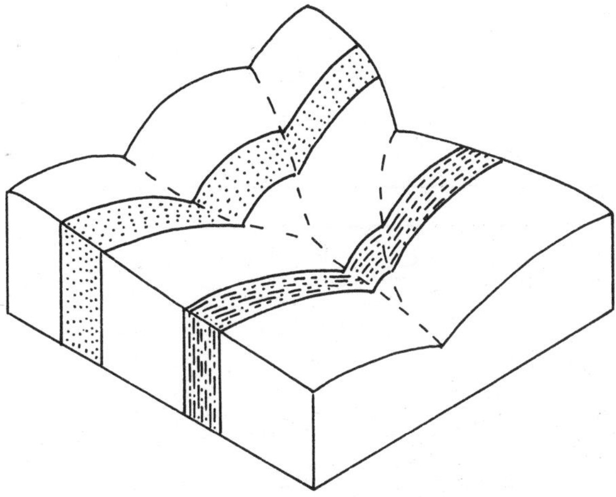

FIGURE 15. Effects of topography on vertical bedding.

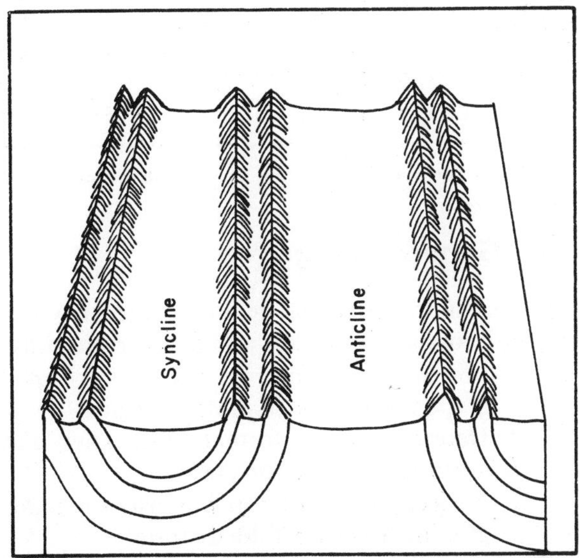

FIGURE 16. Outcrop pattern for nonplunging folds. (Redrawn by permission from A. K. Lobeck, *Geomorphology*, 1939, McGraw-Hill Book Co.)

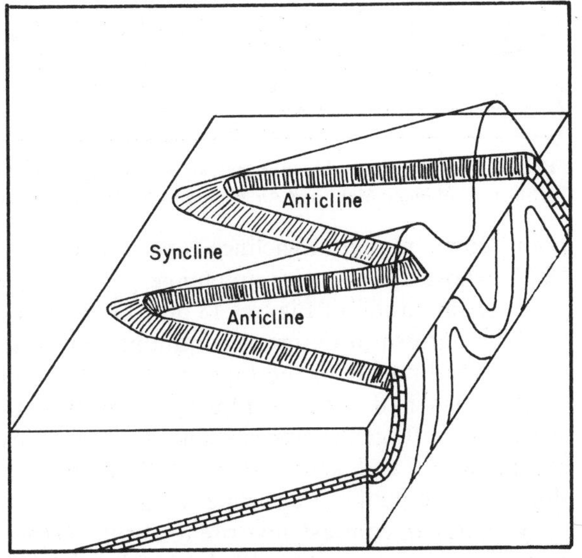

FIGURE 17. Outcrop pattern for plunging folds. (Redrawn by permission from A. K. Lobeck, *Geomorphology*, 1939, McGraw-Hill Book Co.)

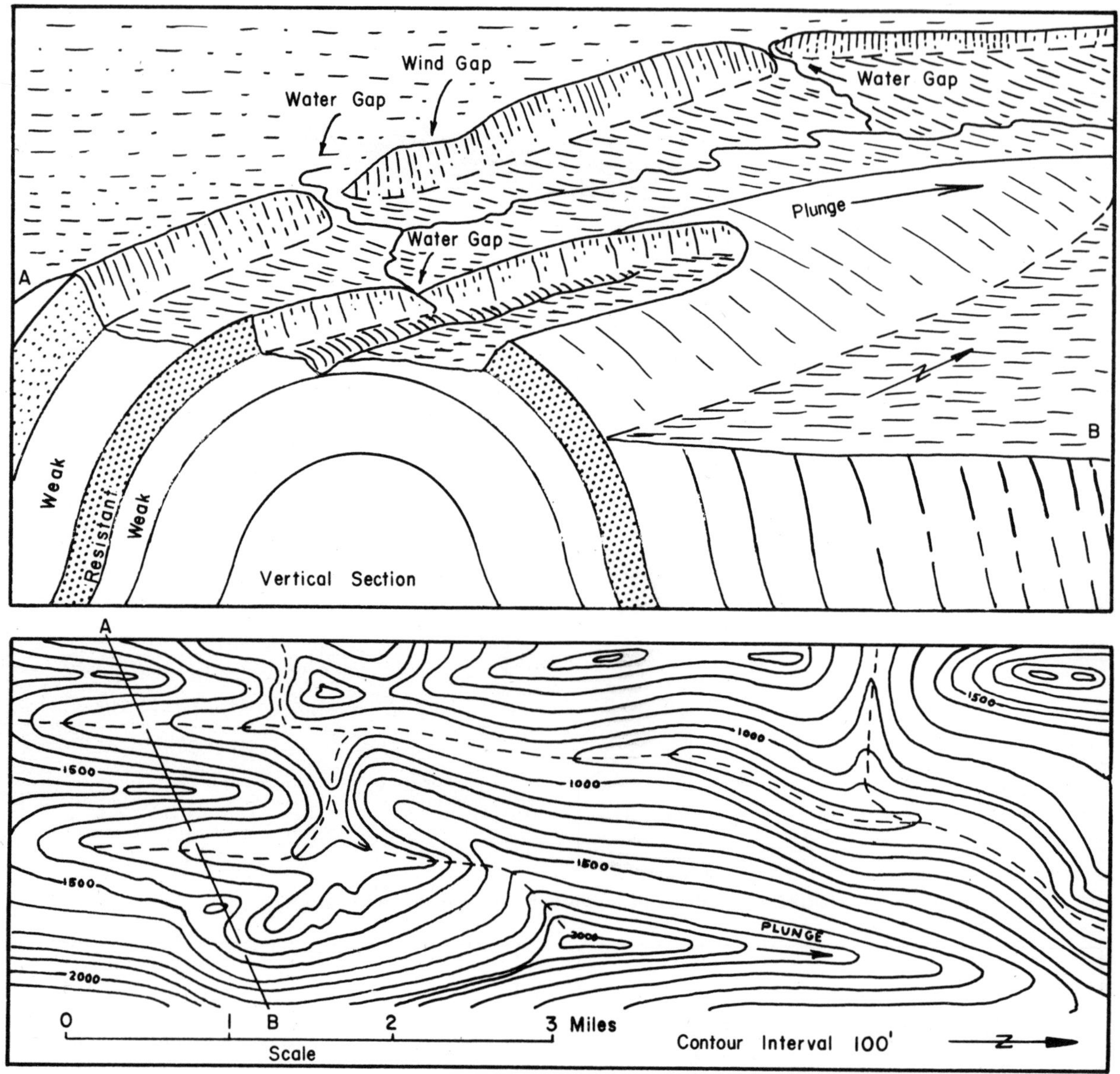

FIGURE 18. Topographic expression of plunging anticline. (Redrawn by permission from A. K. Lobeck and W. J. Tellington, *Military Maps and Air Photographs*, 1944, McGraw-Hill Book Co.)

point down plunge. Synclines form "noses" or "U's" whose apexes point up plunge.

An examination of Figures 18 and 19 indicates that the pattern of outcrops commonly controls the detailed nature of the topography, provided erosion has had time to adjust topography to structure. Soft, gentle slopes form on the plunges of anticlines, and gentle slopes follow the dip slopes on the flanks of anticlines (Fig. 18).

Synclines, in contrast, give rise to abrupt slopes, as the erosion "cuts across" the bedding rather than follows it (Fig. 19).

General Usage

Types of problems that geologists face in working with topographic maps and outcrop patterns:

1. Projection of outcrop pattern on topographic maps for nonfolded strata.
2. Determination of formation thickness and attitude from outcrop patterns.
3. Projection of outcrop patterns on topographic maps for folded strata.

The methods used in solving these problems are demonstrated by means of examples, which follow.

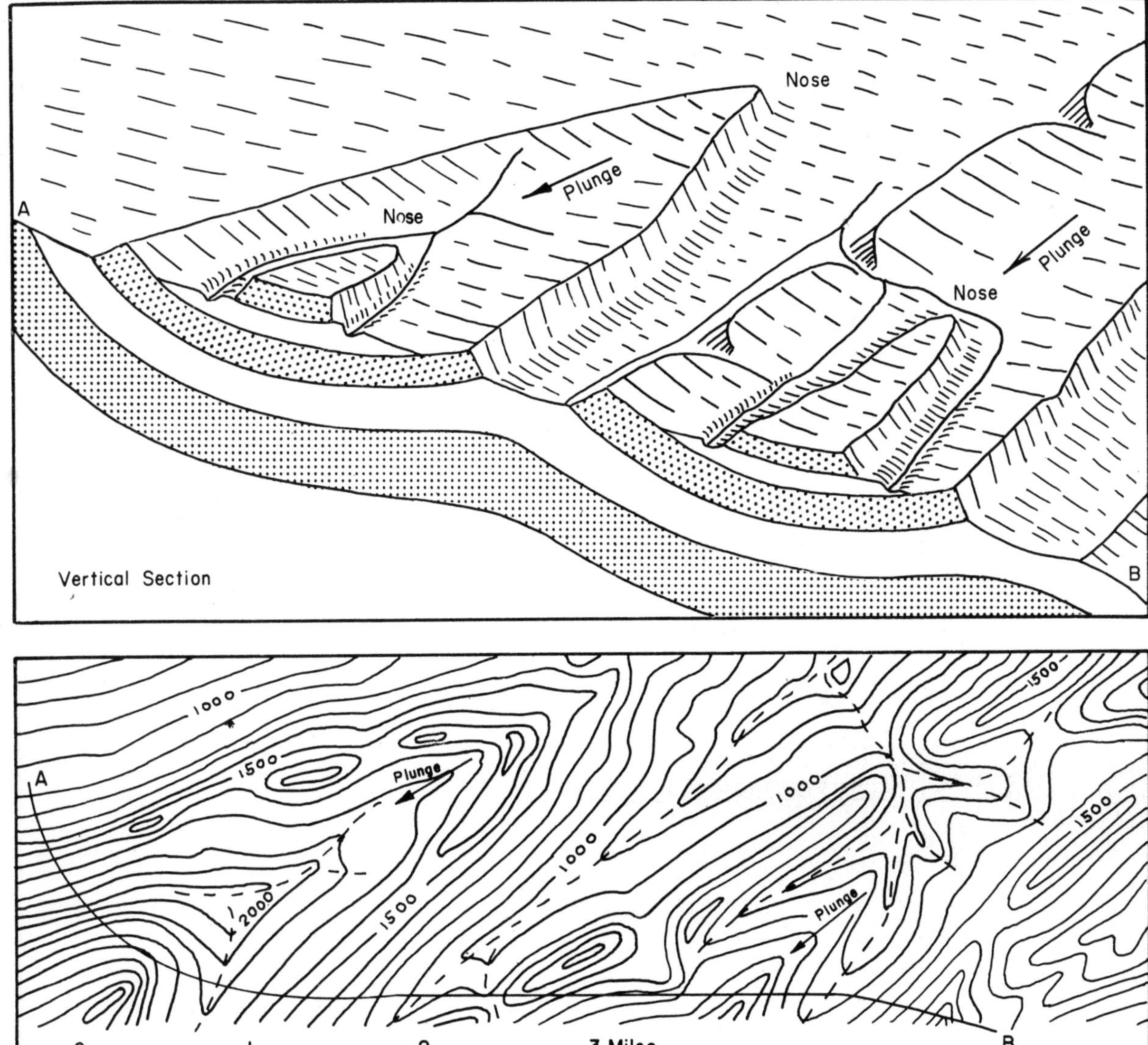

FIGURE 19. Topographic expression of plunging syncline. (Redrawn by permission from A. K. Lobeck and W. J. Tellington, *Military Maps and Air Photographs*, 1944, McGraw-Hill Book Co.)

Application of Descriptive Geometry to Outcrop Determination

PROJECTION OF OUTCROP PATTERNS ON TOPOGRAPHIC MAPS FOR NONFOLDED STRATA

Applications and Limitations: In regions of little outcrop, the ability to predict outcrop patterns commonly must be utilized. This ability can be of great economic value when bedded ore deposits such as iron or coal formations are being exploited in regions with few outcrops.

Data Provided: Topographic map (Fig. 20). The true dip of a uniformly tilted iron formation of Huronian age was measured at 20° at outcrop *A*. The dip direction is due east. The dip measurement was made on a key bed marking the top of the formation. The area is drift-covered for the most part, with few outcrop exposures of the iron formation visible.

Determine: The position of the iron formation

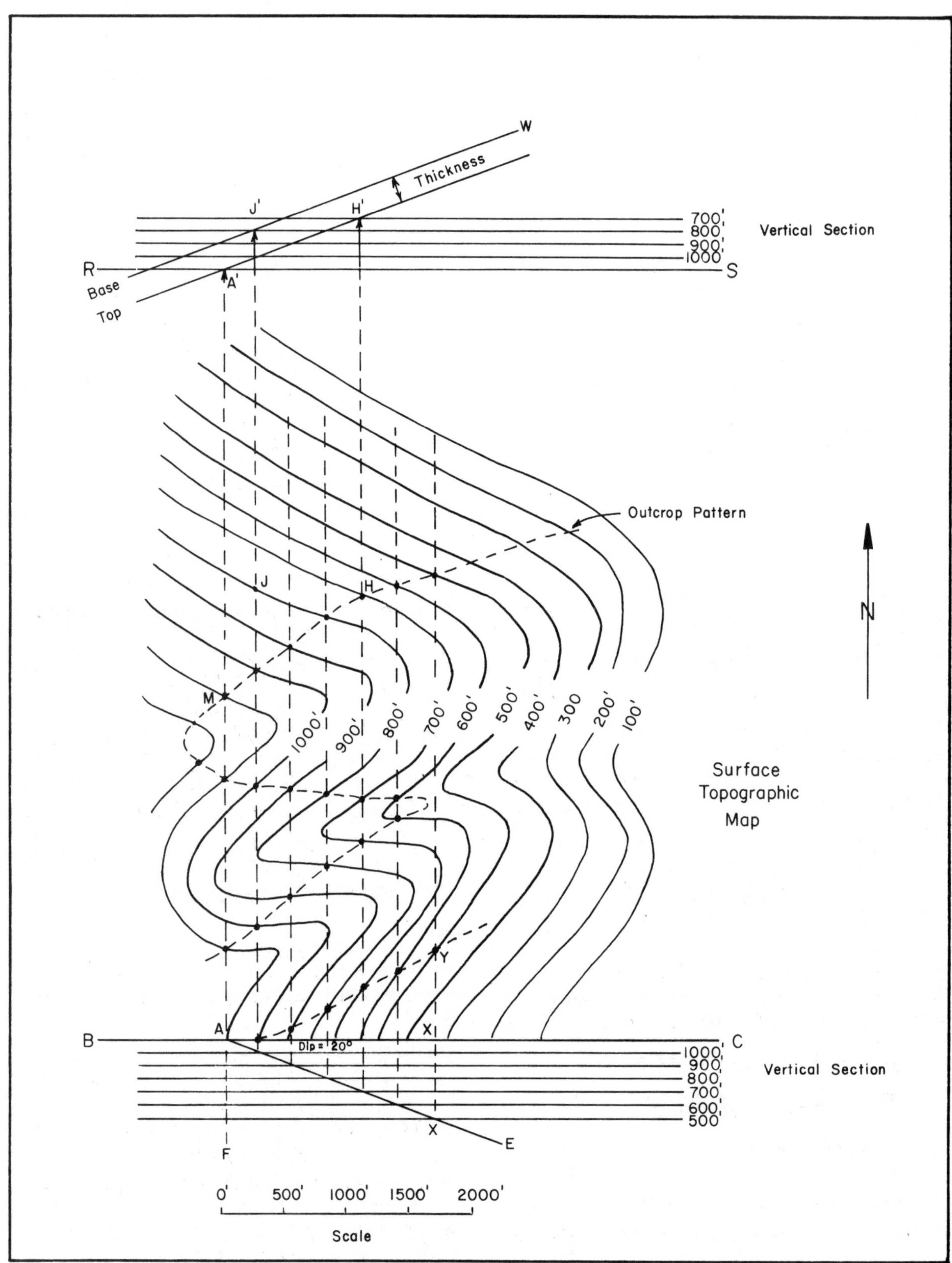

FIGURE 20. Determination of outcrop pattern, formation attitude, and formation thickness for a tilted but nonfolded strata.

below the drift mantle so that a stripping program can be laid out.

Method: Draw in line BAC (Fig. 20) to represent the dip direction. Construct a vertical cross section about BAC as a folding line and lay off the angle $EAC = 20°$ (dip). The elevation at $A = 1100$ feet. Below AB, draw in horizontal lines to represent the 1000-foot, 900-foot, 800-foot etc., elevations. The scale used in the vertical section is the same as that used in the horizontal view. It will be noted that the dip line AE intersects each of the contours, 1000-feet, 900-feet, 800-feet etc. in the vertical section. Project each of these intersection points up to the folding line BC, and then continue each of these lines on, in the horizontal view, perpendicular to BC, until the equivalent topographic contour is intersected. For example, the dip line AE intersects the 500-foot contour in the vertical section at X. X is projected up to the horizontal (X'). A line passing through X' and perpendicular to BC is projected until it intersects the 500-foot topographic contour on the surface map at Y. This procedure is followed for the 600-foot, 700-foot, 800-foot, etc., contours also. By joining the appropriate intersection points on the surface topographic contours, the outcrop pattern for the top of the iron formation may be determined (Fig. 20).

DETERMINATION OF FORMATION THICKNESS AND ATTITUDE FROM OUTCROP PATTERNS

Applications and Limitations: In some regions outcrops are so badly weathered that accurate attitudes cannot be determined by direct means, but it is possible to trace formation contacts by soil colors and so forth. Once the outcrop pattern has been traced on a topographic surface in this way, it is possible to determine its attitude if we have reasonable assurance that the formation is not folded.

Data Provided: Points A, M, and H (Fig. 20) are known to occur on the top of the iron formation at elevations of 1100 feet, 1100 feet, and 700 feet, respectively. Point J (800 feet) is on the base of the iron formation.

Determine: The attitude and thickness of the iron formation.

Method: By joining points A and M which are at the same elevation, the *strike* is established as being due north. A line RS is constructed perpendicular to the extension of AM. A vertical section is constructed about RS as a folding line, and the various topographic contour lines 1000 feet, 900 feet, 800 feet are again shown as they would appear in vertical section. A line through H (elevation, 700 feet) is drawn parallel to AA' and projected into the vertical section until the 700-foot contour line is intersected at H'. The line $A'H'$ now represents the dip line for the iron formation, and the angle $SA'H'$ = the *dip*. A line through J (elevation 800 feet) is drawn parallel to AA' and projected into the vertical section until J' is reached on the 800-foot contour. A line through J parallel to $A'H'$ represents the base of the iron formation as seen in vertical section. A line drawn perpendicular to $A'H'$ (in the vertical section) represents the *stratigraphic thickness* of the iron formation.

PROBLEM 5

PROJECTION OF OUTCROP PATTERNS ON TOPOGRAPHIC MAPS FOR FOLDED STRATA

Applications and Limitations: Geologists are faced with this problem more often than with the nonfolded situation. The method used requires the availability of sufficient elevation points on the strata to construct a structure contour map for the strata.

Data Provided: A topographic map (Fig. 21) on which the structure contours for the desired strata are also shown. The structure contour picture is obtained by methods which will be described in a later chapter.

Determine: The outcrop pattern for the folded strata.

Method: The principle involved is the same as for nonfolded strata. The positions where structure contours intersect their respective topographic contours provide a series of intersection points. Thus the 1600-foot structure contour will intersect the 1600-foot topographic contour at several points on the map (Fig. 21). By joining all adjoining intersection points, the outcrop pattern is determined. In this particular case the student is required to determine the outcrop pattern for the bed whose structure contours are shown in Figure 21. This exercise constitutes Problem 5.

Questions Based on Problem No. 5

1. Would it be possible to determine the general structural picture of this area (Fig. 21) with the topographic information only? If so, how?
2. Do you think that the structures of this area (Fig. 21) have been formed in recent or ancient geological times? Explain.
3. This region (Fig. 21) is located in North America. In what tectonic province do you think that it is located? Explain.
4. What is the approximate average plunge for the folds of this region (Fig. 21)?
5. What is the steepest dip observable in Figure 21?

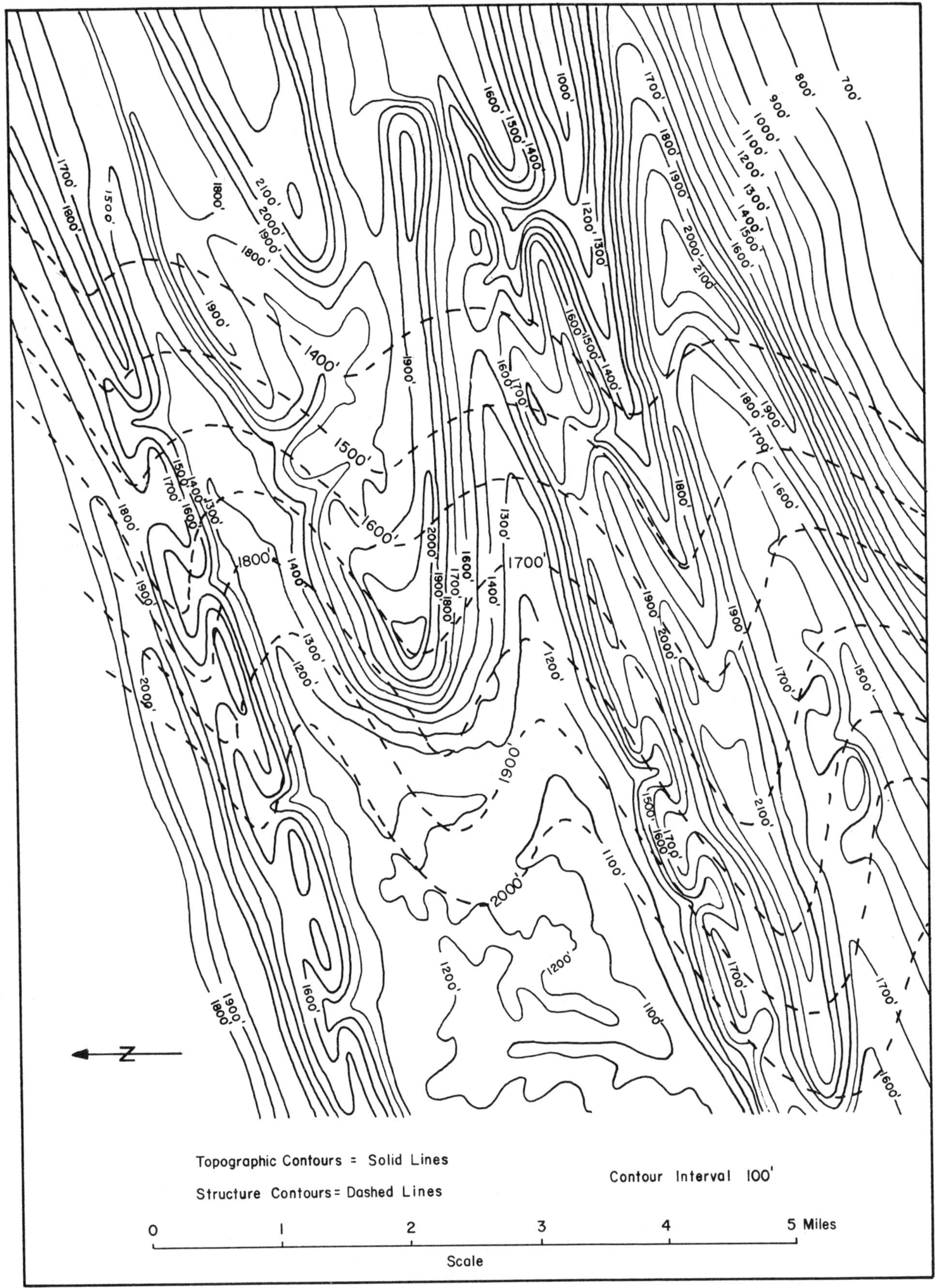

FIGURE 21. Determination of the outcrop pattern for the structure contoured bed.

PROBLEM 6

PROJECTION OF OUTCROPS AND LOCATION OF DISRUPTED ORE SHOOTS

Data Provided: Points *X* and *Y* are located on the base of a limestone formation (tilted but not folded) and point *W* is on the top of the limestone formation. The formation dips due south. A fracture zone striking 135° and dipping due SW at 60° outcrops at point *Z*. The intersection of the fracture zone with the base of the limestone forms an ore shoot. A vertical strike-slip fault striking 070° outcrops at point *V* and is younger than the fracture zone.

Determine: The thickness of the limestone formation and its dip. Show the outcrop pattern for the limestone formation, and determine the outcrop location for the ore shoot and its bearing and inclination. Show the surface projection of the point where the ore shoot is terminated by the strike-slip fault, and determine the elevation of this intersection.

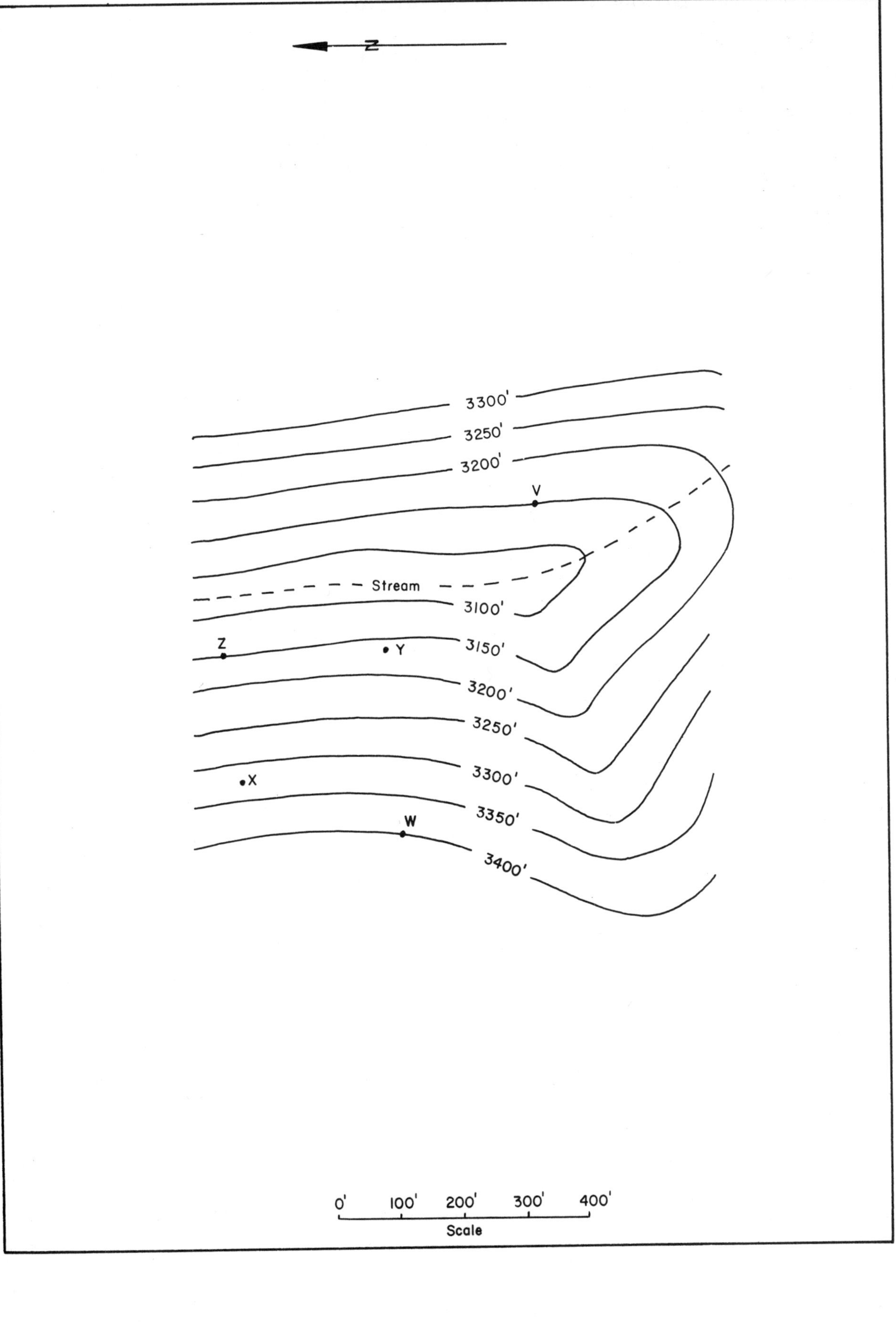
N
3300'
3250'
3200'
V
Stream
3100'
Z
Y
3150'
3200'
3250'
X
3300'
W
3350'
3400'
0'
100'
200'
300'
400'
Scale

References

Dake, C. L., and Brown, J. S. (1925), *Interpretation of Topographic and Geologic Maps,* McGraw-Hill Book Co. Inc., 514 pp.

Eardley, A. J. (1942), *Aerial Photographs, Their Use and Interpretation,* Harper & Brothers, 203 pp.

Lahee, F. H. (1941), *Field Geology,* 4th ed., McGraw-Hill Book Co. Inc., 853 pp.

Lobeck, A. K. (1924), *Block Diagrams,* John Wiley & Sons, Inc., 206 pp.

Lobeck, A. K. (1939), *Geomorphology,* McGraw-Hill Book Co. Inc., 731 pp.

Lobeck, A. K., and Tellington, Wentworth J. (1944), *Military Maps and Air Photographs,* McGraw-Hill Book Co. Inc., 256 pp.

Low, Julian W. (1957), *Geologic Field Methods,* Harper & Brothers, 489 pp.

CHAPTER 3

Construction of Geological Cross Sections

Principles Involved

Geological cross sections illustrate conditions in the subsurface and thus are of tremendous value in economic geology. Cross sections are not difficult to draw when adequate subsurface information is available from bore holes or geophysical surveys, but they may be extremely difficult to construct when only surface information is available.

Folded and faulted layered sequences and igneous intrusions are the main types of geological features which appear in vertical view. An understanding of the fundamental processes involved in folding, faulting, and intrusion is thus an essential requirement for good cross-section construction.

When a region is subjected to stress, the resulting strain will depend upon the competency of the lithological framework involved. The competency of the rocks present is a function of confining pressure, temperature, degree of compaction, fluid content, and so forth. Usually both competent and incompetent beds are present in a region so that various deformational patterns result.

There are three main folding processes: *flexure or competent folding, flow or incompetent folding,* and *shear folding.* There are also a number of special varieties of each process. Figures 22 to 33 and Figure 37 illustrate several types of folding processes. Note the different results for competent and incompetent formations.

There are three main faulting processes involved in the deformation of rocks, and these are dependent upon the nature of the stress application. A brief review of stress principles will be helpful here. In homogeneous isotropic materials, under compression, the compressive stress can be expressed in terms of a set of three mutually perpendicular axes: maximum, minimum, and intermediate stress axes (Fig. 34). When rigid materials are stressed beyond their strength (breaking point), rupture results. The rupture takes the form of two sets of shear planes. Numerous observations in the field and in the laboratory indicate that these two shear directions are bisected by the major stress axis in such a way that this axis forms an angle of approximately 30° with each of the shears (Fig. 35). The intermediate stress axis is parallel to the line of intersection of the two shear planes. The air earth interface is a surface of zero shear and is thus normal to one of the three stress directions. Consequently, the major stress axis is usually horizontal or vertical (Fig. 36).

Figure 36 shows that there are three main fault processes: *thrust faulting, normal faulting, wrench or strike-slip faulting.* Strike-slip faults appear as vertical lines on cross sections and thus present no problem.

Normal faults result mainly from tensional stress and usually form in only slightly deformed environments, although they may also occur in areas which have undergone intense previous deformation. Thus their attitudes remain fairly constant, and they can usually be extended to depth with some degree of confidence (Fig. 44).

Thrust faults are commonly associated with folding processes and may change their attitude at depth (Figs. 38–46). These figures indicate how rock competency controls folding and faulting processes.

General Usage

Accurate cross sections of folded and faulted structures are of great significance in exploration (Figs. 47–50). The ability to predict the position of structural features in the subsurface will allow substantial savings on drilling expenses and will greatly enhance the geologist's reputation if the prediction is confirmed by drilling.

"Compressed" and "exploded" sections are very

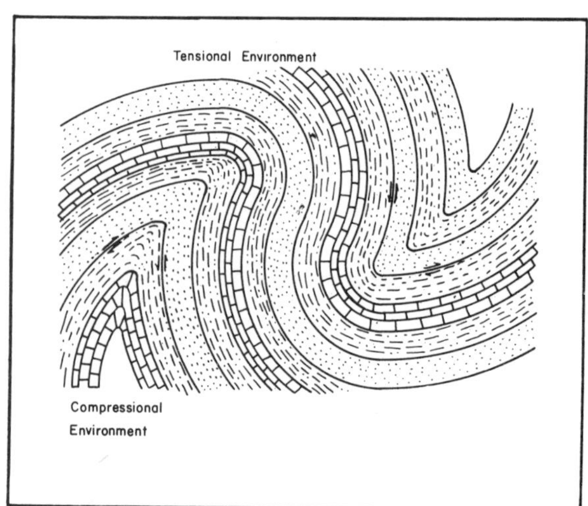

FIGURE 22. Competent or flexure folding. Scale: 1″ = 2000′. Note change in folds' shape with depth.

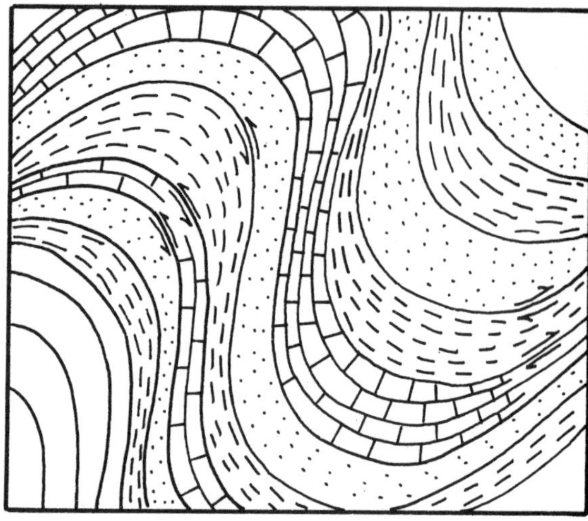

FIGURE 23. Incompetent or flow folding. Scale: 1″ = 2000′.

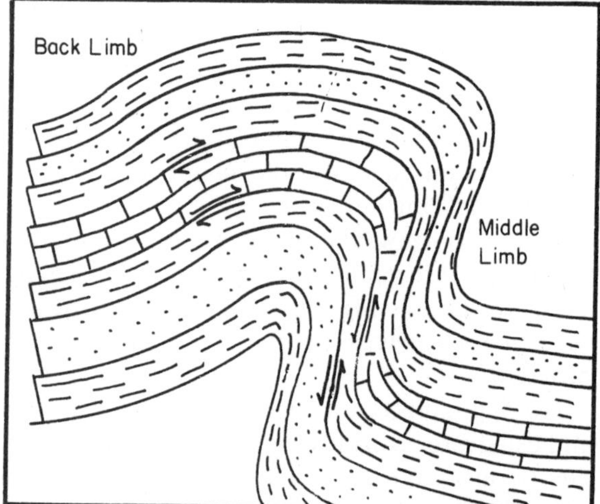

FIGURE 24. Competent folding on the back limbs and thinning on the middle limbs. Scale: 1″ = 2000′.

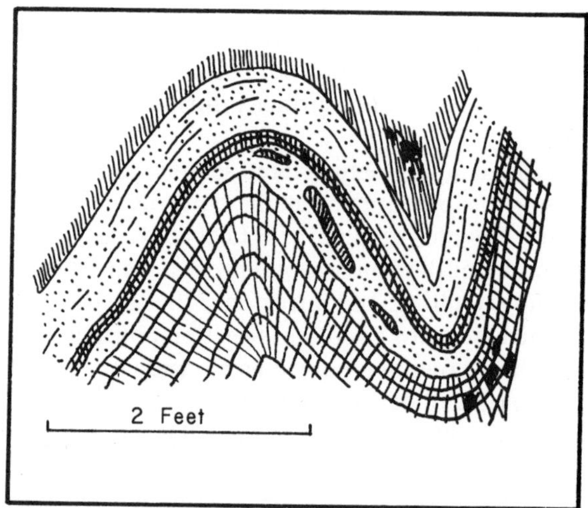

FIGURE 25. Competent folding in sandstone; fracture cleavage in slate. (Redrawn from E. Cloos and A. Hietanen [1941], *Geol. Soc. Am.*, Spec. Paper 35.)

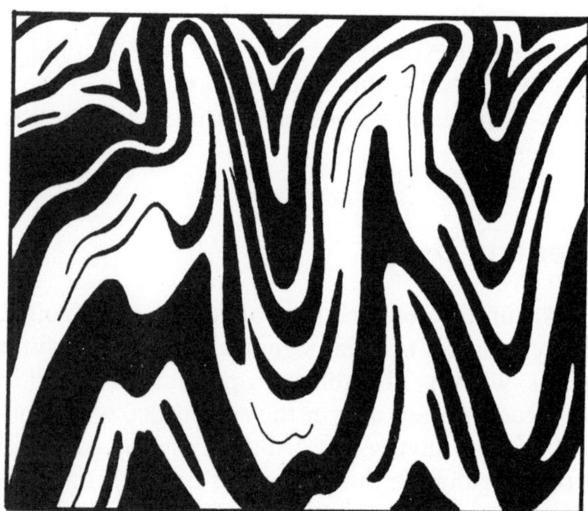

FIGURE 26. Flow folding (plastic flow). Scale: 1″ = 1000′.

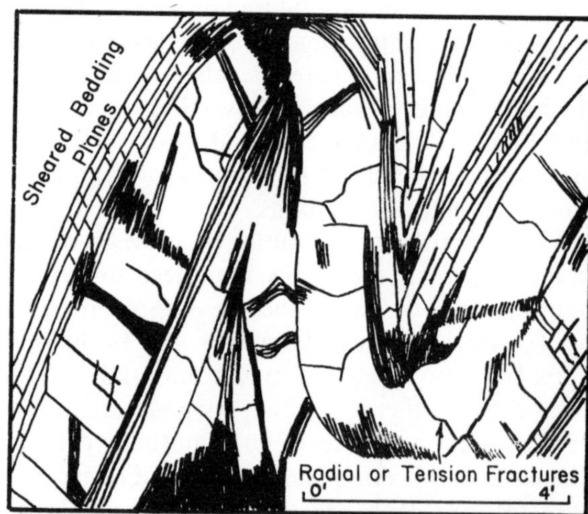

FIGURE 27. Competent folding with radial tension fractures and concentric bedding plane shears. (Redrawn from a photograph of R. Blanchard [1942], in W. H. Newhouse *et al.*, *Ore Deposits as Related to Structural Features*, Princeton University Press.)

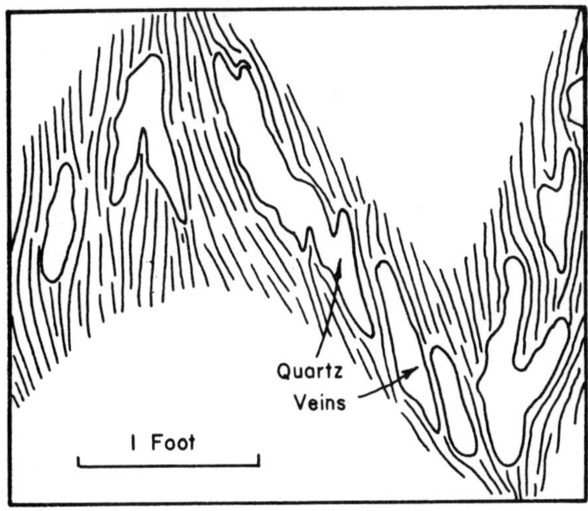

FIGURE 28. Shear folding in alternating competent and incompetent strata. (Redrawn from E. Cloos [1937], *The Application of Recent Structural Methods in the Interpretation of the Crystalline Rocks of Maryland,* vol. 13, Maryland Geological Survey.)

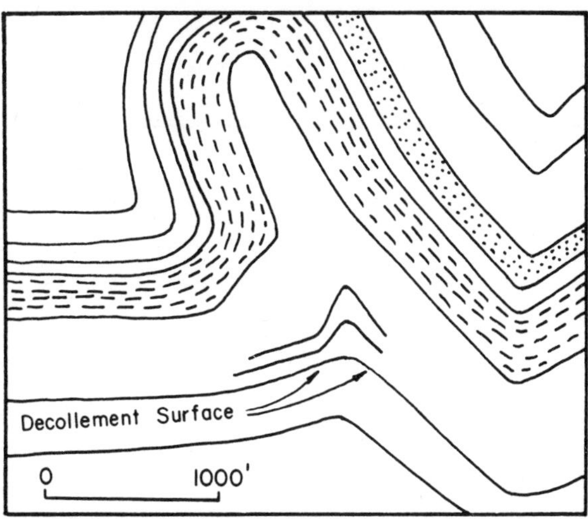

FIGURE 29. Disharmonic folding of a series involving a "decollement" or "detachment" horizon. (Redrawn from N. H. Darton [1940], *U.S. Geol. Surv.,* Prof. Paper 193D.)

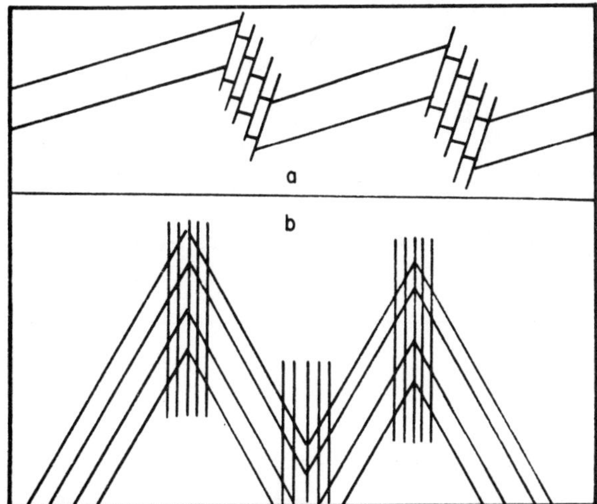

FIGURE 30. (a) Chevron folding (concentration of cleavage on middle limb). (b) Accordion folding (concentration of shearing in axial area of fold). (Both are redrawn by permission from L. U. DeSitter, *Structural Geology,* 1956, McGraw-Hill Book Co.)

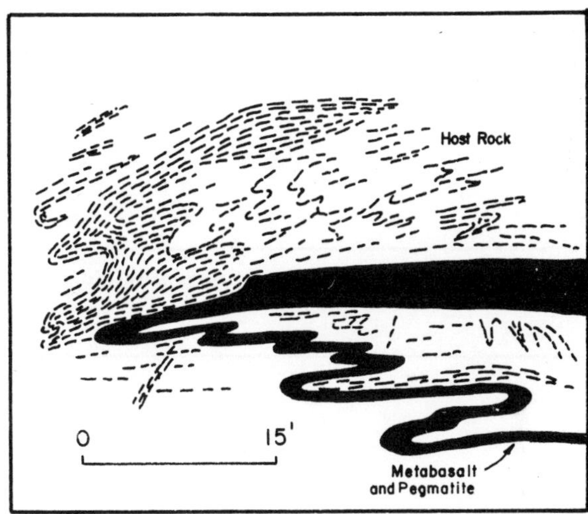

FIGURE 31. Ptygmatic folding. Veins of metabasalt and pegmatite folded ptygmatically by host rock movement. (Redrawn from J. J. Sederholm [1926], *Bull. Comm. Geol. Finlande,* no. 77.)

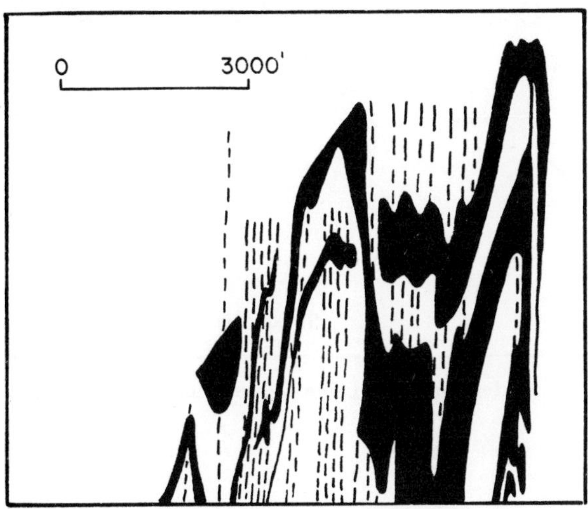

FIGURE 32. Combination of flow folding and shear folding. (Redrawn from M. D. Garrety [1943], *Chem. Eng. and Min. Review,* Melbourne, Australia.)

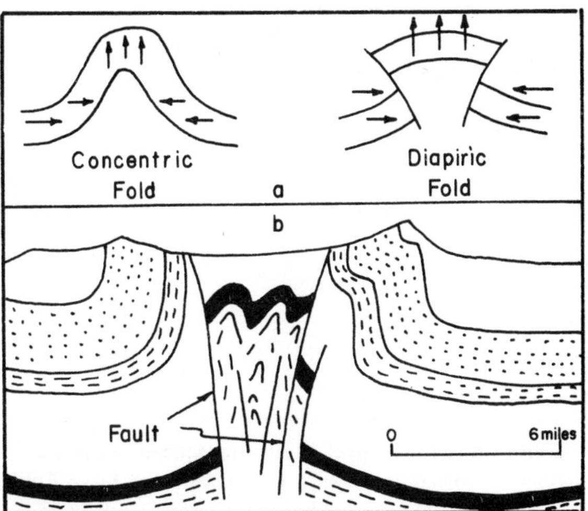

FIGURE 33. Diapiric or piercement folding. Results from a combination of horizontal and vertical movement in an initially competent fold. (Redrawn by permission from L. U. DeSitter, *Structural Geology,* 1956, McGraw-Hill Book Co.)

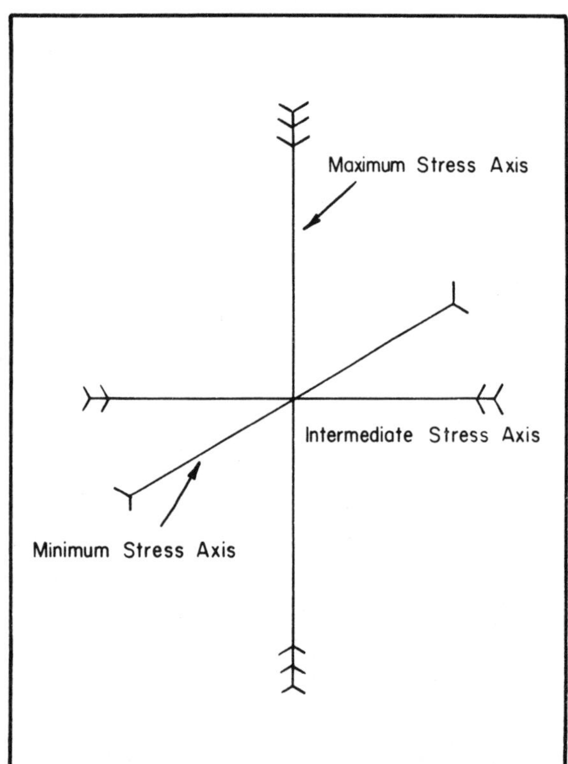

FIGURE 34. Axes of the stress ellipsoid.

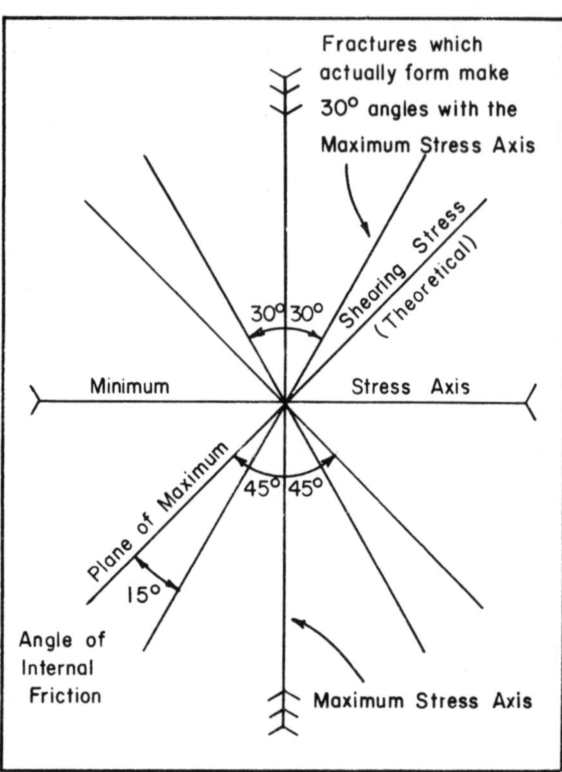

FIGURE 35. Relation of fractures to maximum stress direction.

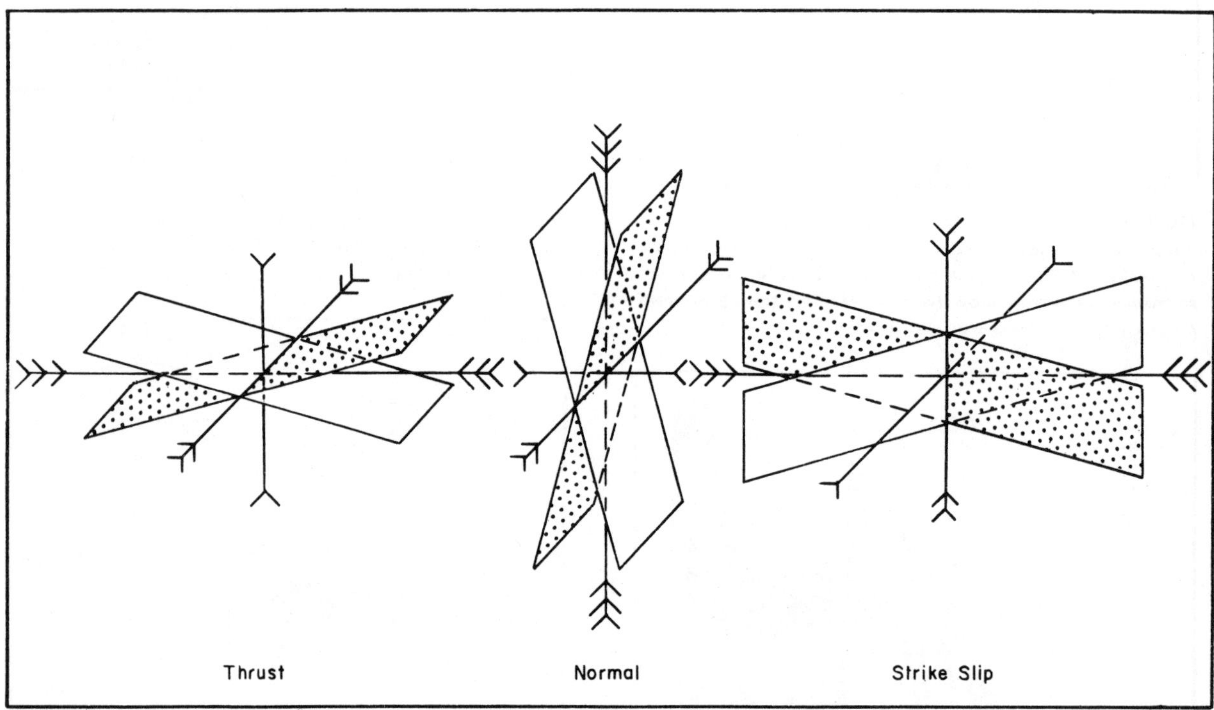

FIGURE 36. Theoretical fault orientations. (Redrawn from E. M. Anderson [1951], *The Dynamics of Faulting and Dyke Formation with Applications to Britain,* Oliver & Boyd Publishers.)

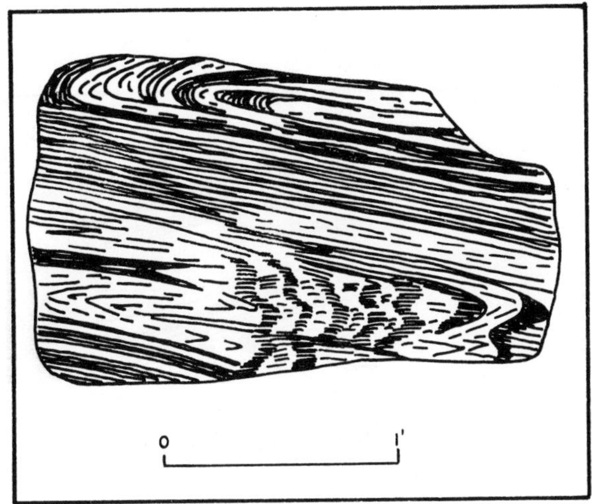

FIGURE 37. Isoclinal flow folding and shear folding in biotite garnet schist near Rawling, New York. (Redrawn from R. Balk [1936], *Bull. Geol. Soc. Am.*, vol. 47.)

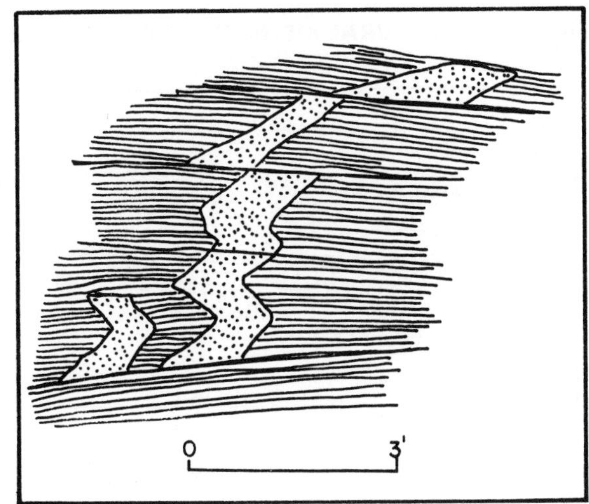

FIGURE 38. Initiation of faulting parallel to cleavage development in the Wissahickon schist. (Redrawn from E. Cloos and A. Hietanen [1941], *Geol. Soc. Am.*, Spec. Paper 35.)

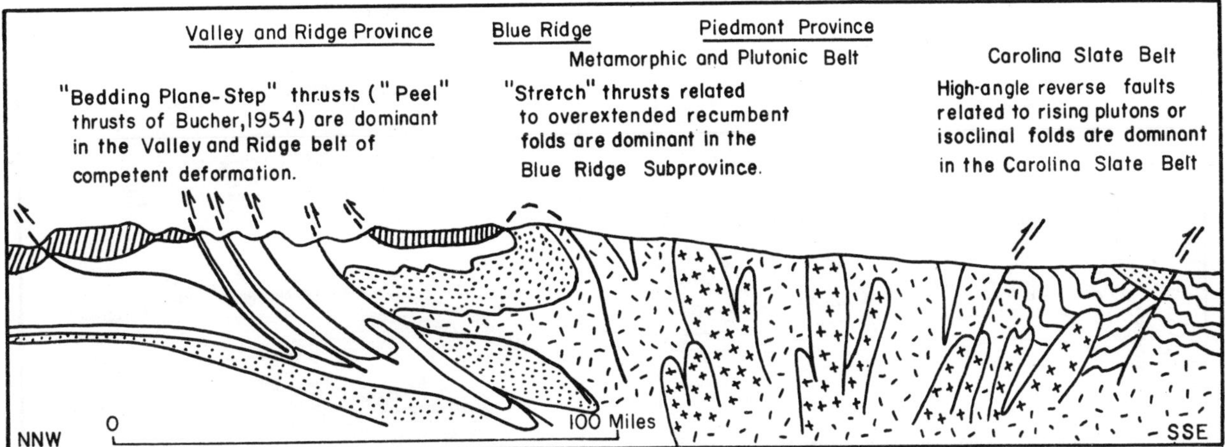

FIGURE 39. Diagrammatic cross section illustrating the positions of various thrust-fault types in the tectonic framework of the Appalachians. (Redrawn from P. B. King [1950], *Bull. Am. Assoc. Petrol. Geol.*, vol. 34.)

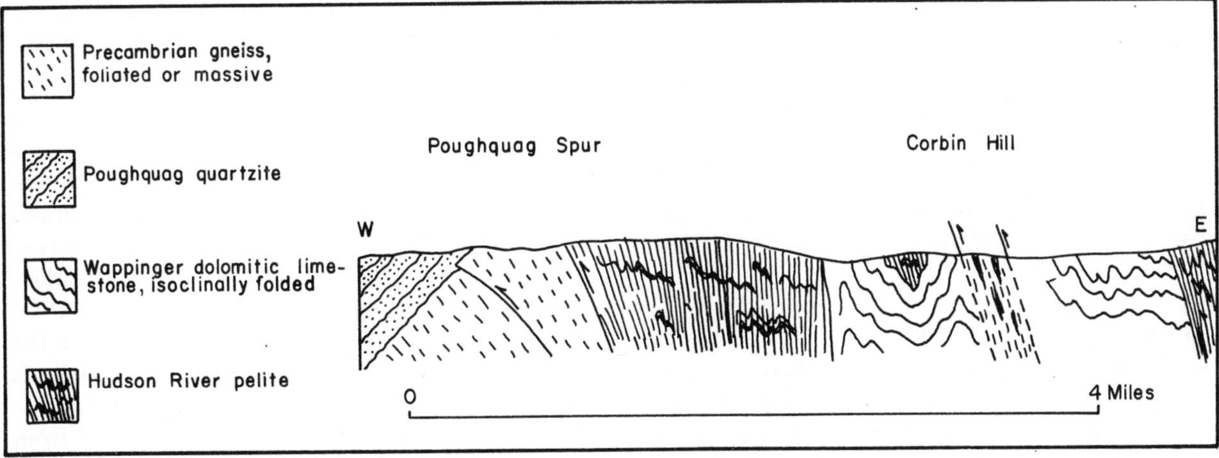

FIGURE 40. Thrust faults related to isoclinal folding, shear folding, and plutonic intrusion in a highly deformed portion of the Appalachians. (Redrawn from R. Balk [1936], *Bull. Geol. Soc. Am.*, vol. 47.)

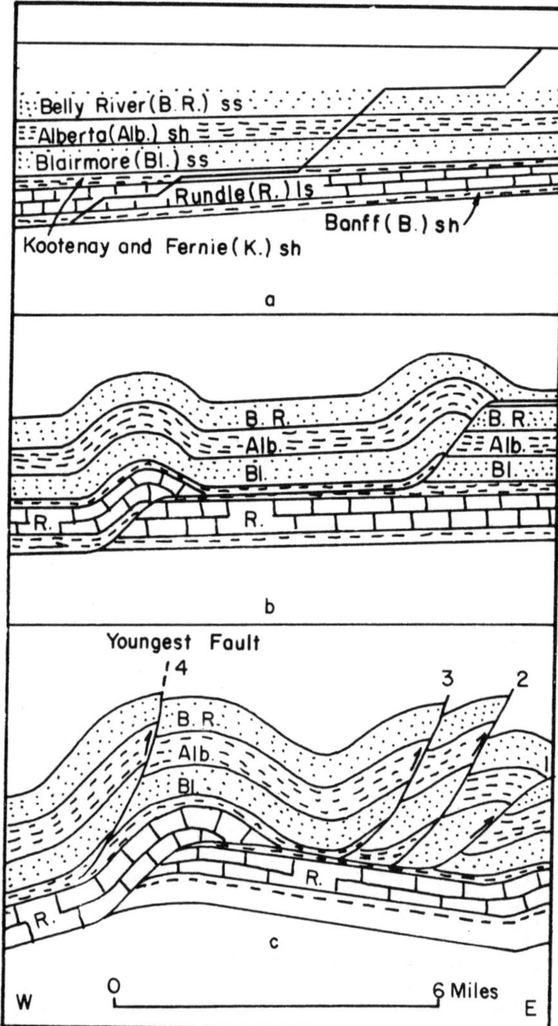

FIGURE 41. Steps involved in "bedding plane-step" thrusting on the disturbed margin of the Western Canada Basin: (a) Bedded sequence before thrusting. Note that faulting is initiated on the incompetent Banff "glide horizon" and moves along this bedding plane until bedding plane friction becomes greater than the rupture strength of the overlying Rundle limestone; (b) Bedding plane-step thrusting. Note the drag effect produced as the hanging wall moves up and against the "buttress" of the footwall; (c) Development of back limb thrust faulting and steepening of main thrust (fault no. 1). (Modified from R. J. W. Douglas [1950], *Geol. Surv. Can.*, Mem. 255.)

FIGURE 42. Steps involved in development of thrust faults related to stretching and thinning of middle limb in overturned anticlines in the Alps. (After Albert Heim [1919], Geologie der Schweiz, C. H. Tanchnitz, Leipzig.)

useful in illustrating the three-dimensional aspects of mountain ranges and petroleum traps (Fig. 71, p. 57). They achieve the same results as isometric diagrams of ore bodies. Isometric diagrams (Figs. 159–162, pp. 155–156) show ore bodies in three dimensions by illustrating the ore body on the various levels of a mine. They are best adapted to ore bodies with greater vertical than horizontal dimension. Petroleum reservoirs, on the other hand, have greater horizontal than vertical dimension and are best illustrated in three dimensions by stacking or compressing vertical sections close together. Eardley (Fig. 51) has attempted to arrange "compressed" vertical sections isometrically, but the distance between vertical sections does not permit much plan view expression of the geological features. The individual features can be traced from section to section with more ease in Figure 71, page 57.

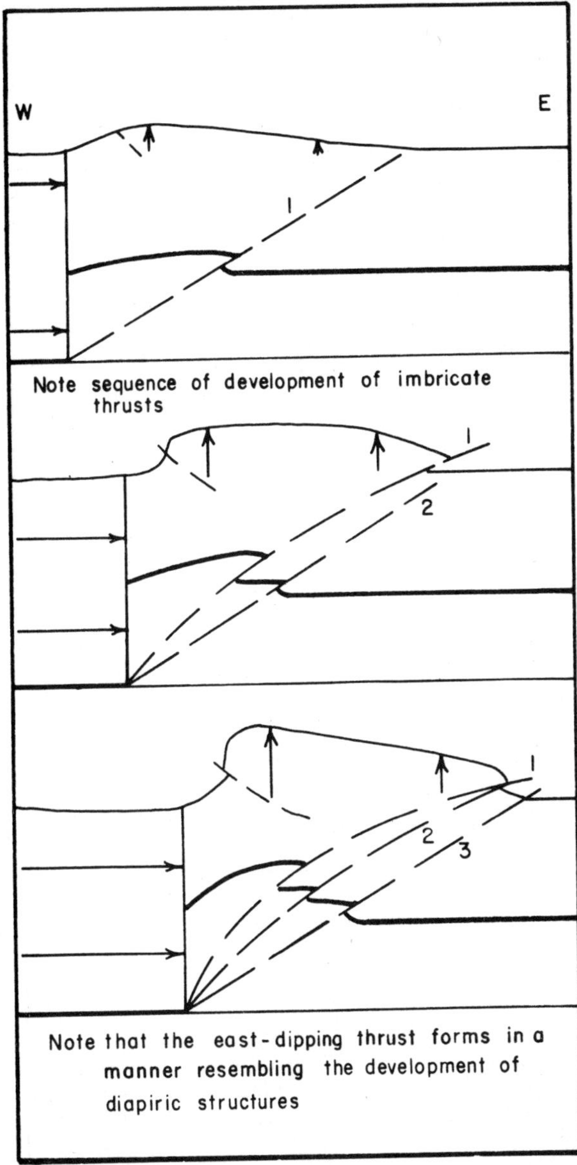

W
E
Note sequence of development of imbricate thrusts
Note that the east-dipping thrust forms in a manner resembling the development of diapiric structures

FIGURE 43. Development of imbricate thrusts, "box" anticlines, and subsidiary reverse thrusts. (From T. A. Link [1949], *Bull. Am. Assoc. Petrol. Geol.*, vol. 33.)

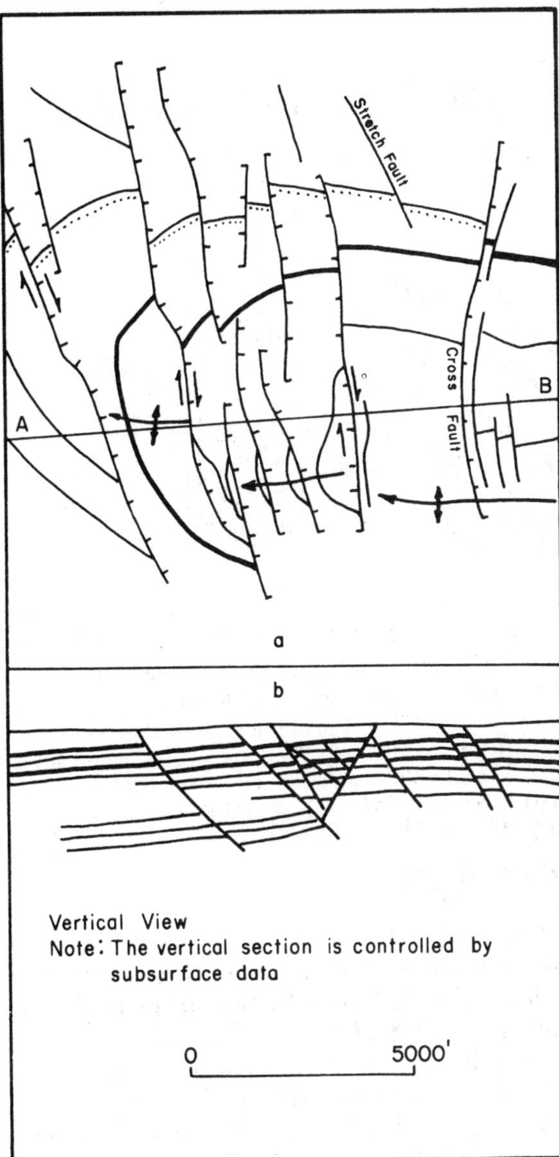

FIGURE 44. Development of cross faults (tensional) and stretch faults (shear) on the crest of the Wilmington anticline, California. (From R. Winterthurn [1943], *California Dept. Nat. Res., Div. of Mines, Bull. 118.*)

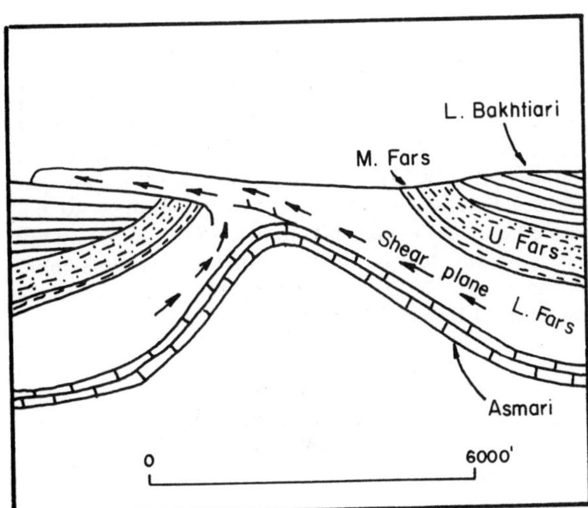

FIGURE 45. Development of "gamma structure" in Iran. This results from the excessive plasticity or incompetency of the Lower Fars evaporites. (From H. G. Busk [1299], *Earth Flexures*, Cambridge University Press.)

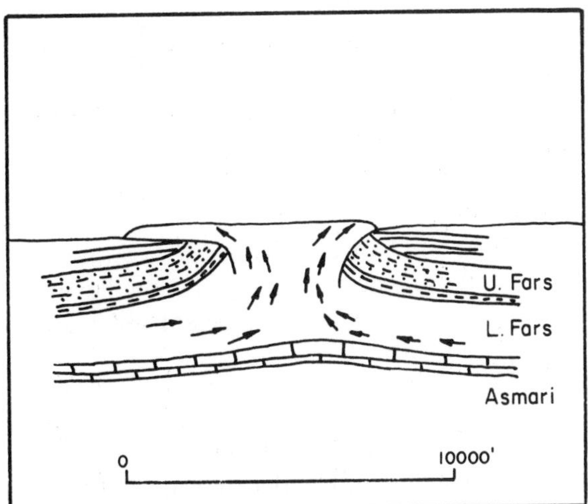

FIGURE 46. Development of "omega structure" in Iran. (From H. G. Busk [1929], *Earth Flexures*, Cambridge University Press.)

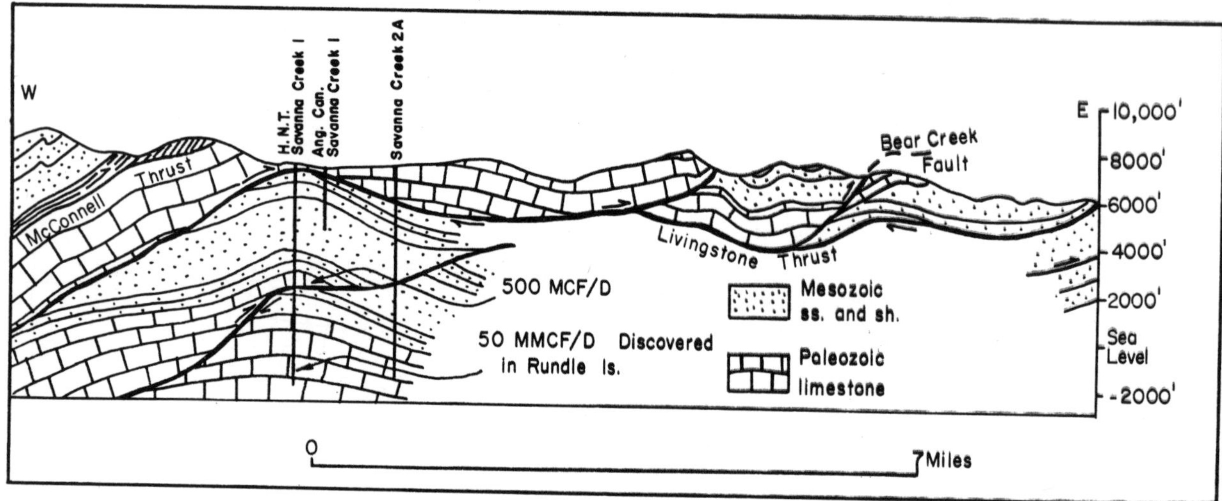

FIGURE 47. Cross section of Savanna Creek structure, Alberta, Canada. The Anglo Canadian well was drilled in the 1930's and was abandoned after passing through the Livingston thrust fault. The Husky-Northern Natural Gas-Target Savanna Creek No. 1 well found a small amount of gas (500 MCF/D) in the Paleozoic limestone above the lower thrust fault but did not penetrate the main limestone porosity before passing through the limestone back into Mesozoic sandstone. The mechanics of faulting involved led the operators to believe that an anticline would exist below the fault also. If this lower fault had been related to asymmetric folding, then a syncline would have occurred below the fault. (Redrawn from an illustration by D. K. Norris which appeared in G. S. Hume [1957], *Bull. Geol. Soc. Am.*, vol. 62.)

Application

A number of geological cross-section construction methods for folds have been evolved, and the method selected should be dependent upon the competency of the rocks involved and the nature of the deformation. When faults occur in folded sequences a careful interpretation of the faulting process involved will permit the prediction of the fault's position at depth, provided sufficient information regarding the angular relations of the faults and the bedding is available.

All of the methods require careful surface geological mapping of attitudes, fault-bedding angular relationships, formation thicknesses, and small-scale structural features along the line of section.

The fold cross-section construction methods to be described in this book are as follows:

1. The "arc" method for flexure (competent) folding.
2. The "arc" method combined with freehand drawing for combined "flow-flexure" folds involving both competent and incompetent beds.
3. The "boundary ray" method for flexure folds involving competent and incompetent beds which have undergone partial compaction rather than plastic flow.

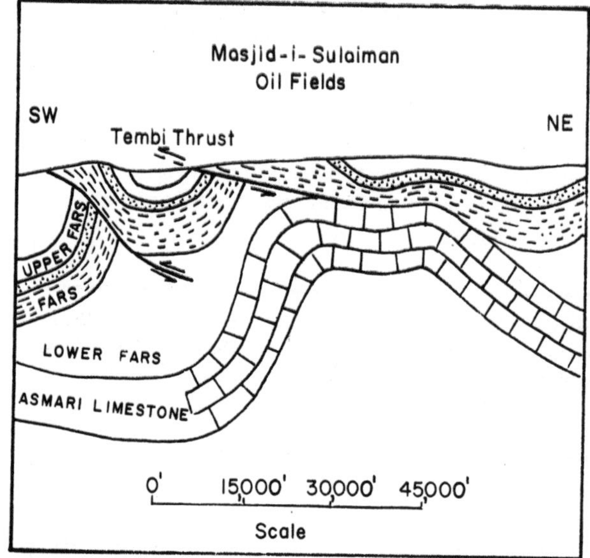

FIGURE 48. Cross section of the important Masjid-i-Sulaiman oil field, Iran. This cross section shows the discordance between surface structure (controlled by the incompetent Fars evaporites, sands, and shales) and the underlying structure of the competent Asmari limestone. (Redrawn from G. W. Lees [1953], *The Science of Petroleum*, Oxford University Press.)

4. The "right section" method for plunging folds. This method is used for flexures involving either competent or incompetent beds.

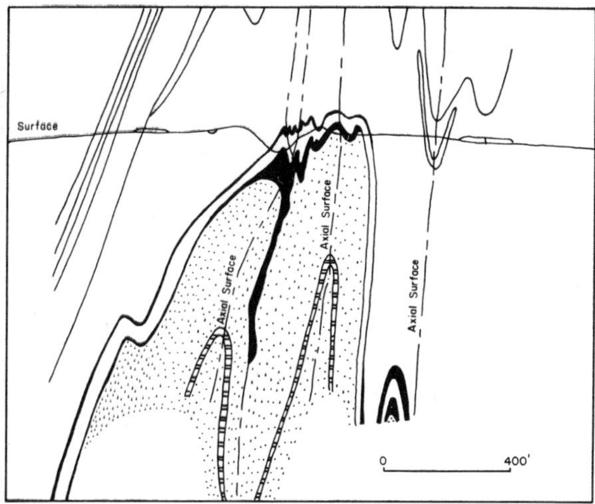

FIGURE 49. Vertical east-west cross section through the Broken Hill district, New South Wales, Australia. Lead zinc ore bodies (black) are concordant with the bedding in the folded gneiss. Note the extreme attenuation in the axis of the synclinal fold near the crest of the major anticline. (Redrawn from J. K. Gustafson, H. C. Burrell, and M. D. Garrety [1950], *Bull. Geol. Soc. Am.*, vol. 61.)

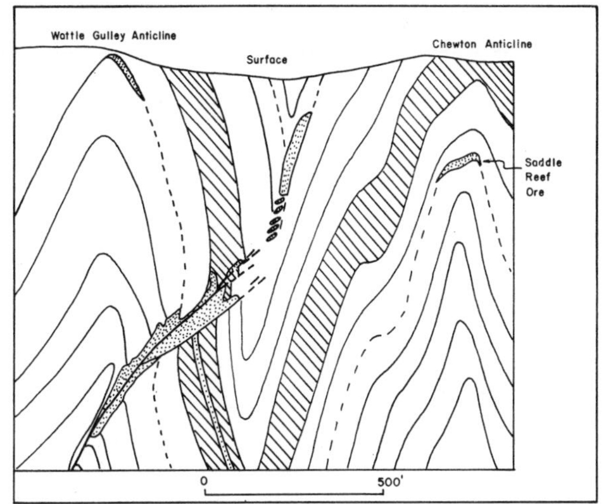

FIGURE 50. Vertical east-west cross section through the Wattle Gulley and Chewton anticlines, Chewton Goldfield, Victoria, Australia. The ore body (stippled) is related to thrust fault and to saddle reef openings on the anticlinal crest. This thrust fault probably originated because of lack of space in the core of the Wattle Gulley anticline, and its path is controlled also by axial plane cleavage in the synclinal axis. (Redrawn from D. E. Thomas [1953], *Geology of Australian Ore Deposits*, Aust. Inst. Min. Met.)

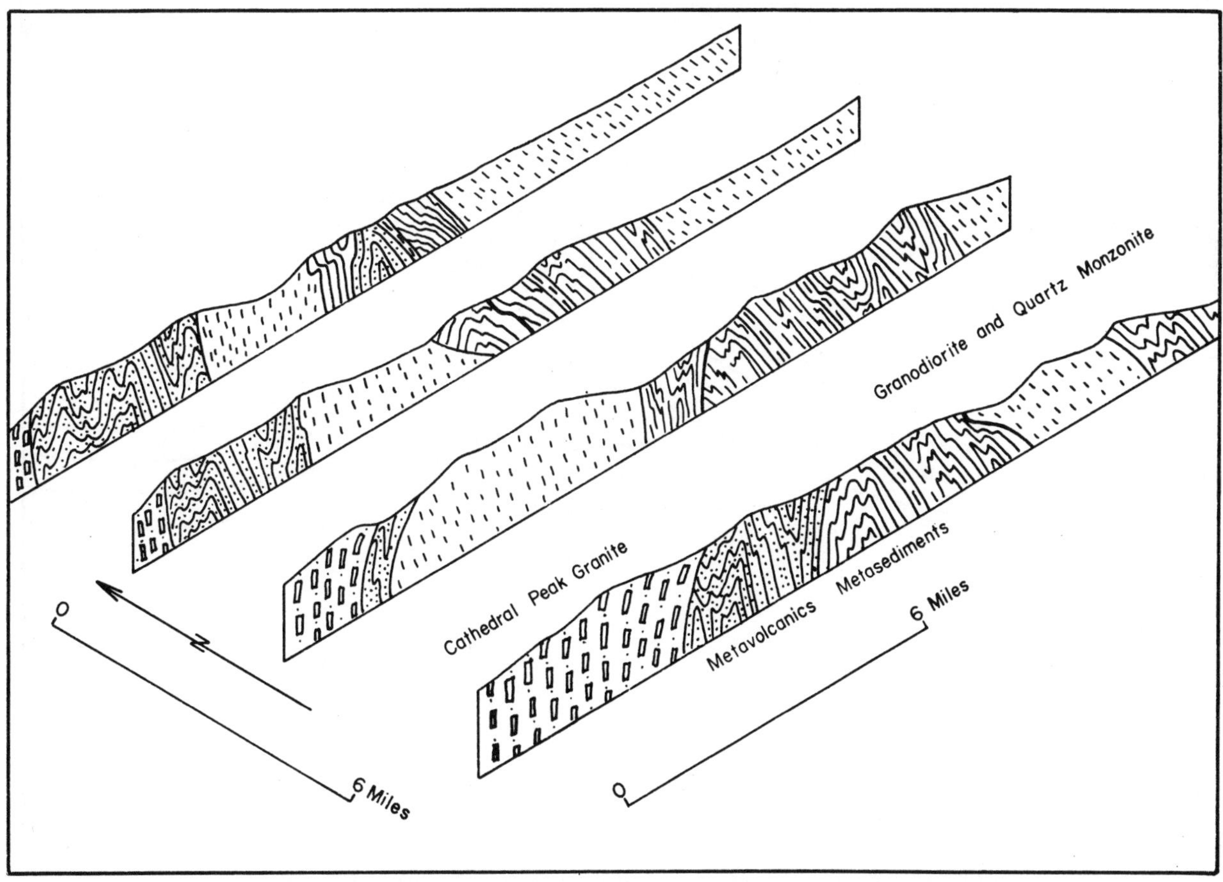

FIGURE 51. Vertical structure sections (arranged isometrically) across the southern Sierra Nevada Mountains (adapted from E. B. Mayo, 1941). (Redrawn from A. J. Eardley [1951], *Structural Geology of North America*, Harper & Brothers.)

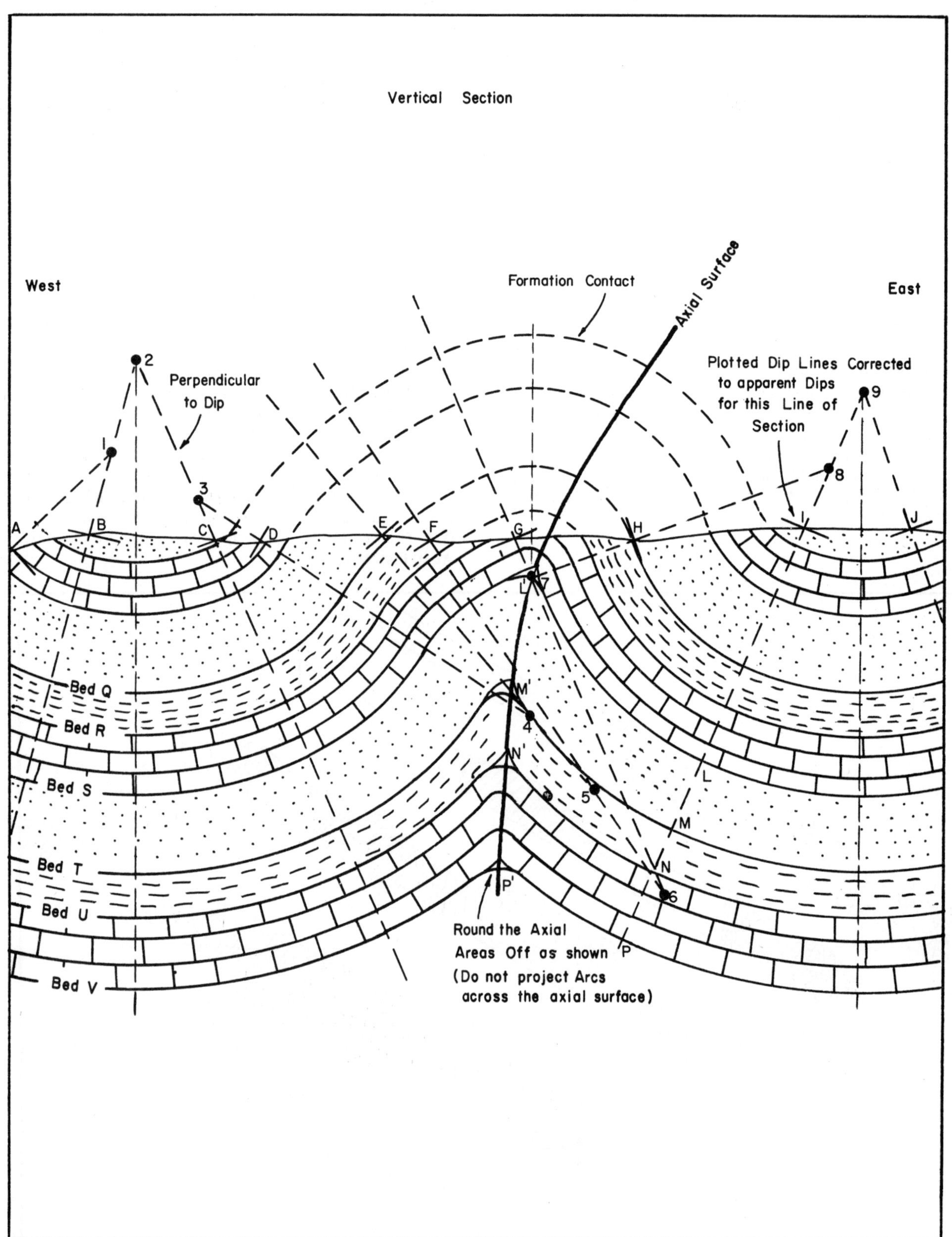

FIGURE 52. Construction of geological cross sections by the "arc" method.

Each of these methods is satisfactory when stress application and rock failure are uniform. Commonly, however, it is necessary to deviate from the normal procedure to make subsurface projections of folds and faults "fit" the geological contacts at the other end of the cross section. This is because stress application and rock failure are not usually uniform and the lithological framework includes rocks of varying competencies.

CONSTRUCTION OF GEOLOGICAL CROSS SECTIONS OF FLEXURE FOLDS BY THE ARC METHOD

Applications and Limitations: This method was originally described by H. G. Busk (1929). It applies only to concentric folds formed by the flexure-folding process. This type of folding is common in mildly deformed oil provinces involving competent strata. Most reservoir formations are competent under deformational conditions at shallow depths. Some flow folding may occur in the incompetent strata above and below the competent formations, but the folded complex will be essentially concentric if a sufficient number of competent strata are present to give an over-all rigidity to the deformed section. When deformational stress is sufficient to cause flow folding or rupture, this method can no longer be used as the folds are no longer concentric. The original reservoir conditions (porosity, permeability, fluid content, and so forth) will be altered by high stresses and the rocks may be no longer suitable for the entrapment of hydrocarbons. The following illustration (Fig. 52) will indicate the method of application.

Data Provided: The attitudes and elevations are known for outcrops *A, B, C, D, E, F, G, H, I,* and *J* (Fig. 52). These points are on a cross section which is perpendicular to the structural trend of the folds of the area. Some of the attitudes may have to be projected along their strike to this line of section if their respective outcrops do not fall exactly on the section line. Some of the strike lines may not be directly perpendicular to the line of strike, and the dips for these outcrops will have to be converted into apparent dips before they are plotted onto the cross section (see Fig. 6, Table 1).

Method: Once all the dips are plotted on the section in their respective positions, then perpendiculars are constructed to these dips as shown in Figure 52. These perpendiculars are extended to intersect the perpendiculars from adjacent outcrops. Thus the perpendicular from *A* intersects the perpendicular from *B* at 1. The dip of the bedding is the same at any point along each perpendicular. Perpendiculars should be drawn through the crests and troughs of all anticlines and synclines even if these actual points were not observed in the field. Such inversion points may be approximated by projection of flank dips, when not observed at the outcrop.

Using the intersection points (1, 2, 3, 4, etc.) as centers and the distances from these centers to the various formation contacts as radii, arcs are swung between each set of adjacent perpendiculars. The center points, radii, and arcs are changed for each succeeding set of adjacent perpendiculars as shown in Figure 52. Thus each horizon can be drawn all the way across the vertical section. The thickness of each formation can be measured along any of the perpendiculars. The position of formation contacts may be obtained from either surface mapping or from bore hole information.

One must not project the arcs across the axial surface, however, as the dip reverses across this surface. This makes it impossible to trace such strata as beds *T, U,* and *V* across the vertical section by the method outlined above, as the arcs *T, U,* and *V* drawn with center 3 would cross the axial surface before coming to the perpendiculars to outcrops *D, E,* and *F.* This problem can be remedied by measuring off formation thicknesses *RS, ST, TU,* and *UV* on the perpendicular to outcrop *I.* With point 8 as center, arcs are swung westward from points *L, M, N,* and *P* until they intersect beds *S, T, U,* and *V* at points *L′, M′, N′,* and *P′*. By joining points *L′, M′, N′,* and *P′,* the position of the *axial surface* is established.

When two adjoining outcrops show parallel dips, then the formation contacts are straight lines between the perpendiculars to these adjacent outcrops. The addition of the vertical perpendiculars through the anticlinal crests and synclinal troughs is particularly useful when dealing with asymmetric folds as the additional perpendicular frequently provides a second center in the critical portion of the fold. Centers 4 and 5 of Figure 53 are examples.

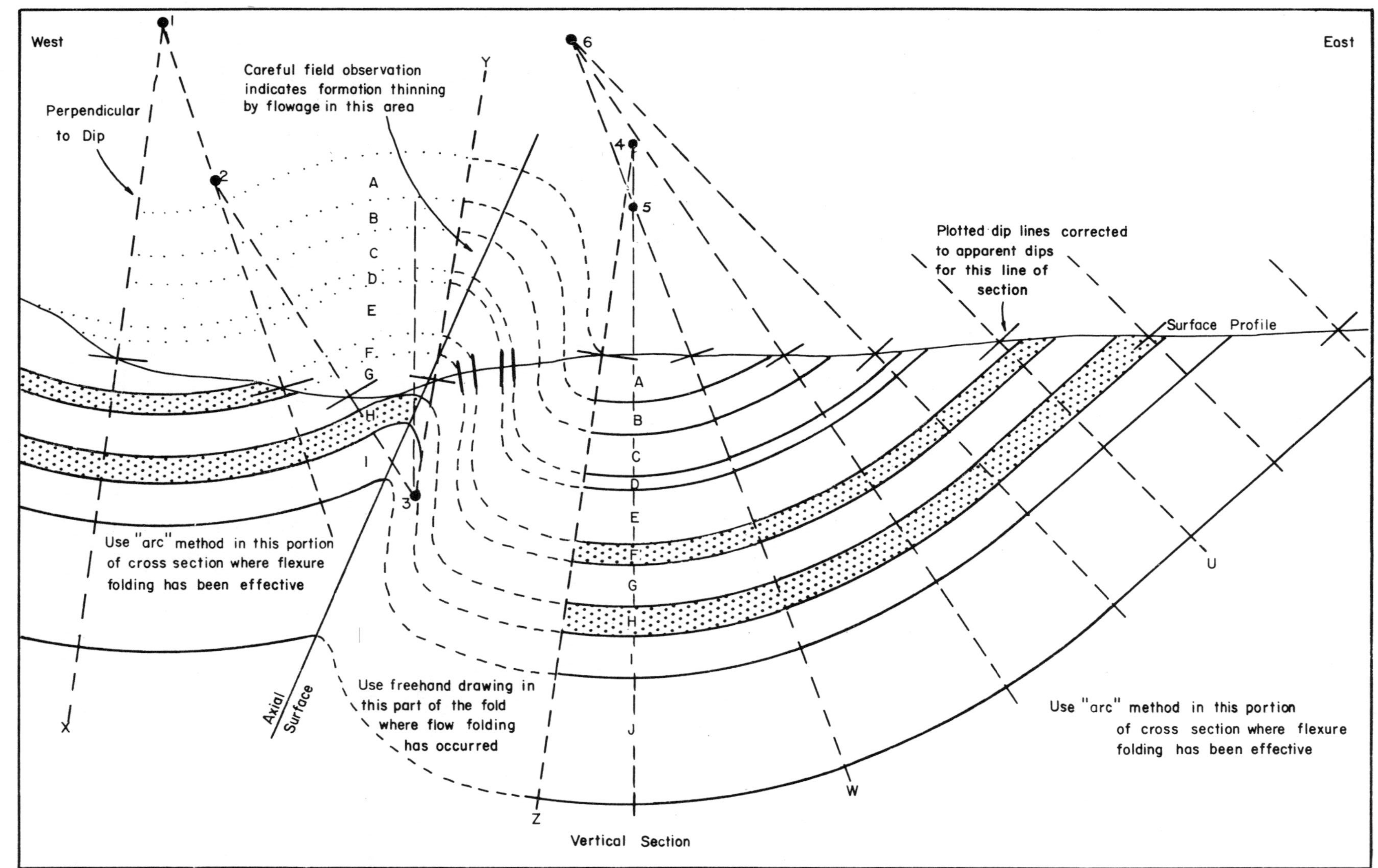

FIGURE 53. **A combination of the "arc" method and freehand drawing is used for folds resulting from both flexure and flow-folding processes.**

CONSTRUCTION OF GEOLOGICAL CROSS SECTIONS OF FOLDS WHICH HAVE FORMED PARTIALLY BY THE FLEXURE PROCESS AND PARTIALLY BY THE FLOW PROCESS

Applications and Limitations: Many folds have been formed by both flexure- and flow-folding processes. Flexure folding is dominant on the gentle limbs of the folds and flowage occurs on the steep or overturned limbs. Or flexure folding may control the competent formations even on steep limbs, with flowage being restricted to the incompetent beds on the steep limbs. These complicated situations are the commonest type of folding in mountainous areas as most stratigraphic sequences contain rocks of varying competency. Careful field observation of formation thickness changes, position of formation contacts, flow-folding phenomena, faulting processes, and so forth, will provide the basic data necessary for the construction of such folds which have been deformed heterogeneously. The method used combines freehand drawing together with either the arc or boundary ray method. The following example will illustrate this combined method.

Data Provided: A west-east surface traverse crossing the structural trend of an area provided the surface dips, formation contacts, and thicknesses shown in Figure 53. It is obvious that some flowage has occurred in the area of vertical dips.

Method: Draw in the formation contacts by the arc method between perpendiculars *X* and *Y* and between perpendiculars *Z* and *U*. There has been no flowage or thinning indicated at the surface between these respective perpendiculars. Now extend the formations from perpendicular *Y* to perpendicular *Z* by means of freehand drawing, making sure that each formation contact passes through the position mapped for that contact on the surface.

CONSTRUCTION OF GEOLOGICAL CROSS SECTIONS BY THE BOUNDARY RAY METHOD

Applications and Limitations: This method was developed by Coates (1945) and Gill (1953) for folds which have undergone compaction rather than plastic flow. Coates and Gill consider that the major factor producing thinning in layered sequences, prior to the initiation of plastic flow, is the varying compactibility of the incompetent members. They believe that the compaction of each individual formation is a function of dip. The analysis which follows is a simplification and modification of the methods of Gill and Coates.

The type of folding process involved in most petroleum provinces is essentially of the flexure type (concentric folds). Plastic flow, recrystallization, and cleavage or shear folding are uncommon. The favorable petroleum reservoir characteristics of rocks are largely destroyed by these processes. Flexure folding is the result of tangential compression, and during this process there may be some thinning on the limbs of folds. This thinning is thought to be the result of compaction of the incompetent members of the deformed sequence. In a layered sequence, the fold pressure increases the compaction of the incompetent layers, and the compaction effectiveness of this fold pressure varies with the degree of dip. Where the beds are horizontal the competent members resist the compressive stress and thus protect the incompetent beds from the compression. The incompetent beds feel the full compression only where the beds are vertical, in which position the compressive stress is transmitted directly through the incompetent beds.

For the purpose of cross-section constructions it is assumed that the amount of compaction is a linear function of the force of compaction, and consequently:

$$\text{The Force of Compaction} = 1 - \frac{\text{Adjacent Side}}{\text{Hypotenuse}}$$
$$= 1 - \text{Cosine of the Dip} \qquad (1)$$

The adjacent side of the dip triangle (Fig. 54) is equivalent to the resistance offered by the competent interbeds. When the dip is vertical, this competent bed resistance is zero, and thus the force of compaction is at a maximum.

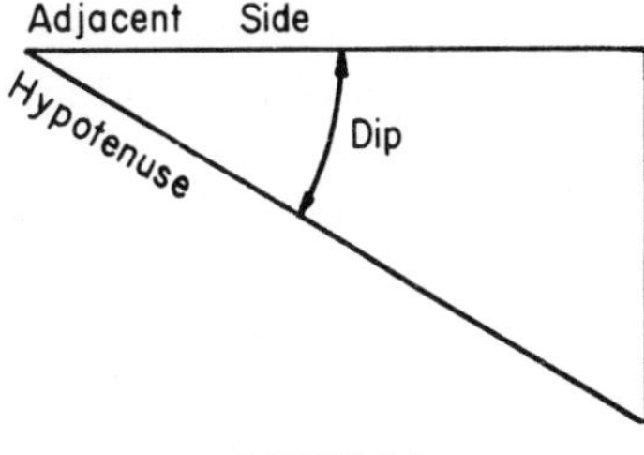

FIGURE 54.

The chief source of error in this equation is related to the assumption that compaction is a linear function of the force of compaction. In actuality there is a minimum force below which no compaction occurs (Fig. 55).

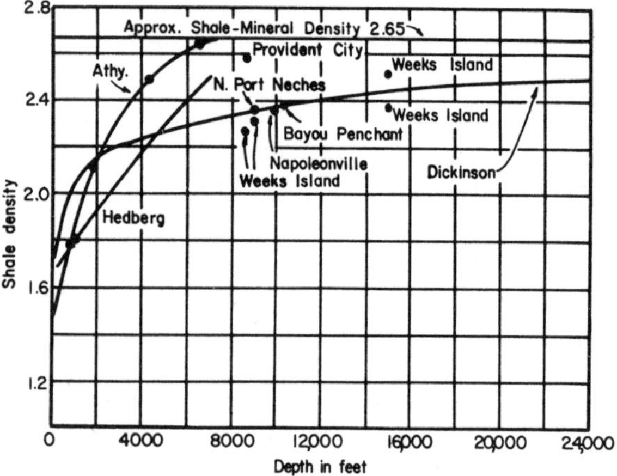

FIGURE 55. Diagram showing the relations between depth and density in shales, as reported by several investigators. (From G. Dickenson [1953], *Bull. Am. Assoc. Petrol. Geol.*, vol. 37.)

As a result of information obtained during petroleum drilling operations a great deal of information has been obtained concerning the amount of compaction which can occur in sediments. Athy (1930), Hedberg (1927), and Dickinson (1953) have all published articles on the subject and their results show that the density of shales increases from around a minimum of 1.5 to a maximum of about 2.65. The greater densities have been obtained from deeply buried shales and presumably from folded shales also. Once the maximum density has been reached, there is no density increase regardless of increase in depth.

For the purposes of constructing geological cross sections by the boundary ray method, it is considered that 50 per cent thinning (= 100 per cent density increase) represents the probable maximum thinning due to compaction. Above these limits thinning is due probably to plastic flow. Plastic flow is considered too irregular and unpredictable to bear mathematical analysis, and thus a maximum thinning of 50 per cent is used for geometrical construction of folds by this method. Thus the force of compaction obtained in the previous equation must be multiplied by 50 per cent to obtain the maximum amount of thinning due to compressive stress.

$$\text{Maximum Thinning (Due to Compression)} = \frac{1 - \text{Cosine of Dip}}{2} \quad (2)$$

The main step involved in this method is the determination of the location of boundary rays which are lines separating zones of different dips. The boundary rays are thus analogous to the "perpendiculars" to the dips of the arc method. Once the boundary rays are located, it is a simple matter to complete the cross section, as one knows automatically where to change dip.

There are several serious limitations to this method although apparently Gill and Coates have used the method with some success in Burma and the Middle East. The separation between thinning by compaction and by plastic flow is not sharp, and one process will grade into the other. The method of Gill and Coates requires parallel formation contacts (Fig. 57), that is, parallel folding. In actuality the shales will be thinned considerably more than sandstones and limestones when compaction affects sediments, and the formation contacts should not be parallel. Thus, this method is unable to cope adequately with sequences involving competent and incompetent strata, but it is fairly satisfactory where the stratigraphic sequence consists of formations of quite similar competencies.

Dallmus (1958) believes that shales in the center of a basin have greater density than shales of equivalent age and depth near the rim of the basin because of pressure differential between the compressional centers of basins and their tensional rims. No allowance has been made for this possibility here, but if this hypothesis is true, then this variable should also be considered in such cases.

Data Provided: The attitudes and elevations must be known for various outcrops along a line of traverse. The attitudes are plotted on a map (Fig. 56). A vertical cross section is desired for this area and is to be drawn along a line (XY) at right angles to the average strike observed in the traverse.

The recent paper by Weller (1959) indicates that there is still much to be learned about compaction. Thus the compactional aspects of the following method are subject to revision as our knowledge of this process increases.

Method: The various outcrop attitudes are projected along their strike lines until they intersect the cross-section line XY (Fig. 56). The dips are

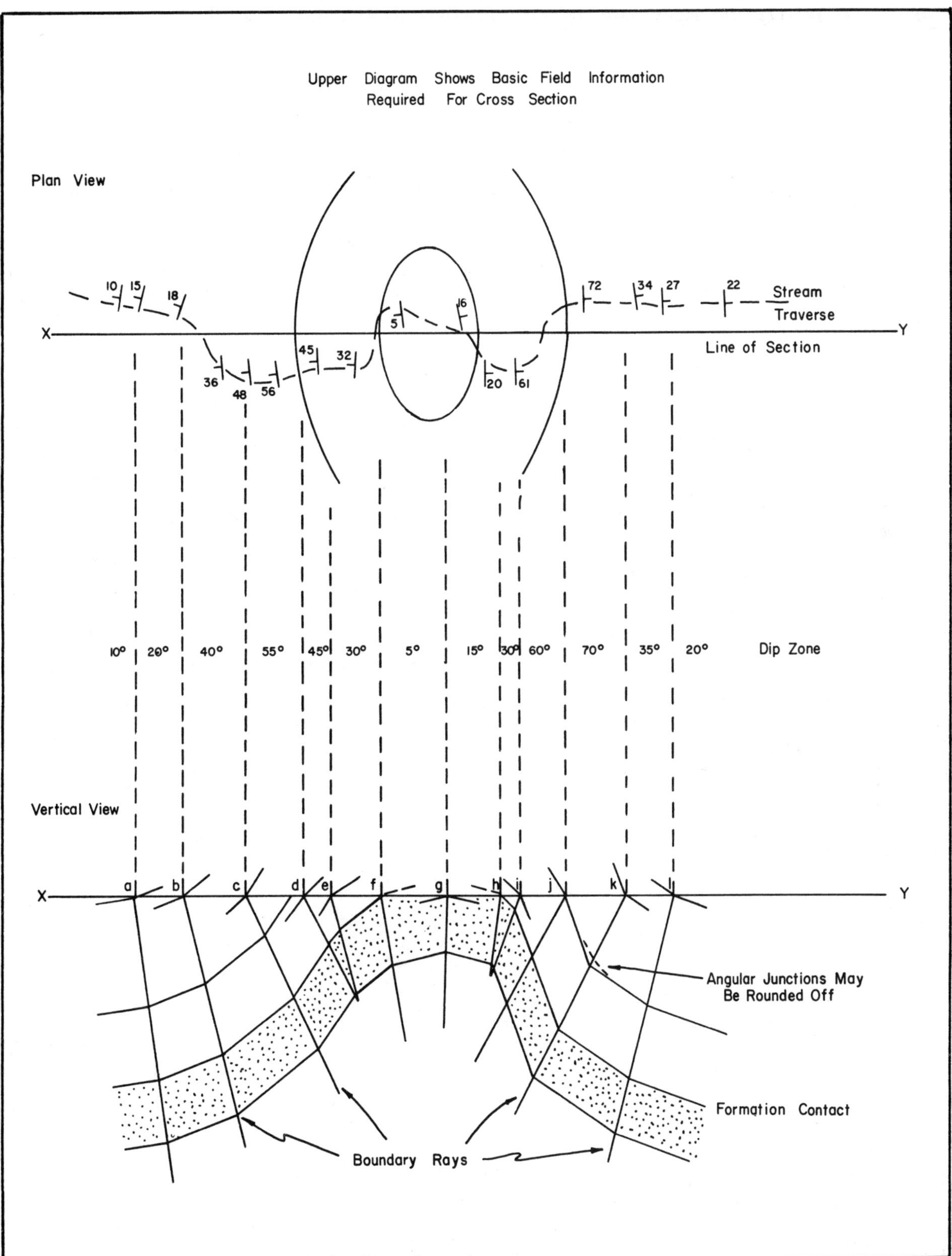

FIGURES 56 (*above*) and 57 (*below*). Construction of a geological cross section allowing for thinning on the limbs of folds by means of boundary rays. (Modified from W. D. Gill [1953], *Bull. Am. Assoc. Petrol. Geol.*, vol. 37.)

converted to apparent dip where necessary (Fig. 6 or Table 1). For any given stretch along the line *XY*, the dips can be grouped or averaged to the nearest 5°. The line *XY* is then divided up into various lengths, each length representing an area whose average dips are indicated to the nearest 5°. The various dip zones will then meet at points *a, b, c, d, e,* and so forth (Fig. 57).

If the adjacent dips are in the same direction at the zone boundaries, then one dip symbol is drawn below the topographic profile and the other dip symbol is drawn above the profile, each representing one of the two adjacent dip zones (Fig. 58).

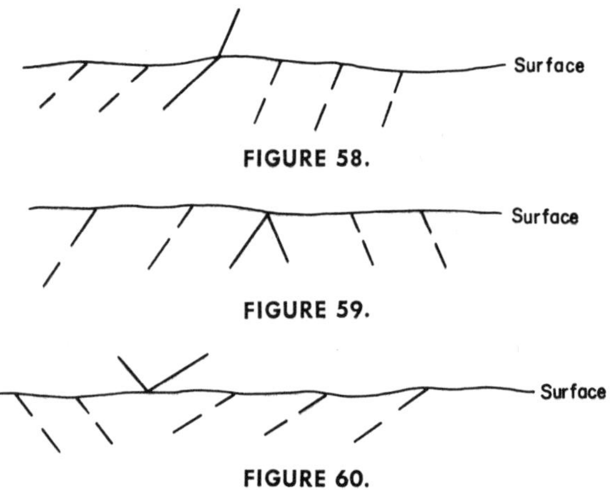

FIGURE 58.

FIGURE 59.

FIGURE 60.

If adjacent dips at zone boundaries are in opposite directions, away from each other, then both dips are drawn below the topographic profile at the boundary position between the two adjacent dip zones (Fig. 59).

If adjacent dips at zone boundaries are in opposite directions and toward each other, then both dips are drawn above the topographic profile (Fig. 60).

The next step is to determine the positions (angular relationships) of the boundary rays for each dip zone boundary on the cross section.

After the amount of maximum thinning for an area has been estimated from numerous observations in the field, the position of the boundary rays can be determined graphically or by tables.

Graphical Method

Thinning = Normal Fm. Thickness × Max. Thinning % for Area × (1 − Cos Dip) (3)

Plot the proportionate thickness calculated for each dip zone below the dip intersection at the sur-

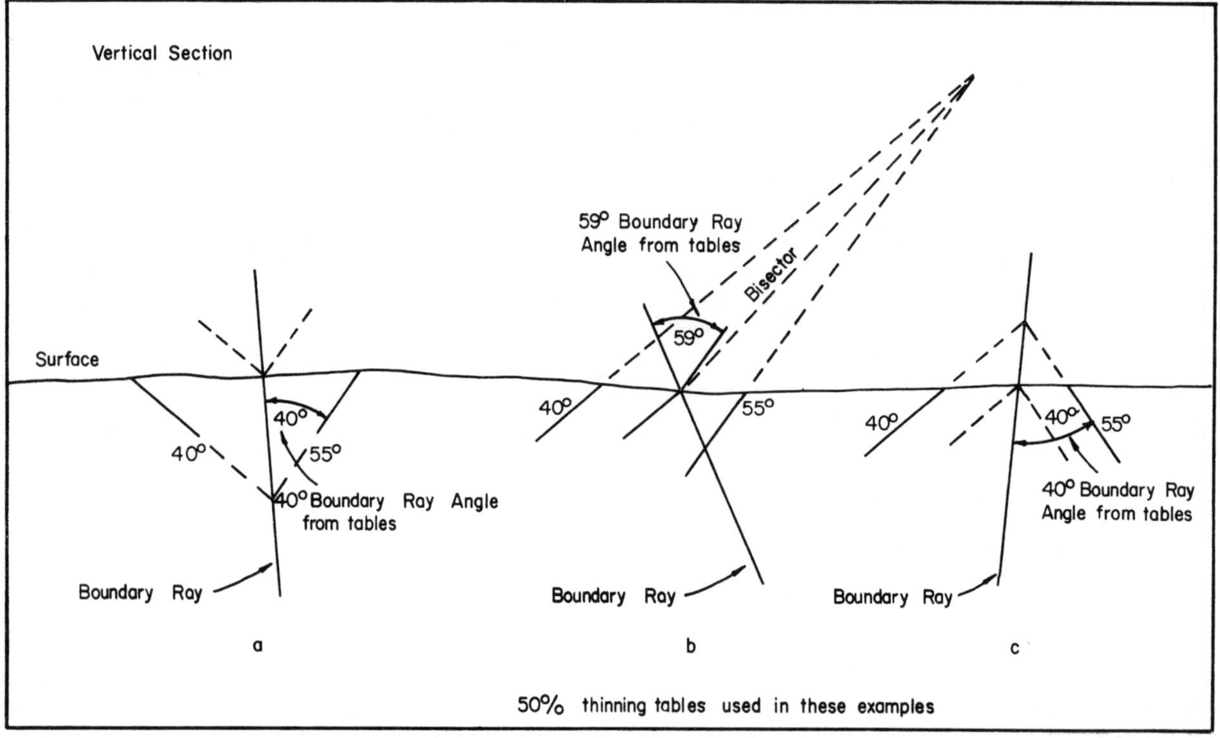

FIGURE 61. Examples illustrating the determination of boundary ray angles and indicating their application at dip zone boundaries. Note that the "bisector" method is used only when adjacent dip zones are in the same direction.

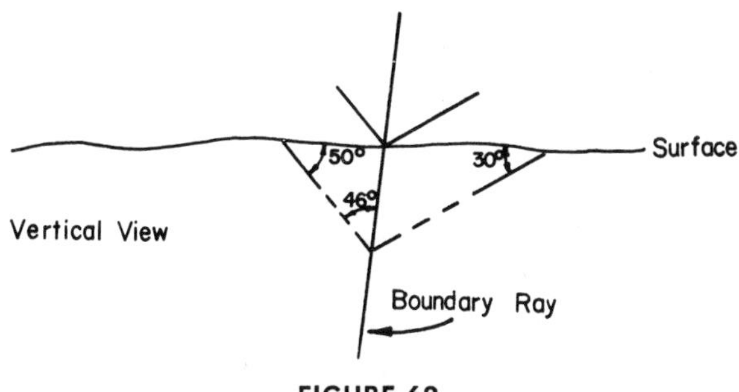

FIGURE 62.

face and thus draw in a lower dip surface for each formation. Note where the lower dip surfaces for each formation intersect. Then the compensated ray may be drawn through the lower intersection points.

Method By Tables: Tables have been drawn up for all possible combinations of dip in 5° units and for values of maximum thinning, ranging up to 50 per cent (Tables 2–10). For example, in the table for 50 per cent thinning, suppose that two adjacent intersecting dip zones had dips of 40° and 55°, respectively (Figs. 61a, 61b, and 61c). Read along from 40° on the ordinate until the projection from 55° on the abscissa is intersected. This gives an angle of 59° for dips in the same direction and an angle of 40° for dips in opposite directions. *This angle is then measured from the steeper dip (55°) in the included angle at the surface dip intersections.* Once these angles have been plotted in the line of section, the boundary rays can be drawn in immediately.

The actual position of boundary rays between adjacent dip zones may be determined by projecting adjacent dips (e.g., 30° and 50°, Fig. 62) until they intersect and then calculating the boundary ray angle (46° in this case) for this intersection. The position where the boundary ray crosses the topographic surface profile locates the point where the opposing dip zones meet. This is an arbitrary approach but is probably as satisfactory as any other method for opposing dips.

Where two rays intersect (Fig. 63), the intermediate of the dip zones involved (75°) is eliminated and the two remaining dips are used to calculate the position of the boundary ray.

Once the boundary rays have been drawn in, the formation contacts and thicknesses can be drawn in. This is done by projecting the formation contacts below the surface, using dips parallel to the appropriate averaged dip for that segment of the fold (segment = that portion of a fold between adjacent boundary rays). The dip is changed every time a boundary ray is crossed. Thus formation contacts can be plotted all the way across the vertical section. Once the formation contacts have been drawn in, the axial areas of the folds (points where formation contacts cross boundary rays) can be rounded off slightly to give a more realistic appearance to the cross sections (Fig. 57).

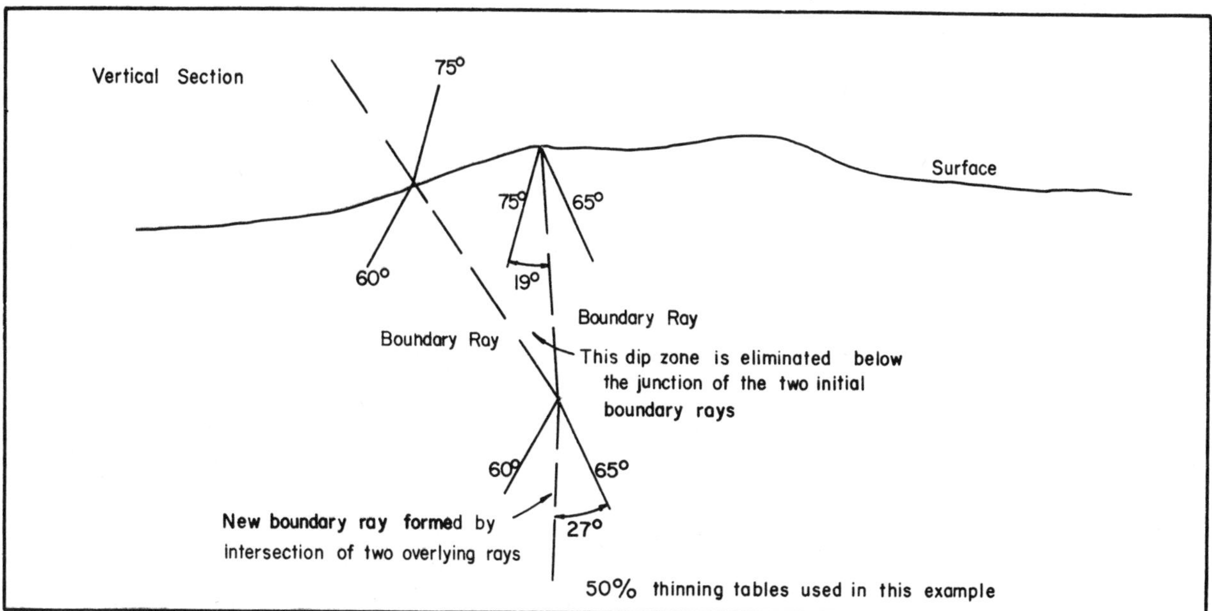

FIGURE 63. Illustrating the determination of a new boundary ray when two boundary rays intersect.

TABLE 2. Boundary Ray Angles for Compactional Thinning of 10 Per Cent

Steeper Dip at Dip Intersection Point (Abscissa)

Gentler Dip at Dip Intersection Point (Ordinate)

0	5	10	15	20	25	30	35	40	45	50	55	60	65	70	75	80	85	90
0	87	84	82	79	76	74	71	68	65	63	60	58	55	52	50	47	45	42
	87	**84**	**82**	**79**	**76**	**74**	**71**	**68**	**65**	**63**	**60**	**58**	**55**	**52**	**50**	**47**	**45**	**42**
5		87	84	81	79	76	73	70	68	65	62	60	57	54	52	49	47	44
		82	**80**	**77**	**74**	**71**	**69**	**66**	**63**	**61**	**58**	**55**	**53**	**50**	**47**	**45**	**42**	**40**
10			86	84	81	78	75	73	70	67	65	62	59	57	54	52	49	47
			77	**75**	**72**	**69**	**66**	**64**	**61**	**58**	**56**	**53**	**50**	**48**	**45**	**43**	**40**	**38**
15				86	83	80	78	75	72	70	67	64	62	59	56	54	51	49
				72	**70**	**67**	**64**	**61**	**59**	**56**	**53**	**51**	**48**	**46**	**43**	**40**	**38**	**35**
20					85	83	80	77	74	72	69	66	64	61	59	56	54	51
					67	**65**	**62**	**59**	**56**	**54**	**51**	**49**	**46**	**43**	**41**	**38**	**36**	**33**
25						85	82	79	77	74	71	69	66	64	61	58	56	53
						62	**60**	**57**	**54**	**52**	**49**	**46**	**44**	**41**	**38**	**36**	**33**	**31**
30							84	82	79	76	74	71	68	66	63	61	58	56
							57	**55**	**52**	**49**	**47**	**44**	**41**	**39**	**36**	**34**	**31**	**29**
35								84	81	79	76	73	71	68	65	63	60	58
								52	**50**	**47**	**44**	**42**	**39**	**36**	**34**	**31**	**29**	**26**
40									83	81	78	76	73	70	68	65	63	60
									47	**45**	**42**	**39**	**37**	**34**	**32**	**29**	**26**	**24**
45										83	81	78	75	73	70	67	65	62
										42	**40**	**37**	**34**	**32**	**29**	**27**	**24**	**22**
50	Example when adjoining										83	80	78	75	72	70	67	65
											37	**35**	**32**	**30**	**27**	**24**	**22**	**19**
55	dips are 85° and 90°											82	80	77	75	72	69	67
												32	**30**	**27**	**25**	**22**	**20**	**17**
60	81° for dips in the same direction												82	80	77	74	71	69
													27	**25**	**22**	**20**	**17**	**15**
65	**3° for opposed dips**													82	80	77	74	72
														22	**20**	**17**	**15**	**12**
70															82	79	77	74
															17	**15**	**12**	**10**
75																82	79	77
																12	**10**	**7**
80																	81	79
																	8	**5**
85																		81
																		3

NOTE: Angles shown in the table are those between the steeper dip and the boundary ray between adjoining dip zones. (Modified after W. D. Gill.)

TABLE 3. Boundary Ray Angles for Compactional Thinning of 15 Per Cent

Steeper Dip at Dip Intersection Point (Abscissa)

Gentler Dip at Dip Intersection Point (Ordinate)	5	10	15	20	25	30	35	40	45	50	55	60	65	70	75	80	85	90
0	87	84	82	79	76	73	70	67	64	62	59	56	53	51	48	46	43	40
	87	**84**	**82**	**79**	**76**	**73**	**70**	**67**	**64**	**62**	**59**	**56**	**53**	**51**	**48**	**46**	**43**	**40**
5		86	83	87	78	75	72	69	67	64	61	58	56	53	50	47	45	43
		82	**79**	**76**	**73**	**70**	**68**	**65**	**62**	**60**	**57**	**54**	**51**	**49**	**46**	**43**	**41**	**38**
10			86	83	80	77	74	71	69	66	63	60	58	55	52	50	47	45
			77	**74**	**71**	**69**	**66**	**63**	**60**	**57**	**55**	**52**	**49**	**47**	**44**	**41**	**39**	**36**
15				85	82	79	76	74	71	68	65	63	60	57	55	52	49	47
				72	**69**	**67**	**64**	**61**	**58**	**55**	**53**	**50**	**47**	**44**	**42**	**39**	**37**	**34**
20					84	81	79	76	73	70	67	65	62	59	57	54	51	49
					67	**64**	**62**	**59**	**56**	**53**	**50**	**48**	**45**	**42**	**40**	**37**	**35**	**32**
25						83	81	78	75	72	70	67	64	61	59	56	54	51
						62	**59**	**57**	**54**	**51**	**48**	**46**	**43**	**40**	**38**	**35**	**32**	**30**
30							83	80	77	74	72	69	66	64	61	58	56	53
							57	**54**	**52**	**49**	**46**	**43**	**41**	**38**	**35**	**33**	**30**	**28**
35								82	79	77	74	71	68	66	63	60	58	55
								52	**49**	**47**	**44**	**41**	**39**	**36**	**33**	**31**	**28**	**26**
40									81	79	76	73	71	68	65	62	60	57
									47	**45**	**42**	**39**	**36**	**34**	**31**	**28**	**26**	**23**
45										81	78	75	73	70	67	65	62	59
										42	**40**	**37**	**34**	**31**	**29**	**26**	**24**	**21**
50											80	78	75	72	69	67	64	62
											37	**35**	**32**	**29**	**27**	**24**	**21**	**19**
55												80	77	74	72	69	66	64
												32	**30**	**27**	**24**	**22**	**19**	**17**
60	78° for dips in the same direction												79	77	74	71	68	66
													27	**25**	**22**	**19**	**17**	**14**
65	**3° for opposed dips**													80	76	74	71	70
														22	**20**	**17**	**15**	**12**
70															78	76	73	71
															17	**15**	**12**	**10**
75																78	76	73
																12	**10**	**7**
80																	78	75
																	7	**5**
85																		78
																		3

NOTE: Angles shown in the table are those between the steeper dip and the boundary ray between adjoining dip zones. (Modified after W. D. Gill.)

TABLE 4. Boundary Ray Angles for Compactional Thinning of 20 Per Cent

Steeper Dip at Dip Intersection Point (Abscissa)

Gentler Dip at Dip Intersection Point (Ordinate)

0	5	10	15	20	25	30	35	40	45	50	55	60	65	70	75	80	85	90
0	87	84	81	78	75	72	69	66	63	61	58	55	52	49	47	44	41	39
	87	**84**	**81**	**78**	**75**	**72**	**69**	**66**	**63**	**61**	**58**	**55**	**52**	**49**	**47**	**44**	**41**	**39**
5		86	83	80	77	74	71	68	65	62	60	57	54	51	49	46	43	41
		82	**79**	**76**	**73**	**70**	**67**	**64**	**61**	**59**	**56**	**53**	**50**	**47**	**45**	**42**	**39**	**37**
10			85	82	79	76	73	70	67	64	62	59	56	53	51	48	45	43
			77	**74**	**71**	**68**	**65**	**62**	**60**	**57**	**54**	**51**	**48**	**45**	**43**	**40**	**37**	**35**
15				84	81	78	75	72	69	66	64	61	58	55	52	50	47	45
				72	**69**	**66**	**63**	**60**	**57**	**55**	**52**	**49**	**46**	**43**	**41**	**38**	**35**	**33**
20					83	80	77	74	71	68	66	63	60	57	54	52	49	47
					67	**64**	**61**	**58**	**55**	**53**	**50**	**47**	**44**	**41**	**39**	**36**	**33**	**31**
25						82	79	76	73	70	68	65	62	59	56	54	51	48
						62	**59**	**56**	**53**	**50**	**48**	**45**	**42**	**39**	**37**	**34**	**31**	**29**
30							81	78	75	72	70	67	64	61	58	56	53	50
							57	**54**	**51**	**48**	**46**	**43**	**40**	**37**	**35**	**32**	**29**	**27**
35								80	77	75	72	69	66	63	60	58	55	52
								52	**49**	**46**	**44**	**41**	**38**	**35**	**33**	**30**	**27**	**25**
40									79	77	74	71	68	65	62	60	57	54
									47	**44**	**41**	**39**	**36**	**33**	**30**	**28**	**25**	**23**
45										79	76	73	70	67	65	62	59	56
										42	**39**	**37**	**34**	**31**	**28**	**26**	**23**	**21**
50											78	75	72	69	67	64	61	59
											37	**34**	**32**	**29**	**26**	**24**	**21**	**18**
55												77	74	71	69	66	63	61
												32	**29**	**27**	**24**	**21**	**19**	**16**
60	74° for dips in the same direction												76	73	71	68	65	63
													27	**25**	**22**	**19**	**17**	**14**
65	**3° for opposed dips**													76	73	70	67	65
														22	**20**	**17**	**14**	**12**
70															75	72	70	67
															17	**15**	**12**	**10**
75																75	72	69
																12	**10**	**7**
80																	74	71
																	7	**5**
85																		74
																		3

NOTE: Angles shown in the table are those between the steeper dip and the boundary ray between adjoining dip zones. (Modified after W. D. Gill.)

TABLE 5. Boundary Ray Angles for Compactional Thinning of 25 Per Cent

Steeper Dip at Dip Intersection Point (Abscissa)

Gentler Dip at Dip Intersection Point (Ordinate)

0	5	10	15	20	25	30	35	40	45	50	55	60	65	70	75	80	85	90
0	87	84	81	78	74	71	68	65	62	59	56	54	51	48	45	42	40	37
	87	**84**	**81**	**78**	**74**	**71**	**68**	**65**	**62**	**59**	**56**	**54**	**51**	**48**	**45**	**42**	**40**	**37**
5		86	83	79	76	73	70	67	64	61	58	55	52	50	47	44	41	39
		82	**79**	**76**	**73**	**70**	**66**	**63**	**60**	**57**	**55**	**52**	**49**	**46**	**43**	**40**	**38**	**35**
10			84	81	78	75	72	69	66	63	60	57	54	51	49	46	43	41
			77	**74**	**71**	**68**	**65**	**62**	**59**	**56**	**53**	**50**	**47**	**44**	**41**	**39**	**36**	**33**
15				83	80	77	74	71	68	65	62	59	56	53	50	48	45	42
				72	**69**	**66**	**63**	**60**	**57**	**54**	**51**	**48**	**45**	**42**	**39**	**37**	**34**	**31**
20					82	79	76	73	70	67	64	61	58	55	52	49	47	44
					67	**64**	**61**	**58**	**55**	**52**	**49**	**46**	**43**	**40**	**38**	**35**	**32**	**30**
25						81	78	75	72	69	66	63	60	57	54	51	49	46
						62	**59**	**56**	**53**	**50**	**47**	**44**	**41**	**38**	**36**	**33**	**30**	**28**
30							80	77	73	71	67	65	62	59	56	53	50	48
							57	**54**	**51**	**48**	**45**	**42**	**39**	**37**	**34**	**31**	**28**	**26**
35								78	75	72	69	64	63	61	58	55	52	50
								52	**49**	**46**	**43**	**40**	**37**	**35**	**32**	**29**	**27**	**24**
40									77	74	71	68	65	62	60	57	54	51
									47	**44**	**41**	**38**	**35**	**33**	**30**	**27**	**25**	**22**
45										76	73	70	67	64	62	59	56	53
										42	**39**	**36**	**33**	**31**	**28**	**25**	**23**	**20**
50											75	72	69	66	63	61	58	55
											37	**34**	**31**	**29**	**26**	**23**	**21**	**18**
55	69° for dips in the same direction											74	71	68	65	63	60	57
												32	**29**	**27**	**24**	**21**	**19**	**16**
60	**3° for opposed dips**												73	70	67	65	62	59
													27	**24**	**22**	**19**	**16**	**14**
65														72	69	67	64	61
														22	**20**	**17**	**14**	**12**
70															71	69	66	63
															17	**15**	**12**	**10**
75																71	68	65
																12	**10**	**7**
80																	70	67
																	7	**5**
85																		69
																		3

NOTE: Angles shown in the table are those between the steeper dip and the boundary ray between adjoining dip zones. (Modified after W. D. Gill.)

TABLE 6. Boundary Ray Angles for Compactional Thinning of 30 Per Cent

Steeper Dip at Dip Intersection (Abscissa)

Gentler Dip at Dip Intersection Point (Ordinate)

0	5	10	15	20	25	30	35	40	45	50	55	60	65	70	75	80	85	90
0	87	84	80	77	74	71	67	64	61	58	55	52	49	46	43	40	38	35
	87	**84**	**80**	**77**	**74**	**71**	**67**	**64**	**61**	**58**	**55**	**52**	**49**	**46**	**43**	**40**	**38**	**35**
5		85	82	79	76	72	69	66	63	60	57	54	51	48	45	42	39	37
		82	**79**	**75**	**72**	**69**	**66**	**63**	**59**	**56**	**53**	**50**	**47**	**45**	**42**	**39**	**36**	**33**
10			84	81	77	74	71	68	65	62	58	55	52	50	47	44	41	38
			77	**74**	**70**	**67**	**64**	**61**	**58**	**55**	**52**	**49**	**46**	**43**	**40**	**37**	**34**	**32**
15				82	79	76	73	70	66	63	60	57	54	51	48	45	43	40
				72	**69**	**65**	**62**	**59**	**56**	**53**	**50**	**47**	**44**	**41**	**38**	**35**	**33**	**30**
20					81	78	74	71	68	65	62	59	56	53	50	47	44	42
					67	**64**	**60**	**57**	**54**	**51**	**48**	**45**	**42**	**39**	**36**	**34**	**31**	**28**
25						79	76	73	70	67	64	61	57	55	52	49	46	43
						62	**59**	**56**	**52**	**49**	**46**	**43**	**40**	**38**	**35**	**32**	**29**	**27**
30							78	75	72	68	65	62	59	56	53	50	48	45
							57	**54**	**51**	**48**	**45**	**42**	**39**	**36**	**33**	**30**	**28**	**25**
35								77	73	70	67	64	61	58	55	52	49	47
								52	**49**	**46**	**43**	**40**	**37**	**34**	**31**	**28**	**26**	**23**
40									75	72	69	66	63	60	57	54	51	48
									47	**44**	**41**	**38**	**35**	**32**	**29**	**27**	**24**	**21**
45										74	71	68	65	61	59	56	53	50
										42	**39**	**36**	**33**	**30**	**27**	**25**	**22**	**19**
50											72	69	66	63	60	57	54	52
											37	**34**	**31**	**28**	**25**	**23**	**20**	**18**
55												71	68	65	62	59	56	53
												32	**29**	**26**	**24**	**21**	**18**	**16**
60	65° for dips in the same direction												70	67	64	61	58	55
													27	**24**	**21**	**19**	**16**	**14**
65	**3° for opposed dips**													69	66	63	60	57
														22	**19**	**17**	**14**	**11**
70															68	65	62	59
															17	**15**	**12**	**9**
75																67	64	61
																12	**10**	**7**
80																	66	63
																	7	**5**
85																		65
																		3

NOTE: Angles shown in the table are those between the steeper dip and the boundary ray between adjoining dip zones. (Modified after W. D. Gill.)

TABLE 7. Boundary Ray Angles for Compactional Thinning of 35 Per Cent

Steeper Dip at Dip Intersection Point (Abscissa)

Gentler Dip at Dip Intersection Point (Ordinate)	5	10	15	20	25	30	35	40	45	50	55	60	65	70	75	80	85	90
0	87	83	80	77	73	70	67	63	60	57	54	51	48	45	42	39	36	33
	87	**83**	**80**	**77**	**73**	**70**	**67**	**63**	**60**	**57**	**54**	**51**	**48**	**45**	**42**	**39**	**36**	**33**
5		85	82	78	75	72	68	65	62	59	55	52	49	46	43	40	37	35
		82	**78**	**75**	**72**	**68**	**65**	**62**	**59**	**55**	**52**	**49**	**46**	**43**	**40**	**37**	**34**	**32**
10			83	80	76	73	70	67	63	60	57	54	51	48	45	42	39	36
			77	**73**	**70**	**67**	**63**	**60**	**57**	**54**	**51**	**47**	**44**	**41**	**38**	**36**	**33**	**30**
15				81	78	75	71	68	65	62	58	55	52	49	46	43	40	37
				72	**68**	**65**	**62**	**59**	**55**	**52**	**49**	**46**	**43**	**40**	**37**	**34**	**31**	**29**
20					80	76	73	70	66	63	60	57	54	51	48	45	42	39
					67	**63**	**60**	**57**	**54**	**50**	**47**	**44**	**41**	**38**	**35**	**33**	**30**	**27**
25						78	75	71	68	65	62	58	55	52	49	46	43	40
						62	**58**	**55**	**52**	**49**	**46**	**43**	**40**	**37**	**34**	**31**	**28**	**25**
30							76	73	70	66	63	60	57	54	51	48	45	42
							57	**54**	**50**	**47**	**44**	**41**	**38**	**35**	**32**	**29**	**26**	**24**
35								75	71	68	65	62	58	55	52	49	46	43
								52	**49**	**45**	**42**	**39**	**36**	**33**	**30**	**28**	**25**	**22**
40									73	70	66	63	60	57	54	51	48	45
									47	**44**	**41**	**37**	**34**	**32**	**29**	**26**	**23**	**20**
45										72	68	65	62	59	55	52	49	46
										42	**39**	**36**	**33**	**30**	**27**	**24**	**21**	**19**
50											70	66	63	60	57	54	51	48
											37	**34**	**31**	**28**	**25**	**22**	**20**	**17**
55												68	65	62	59	56	53	50
												32	**29**	**26**	**23**	**20**	**18**	**15**
60	60° for dips in the same direction												67	63	60	57	54	51
													27	**24**	**21**	**18**	**16**	**13**
65	**2° for opposed dips**													65	62	59	56	53
														22	**19**	**17**	**14**	**11**
70															64	61	58	54
															17	**14**	**12**	**9**
75																62	59	56
																12	**10**	**7**
80																	61	58
																	7	**5**
85																		60
																		2

NOTE: Angles shown in the table are those between the steeper dip and the boundary ray between adjoining dip zones. (Modified after W. D. Gill.)

TABLE 8. Boundary Ray Angles for Compactional Thinning of 40 Per Cent

Steeper Dip at Dip Intersection Point (Abscissa)

Steeper Dip at Dip Intersection Point (Ordinate)

0	5	10	15	20	25	30	35	40	45	50	55	60	65	70	75	80	85	90
0	87	83	80	76	73	69	66	62	59	56	52	49	46	43	40	37	34	31
	87	**83**	**80**	**76**	**73**	**69**	**66**	**62**	**59**	**56**	**52**	**49**	**46**	**43**	**40**	**37**	**34**	**31**
5		85	81	78	74	71	67	64	60	57	54	51	47	44	41	38	35	32
		82	**78**	**75**	**71**	**68**	**64**	**61**	**58**	**54**	**51**	**48**	**45**	**41**	**38**	**35**	**33**	**30**
10			83	79	76	72	69	65	62	59	55	52	49	46	43	39	37	34
			77	**73**	**70**	**66**	**63**	**59**	**56**	**53**	**49**	**46**	**43**	**40**	**37**	**34**	**31**	**28**
15				81	77	74	70	67	63	60	57	53	50	47	44	41	38	35
				72	**68**	**65**	**61**	**58**	**55**	**51**	**48**	**45**	**42**	**39**	**36**	**33**	**30**	**27**
20					79	75	72	68	65	61	58	55	52	48	45	42	39	36
					67	**63**	**60**	**56**	**53**	**50**	**47**	**43**	**40**	**37**	**34**	**31**	**28**	**26**
25						77	73	70	66	63	60	56	53	50	47	44	40	38
						62	**58**	**55**	**52**	**48**	**45**	**42**	**39**	**36**	**33**	**30**	**27**	**24**
30							75	71	68	64	61	58	54	51	48	45	42	39
							57	**53**	**50**	**47**	**43**	**40**	**37**	**34**	**31**	**28**	**25**	**23**
35								73	69	66	62	59	56	53	49	46	43	40
								52	**48**	**45**	**42**	**39**	**36**	**33**	**30**	**27**	**24**	**21**
40									71	67	64	61	57	54	51	48	45	41
									47	**43**	**40**	**37**	**34**	**31**	**28**	**25**	**22**	**20**
45										69	66	62	58	55	52	49	46	43
										42	**39**	**35**	**32**	**29**	**26**	**23**	**21**	**18**
50											67	64	60	57	54	50	47	44
											37	**34**	**31**	**28**	**25**	**22**	**19**	**16**
55												65	62	58	55	52	49	46
												32	**29**	**26**	**23**	**20**	**17**	**15**
60	55° for dips in the same direction												63	60	57	53	50	47
													27	**24**	**21**	**18**	**15**	**13**
65	**2° for opposed dips**													61	58	55	52	48
														22	**19**	**16**	**14**	**11**
70															60	56	53	50
															17	**14**	**12**	**9**
75																58	55	51
																12	**10**	**7**
80																	56	53
																	7	**5**
85																		55
																		2

NOTE: Angles shown in the table are those between the steeper dip and the boundary ray between adjoining dip zones. (Modified after W. D. Gill.)

TABLE 9. Boundary Ray Angles for Compactional Thinning of 45 Per Cent

Gentler Dip at Dip Intersection Point (Ordinate) \ Steeper Dip at Dip Intersection Point (Abscissa)	0	5	10	15	20	25	30	35	40	45	50	55	60	65	70	75	80	85	90
0		86	83	79	76	72	68	65	61	58	54	51	48	44	41	38	35	32	29
		86	**83**	**79**	**76**	**72**	**68**	**65**	**61**	**58**	**54**	**51**	**48**	**44**	**41**	**38**	**35**	**32**	**29**
5			84	81	77	73	70	66	63	59	56	52	49	46	42	39	36	33	30
			81	**78**	**74**	**71**	**67**	**64**	**60**	**57**	**53**	**50**	**46**	**43**	**40**	**37**	**34**	**31**	**28**
10				82	78	75	71	68	64	61	57	54	50	47	44	40	37	34	31
				76	**73**	**69**	**66**	**62**	**59**	**55**	**52**	**48**	**45**	**42**	**39**	**35**	**32**	**29**	**26**
15					80	76	72	69	65	62	58	55	52	48	45	42	38	35	32
					71	**68**	**64**	**61**	**57**	**54**	**50**	**47**	**44**	**40**	**37**	**34**	**31**	**28**	**25**
20						77	74	70	67	63	60	56	53	49	46	43	40	36	33
						66	**63**	**59**	**56**	**52**	**49**	**46**	**42**	**39**	**36**	**33**	**30**	**27**	**24**
25							75	72	68	65	61	58	54	51	47	44	41	38	35
							62	**58**	**54**	**51**	**48**	**44**	**41**	**38**	**35**	**31**	**28**	**26**	**23**
30								73	69	66	62	59	55	52	49	45	42	39	36
								57	**53**	**50**	**46**	**43**	**40**	**36**	**33**	**30**	**27**	**24**	**21**
35									71	67	64	60	57	53	50	46	43	40	37
									52	**48**	**45**	**41**	**38**	**35**	**32**	**29**	**26**	**23**	**20**
40										69	65	61	58	54	51	48	44	41	38
										47	**43**	**40**	**37**	**33**	**30**	**27**	**24**	**21**	**19**
45											66	63	59	56	52	49	46	42	39
											42	**38**	**35**	**32**	**29**	**26**	**23**	**20**	**17**
50												64	61	57	54	50	47	44	40
												37	**33**	**30**	**27**	**24**	**21**	**18**	**15**
55													62	58	55	52	48	45	41
													32	**29**	**25**	**22**	**20**	**17**	**14**
60	49° for dips in the same direction													60	56	53	49	46	43
														27	**24**	**21**	**18**	**15**	**12**
65	**2° for opposed dips**														58	54	51	47	44
															22	**19**	**16**	**13**	**11**
70																56	52	49	45
																17	**14**	**11**	**9**
75																	53	50	47
																	12	**9**	**7**
80																		51	48
																		7	**5**
85																			49
																			2

NOTE: Angles shown in the table are those between the steeper dip and the boundary ray between adjoining dip zones. (Modified after W. D. Gill.)

TABLE 10. Boundary Ray Angles for Compactional Thinning of 50 Per Cent

Steeper Dip at Dip Intersection Point (Abscissa); rows: Gentler Dip at Dip Intersection Point (Ordinate)

0	5	10	15	20	25	30	35	40	45	50	55	60	65	70	75	80	85	90
0	86	83	79	75	71	68	64	60	57	53	50	46	43	39	36	33	30	27
	86	**83**	**79**	**75**	**71**	**68**	**64**	**60**	**57**	**53**	**50**	**46**	**43**	**39**	**36**	**33**	**30**	**27**
5		84	80	76	73	69	65	62	57	54	51	47	44	40	37	34	31	28
		81	**78**	**74**	**70**	**66**	**63**	**59**	**56**	**52**	**48**	**45**	**42**	**38**	**35**	**32**	**29**	**26**
10			81	78	74	70	66	63	59	56	52	48	45	42	38	35	32	29
			76	**73**	**69**	**65**	**62**	**58**	**54**	**51**	**47**	**44**	**40**	**37**	**34**	**31**	**28**	**25**
15				79	75	71	68	64	60	57	53	50	46	43	39	36	33	30
				71	**68**	**64**	**60**	**57**	**53**	**50**	**46**	**43**	**39**	**36**	**33**	**30**	**26**	**24**
20					76	73	69	65	61	58	54	51	47	44	40	37	34	31
					66	**63**	**59**	**55**	**52**	**48**	**45**	**41**	**38**	**35**	**32**	**28**	**25**	**22**
25						74	70	66	63	59	55	52	48	45	41	38	35	31
						61	**58**	**54**	**51**	**47**	**44**	**40**	**37**	**34**	**30**	**27**	**24**	**21**
30							71	68	64	60	57	53	49	45	42	39	36	32
							56	**53**	**49**	**46**	**42**	**39**	**36**	**32**	**29**	**26**	**23**	**20**
35								69	65	61	58	54	51	47	43	40	37	33
								51	**48**	**44**	**41**	**38**	**34**	**31**	**28**	**25**	**22**	**19**
40									66	63	59	55	52	48	45	41	38	34
									47	**43**	**40**	**36**	**33**	**30**	**26**	**23**	**20**	**18**
45										64	60	56	53	49	46	42	39	35
										42	**38**	**35**	**31**	**28**	**25**	**22**	**19**	**16**
50											61	58	54	50	47	43	40	36
											37	**33**	**30**	**27**	**24**	**21**	**18**	**15**
55												59	55	51	48	44	41	37
												32	**28**	**25**	**22**	**19**	**16**	**14**
60													56	53	49	45	42	38
													27	**24**	**20**	**18**	**15**	**12**
65														54	50	46	43	39
														22	**19**	**16**	**13**	**10**
70															51	48	44	40
															17	**14**	**11**	**9**
75																49	45	42
																12	**9**	**7**
80																	46	42
																	7	**5**
85																		44
																		2

44° for dips in the same direction

2° for opposed dips

NOTE: Angles shown in the table are those between the steeper dip and the boundary ray between adjoining dip zones. (Modified after W. D. Gill.)

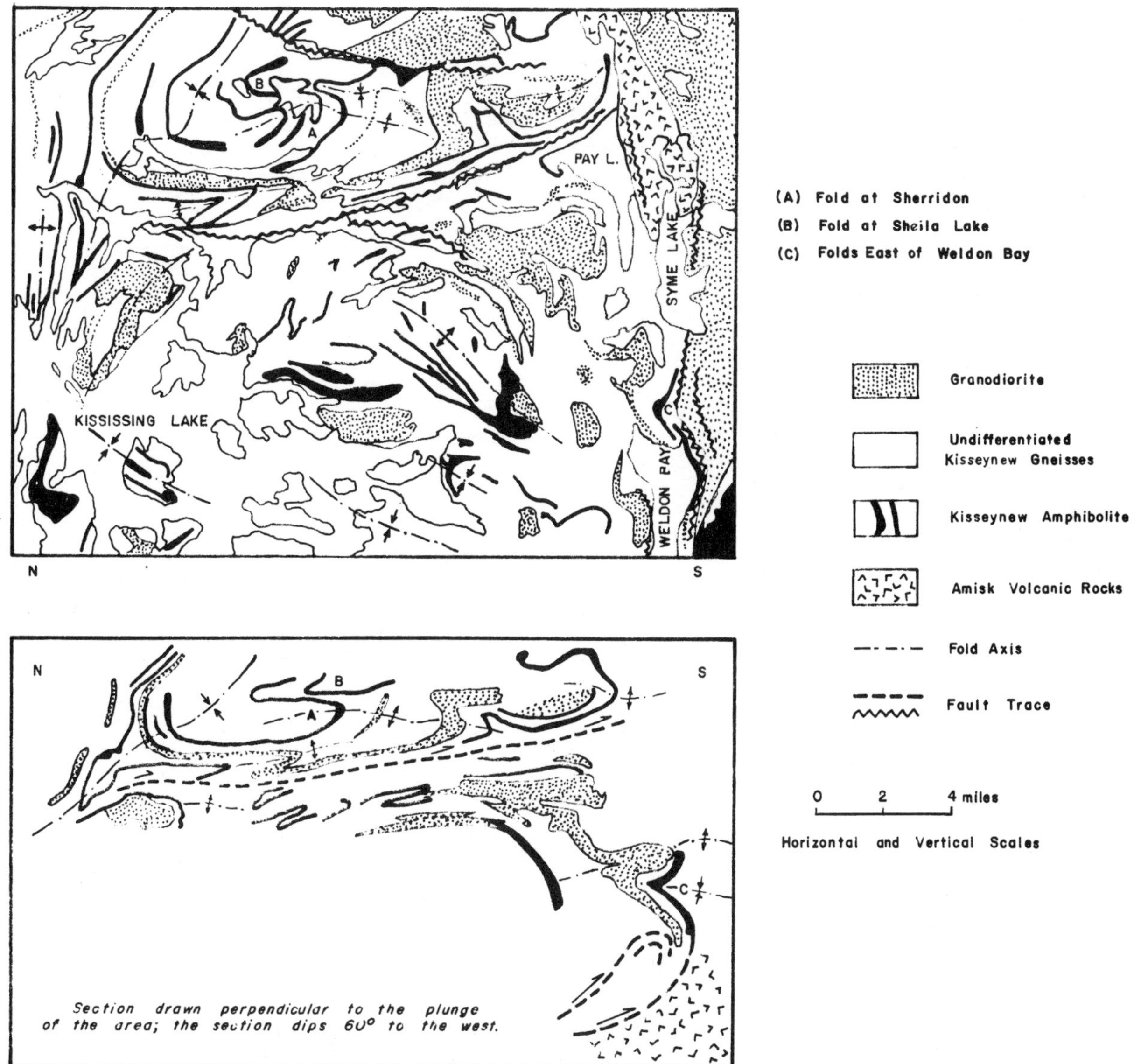

FIGURE 64 (*above*). Fold pattern in the Sherridon area of northern Manitoba, Canada. (Redrawn from J. Kalliokoski [1953], *Geol. Surv. Can.*, Bull. 25.)

FIGURE 65 (*below*). Geological cross section (a "right section") from Sherridon to Weldon Bay, Northern Manitoba, Canada. (Redrawn from J. Kalliokoski [1953], *Geol. Surv. Can.*, Bull. 25.)

CONSTRUCTION OF RIGHT SECTIONS NORMAL (PERPENDICULAR) TO THE PLUNGE OF GEOLOGICAL STRUCTURES

Applications and Limitations: Previous cross-section methods described were for areas involving little or no plunge. Many intensely deformed areas have been affected by several periods of folding. Kalliokoski (1953) and Stockwell (1950) have described such structures in the Precambrian of northern Manitoba, and White and Jahns (1950) have discussed multiple folding in Vermont. Figures 64 and 65 indicate some of the results of folded structures which have been affected by later tilting in the same area. The folds illustrated were formed by flow- and shear-folding processes. The entire pattern of axial plane traces on the surface is changed.

The fold pattern in the Sherridon area of northern Manitoba (Fig. 66) appears to be dominated

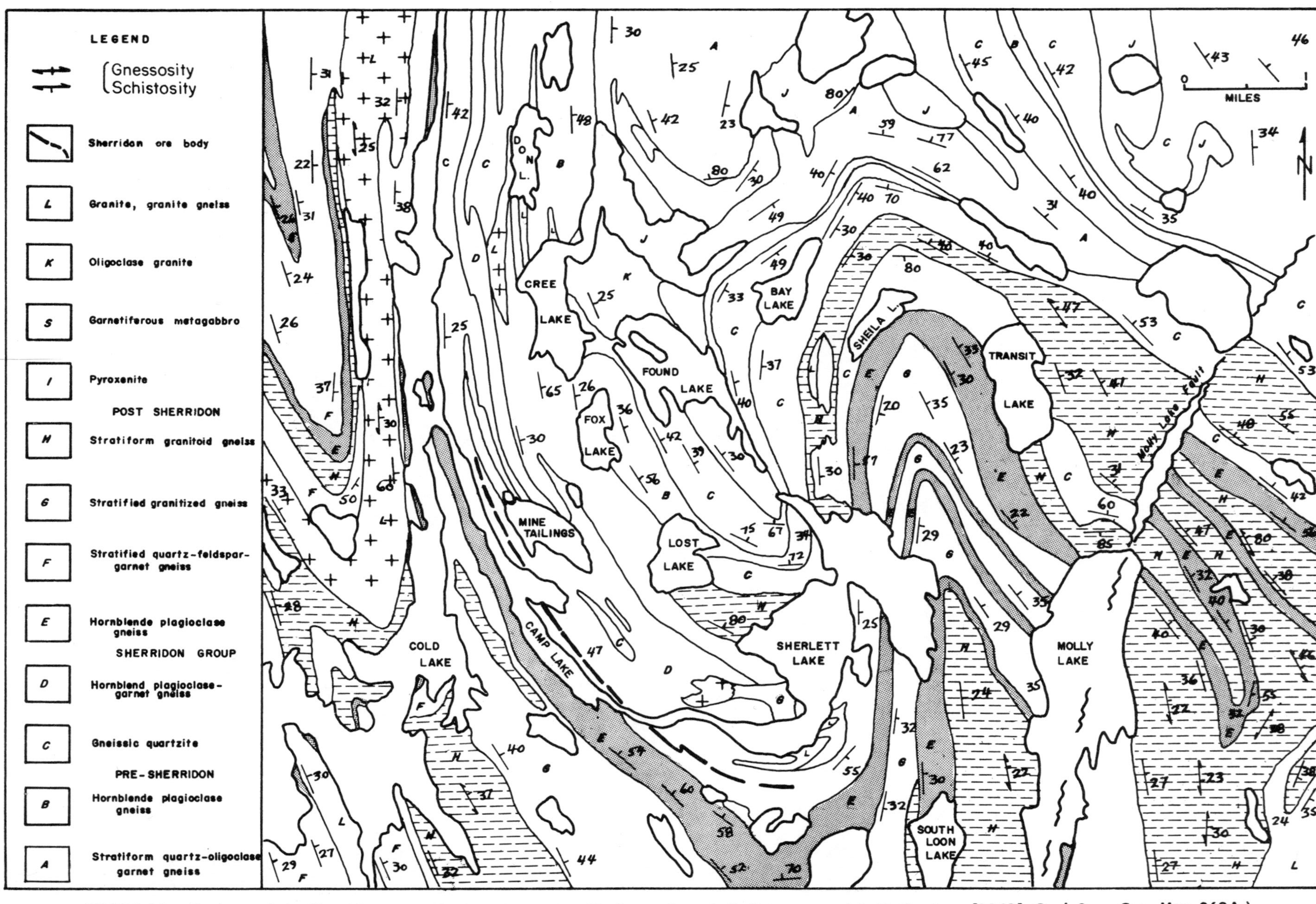

FIGURE 66. Geology of the Sherridon area, Northern Manitoba. (Redrawn from J. D. Bateman and J. M. Harrison [1943], *Geol. Surv. Can.*, Map 862A.)

by north-south fold axes. Closer study of the area, with particular attention to plunge directions of minor structures, indicated that the region is dominated by recumbent folds, overturned to the south and plunging east-northeast. This relationship is illustrated very clearly by means of a section drawn perpendicular to the plunge (Fig. 65). The *plunge* of a line is the angle between that line and the horizontal as measured in a vertical plane. An *axial line* or *axis* of a fold is a line along a surface of a particular bed where the degree of curvature, considered in three dimensions, is greatest. The *axial plane* or *axial surface* of a fold is the plane or surface that contains all the axial lines. A *crest line* is a line along the highest part of a bed, and the *crestal plane* or crestal surface is a plane or surface containing all the crest lines. A *trough line* is a line along the lowest part of a bed and the *trough plane* or *trough surface* is a plane or surface containing all the trough lines. The *axial trace* is the intersection line which the axial plane or axial surface makes with either the earth's surface or with any other surface. A *cylindrical fold* is one in which all the plunges parallel one another.

Figures 67 and 68 show the changes in formation thickness which become apparent when tilting influences previously folded structures. Conventional vertical cross sections through such tilted structures show apparent dips and apparent thicknesses rather than true structural dips and true thicknesses. For cylindrical folds it is necessary to construct sections normal (perpendicular) to the plunge if the true curvature and thickness are to be revealed. The method which is described here is adapted from Stockwell (1950) and applies only to plunging folds. It requires structural information from the entire surface extent of a structure rather than from a single line of traverse. It is based on the assumption that the thickness of the beds is constant down the plunge. Stockwell (1950) uses the term *right* section and defines it as an end-view section of an anticline or syncline, looking up the plunge in the case of synclines and down the plunge in the case of anticlines. The following example will illustrate the procedure involved.

Data Provided: The surface geological information for a syncline shown in Figure 69 is available (solid lines).

Determine: Construct a right section normal to the plunge of the syncline to illustrate the true configuration of the structure.

Method: Examine Figure 69 and determine the average bearing and inclination of plunge lines. The plunge can be determined by taking any two planes on the map (Fig. 69), such as the intersection of bedding and cleavage, or the intersection of two bedding planes (e.g., intersection of bedding planes at outcrop *X*, 342/48° WSW, with bedding planes at outcrop *Y*, 315/28°SW), and

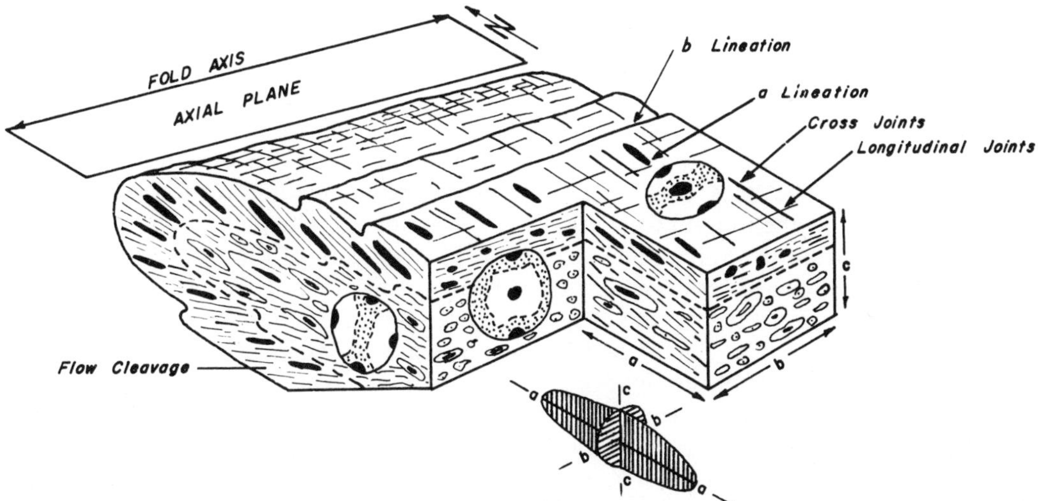

FIGURE 67. Recumbent fold. The fold axis is horizontal and strikes east-west. The *a* lineation is the direction of flowage in the flow cleavage planes. This is also known as the direction of "tectonic transport." The *a* lineation plunges to the south at a low inclination. The *b* lineation is the direction of "rotation around fold axes" during folding. The c axis is perpendicular to the flow cleavage. The mica diagrams are girdles around the *a* lineation. Dark elongate shapes are pebbles or oölites. (Redrawn and modified from E. Cloos [1946], *Geol. Soc. Am.*, Mem. 18.)

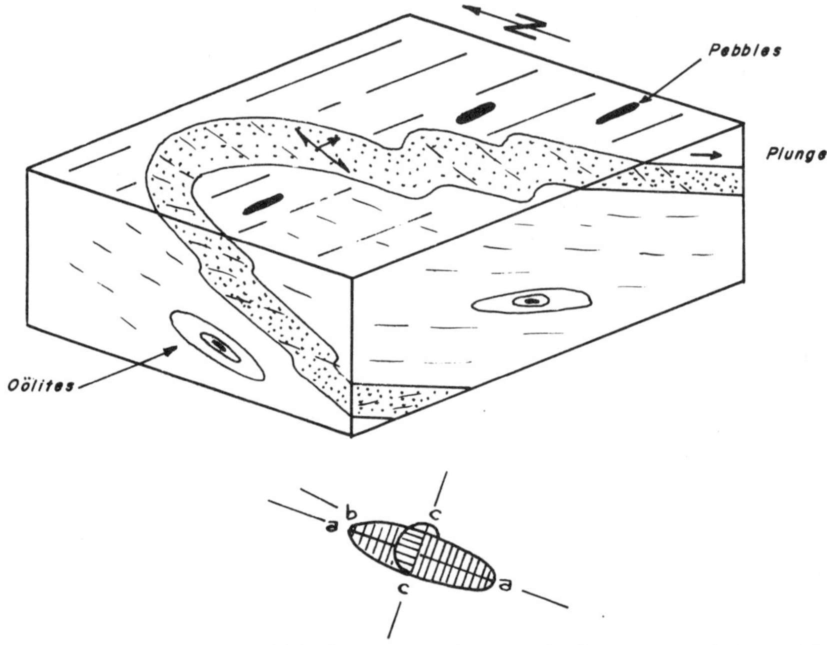

FIGURE 68. Recumbent fold plunging to the east. Surface traces of the axial planes of the folds and drag folds strike north-south, although the major direction of folding is still along east-west lines.

determining the bearing and inclination of the line of intersection of the two planes. This may be accomplished by the intersecting plane method of Chapter 1 or by stereographic methods described in Chapter 8. In the example mentioned, the plunge of the intersection line approximates due south and 20° of inclination. This appears to be the average for all of the plunge lines.

Draw lines AB perpendicular to the average bearing of the plunge lines, and then draw perpendiculars to AB through points A and B.

Then select any points C, E, F, etc., on one of the formation contacts, and draw lines CC', EE', FF', etc., parallel to AB. The lines $C'C''$, $E'E''$, $F'F''$ are then drawn in on the longitudinal sections with a 20° plunge from the horizontal. The lines BH and AJ are established by making the angles $C'BH$ and $DAJ = 70°$, which is the complement of the 20° plunge angle. The lines BH and AJ thus represent the traces of the right sections as seen in the longitudinal view. Then using A or B as centers, and BE'', BC'', AF'' as radii, draw in the arcs $E''E'''$, $C''C'''$, and $F''F'''$, etc. Finally draw in lines $E'''E''''$, $C'''C''''$, and $F'''F''''$ parallel to AB, making the lengths of these lines equal to EE', CC' and FF', respectively. The points E'''', C'''', F'''' thus establish the position of the formation contact in their right section. This procedure may be repeated for numerous points to establish the complete structural picture for the right section. The process may be speeded up if proportional dividers are available by setting the dividers in the ratio of $CW : BC''$. With this ratio, the distance CW is quickly reduced to WC''''. The same ratio can be applied to any points on the plan view.

It is observed that the plunge lines for the cleavage planes and drag folds are in sympathy with those of the formation contacts. Evidently these secondary structures are of the dependent type. Secondary structures may not always be dependent upon major structural processes, however. A stereographic method for testing this relationship is described in Chapter 8.

The position of the trace of the plane in plan view is unknown. It can be located easily in the right section by joining the points of maximum curvature (L, M, N, P, etc.). These points can be found in plan view by reversing the procedure just described. The trace of the trough plane is located by joining the lowest points on each formation contact. The positions of the traces of the axial and crestal surfaces are seen to diverge greatly in both plan view and right section. Note the change in direction of drag-fold movement for opposite sides of the axial surface. This surface is therefore not imaginary but of true structural significance.

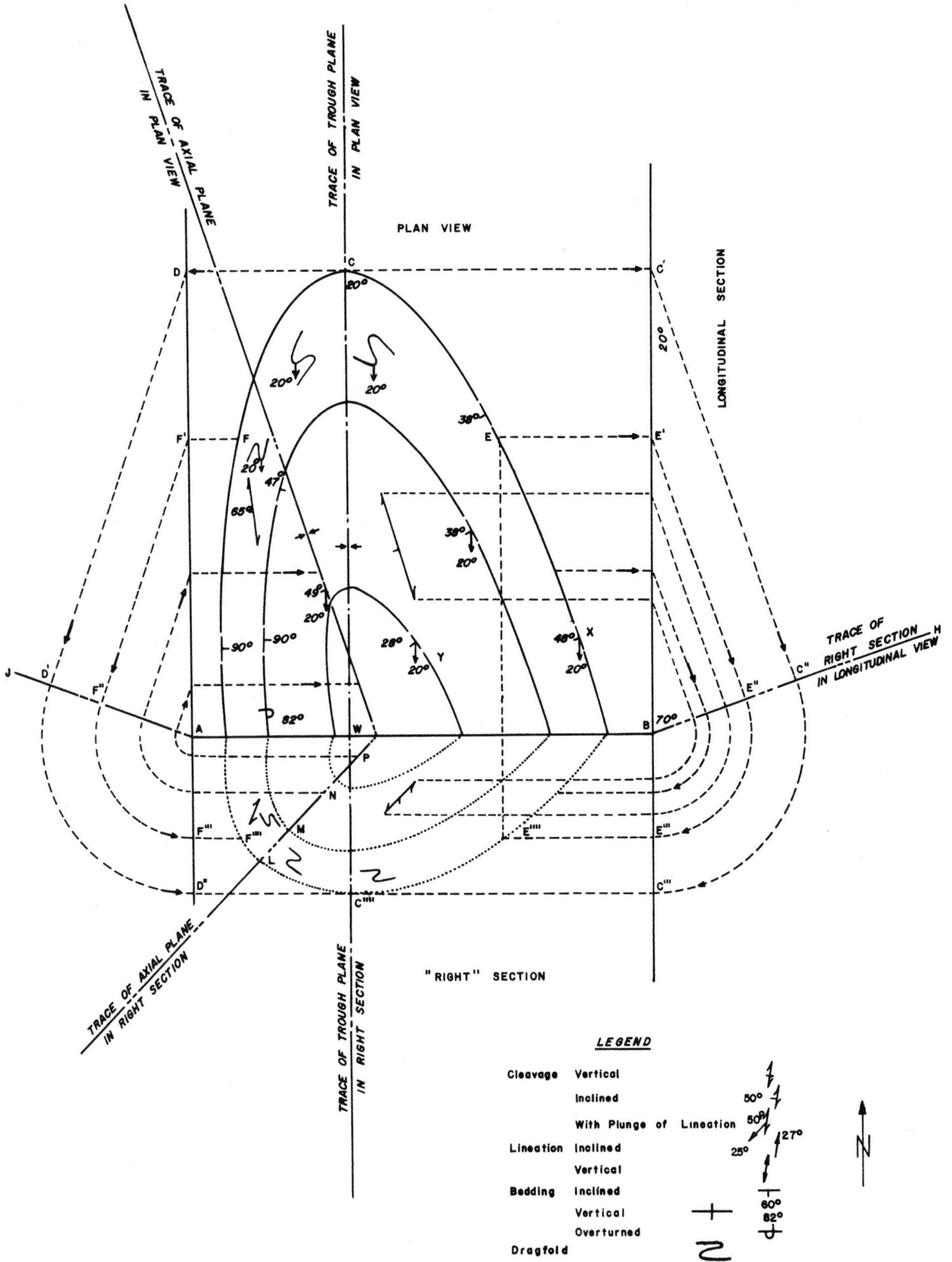

FIGURE 69. Illustrating the construction of "right sections" normal to the regional plunge. The fold illustrated is a cylindrical, parallel, overturned syncline, plunging 20° to the south. (Redrawn from C. H. Stockwell [1950], *Proc. Geol. Assoc. Can.*, vol. 3.)

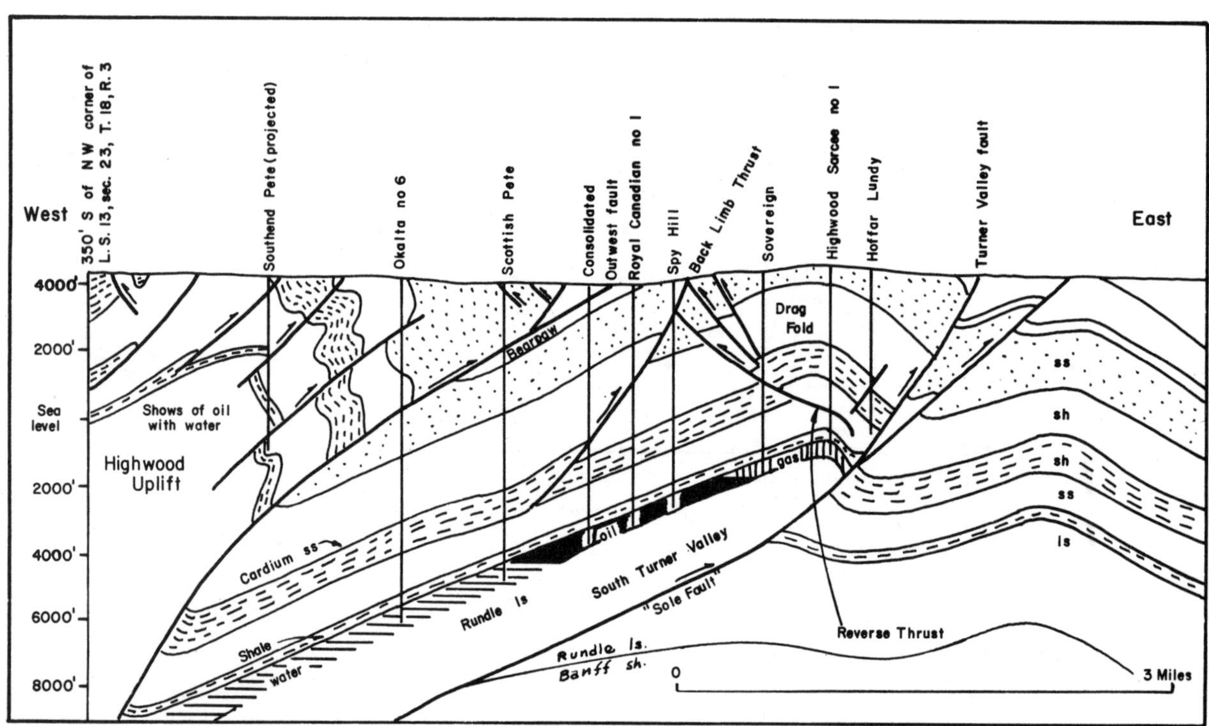

FIGURE 70. Cross section through the southern portion of the Turner Valley oil field, Alberta, Canada. (Redrawn from G. S. Hume [1940], *Geol. Surv. Can.*, Paper 40-8.)

PROBLEM 7 (Fig. 70)

INTERPRETATION OF A GEOLOGICAL CROSS SECTION

Questions Based on Problem No. 7

1. Discuss the mechanics and time of origin of all of the structures shown on this cross section.
2. Label all the features in such a way as to show the relative time of development of each feature.
3. Would you expect the syncline lying below the "drag fold" and beneath the "sole" fault to be wider or narrower if the sole fault had originated by a mechanism other than that which you have interpreted? Refer to Figures 41 and 42.
4. Discuss the economic aspects of this syncline interpretation.

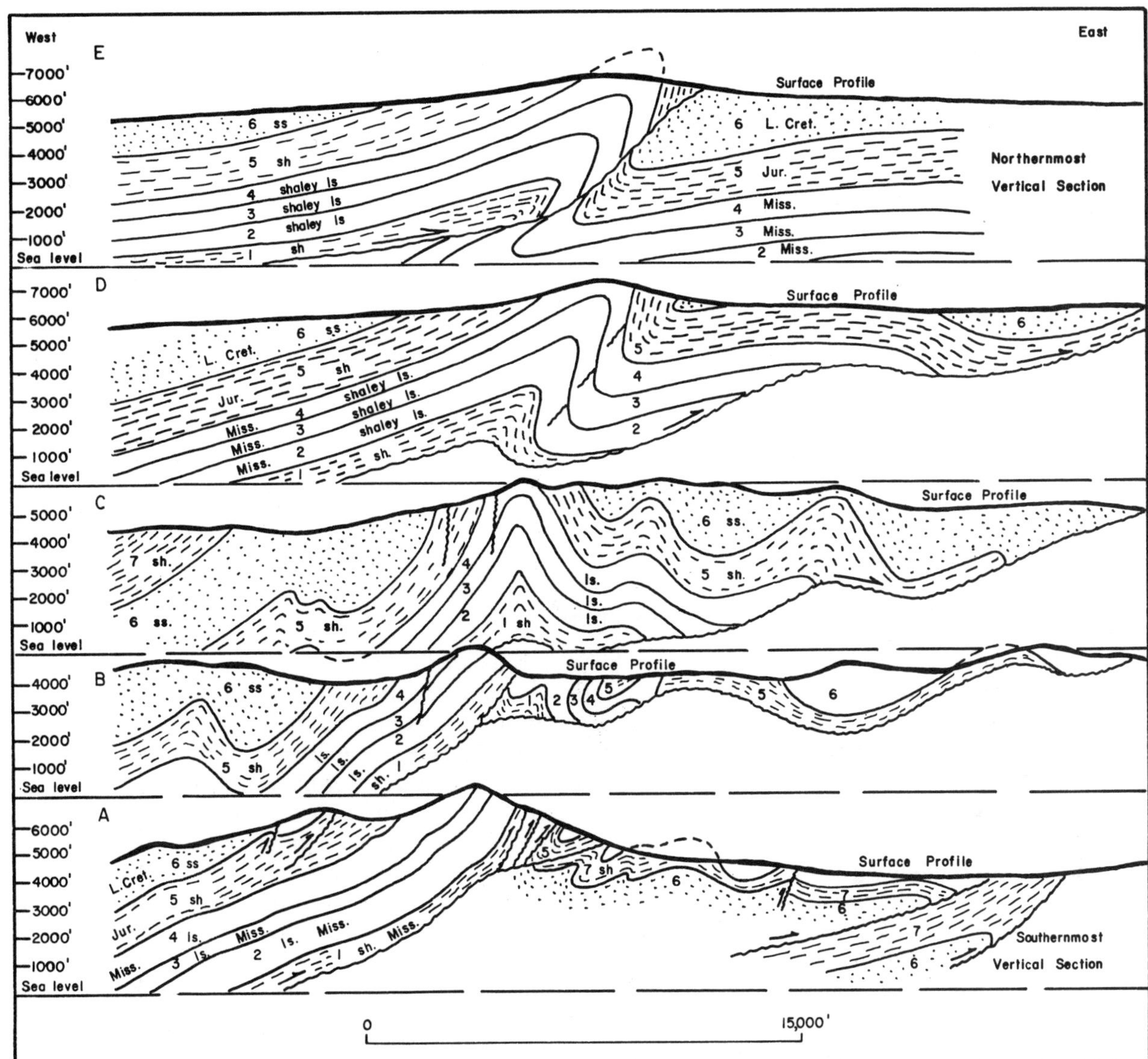

FIGURE 71. The use of "compressed" or "exploded" sections to illustrate the changing structural pattern along the strike of a mountain range.

PROBLEM 8 (FIG. 71)

THE USE OF "COMPRESSED" OR "EXPLODED" SECTIONS TO ILLUSTRATE THE CHANGING STRUCTURAL PATTERN ALONG THE STRIKE OF A MOUNTAIN RANGE

These vertical sections, through an anticlinal structure in the foothills of southern Alberta, are actually separated from each other by 10 miles, but they have been "compressed" together so that individual structural features can be traced visually from one section to the next without any difficulty. It is therefore simple to determine the changing structural mechanics along strike. The evolution of each structural feature can be followed visually with ease.

Discuss the mechanics and time of origin of the structural features illustrated. Discuss the lithological framework of the region and its control of structural developments.

PROBLEM 9 (FIG. 72)

INTERPRETATION OF A GEOLOGICAL CROSS SECTION

Description of Area Shown in Figure 72: This area is located on the disturbed margin (i.e., the western edge) of the Western Canada deformational basin (Fig. 73). Areas of more intense deformation lie to the west. The regional dip of this basin rises gradually to the east toward the stable craton (Laurentian shield). The Western Canada deformational basin is only a segment of what was originally the much larger Cordilleran geosyncline. The deepest portion of the Cordilleran geosyncline lay much farther to the west, and consequently all the formations shown on this cross section dipped regionally to the west prior to the folding and faulting which caused the smaller Rocky Mountain or Western Canada deformational basin to be formed on the eastern side of the larger Cordilleran geosyncline. This region has been affected slightly by the Jurassic Nevadan revolution and considerably by the Late Cretaceous Laramide revolution. The westward regional dip, which has persisted in this area since the initiation of the Cordilleran geosyncline, resulted from greater subsidence to the west in the deeper portions of the geosyncline. The gas reservoir at *C* has a higher reservoir pressure than would normally be expected for this depth.

Questions Based on Problem No. 9

1. There are several folding and faulting processes (mechanics of origin) involved in the area illustrated. What are they? Show where each process has been active on the cross section.
2. Which type of fault came into existence initially? Why? Indicate by numbers the relative age of the various faults shown (no. 1 for the oldest one).
3. Describe the folds and faults as completely as possible (geometrically and genetically).
4. Show the position and orientation of drag folds if they formed, tension fractures, concentric shears (and movement direction), fracture cleavage.
5. Which structure would you drill initially if you had only the surface geological information available? Why?
6. Outline the complete tectonic history of the region, including an analysis of the time of migration, time of accumulation and entrapment of hydrocarbons in the area. Be sure to explain the reasons why the distribution of reservoir fluids is as shown.
7. Do you think that the structures shown on the accompanying diagram could actually occur in the same region? If so, why?
8. Is it more important to be able to recognize the process (mechanics of origin) involved in the formation of a structure or to be able to describe it from a descriptive point of view? Which comes first, the description or the genetic interpretation?

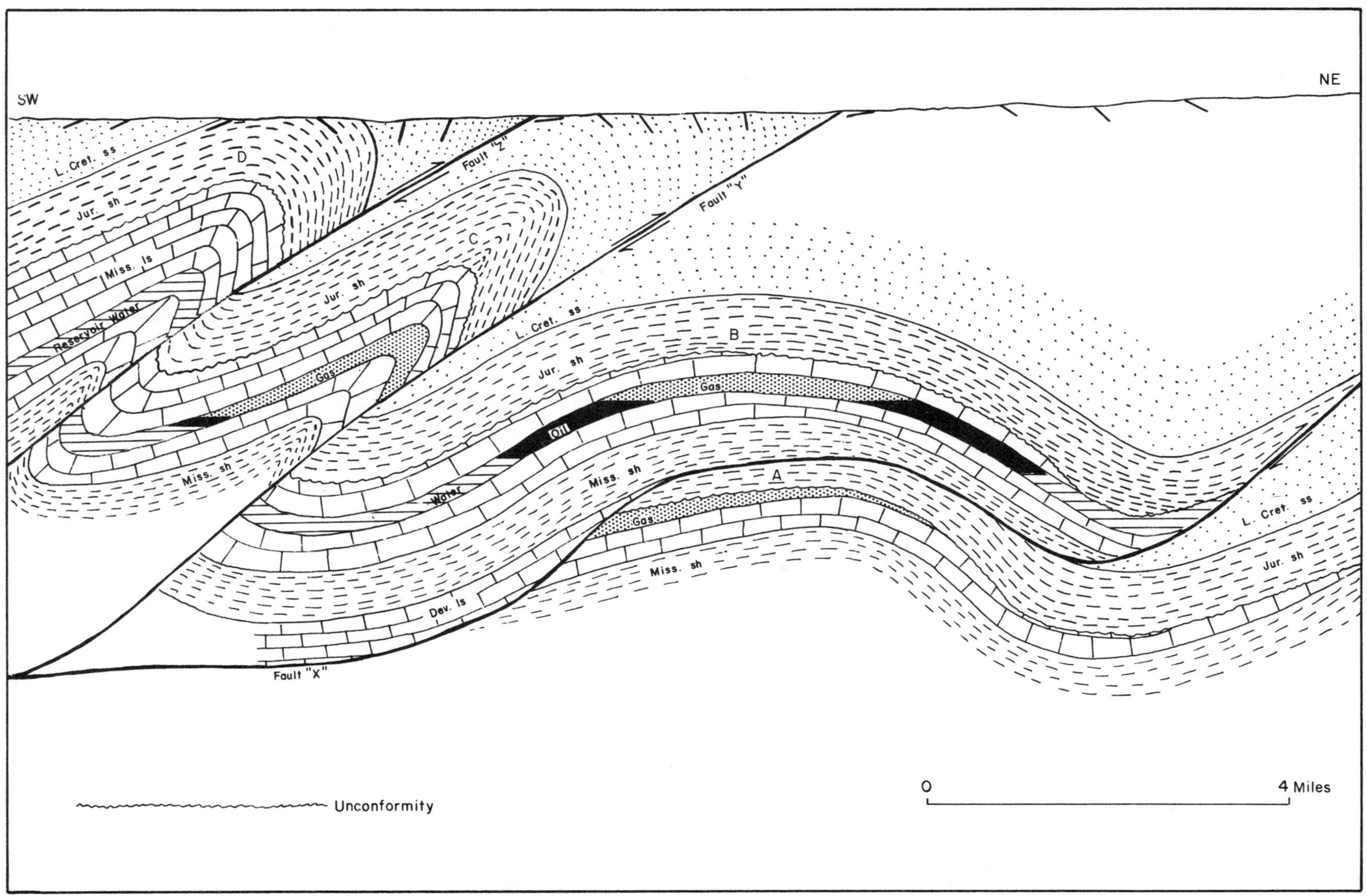

FIGURE 72. For use with Problem 9.

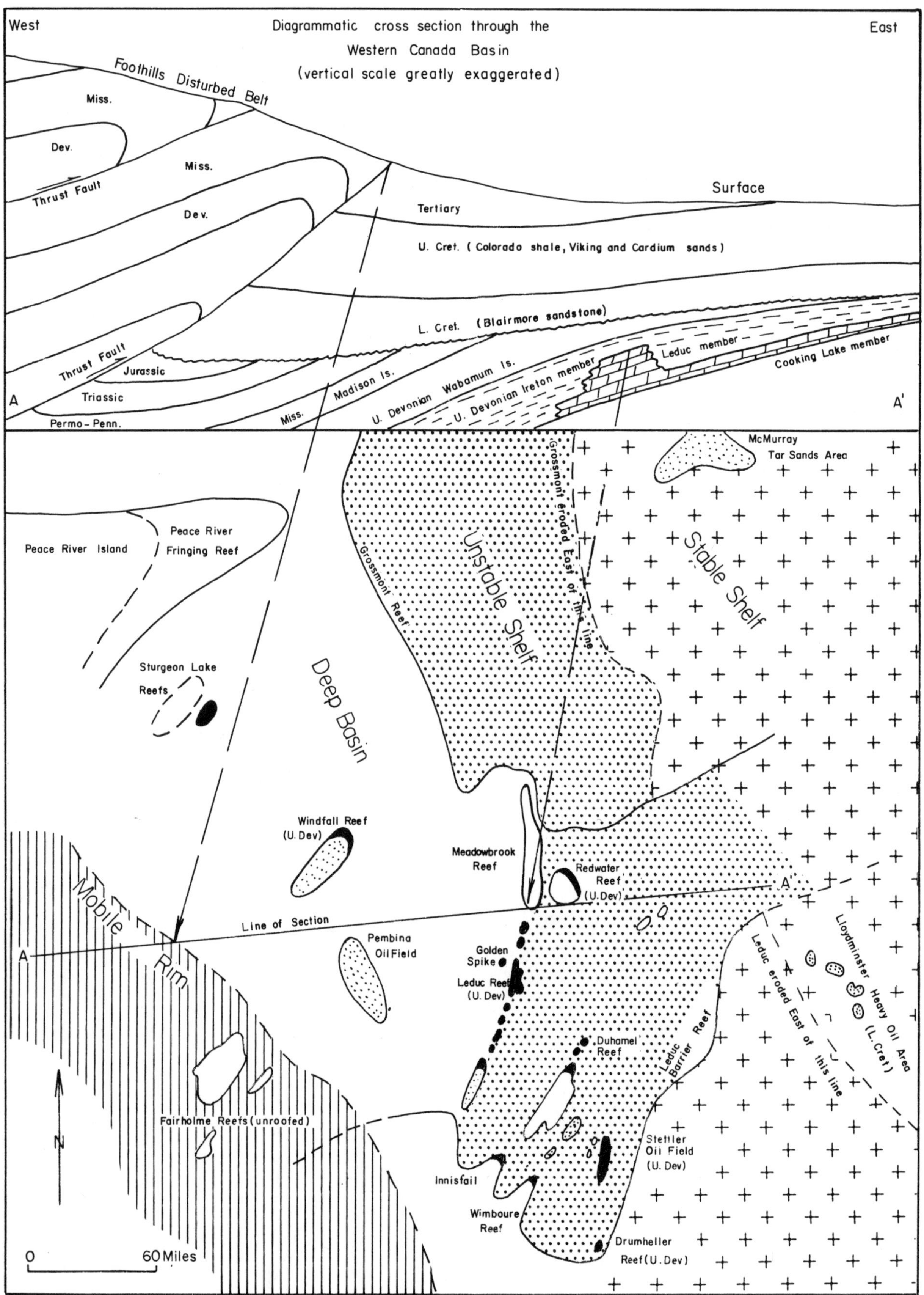

FIGURE 73. Tectonic framework of the Western Canada Basin in Alberta.

Table 11. **Stratigraphic Section (Descending Sequence)**

Age	Formation Name	Approximate Stratigraphic Thickness	Angle Made with Fault Surface	Lithology
Upper Cretaceous	Belly River formation	700′	30°	Sandstone (graywacke), gray to green, cross-bedded; some coal beds.
Upper Cretaceous	Colorado shale	3000′	5°	Consists of black to dark gray, fissile, marine shale with occasional sandstone interbeds.
Lower Cretaceous	Upper Blairmore	1000′	30°	Often divided into upper and lower members.
	Lower Blairmore	875′	30°	Consists of sandstone (graywacke), gray and greenish, often conglomeratic; some interbeds of gray, green, and reddish carbonaceous shale.
Lower Cretaceous or Jurassic	Kootenay formation	750′	5°	Shale, dark gray, carbonaceous, and coaly. Occasional sandy interbeds.
Jurassic	Fernie group	1275′	30°	Shale, limy, dark gray; and limestone, dark brownish gray; some sandy shale interbeds.
Mississippian	Rundle formation (Madison group)	2000′	30°	Limestone, medium to dark gray, massive, thick-bedded, usually competent, often dolomitized locally. In this region the Rundle contains porous stringers which often act as petroleum reservoirs.
Mississippian	Banff formation	500′	2° flattening out to 0°	Shale, dark brownish gray, locally limy and cherty. Is an excellent zone for the initiation of thrusts.

NOTE: The thicknesses used in this problem are only approximations of the actual thicknesses involved in this area.

PROBLEM 10 (FIG. 74)

CONSTRUCTION OF A GEOLOGICAL CROSS SECTION BY THE ARC METHOD AND THE EVALUATION OF A TILTED RESERVOIR BELOW AN UNCONFORMITY

This is an intermediate level problem involving the principles of the arc method as well as the use of ingenuity and imagination—qualities which the student of structural geology should attempt to cultivate.

Data Provided: A west-east surface traverse that crosses the general structural trend of an area near the disturbed belt of the Western Canada Basin yielded the strike, dip, and elevation data shown in plan view (Fig. 74). An exploratory well drilled near the west end of the traverse yielded the stratigraphic and dip information shown in vertical view (Fig. 74). A porous and oil stained member of the Mississippian Madison group was penetrated between depths of 5050 and 5600 feet. Careful examination of drill cores gave the dip information shown on the well log illustrated in the vertical view. It will be noted that the dips are 20° steeper below the unconformity which truncates the Madison group. This is due to a 20° westward regional tilt which developed in the sediments prior to the uplifting which caused the pre-Blairmore erosion surface. The area of maximum Mississippian, Permo-Pennsylvanian, Triassic, Jurassic, and Cretaceous sedimentation lies in the mountains west of the disturbed belt. Figure 73 shows diagrammatic views of the tectonic framework of the Western Canada Basin. Note that the regional dip rises to the east. Numerous Mississippian oil and gas fields occur in the eastern foothills and just east of the foothills.

Examination of the surface elevation data reveals a valley near the east end of the traverse. Oil seeps were noted in outcrops of the Viking (or Newcastle) sandstone, at the top (Dakota sand) of the Blairmore (Kootenai) sequence, and in the vicinity of the unconformity surface. The dips in the Mississippian (Madison) strata below the unconformity were noted to be 20° steeper than in the overlying Mesozoic strata.

Method: Draw a west-east cross-sectional view of the subsurface structural conditions. Use the top of the oil well log (shown in vertical view) as the reference point from which to commence drawing the topographic profile for the area. Project all strike information to a west-east line and convert true dips to apparent dips (see Fig. 6 or Table 1). Normally it is necessary to take topography into consideration in projecting outcrop information to a section line. The projection distance and elevation changes are small enough in this case so that the effects of topography can be neglected. Draw the topographic profile for the area and then plot all apparent dips on this profile. Then proceed to draw in the subsurface structural picture for the formations both above and below the unconformity. Bear in mind that dip must be assumed to be constant between adjoining outcrops of similar dip.

Questions Based on Problem No. 10

1. Indicate the best location of a well to test the Viking sand reservoir. Where would the best location to test the Madison possibilities be found?
2. What is the maximum thickness of formations that have been eroded from the crestal portion of the structure for the formations shown on the cross section?
3. Show the position of the traces of axial and crestal surfaces.
4. Which is the best surface to use as a guide for locating exploratory wells—crestal or axial surface?
5. Where could a vertical drill hole be located so as to encounter a reversal of dip?
6. How should the possible trap in the Madison porous zone be classified?
7. Did petroleum migrate up the regional dip prior to or after the formation of anticlinal traps? Explain.
8. Summarize the tectonic history of the area.

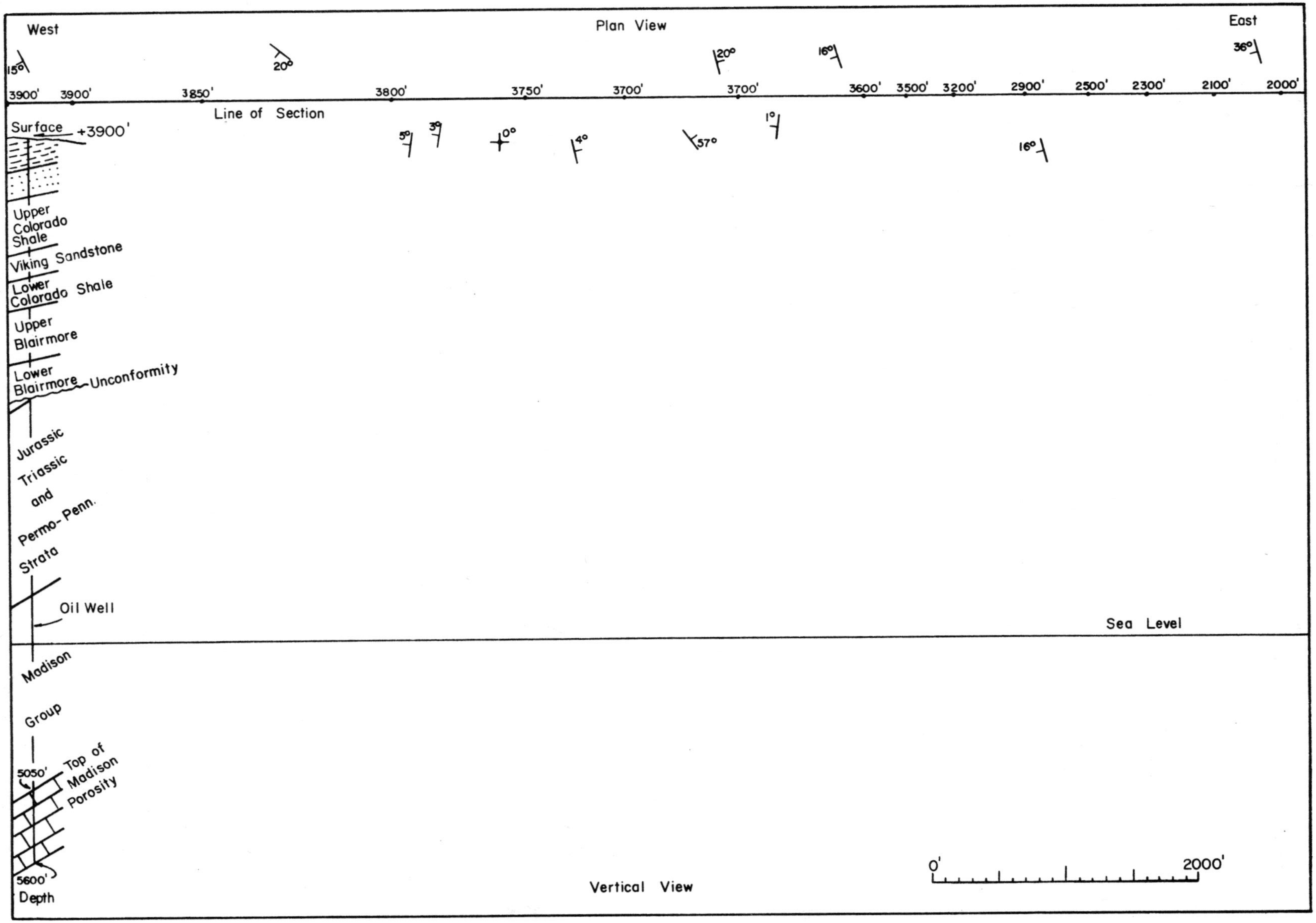

FIGURE 74. For use with Problem 10.

PROBLEM 11 (FIG. 75)

CONSTRUCTION OF A GEOLOGICAL CROSS SECTION BY THE BOUNDARY RAY METHOD AND THE INTERPRETATION OF A THRUST FAULT PATTERN IN THE SUBSURFACE

This is an advance level problem involving the theory of thrust faulting as well as the boundary ray method. The problem is based on a modification of a cross section of the Livingston thrust sheet which accompanies R. J. W. Douglas' memoir on the Callum Creek, Langford Creek, and Gap Map Areas, Alberta, Canada (1950). The Livingston thrust is located near the eastern margin of the disturbed foothills belt in southern Alberta (Fig. 73). The author has not followed the exact details of stratigraphy and so forth reported by Douglas but has used his map areas simply to illustrate the use of this method and the mechanics of origin of certain types of thrust faults.

Data Provided: A surface profile traversing from southwest to northeast across the structural trend of the Livingston Range of southern Alberta, Canada, yielded the strike, dip, elevation, and stratigraphic relations shown in Figure 75. It is necessary to draw a structural cross section for the area. The boundary ray method will be used as compression is believed to have caused some thinning of the folded strata. In this particular area, there is insufficient information to indicate the exact amount of thinning which has occurred. The 10 per cent thinning table adapted from W. D. Gill (1953) will be used in determining the position of boundary ray in the cross section. At the present time the student is concerned more with learning how to use this method than with the selection of the correct thinning table.

The pertinent portion of the stratigraphic section for the area is summarized in Table 11 (p. 61). Note that the section consists of alternating competent and incompetent strata. Field experience in this area indicates that thrust faults were initiated on glide planes, such as the Banff shale, and that the thrusts have followed a steplike pattern up to the surface (Fig. 41). The thrusts are believed to have started as bedding plane shear phenomena in the Banff portion of the section. When friction built up to such a point that upward movement had to occur to relieve the additional stress, then the thrust fault turned up into the overlying competent Rundle limestone, cutting this formation at approximately 30° to the direction of stress which is believed to have been parallel to the bedding. After the Rundle and Fernie are traversed, another glide zone is encountered in the Kootenay, and the thrusts flatten out again. Thus a steplike pattern is followed by thrusts before they reach the surface. The angles at which thrusts traverse the various formations in this area are indicated in the stratigraphic chart (Table 11) on page 61. The angles chosen agree quite closely with field observations in this region.

Method: After locating the boundary rays and formation contacts in the cross section, it is necessary to project the thrust fault down into the subsurface, and the angular relations indicated in the chart must be observed closely if the correct subsurface structural picture is to be obtained.

From information obtained elsewhere in this region, the net slip, measured along the fault surface, was determined to be 22,500 feet. This thrust is believed to be a dip-slip fault. Show the position and configuration of the Rundle reservoir below the fault surface. This is accomplished by moving back 22,500 feet along the fault surface from each point where a formation contact (of the hanging wall) touches the upper surface of the thrust fault surface. In this manner the intersection of formation contacts (of the footwall) with the underneath side of the fault can be located (points *A, B, C, D* of Fig. 76).

For each dip zone below the thrust surface, the angle between bedding and thrust surface (Table 11, column 4) must conform with the angle at which the fault is supposed to traverse the formation immediately underlying the fault surface (Fig. 76). For example, if the Rundle formation immediately underlies the fault, then the fault-bedding angle

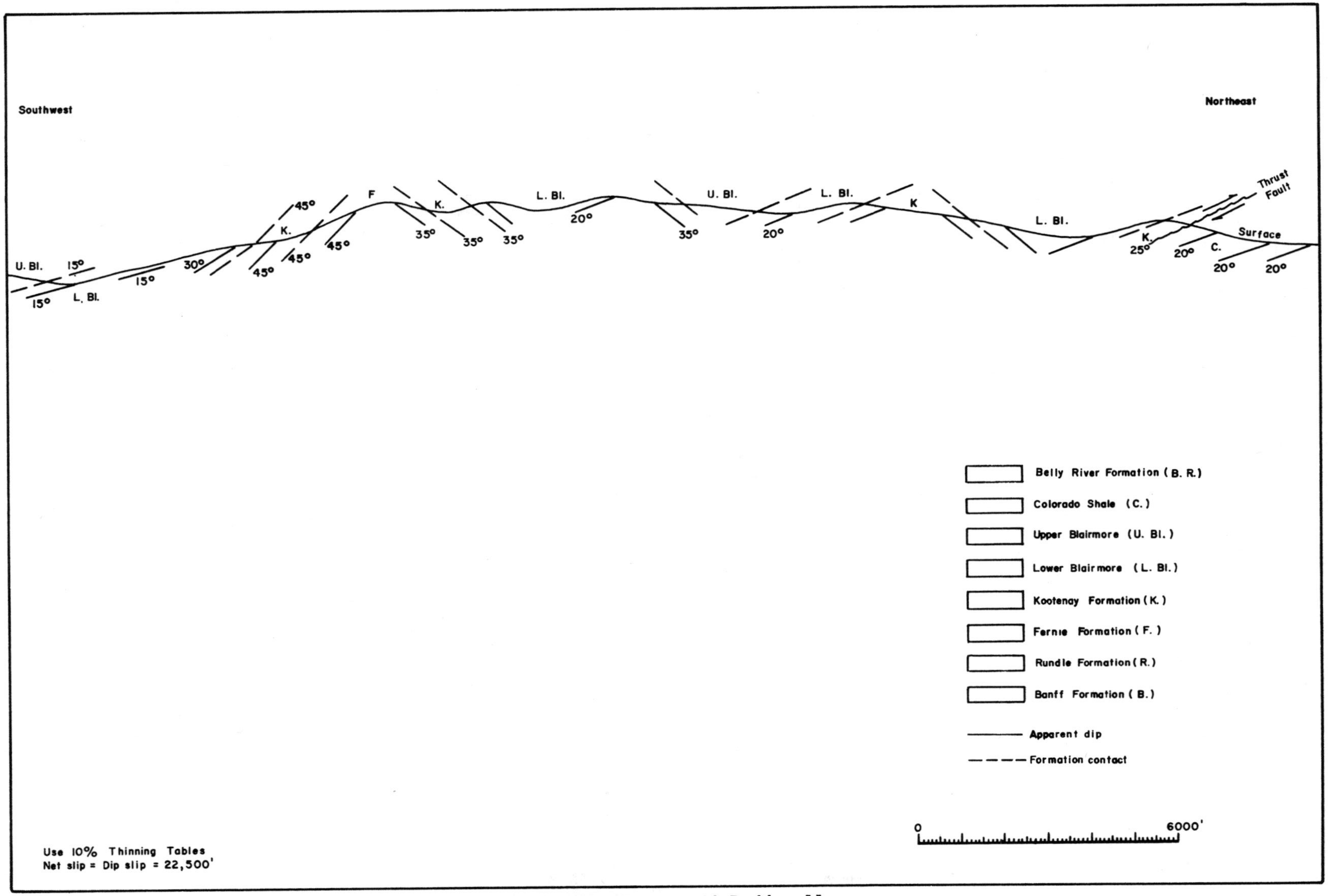

Southwest

Northeast

U. Bl. 15° 15° L. Bl. 15° 30° 45° K. 45° 45° 45° 45° F K. 35° 35° 35° L. Bl. 20° U. Bl. 35° 20° L. Bl. K L. Bl. K. 25° 20° C. 20° 20° Thrust Fault Surface

Belly River Formation (B. R.)

Colorado Shale (C.)

Upper Blairmore (U. Bl.)

Lower Blairmore (L. Bl.)

Kootenay Formation (K.)

Fernie Formation (F.)

Rundle Formation (R.)

Banff Formation (B.)

Apparent dip

Formation contact

0 6000'

Use 10% Thinning Tables
Net slip = Dip slip = 22,500'

FIGURE 75. For use with Problem 11.

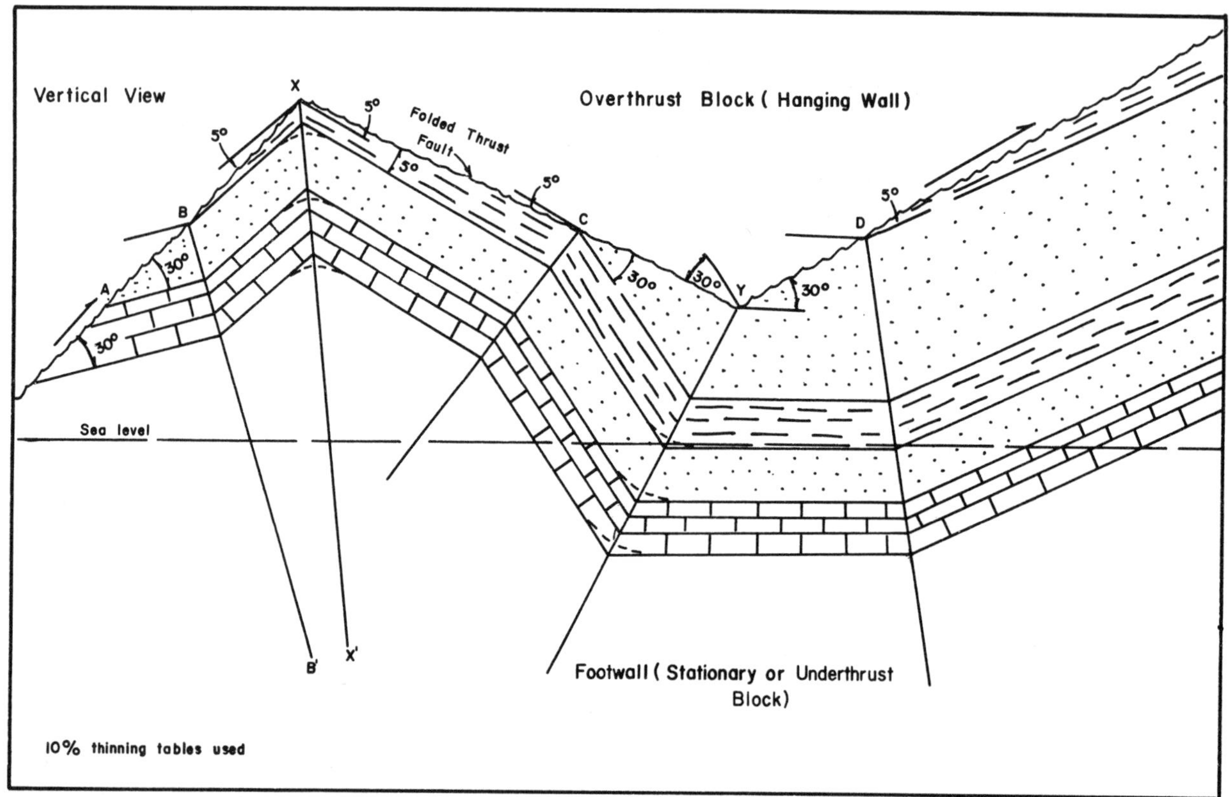

FIGURE 76. Angular relations between bedding and fault must be maintained in the footwall also. This necessitates the location of new boundary rays at points where formation contacts intersect the fault (at *B*, *C*, and *D*) and where the dip of the fault changes (at points *X* and *Y*). If only a thin wedge of new formation is involved before the next boundary ray (*XX′*) is reached (e. g., between points *B* and *X*), then the new boundary ray (*BB′* in this case) could be eliminated.

should be 30° for the Rundle dip zone. If the Kootenay immediately underlies the fault, then the fault-bedding angle should be 5° for the Kootenay dip zone. This requires the construction of a new set of boundary rays underneath the fault (Fig. 76).

The angular junctions should be rounded off after the mechanics of cross-section construction have been completed to give the structures a more natural appearance. A little freehand adjustment of the formation contacts projected across the vertical section to the contact positions indicated at the surface may be necessary as the deformation has not been homogeneous and also because of possible drafting inaccuracies on the part of the student.

Questions Based on Problem No. 11

1. What are the maximum and minimum thicknesses observed for the Rundle formation on the cross section?
2. Did thrusting largely precede folding in this area or is thrusting the result of folding?
3. Is there any location above the fault which could be recommended as a potential Rundle test site? Explain.
4. Could you recommend any location to drill for a potential Rundle reservoir below the fault surface? If so, where?
5. What is the postfaulting tectonic history of this area?
6. What is the advantage of this cross-section construction method as compared to the arc method?
7. What are the limitations of this method? Give some thought to this question.

PROBLEM 12 (Fig. 66, Plate 1)

CONSTRUCTION OF A RIGHT SECTION NORMAL (PERPENDICULAR) TO THE PLUNGE OF FOLDED FORMATIONS

This is an intermediate level problem. An air photo mosaic (Plate 1 of the series of photographs that are printed at the end of the text) is provided to give the reader an additional view of this classic area.

Data Provided: Figure 66 shows a map of the Sherridon area in northern Manitoba which was mapped by J. D. Bateman and J. M. Harrison (1943). The regional tectonics of the area are indicated in Figures 166 and 167. The position of the Sherridon ore body is shown on the map (Fig. 66).

Determine: Draw a right section of the area perpendicular to the plunge to illustrate the true structural picture of the district. Show all construction lines and list the steps involved in your method.

Method: Determine the regional plunge of the structures shown on the map, and construct a right section perpendicular to the plunge direction. If time is limited, the student may select a single fold, for example the Sheila Lake fold, and draw a right section for this fold only.

Questions Based on Problem No. 12

1. Outline the structural history of the district.
2. Discuss the structural control of ore reposits in this district.
3. Is there any evidence of plunge available on the map directly without calculating its value by orthographic or stereographic projection? Explain.

References

Anderson, E. M. (1951), *The Dynamics of Faulting and Dyke Formation with Applications to Britain,* Oliver & Boyd Publishers, Edinburgh and London, 206 pp.

Athy, L. F. (1930), Density, Porosity and Compaction of Sedimentary Rocks, *Bull. Am. Assoc. Petrol. Geol.,* vol. 14, pp. 1–24.

Balk, Robert (1936), Structural and Petrologic Studies in Dutchess County, New York, *Bull Geol. Soc. Am.,* vol. 47, pp. 685–774.

Balk, Robert (1937), Structural Behavior of Igneous Rocks. *Geol. Soc. Am.,* Mem. 5, 177 pp.

Bateman, J. D., and Harrison, J. M. (1943), Geology of the Sherridon Map Area, Manitoba, *Geol. Surv. Can.,* Map 862A.

Blanchard, Roland (1942), Mount Isa Ore Geology, *Ore Deposits as Related to Structural Features,* Princeton University Press, pp. 148–154.

Bucher, W. H. (1955), Deformation in Orogenic Belts, *Geol. Soc. Am.,* Special Paper No. 62, pp. 343–368.

Busk, H. G. (1929), *Earth Flexures,* Cambridge University Press, 106 pp.

Campbell, J. D. (1951), Some Aspects of Rock Folding by Shearing Deformation, *Am. Jour. Sci.,* vol. 249, pp. 625–639.

Cloos, E. (1937), *The Application of Recent Structural Methods in the Interpretation of the Crystalline Rocks of Maryland,* The Johns Hopkins Press, 105 pp.

Cloos, E., and Hietanen, A. (1941), Geology of the Martic Overthrust and the Glenarm Series in Pennsylvania and Maryland, *Geol. Soc. Am.,* Special Paper No. 35, 207 pp.

Coates, J. (1945), The Construction of Geological Sections, *Quart. Jour. Geol. Min. Met. Soc. India,* vol. 17, no. 1.

Dahlstrom, C. D. A. (1954), Statistical Analysis of Cylindrical Folds. *Trans. Can. Inst. Min. Met.,* vol. LVII, pp. 140–145.

Dallmus, K. F. (1958), Mechanics of Basin Evolution and Its Relation to the Habitat of Oil in the Basin, in Habitat of Oil, a Symposium conducted by the Am. Assoc. Petrol. Geol., pp. 883–931.

DeSitter, L. U. (1956), *Structural Geology,* McGraw-Hill Book Co., Inc., 552 pp.

Dickinson, G. (1953), Geological Aspects of Abnormal Reservoir Pressures on Gulf Coast Louisiana, *Bull. Am. Assoc. Petrol. Geol.,* vol. 37, pp. 410–432.

Douglas, R. J. W. (1950), Callum Creek, Langford Creek, and Gap Map Areas, Alberta, *Geol. Surv. Can.,* Mem. 255.

Eardley, A. J. (1938), Graphic Treatment of Folds in Three Dimensions, *Bull. Am. Assoc. Petrol. Geol.,* vol. 22, pp. 483–489.

Eardley, A. J. (1951), *Structural Geology of North America,* Harper & Brothers, 624 pp.

Engel, A. E. J., and Engel, C. G. (1953), Grenville Series in the Northwest Adirondack Mountains, New York, *Bull. Geol. Soc. Am.,* vol. 64, pp. 1013–1097.

Fairbairn, H. W. (1949), *Structural Petrology of Deformed Rocks,* 2nd ed., Addison-Wesley Publishing Co., Inc., 344 pp.

Gill, W. D. (1953), Construction of Geological Sections of Folds with Steep Limb Attenuation, *Bull. Am. Assoc. Petrol. Geol.,* vol. 37, pp. 2389–2406.

Gustafson, J. K., Burrell, H. C., and Garretty, M. D. (1950), Geology of the Broken Hill Ore Deposit, *Bull. Geol. Soc. Am.,* vol. 61, pp. 1369–1438.

Hafner, W. (1951), Stress Distributions and Faulting, *Bull. Geol. Soc. Am.,* vol. 62, pp. 373–398.

Hedberg, H. D. (1927), The Effect of Gravitational Compaction on the Structure of Sedimentary Rocks, *Bull. Am. Assoc. Petrol. Geol.,* vol. 10, pp. 1035–1072.

Heim, A. (1919), *Geologie der Schweiz,* C. H. Tauchnitz, Leipzig, Bd. 1, 704 pp.

Herold, S. C. (1933), Projection of Dip Angle on Profile Section, *Bull. Am. Assoc. Petrol. Geol.,* vol. 17, pp. 740–742.

Hills, E. S. (1940), *Outlines of Structural Geology,* Methuen & Co., Ltd., London, 172 pp.

Hume, G. S. (1940), The Structure and Oil Prospects of the Foothills of Alberta Between Highwood and Bow Rivers, *Geol. Surv. Can.,* Paper 40–8.

Hume, G. S. (1957), Fault Structures in the Foothills and Eastern Rocky Mountains of Southern Alberta, *Bull. Geol. Soc. Am.,* vol. 68, pp. 395–412.

Kalliokoski, J. (1953), Interpretations of the Structural Geology of the Sherridon-Flin Flon Region, Manitoba, *Geol. Surv. Can.,* Bull. 25.

King, P. B. (1950), Tectonic Framework of the Southeastern States, *Bull. Am. Assoc. Petrol. Geol.,* vol. 34, pp. 635–671.

Lee, G. M. (1953), Persia, *Science of Petroleum,* Oxford University Press, London, pp. 73–82.

Link, T. A. (1949), Interpretation of Foothills Structures, Alberta, Canada, *Bull. Am. Assoc. Petrol. Geol.,* vol. 33, pp. 1475–1501.

Mackin, J. H. (1950), The Down-Structure Method of Viewing Geologic Maps, *Jour. Geol.,* vol. 58, pp. 55–72.

McKinstry, H. E. (1955), Structure of Hydrothermal Ore Deposits, *Econ. Geol.,* 50th Anniv. Vol., pp. 170–225.

Mertie, J. B., Jr. (1944), Calculation of Thickness in Parallel Folds, *Bull. Am. Assoc. Petrol. Geol.,* vol. 78, pp. 1376–1385.

Mertie, J. B., Jr. (1947), Delineation of Parallel Folds and Measurements of Stratigraphic Dimension, *Bull. Geol. Soc. Am.,* vol. 58, pp. 779–802.

Mertie, J. B., Jr. (1948), Application of Brianchon's Theorem to Construction of Geologic Profiles, *Bull. Geol. Soc. Am.,* vol. 59, pp. 767–786.

Moench, R. H., Harrison, J. E., and Sims, P. K. (1958), Precambrian Folding in the Central Part of the Front Range Mineral Belt, Colorado (abstract), *Bull. Geol. Soc. Am.,* vol. 69, p. 1737.

Nevin, C. M. (1949), *Principles of Structural Geology,* 4th ed., John Wiley & Sons, Inc., 410 pp.

Rich, J. L. (1934), Mechanics of Low-Angle Overthrust Faulting as Illustrated by Cumberland Thrust Block, Virginia, Kentucky, and Tennessee, *Bull. Am. Assoc. Petrol. Geol.,* vol. 18, pp. 1584–1596.

Scott, J. C., Hennessey, W. J., and Lamon, R. S. (1958), Savanna Creek Gas Field, Alberta, *Bull. Can. Inst. Min. Met.,* vol. 51, pp. 270–278.

Sederholm, J. J. (1926), On Migmatites and Associated Pre-Cambrian Rocks of Southwestern Finlande, *Bull. Comm. Géol. Finlande,* No. 77, pp. 69–81.

Stockwell, C. H. (1950), The Use of Plunge in the Construction of Cross-Sections of Folds, *Proc. Geol. Assoc. Can.,* vol. 3, pp. 97–121.

Tainsh, H. R. (1950), An Aid to the Forecasting of Underground Structures, *Proc. 18th Internat. Geol. Congress, 1948* (London), Pt. 6.

Thomas, D. E. (1953), The Castlemaine-Chewton-Fryerstown Goldfield, in *Geology of Australian Ore Deposits,* Aust. Inst. Min. Met., pp. 1042–1053.

Weller, J. Marvin (1959), Compaction of Sediments, *Bull. Am. Assoc. Petrol. Geol.,* vol. 43, pp. 273–310.

White, W. S., and Johns, R. H. (1950), Structure of Central and East-Central Vermont, *Jour. Geol.,* vol. 58, pp. 179–220.

Wilson, G. (1952), Ptygmatic Structures and Their Formation, *Geol. Magazine,* vol. LXXXIX, pp. 1–21.

CHAPTER 4

Structure Contour Maps

Terminology and Principles Involved

A *structure contour* is an imaginary line connecting points of equal elevation on a single horizon, usually the top or bottom of a sedimentary bed or formation.

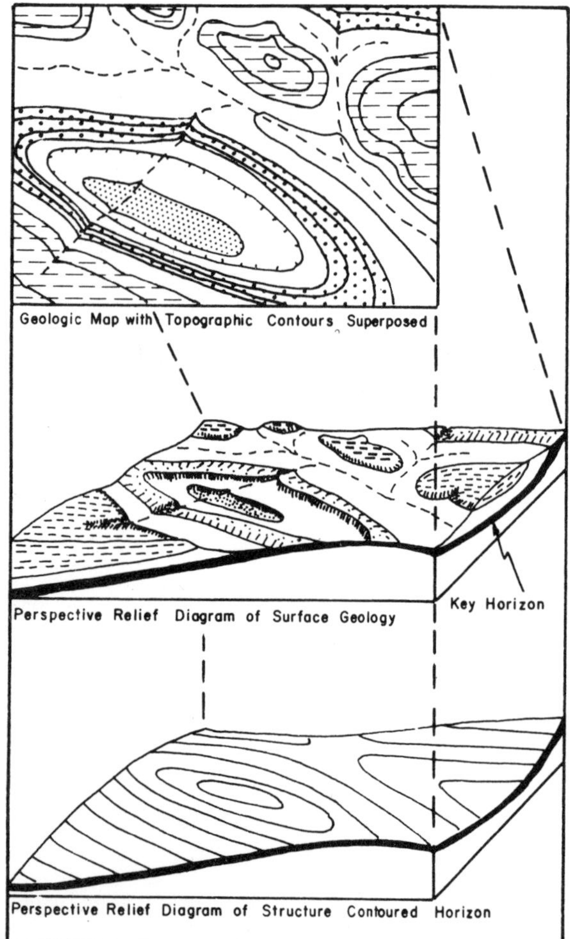

FIGURE 77. Illustrating the relationship between surface geology, topographic relief, and structure contours. (Modified from A. J. Eardley [1941], *Aerial Photographs, Their Use and Interpretation,* Harper & Brothers.)

A *structure contour map* depicts the configuration of a rock surface by contour lines joining points of equal elevation, generally referred to mean sea level as the datum plane. The contoured surface whose configuration is depicted is usually a key horizon (= good mappable formation contact). Structure contour maps are thus analogous to topographic contour maps except that the latter show the configuration of the earth's surface rather than the configuration of one key horizon (Fig. 77).

There are a number of general rules to consider in drawing structure contour maps:

1. Every contour line must pass between those points whose elevation values are higher and lower, respectively, than that of the contour.
2. No contour should cross over itself or over another contour, with the exception of overturned or recumbent folds and reverse faults. Usually contours are not shown for that portion of a datum surface lying below a thrust sheet. These hidden portions may be shown as dotted or dashed lines.
3. Contours may merge (touch) into a single line only where the contoured surface is vertical or where faulting has displaced the contoured surface along the strike by an amount equal to, or exceeding, the contour interval (Fig. 80).
4. Small closed depressions are indicated by hachured lines with the hachures pointing toward the bottom of the depression (= depression contours).
5. A better result is obtained in less time if contours are constructed by bands of several lines, rather than a single line at a time.
6. Contour maps may be read more easily if every fifth, or tenth, etc., contour is made heavier than the others.

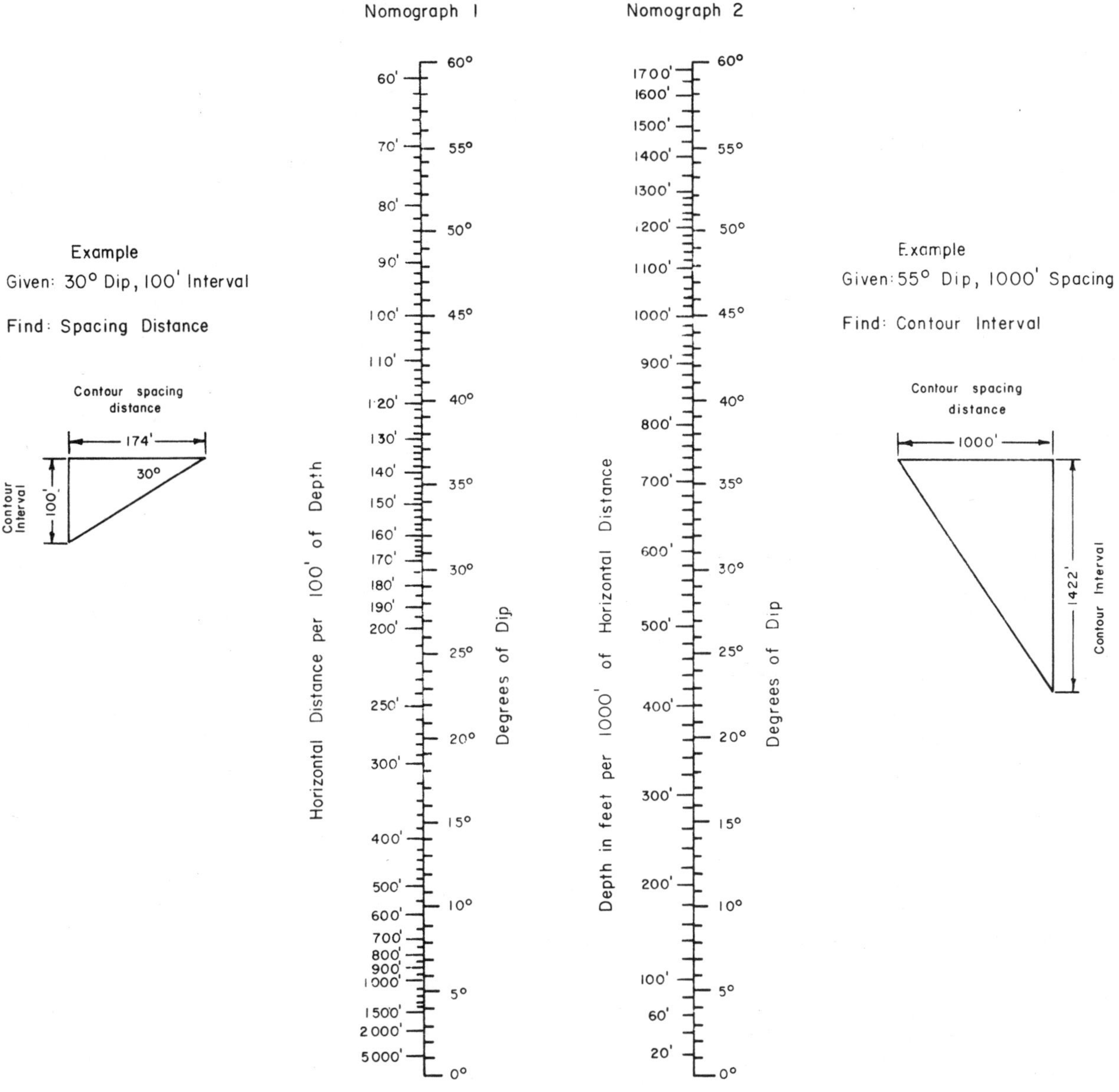

FIGURE 78. Nomograph for converting degrees of dip to structure contour spacing distance. (Reprinted with permission from C. M. Nevin, *Principles of Structural Geology*, 1949, John Wiley & Sons, Inc. and Chapman & Hall, Ltd. Additions and slight modifications have been made to the original drawing by Nevin.)

7. The contour interval selected should depend on:

a. The density of control points available—there should be more contours when more data is available.
b. Accuracy of the elevations—the contour interval should be greater than the limits of error involved.
c. The steepness of the dips involved—use a smaller contour interval for gentle structures than for steep structures.
d. Scale of the map—the contour interval

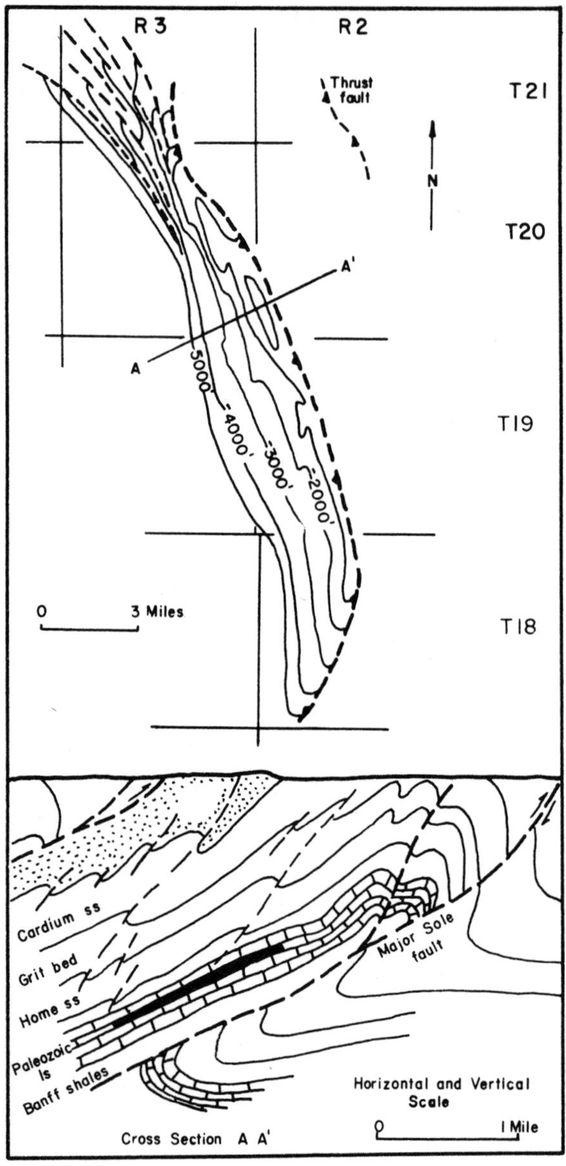

FIGURE 79. Structure contour map for an overturned faulted anticline. The structure illustrated is the Turner Valley anticline in the foothills belt of southwestern Alberta, Canada. Structure contours are on top of the Madison limestone. (Redrawn from T. H. Link [1949], *Bull. Am. Assoc. Petrol. Geol.*, vol. 33.)

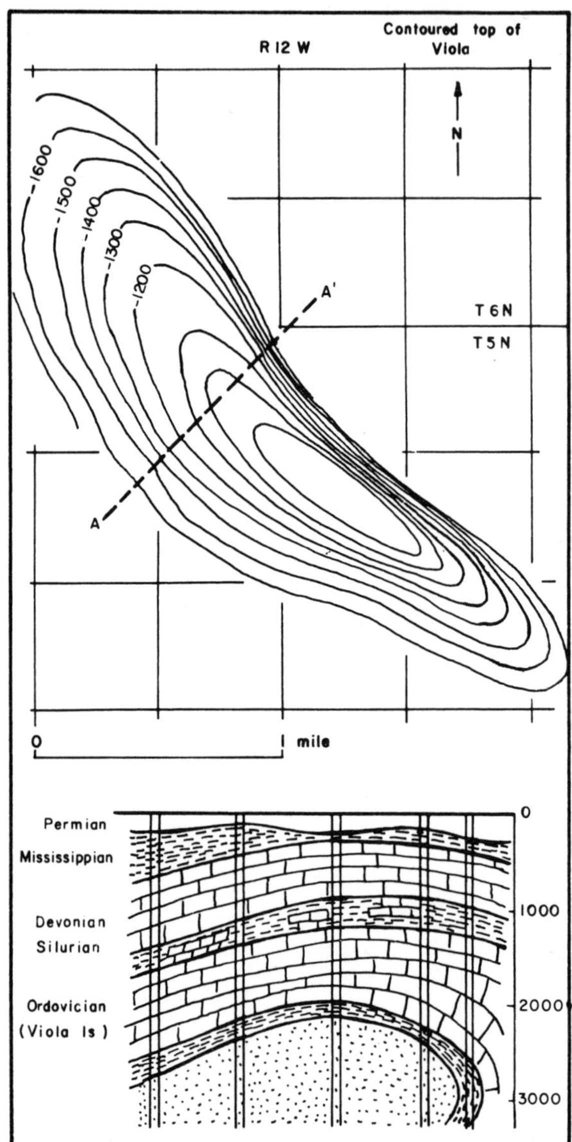

FIGURE 80. Structure contour map and cross section for an overturned anticline. Note the contour packing on the overturned limb. The structure illustrated is the Apache oil pool in Oklahoma. Structure contours are on top of the Viola limestone. (Redrawn from V. C. Scott [1945], *Bull. Am. Assoc. Petrol. Geol.*, vol. 29.)

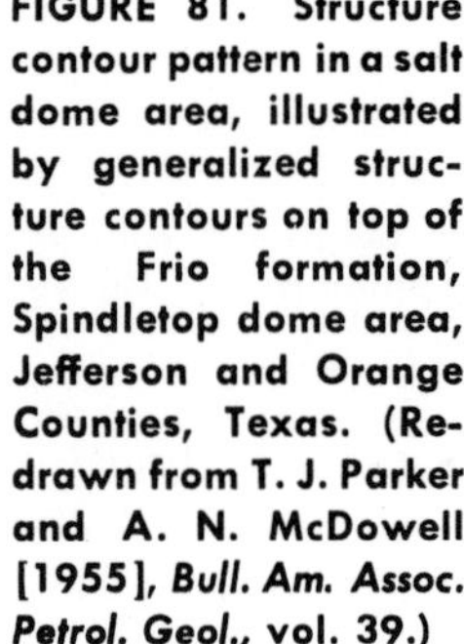

FIGURE 81. Structure contour pattern in a salt dome area, illustrated by generalized structure contours on top of the Frio formation, Spindletop dome area, Jefferson and Orange Counties, Texas. (Redrawn from T. J. Parker and A. N. McDowell [1955], *Bull. Am. Assoc. Petrol. Geol.*, vol. 39.)

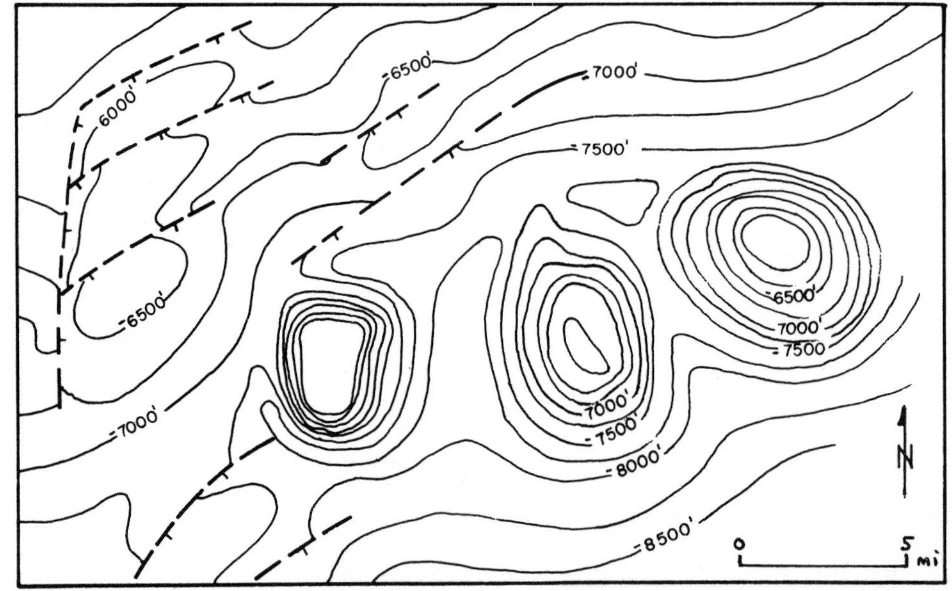

should be decreased as the size of the map increases.

8. The spacing between structure contours is dependent upon the dip of the structures being illustrated. This relationship is illustrated in Figure 78. The structure contour spacing distance may be computed by using the equation:

$$\text{Spacing} = \text{Contour Interval} \times \text{Cotangent of Dip}$$

9. Study the regional geology of the area being worked, and obtain a good idea of the type of structures involved (Figs. 79 to 90). Decide whether one should expect to use equally spaced contours or not. Usually the spacing between contours will be steeper on the flanks of oil-producing anticlines than along the plunge or in the crestal area of the folds. The various control points should be tied together, not in the simplest manner possible, but rather in a manner which would coincide with the type of structures which might be expected in the area. If the nature of folding is well known for the area involved, then the structures should be contoured so as to correlate with the regional trend of the area.

10. Keeping the above limitations in mind, most contour maps can be improved by using multiple dividers to divide the distance up exactly between control points. If multiple dividers are not available, then a standard engineer's scale can be used in the following manner:

Suppose elevations are known for points A, B, C, D, etc., all on the same key horizon which is to be contoured (Fig. 91):

On one of the six scales available on the standard engineer's triangular scale, lay off any line AC' such that the distance $AC' = 335$ feet (i.e., 350 feet − 15 feet). Use that scale (of the six available) which makes AC' as close in length to AC as possible. On AC' mark off points where +300-foot, +250-foot, +200-foot, etc., contours should fall on the line AC. This procedure can be followed for lines AB, AD, etc. Once the 300-foot, 250-foot, etc., contour points have been determined for each line, the various 300-foot points can be joined up along each line to give the position of the 300-foot contour across the map. A similar procedure is used for each of the other contours. It will be noted that careful contouring by this method can reveal structural features that might otherwise be overlooked.

11. When the key bed being contoured appears on the surface, then a number of different elevations may be obtained on the key bed along its outcrop, until the regional dip carries it either below the surface or the bed becomes eroded away entirely. When this happens, the elevations should be continued on underlying or overlying parallel beds and the appropriate stratigraphic thickness should be added or subtracted to reduce the elevations to the original datum (Fig. 92). Sometimes several beds must be used in addition to the key horizon to outline a structure. The stratigraphic thicknesses may be obtained by noting the outcrop widths (stratigraphic thickness = outcrop width × sin dip). Depth may then be calculated by using the equation (Fig. 92):

$$\text{Depth} = \text{Stratigraphic Thickness} \times \text{Secant Dip}$$

Depth may also be computed by using the accompanying alignment diagram (Fig. 93).

12. Because structure contour maps are commonly designed to guide in the selection of drilling sites on anticlines, it is generally a good idea to make the map just as conservative with respect to number, area, and height of anticlines as the datum elevations will permit.

13. It is desirable that the geologist contour his map while he is still in the field so that he can check the correctness of his conclusions wherever possible. This is very important as it is sometimes inconvenient and costly to return to the field later.

14. When structure contours cross fold axes, a change in the strike of the contour occurs. If the folds are plunging, then a zigzag pattern results (Fig. 89). Over plunging anticlines a "V" or "U" is formed whose apex points down plunge. For synclines the apex points up plunge.

15. A reversal of dip occurs over fold axes. Therefore the highest (for anticlines) and lowest (for synclines) contours are repeated at folding axes—the highest or lowest contour will occur on each side of the axis (Fig. 89). Because of this reversal in dip over fold axes a widening or narrowing of the contour spacing may occur in the axial areas.

16. It is desirable to maintain a constant rate of dip (equal contour spacing) and make only gradual changes in strike unless the contour data forces rapid changes in strike and dip. Anomalous areas where strikes and dips differ from the remainder of the map area should be carefully studied for possible faults.

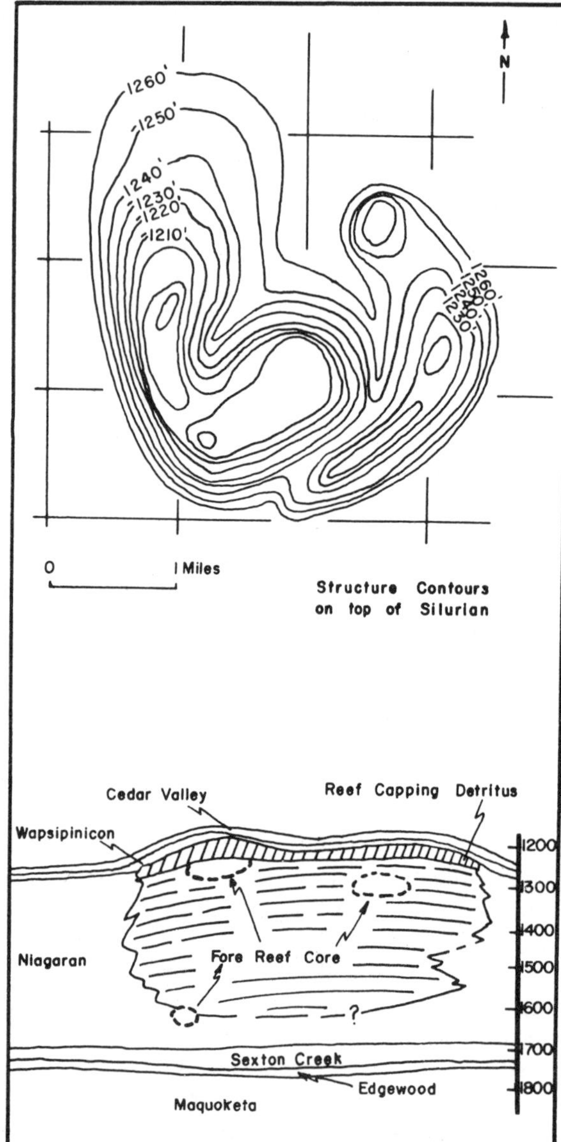

FIGURE 82. Structure contour map and cross section of the Marine Pool in Illinois. This oil trap is a Silurian biohermal reef. Structure contours are on top of the Silurian. (Redrawn from H. A. Lowenstam [1948], Am. Assoc. Petrol. Geol., vol. III of *Structure of Typical American Oil Fields.*)

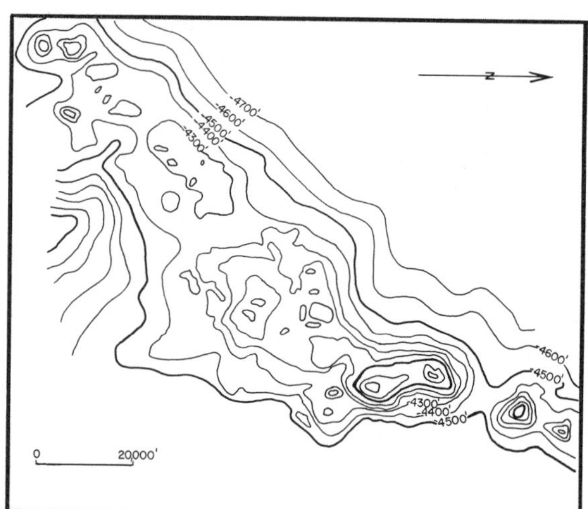

FIGURE 83. Structure contour map illustrating the structural configuration in a reef area. The configuration illustrated is for the top of the Canyon Reef in Scurry County, Texas. (From *World Oil,* vol. 133, no. 4.)

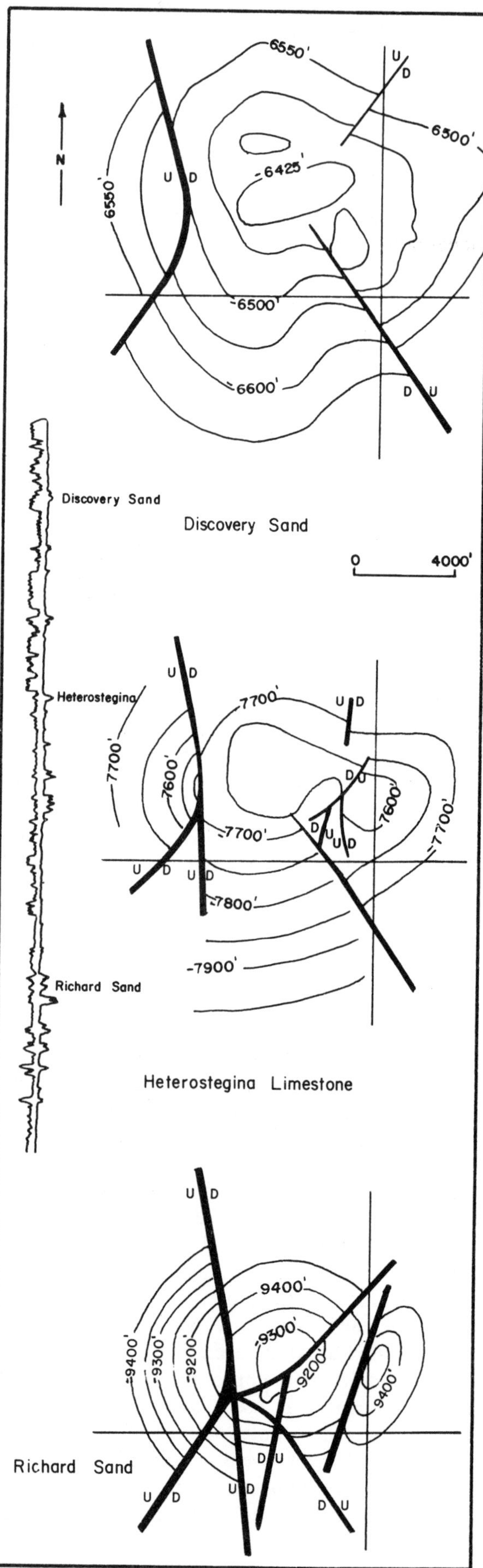

FIGURE 84. Structure contour maps over a faulted salt dome structure. This is the University field in Louisiana. (Redrawn from G. Atwater [1948], *Geophysical Case Histories,* vol. I, Soc. Expl. Geophy.)

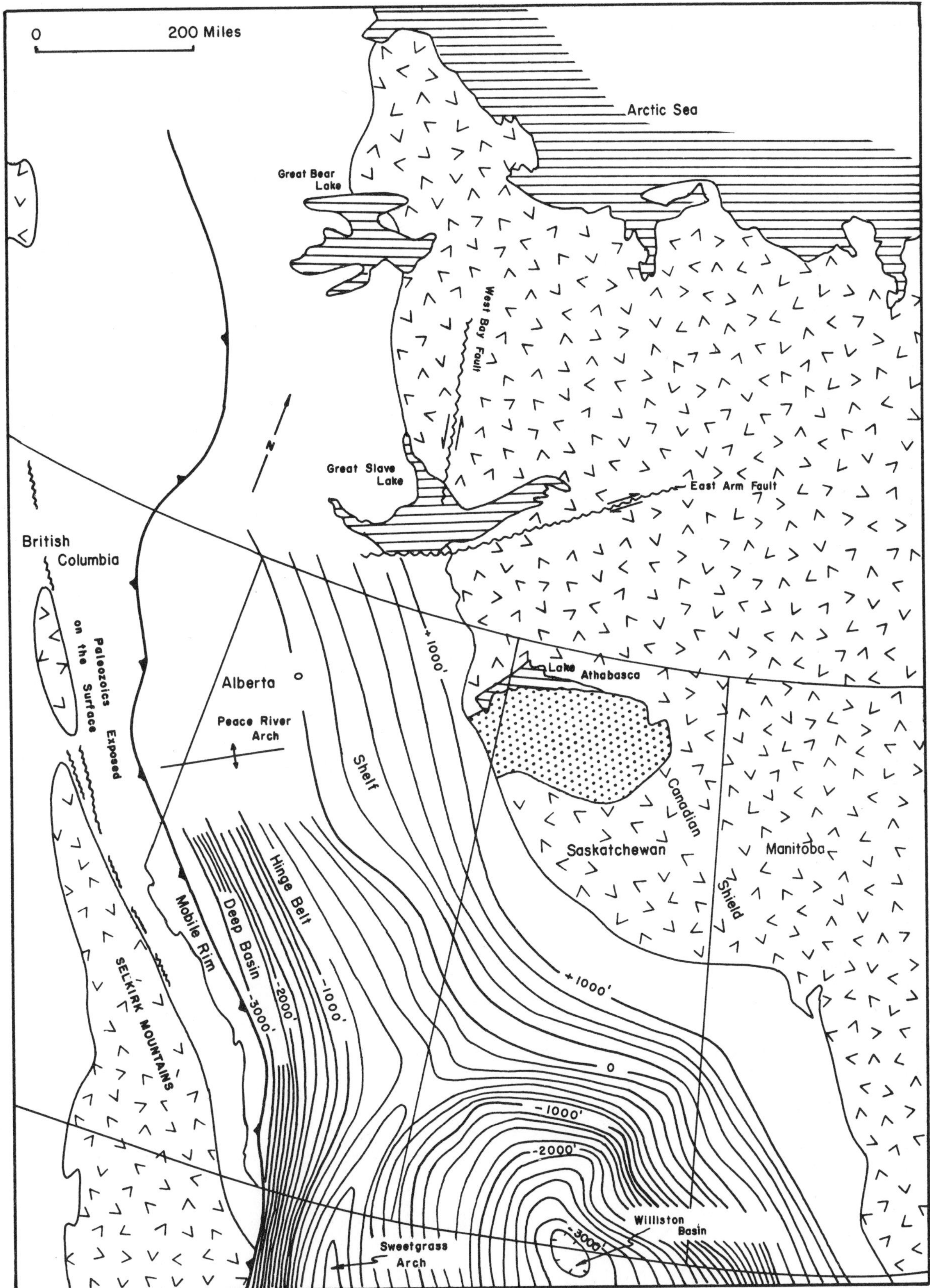

FIGURE 85. Tectonic configuration of an entire basin area as illustrated by contours. The area shown is the Western Canada Basin. Contours are on top of the eroded Paleozoic surface.

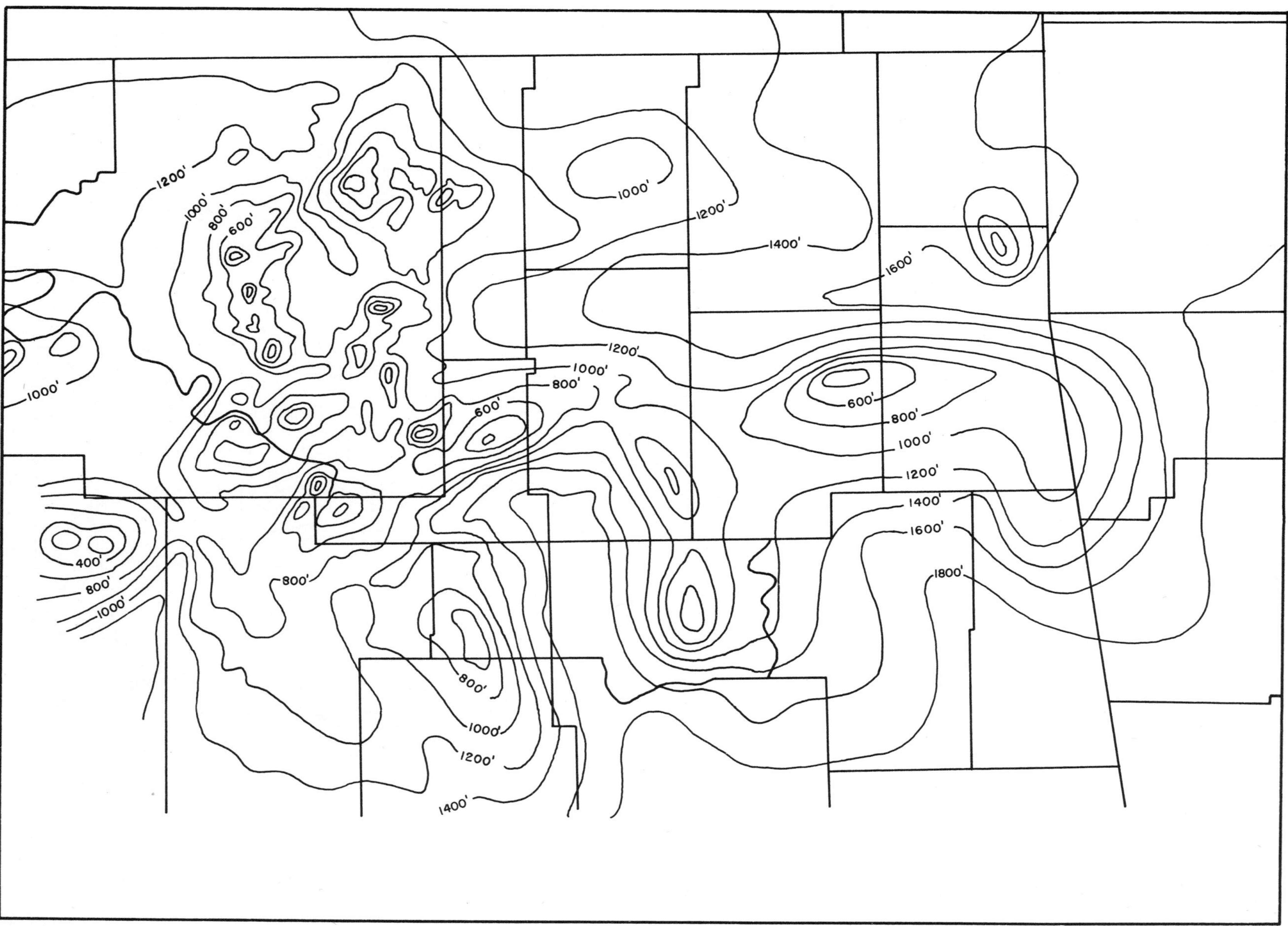

FIGURE 86. Contour map illustrating basement configuration. Shown by means of isopach lines of original thickness of pre-Simpson beds. (Redrawn from H. A. Ireland [1955], *Bull. Am. Assoc. Petrol. Geol.*, vol. 39.)

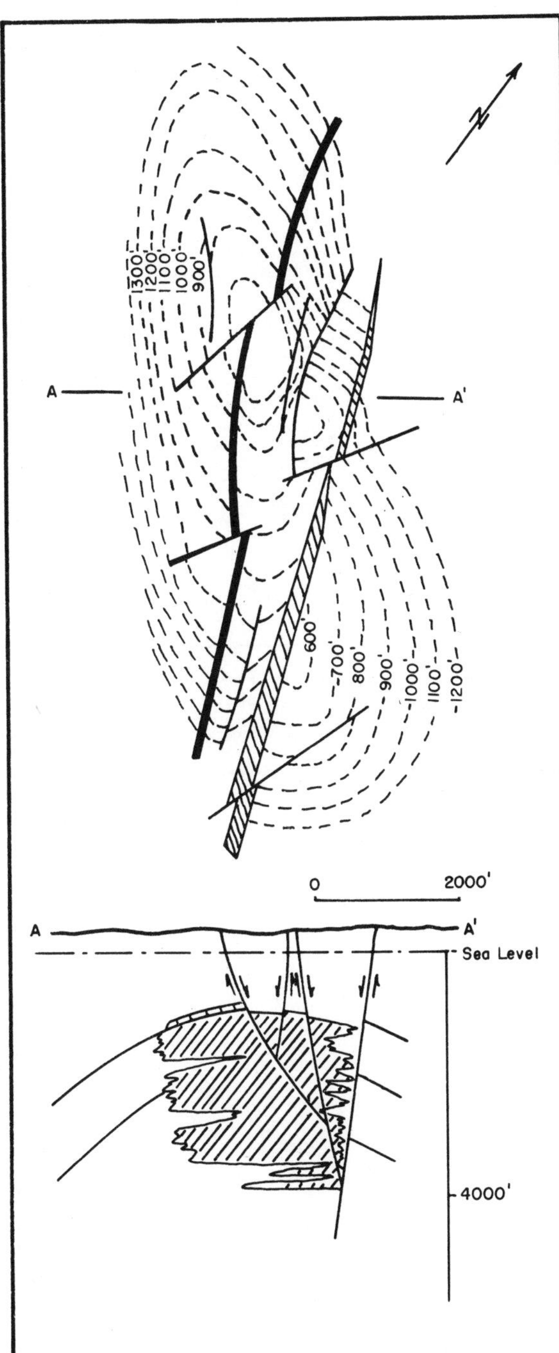

FIGURE 87. Structure contour map and cross section for a normal faulted anticline. The structure shown is the Inglewood oil field in California. (Redrawn from H. L. Driver [1943], *Calif. Dept. Nat. Res., Div. of Mines, Bull. 118.)*

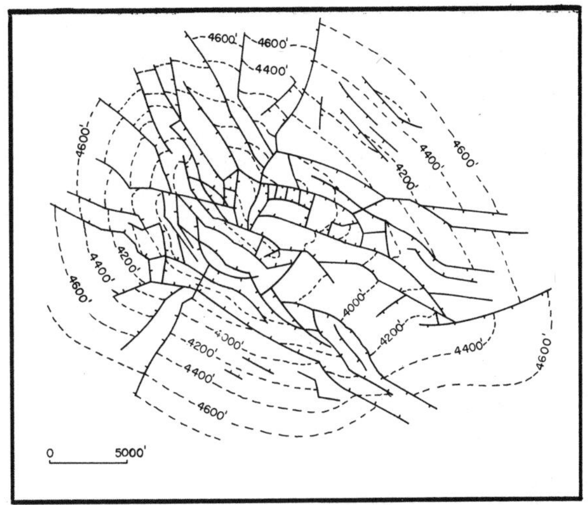

FIGURE 88. The collapsed top of an anticline illustrated by means of structure contours. The structure shown is the Hawkins oil field in Texas. (From E. A. Wentlandt [1951], *Univ. of Texas Publication No. 5116.)*

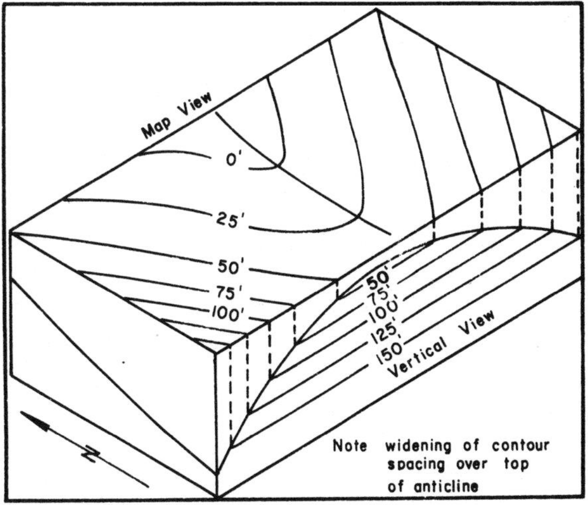

FIGURE 89. Illustrating the change in contour spacing which occurs over the top of an anticline.

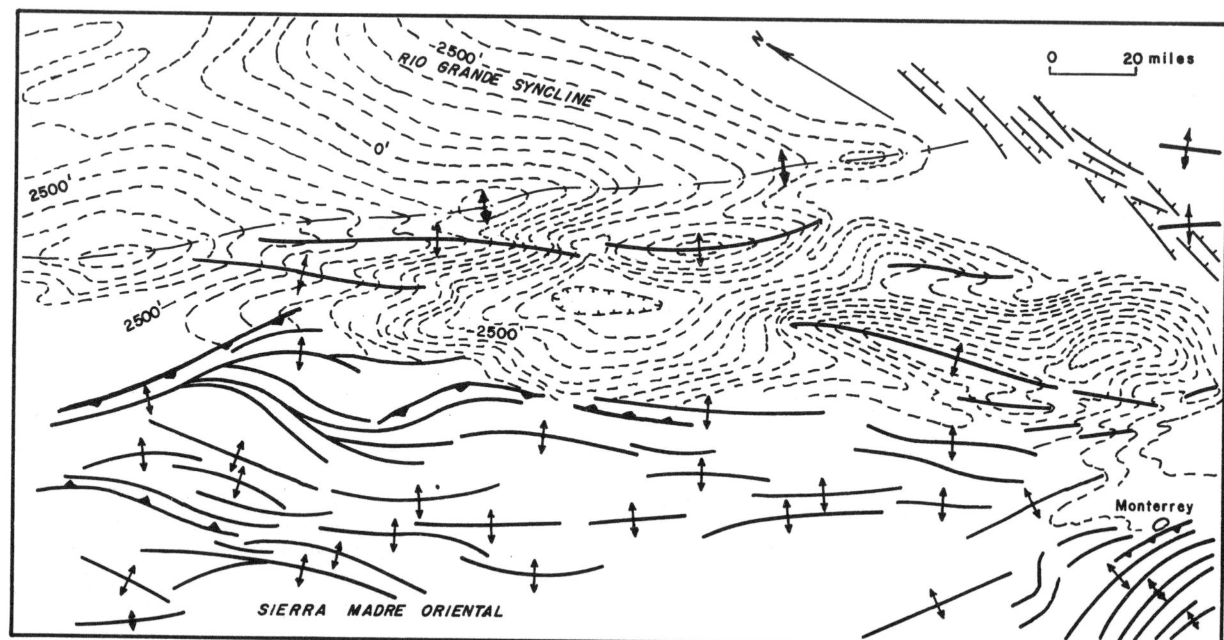

FIGURE 90. Structure contour configuration of the mobile rim portion of a sedimentary basin. The area illustrated is on the western margin of the Gulf Coast Basin in northern Mexico. Structure contours are on top of the Georgetown limestone (Cretaceous). (Redrawn from the Tectonic Map of the United States [1944], Am. Assoc. Petrol. Geol.)

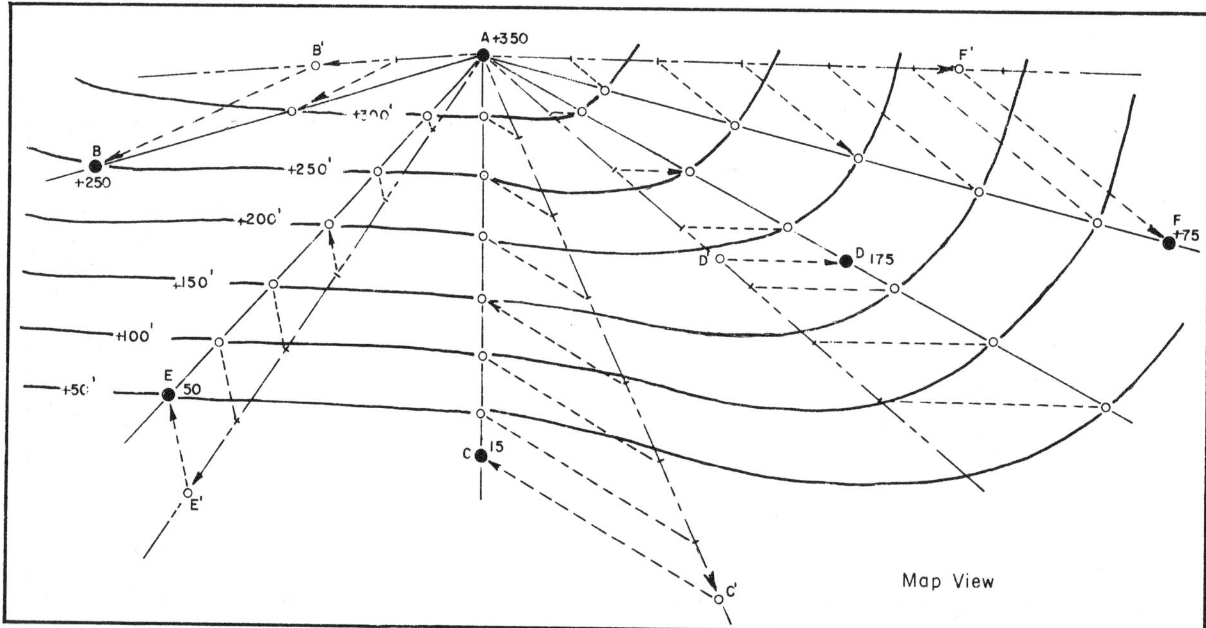

FIGURE 91. If multiple dividers are not available, then the exact contour spacing may be determined with an engineer's scale and the method illustrated here.

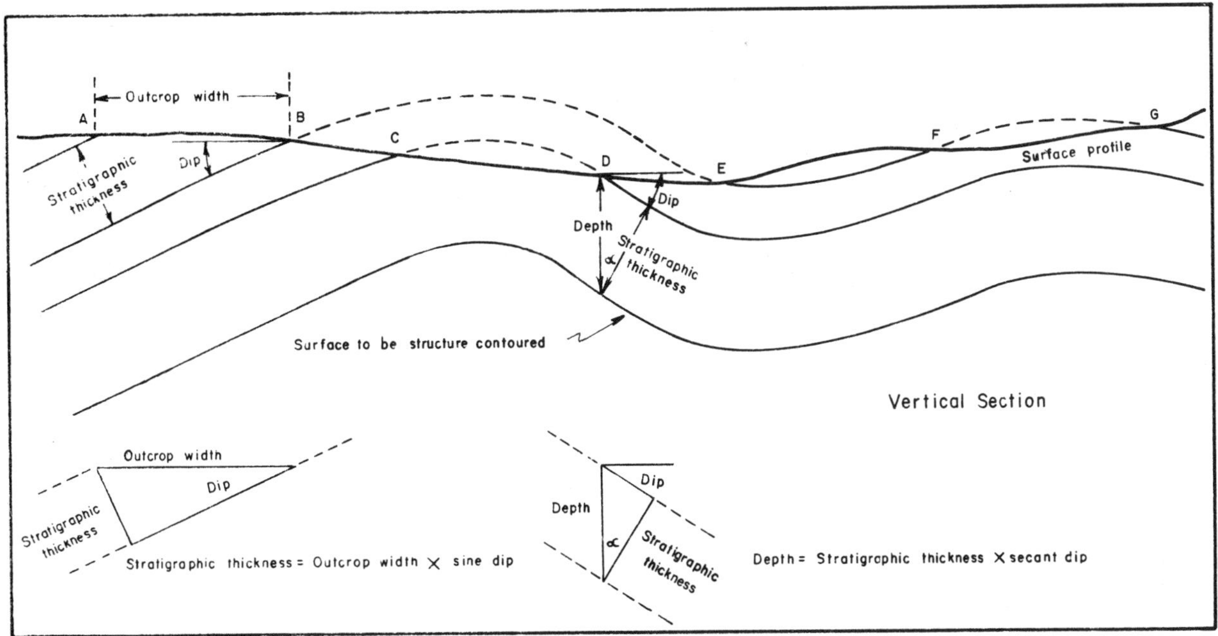

FIGURE 92. Illustrating the method used in converting elevation information from several stratigraphic horizons to one marker bed. The steps involved in deriving the second equation appear on page 125.

17. A fault is usually represented on most geological maps as a single line. A single line usually cannot be used on structure contour maps, however, as normal faults invariably create a zone where the datum surface is absent. This situation can be easily understood by the following vertical section diagram (Fig. 95).

The only exception for normal faults is when the fault is vertical, and then there would be no datum gap on the contour map. However, there may still be a horizontal separation of all strata along the fault trace. In plan view the area of datum gaps increases as the fault dip decreases.

The size of the datum gap or overlap can be determined on the structure contour maps if there are sufficient datum control points to determine the contour pattern for each fault block and at least three wells that have penetrated the fault plane. The three fault penetration points are then used to determine the strike and dip of the fault surface (using the three-point method or a simplification of this method). The method used is shown in Figures 95 and 96.

General Usage

Structure contour maps may be used to illustrate large-scale features such as the tectonic configuration of an entire basin (Fig. 85) or features as small as an individual anticline (Fig. 80). It is very important to have an idea of the general type of structure to be expected in the area as the shape of an anticline (Figs. 79, 80, 87, 88) is different from that of a reef (Figs. 82, 83) or a salt dome (Fig. 81). There is considerable similarity between individual structures within the same tectonic element of a tectonic province. Figure 90 illustrates anticlinal structures on the mobile rim of the Rio Grande embayment. Figure 86 illustrates the type of structural picture existing over basement highs on the stable shelf of Kansas.

One of the most important uses of structure contour maps is the portrayal of the progressive development of structural features from one geological period to another. Figure 84 illustrates the structural configuration of a salt dome at several stratigraphic levels. The progressive development of structures can be illustrated even more satisfactorily when isopach maps are used in conjunction with structure contour maps. The student will be assigned a problem of this type in a later chapter.

Application

The principles described above may be applied to various types of structural information. The

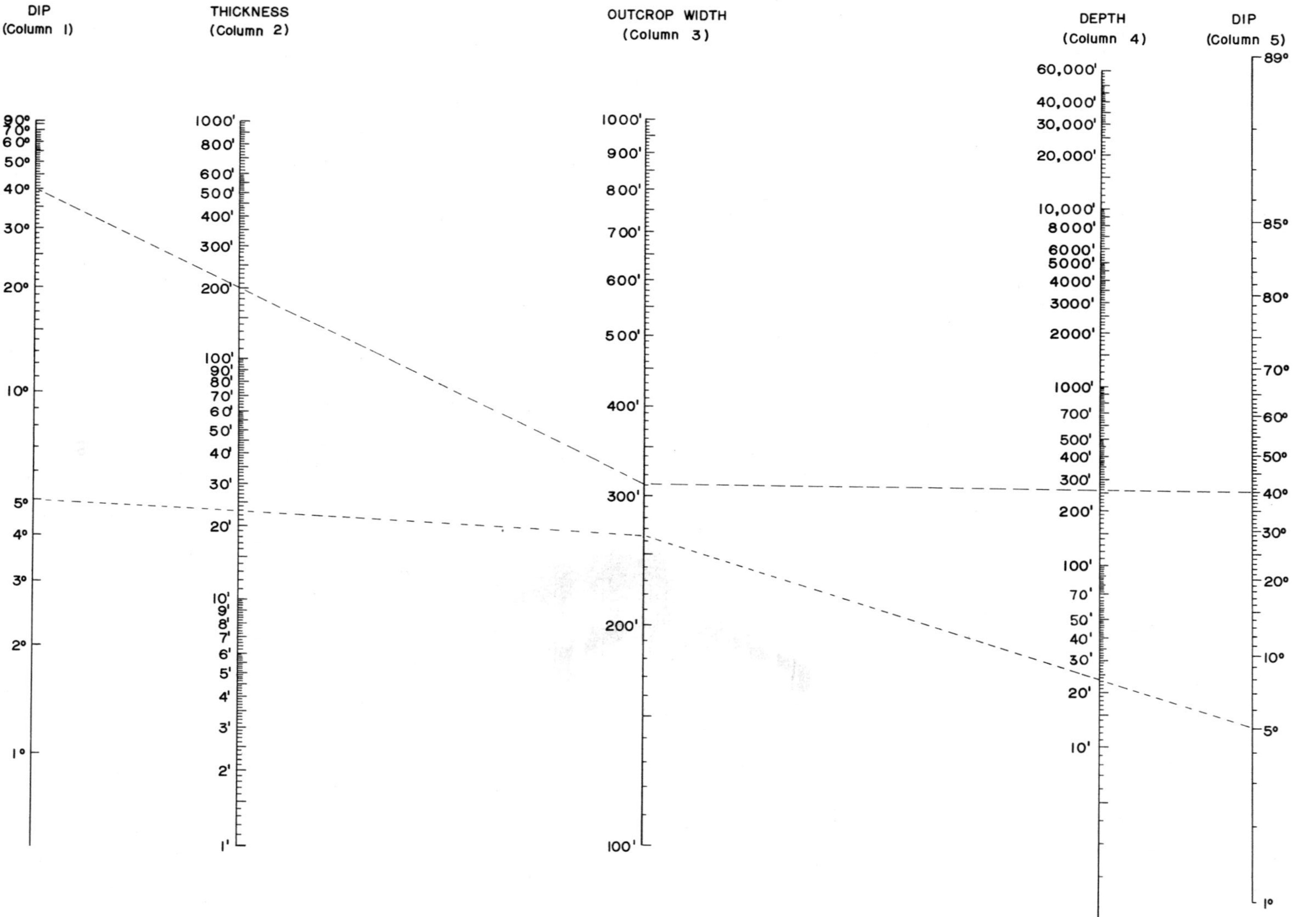

EXAMPLES:

GIVEN: A bed with a stratigraphic thickness of 2000 feet dipping at 40°. FIND: The depth to the top of the bed. PROCEDURE: Join 40° on column 1 to 200' on column 2 and project this line to intersect column 3 at 311'. Now join 311' on column 3 to 40° on column 5 and read off 260' on column 4. Multiply 260' by 10 to give a depth of 2600'.

GIVEN: A bed with stratigraphic thickness of 229' dipping at 5°. FIND: The depth to the top of the bed. PROCEDURE: Join 5° on column 1 to 229' on column 2 and project this line to intersect column 3 at 264'. Now join 264' on column 3 to 5° on column 5 and read off a depth of 232' on column 4.

FIGURE 93. Alignment diagram for computing the depth to a certain horizon when stratigraphic thickness and dip are known. (Modified from H. S. Palmer [1918], *U.S. Geol. Surv.*, Prof. Paper 120G.)

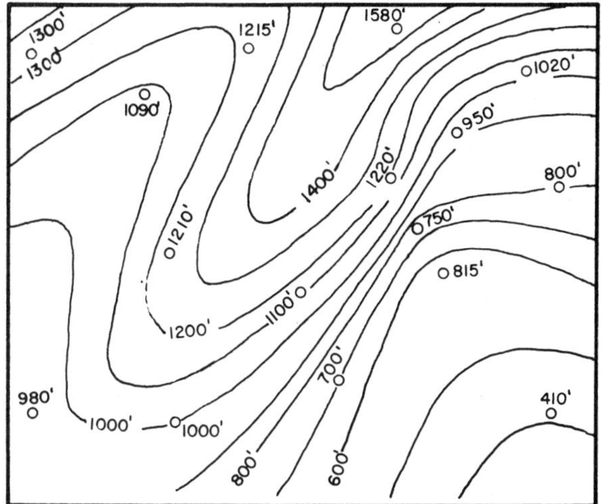

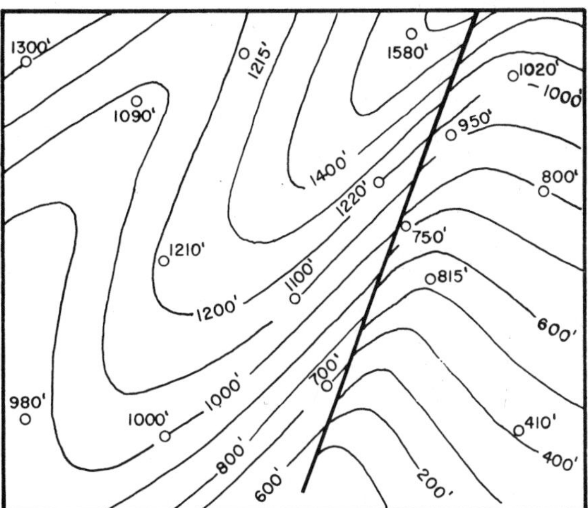

FIGURE 94. Illustrating the detection of a fault by structure contour methods. (From J. W. Low [1951], *Subsurface Geologic Methods*, 2nd ed., Colorado School of Mines, Fig. 479.)

method used and its accuracy depend upon the type of data which is available:

1. No Topographic Control (Form Line[1] Maps):
   a. Strike and dip information (or dip component data) is available from geological field work, but formation boundaries cannot be mapped due to uniformity of the exposed strata and/or a youthful stage of erosion.
   b. Formation boundaries are available, but strike and dip information is estimated only. This data is taken from air photographs.
   c. Strike and dip information and formation boundaries are both available.
2. Topographic Control Available (Structure Contour Maps):
   d. Formation boundaries (from air photographs) and topographic maps. Strike and dip information estimated or not available.
   e. Strike and dip information and formation boundaries are both available.
   f. Formation boundaries available from subsurface drilling information.
   g. No attitude determinations available. Fault and formation boundaries available from subsurface or surface information.
   h. Structure contouring of veins, fractures, and so forth, as a means of revealing ore shoots.

[1] Form lines are structure contour lines which represent the general form or shape of structures without any absolute elevation values indicated.

FORM LINE CONTOURING FROM STRIKE AND DIP INFORMATION ONLY

Applications and Limitations: In some regions it is impossible to trace key beds across the entire map area, owing to inadequate exposure, or key beds may not be recognizable owing to the uniformity of the stratigraphic section which is exposed. In areas of recently formed structures, such as in the Middle East, erosion has not cut through some of the surface limestones and only one stratigraphic unit is exposed, even over anticlinal crests. In such situations the form line map must be constructed on the basis of only strike and dip information. This method has the same limitations as all form line maps—absolute values cannot be placed on the contours. However, the spacing between contours can be controlled quite accurately by means of Figure 78 and Table 12.

Data Provided: Accurately measured strike and dip information or dip component information plotted on a suitable base map.

Determine: Form line map for the area and amount of structural closure for the geological features of the area.

Method: Select a suitable contour interval for the map. Then place spacing lines about each strike and dip symbol on the map as in Figure 97.

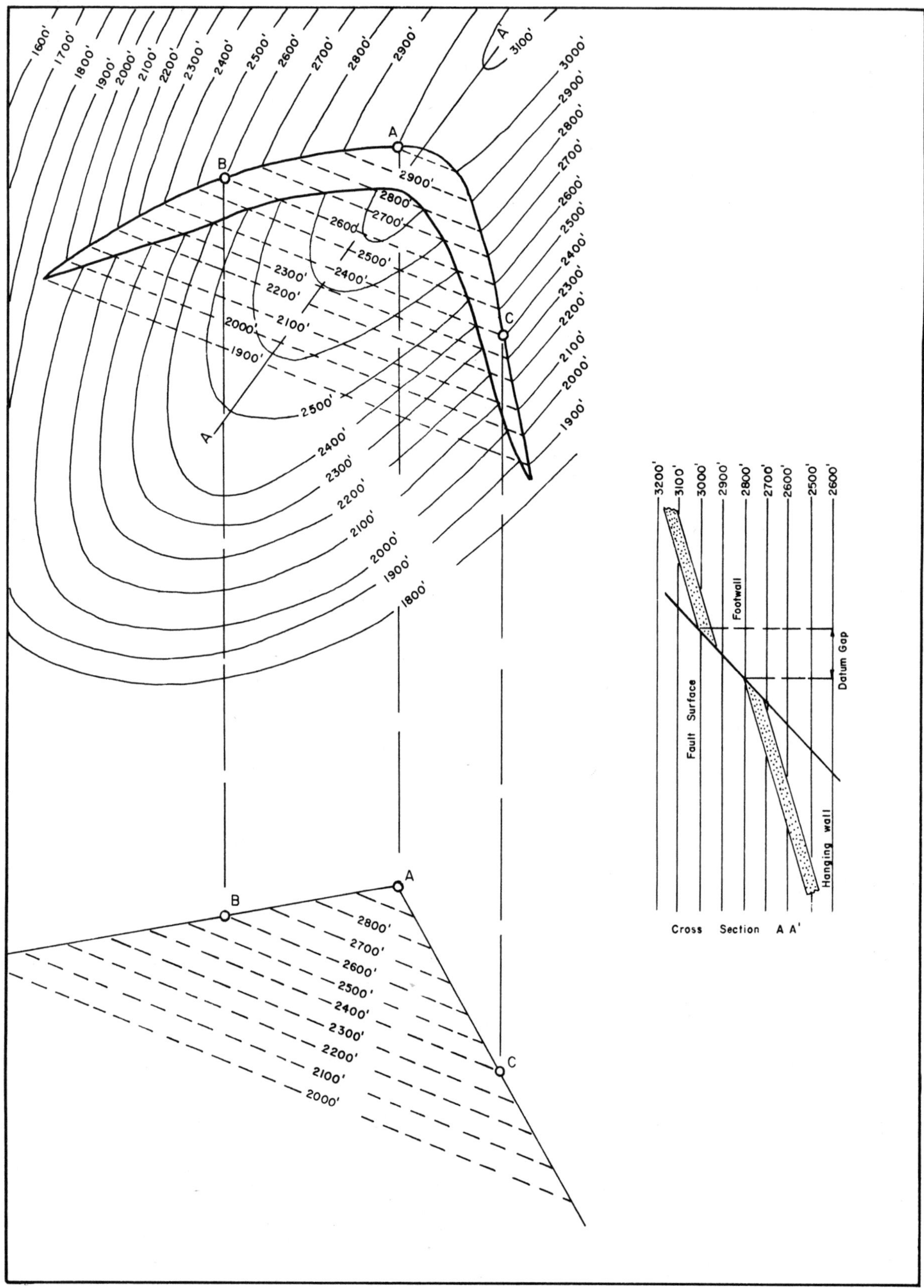

FIGURE 95. Method for determining the structure contour pattern over a normal fault and the extent of the datum gap.

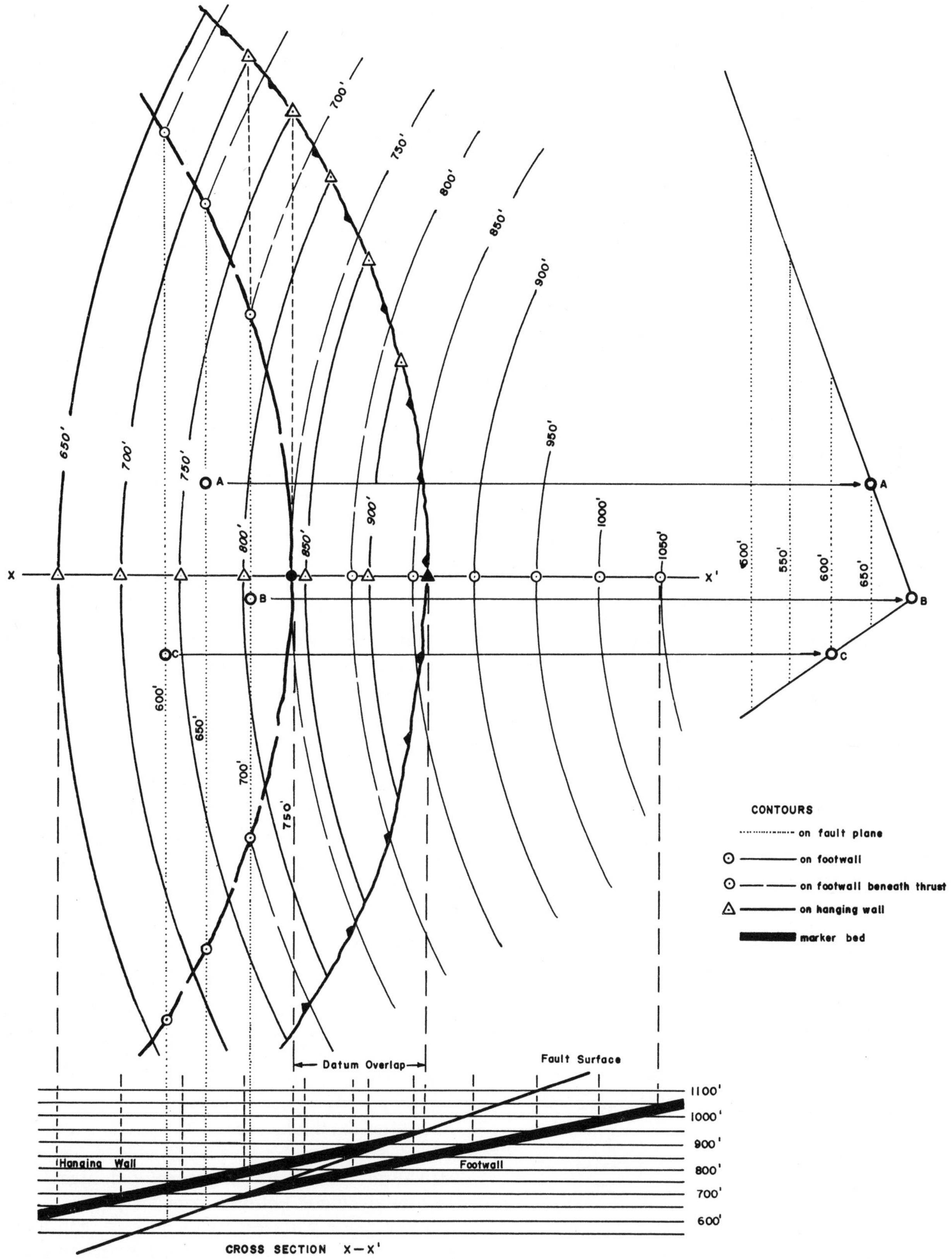

FIGURE 96. Method for determining the structure contour pattern over a thrust fault and the extent of the datum overlap.

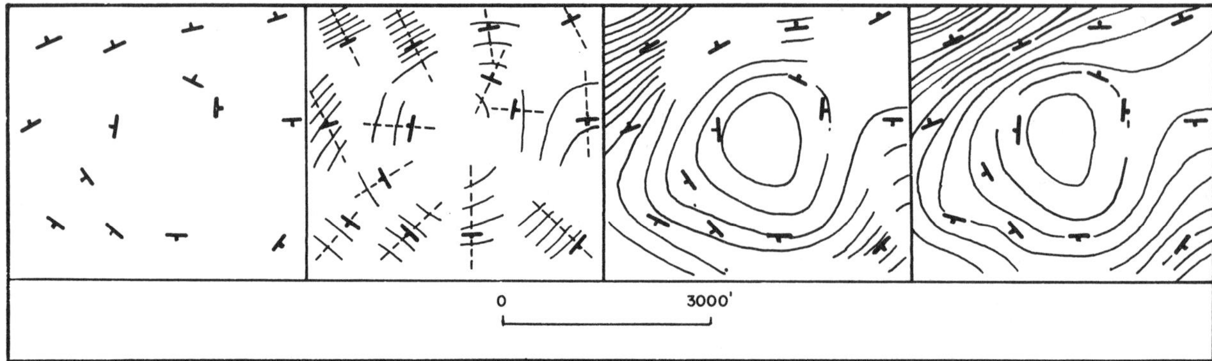

FIGURE 97. Method used in drawing form line maps when only strike and dip information is available. (Modified from J. W. Low [1957], *Geologic Field Methods*, Harper & Brothers.)

The spacing is determined by means of the nomographs in Figure 78. After a few contour spacings have been drawn in to scale, it is usually possible to estimate the remainder by eye. If one or two strategically located elevation points are known for the area, then the contouring can be started at one of these points (Fig. 97). Actually, further topographic control will be of little value to this method unless it can be related to some key horizon. When topographic information is not available, the first step will be to draw in all anticlinal and synclinal axes. Then start drawing the form lines on what appears to be the largest and highest structure so that the major structural picture evolves first. The subsidiary features can be drawn in later. The form lines must be drawn parallel to the strike and dip symbols. When a fold axis is traversed by a form line, then a change in the strike of the form line must be made, even though strike and dip symbols are not present in this vicinity.

In some areas of low dip it is very difficult to obtain accurate strikes by direct methods. However, it is nearly always possible to obtain dip components. Structure contour spacing can be computed

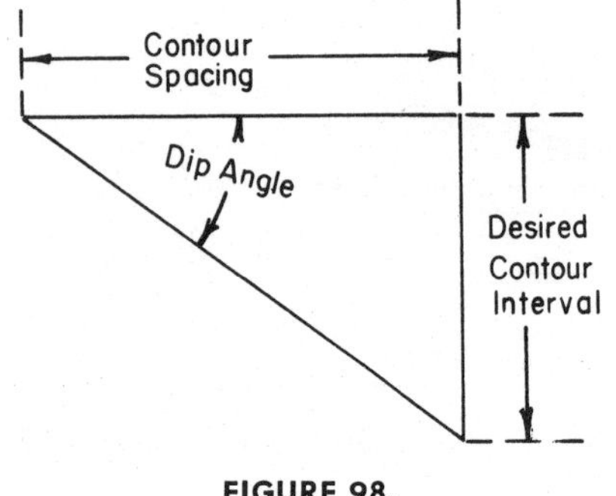

FIGURE 98.

from dip component information using the following equation (Fig. 98):

$$\text{Cotangent Dip Angle} = \frac{\text{Structure Contour Spacing}}{\text{Desired Contour Interval}}$$

and,

$$\text{Structure Contour Spacing} = \text{Contour Interval} \times \text{Cotangent Dip Angle}$$

Figure 99 indicates an area where several dip component lines are shown (4°, 5°, 3°, and 4°). The contour spacing along each line is computed by the above equation and the cotangent tables in the appendix. Adjacent dip component lines are projected until they intersect at *X, Y,* and *Z,* and the computed contour spacings are laid off on the respective dip component lines, starting with the *X* intersection point. Structure contours are then drawn through the spacing points on each dip component line.

FORM LINE CONTOURING FROM FORMATION BOUNDARIES AND LIMITED ATTITUDE AND ELEVATION CONTROL

Applications and Limitations: In regions where formation contacts and dip slopes show up nicely on air photographs, it is possible to draw form lines after the dip has been estimated at a number of key spots on the air photos. Reconnaissance structural evaluations of unexplored areas are commonly made entirely from air photographs and are made with less time and cost than field geological methods. Field studies can then be concentrated on the areas of critical interest.

Method: This method assumes that only the sim-

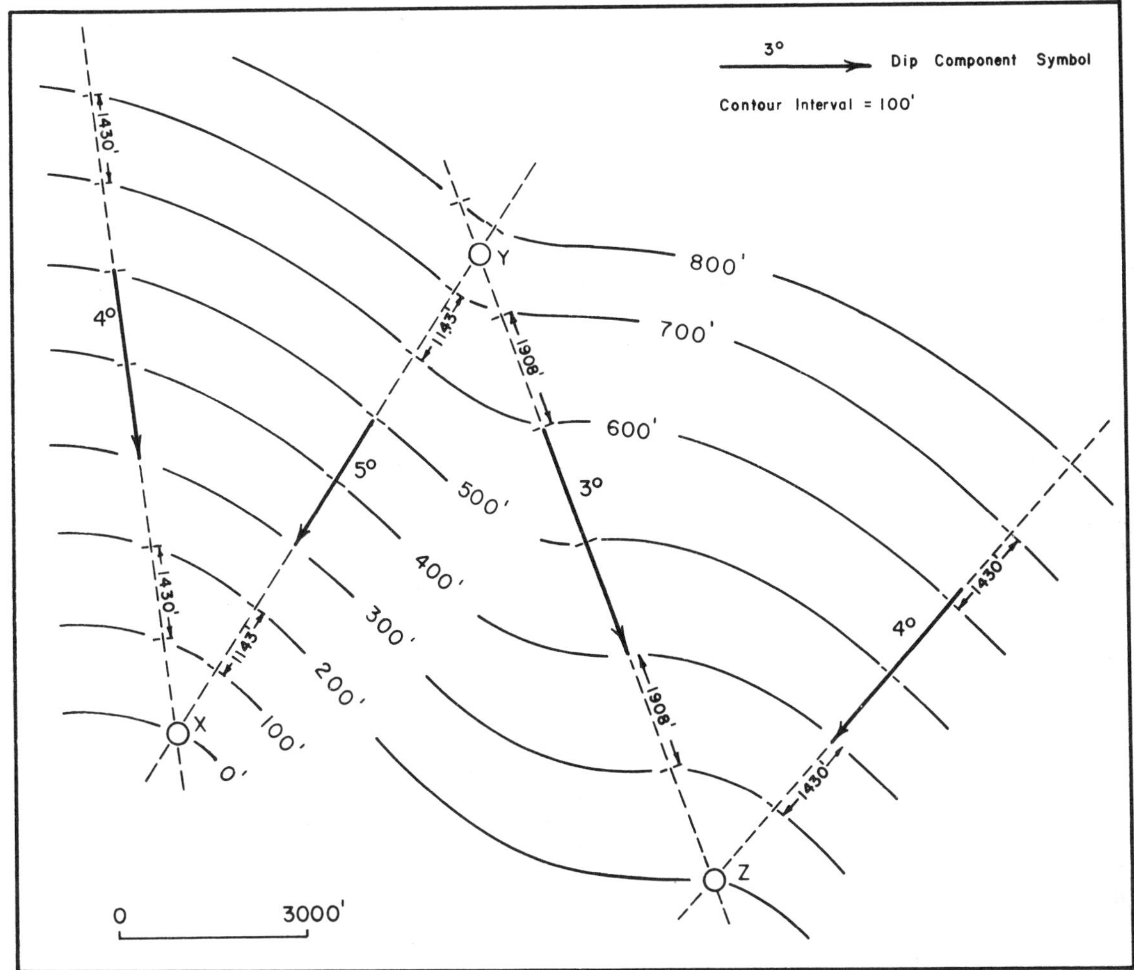

FIGURE 99. Drawing structure contour or form line maps from dip component information.

ple lens type of pocket stereoscope is available to the geologist. Costly equipment such as stereoplanigraphs, aerocartographs, multiplex aeroprojectors, stereocomparographs, or Kelsh plotters give more accurate results but are not available to the field geologist confronted with only occasional air photograph problems. Desjardins (1950) has given several formulae for computing dip from air photographs:

$$\text{Tangent Dip} = \frac{\text{Focal Length} \times \text{Parallex Difference Between Two Points}}{\text{Theoretical Photo Base} \times \text{Photo Distance Between Two Points}}$$

Again, this type of information is not handled or obtained easily by occasional photogeologists. However, dip estimates can be made directly from stereoscopic observations provided the effect of exaggerated relief is allowed for. In areas of high dips it is usually possible to locate areas of both vertical dip and areas of zero dip (along fold axes). It is then possible to estimate the intervening dips between these two extremes. The task is simplified greatly if a few scattered attitude or elevation control points are available from maps of the regional area. The principles described in the chapter on outcrop patterns will be very useful at this point. After a sufficient number of dips have been estimated, the procedure is similar to that outlined previously on p. 84.

Miller (1950) has suggested a practical and rapid method for dip estimation in regions where topographic control is available. The following excerpt is from Miller, with one or two small alterations by the present author:

Since photographs are taken at different scales, by cameras of different focal lengths and from different heights, it is to be expected that the magnitude of vertical exaggeration will not be the

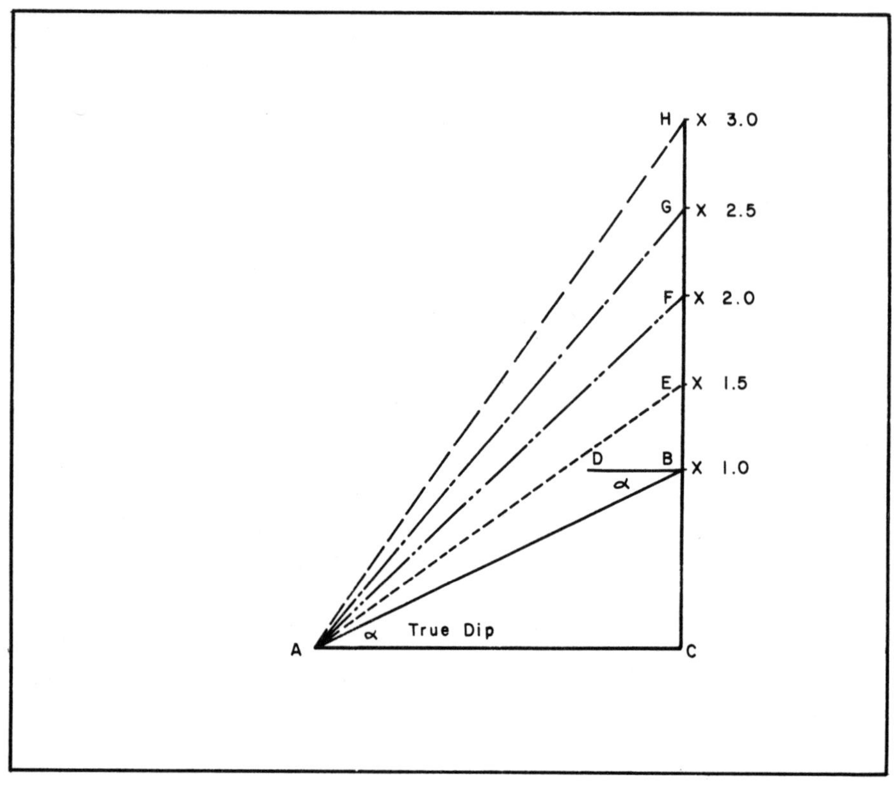

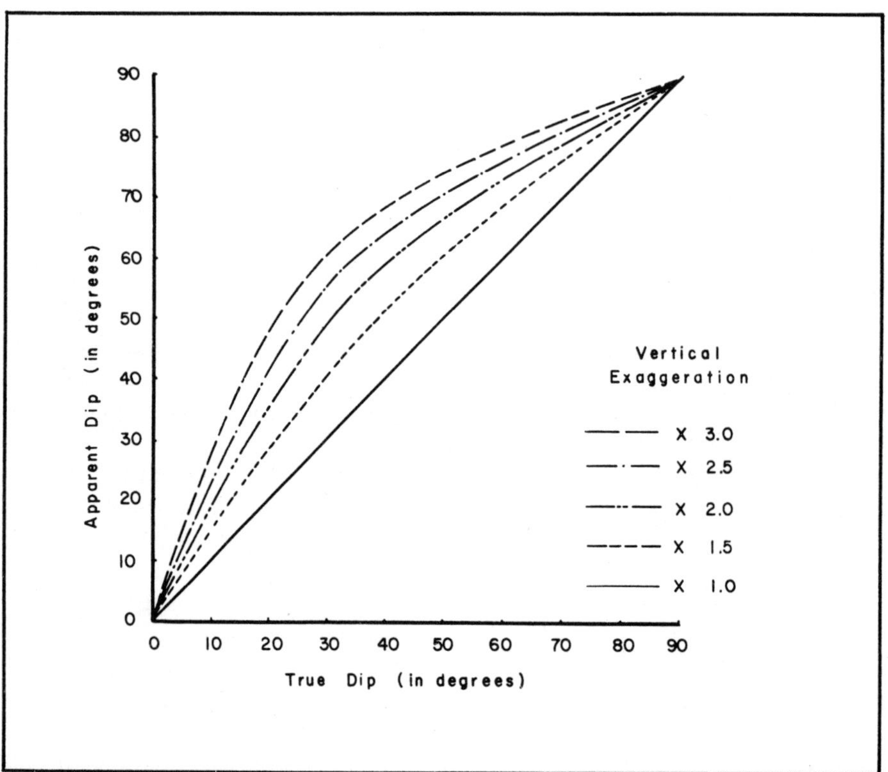

FIGURES 100 (*above*) and 101 (*below*). **Method used in allowing for vertical exaggeration when using air photographs for structure contour purposes. (From V. C. Miller [1950], *Bull. Am. Assoc. Petrol. Geol.*, vol. 34.)**

same for all aerial photographs. However, for a single flight strip, or for adjacent strips taken at approximately the same scale with the same equipment, it may reasonably be assumed that vertical exaggeration is practically uniform for all photographs in the group. This assumption is true if there is approximate uniformity of separation of centers of consecutive photographs. If the magnitude of exaggeration can be determined, it is possible to set up a definite relation between true and apparent slope or dip. (In this paper, the term *apparent* refers to the way ground images appear on aerial photographs. *Apparent* slopes, then, are vertically distorted or exaggerated true slopes.)

Consider Figure 100:

Angle *ABD* represents the true value of dip (or slope).

Angle *BAC* = angle *ABD* (alternate angles).

Therefore angle *BAC* represents true dip.

Side *CB* represents the true height or topographic relief of the dip.

If a vertical exaggeration of ×1.5 exists on photographs of this dip, height *CB* will appear as *CE,* 1.5 times as great as the original height, *CB.*

Angle *EAC* will then be the apparent dip, as seen through the stereoscope.

Similarly, with exaggerations of ×2.0, ×2.5, and ×3.0, the dip will appear to be equal to angle *FAC,* angle *GAC,* and angle *HAC.*

From plane geometry, it is seen that the lines *CB, CE, CF, CG,* and *CH* are proportional to the tangents of the respective apparent dip angles, since the base *AC* is constant in all cases. This brings out one extremely important fact: dip exaggeration is not directly proportional to vertical exaggeration.

The relation between apparent and true dip can be plotted on graph paper (Fig. 101). True dip is plotted along the horizontal axis; apparent dip along the vertical. For example, if true dip is 30°, exaggerations of ×1.5, ×2.0, ×2.5, and ×3.0 will give apparent dips of 41°, 49°, 55½°, and 60½°, respectively.

Constructions similar to Figure 100 were made for true dips ranging from 1° to 85°. Data obtained and plotted determined the lines shown in Figure 101 which represent the several exaggerations.

Now what does all this mean? It means that if the vertical exaggeration of a pair (or group) of photographs can be determined, a means is available to transfer estimated apparent dips or slopes into more nearly accurate true values.

Figure 101 shows, in addition to the lines representing vertical exaggeration, 11 separately plotted points. One is seen to fall on the × 3.0 line; another falls close to the × 2.0 line. The others are scattered in the intervening zone, the average position being roughly coincidental with the line of × 2.5 exaggeration.

The points were determined in the following way:

1. On topographic maps covering the area shown on a set of photographs, 11 different slopes of constant gradient were chosen. Knowing the map scale and contour interval, it was routine procedure to determine the actual (or true) magnitude of each slope. (Slope may be determined by trigonometry or by plotting horizontal and vertical lengths to scale.)

2. The slopes for which measurements were made on the maps were then located on the photographs. Corresponding apparent magnitudes were then estimated.

3. Thus for each slope, two values were obtained: apparent and true. These data were then plotted on the graph. For example, one slope whose true gradient was 36° appeared to be 60° when seen through the stereoscope. Another which appeared on the photographs as 35° was found to be actually 17°.

Though these points do not fall on a single line of constant exaggeration, they nevertheless fall close enough to the value ×2.5 to warrant the assumption that this is the approximate vertical exaggeration of the photographs.

Since one's ability to judge apparent slope is subject to errors of a few degrees, the failure of the points to coincide perfectly with a single exaggeration value is to be expected. Nevertheless, the general order of magnitude is clearly indicated.

If photograph study follows or accompanies preliminary field investigations, a sufficient number of true slopes, or dips, may be measured in the field by Brunton or plane table to permit determination of photograph exaggeration.

Once vertical exaggeration has been determined, it is a simple matter to reduce future apparent slope or dip estimates to true values. Merely estimate the dip, as seen through the stereoscope, refer to the graph, and read off the corresponding true dip.

When no map or field control is possible, it is felt that an assumed exaggeration is of considerable value. Though its true magnitude is not known, dips or slopes determined by an assumed exaggeration will have a constant and sensible relation to each other. If field checks are made after interpretation, correction of dip is facilitated by the fact that error is uniform. A common vertical exaggeration is approximately $\times 2.5$, and it is suggested that assumed exaggeration be of this order of magnitude.

Regardless of how exaggeration is determined, the relation of true and apparent dip or slope is still that which has been described, and the usefulness of Figure 101 is maintained.

FORM LINE CONTOURING FROM ATTITUDE AND FORMATION CONTACT INFORMATION

Applications and Limitations: This type of information is usually available only from field mapping although it can be obtained less accurately from air photographs. The procedure is similar to that described in the first method discussed (p. 84) but with the added advantage that the structural relief can be related to actual stratigraphic horizons. However, absolute elevation values still must be omitted from the contours.

STRUCTURE CONTOURING FROM FORMATION BOUNDARIES AND TOPOGRAPHIC CONTROL

Applications and Limitations: In many regions topographic mapping and air photographs are available, whereas geological maps even of a preliminary nature may not be available. This is because topographic maps are used by various types of scientists and engineers (forestry, conservation, reclamation, ground water, highway and rail construction, etc.) and specialized government studies of a geological nature usually lag behind the topographic surveys by several or even many years. It may be desirable to have structure contour maps for an area without actually conducting a field examination. Structure contour studies by plane table field methods are slow and costly and are limited by weather conditions. Sufficiently accurate maps can be obtained for preliminary evaluation purposes without actually conducting field surveys.

Methods: Air photographs are examined stereoscopically and a key marker bed is selected for structure contour purposes. The bed chosen has to be one that can be traced readily on the air photos. The position of the bed is transferred to the topographic map as accurately as possible. Distinctive topographic points observed on the air photographs along the trace of the key bed usually can be located without difficulty on the topographic map. A limiting error of ± 25 feet of vertical elevation is usually obtainable when the air photos and topographic maps are of good quality. The horizontal error may be greater but is less significant, as elevation control is of prime importance in reconnaissance surveys of this type. Structure contouring is commenced as soon as a sufficient number of elevation points are obtained for any one horizon. It will be possible to determine the dip and strike for the strata involved as soon as three or more elevation points are available for any one strata. With dip information available it may be desirable to use more than one key mappable horizon by reducing surface elevations to the structure contour datum (Fig. 93).

STRUCTURE CONTOURING WITH ATTITUDE, FORMATION BOUNDARY, AND TOPOGRAPHIC CONTROL

Applications and Limitations: This approach involves the maximum amount of field information and provides the most accurate structure contour maps. Formation boundaries must be well exposed. Many of the surface structures of the Rocky Mountain region have been mapped by this method.

Data Provided: Figure 102 shows four elevation-controlled outcrops on the same formation boundary.

Method: The structure contour spacing is determined for each outcrop (Table 12), and spacing guide points are placed along the dip direction lines for each outcrop (Fig. 102). Points of equal elevation are joined by smooth contour lines. The contour lines should parallel the strike symbols near each of the outcrops. This additional strike control makes the map more accurate than it would be if elevation control only were available, as in subsurface mapping. In areas of strong and rapidly changing structural patterns, the addi-

Table 12. Structure Contour Spacing Distance in Meters for Various Dip Angles

Dip	Spacing for 10-Meter Contour Interval	Spacing for 25-Meter Contour Interval	Spacing for 50-Meter Contour Interval	Spacing for 100-Meter Contour Interval
1°	572.2	1431.0	2832	5724
2	284.0	710.0	1420	2840
3	190.6	476.5	953	1906
4	143.0	357.5	715	1430
5	114.4	286.0	572	1144
6	94.6	236.5	473	946
7	81.0	202.5	405	910
8	70.8	177.0	354	708
9	62.8	157.0	314	628
10	56.8	144.0	284	568
11	51.4	128.5	257	514
12	47.0	117.5	235	470
13	43.4	108.5	217	434
14	40.1	100.5	201	402
15	37.4	93.5	187	374
16	34.8	87.0	174	348
17	32.8	82.0	164	328
18	30.8	77.0	154	308
19	29.0	72.5	145	290
20	27.4	68.5	137	274
21	26.0	65.0	130	260
22	24.6	61.5	123	246
23	23.4	58.5	117	234
24	22.4	56.0	112	224
25	21.4	53.5	107	214
26	20.6	51.5	103	206
27	19.6	49.0	98	196
28	18.8	47.0	94	188
29	18.0	45.0	90	180
30	17.2	43.0	86	172
31	16.6	41.5	83	166
32	16.0	40.0	80	160
33	15.4	38.5	77	154
34	14.8	37.0	74	148
35	14.2	35.5	71	142
36	13.8	34.5	69	138
37	13.4	33.5	67	134
38	12.8	32.0	64	128
39	12.4	31.0	62	124
40	12.0	30.0	60	120
41	11.6	29.0	58	116
42	11.2	28.0	56	112
43	10.8	27.0	54	108
44	10.4	26.0	52	104

NOTE: This table can be used for footage intervals also. Thus a 100′ contour interval map would have 568′ spacing between contours if the dip is 10°.

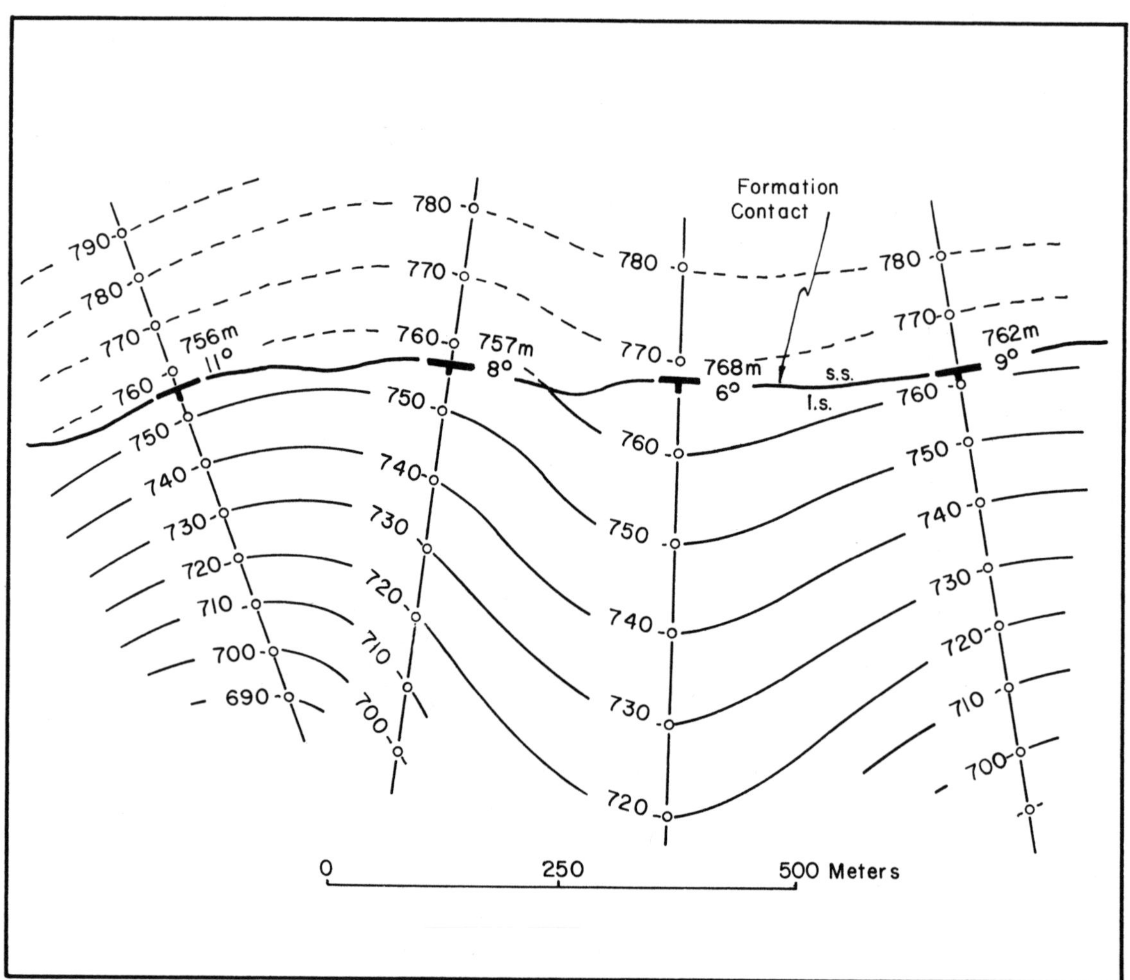

FIGURE 102.

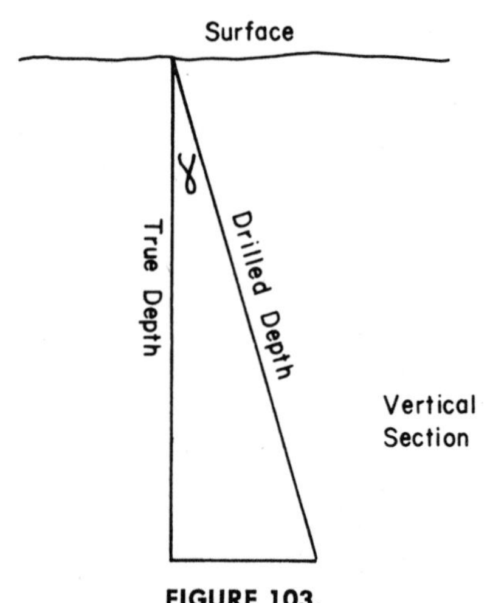

FIGURE 103.

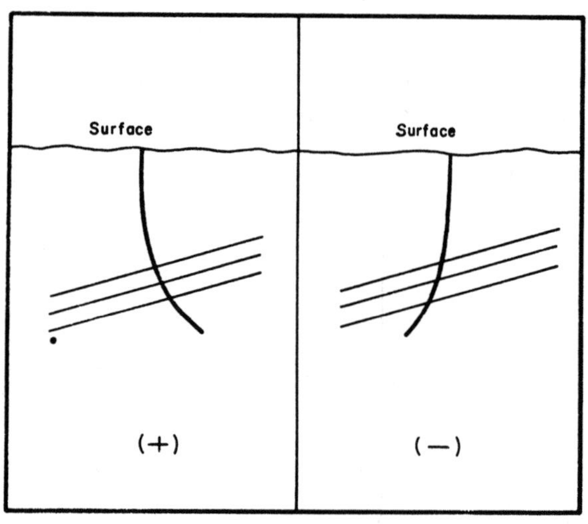

FIGURE 104.

tional guidance provided by strike control is very important.

When elevation control is available for several formation contacts on a map, then all of this information must be used as outlined in Rule 11, p. 73. Attitude data will be used to control the contour spacing pattern in the areas between formation contacts.

STRUCTURE CONTOURING FROM SUBSURFACE FORMATION BOUNDARY INFORMATION (TOPOGRAPHIC CONTROL AVAILABLE)

Applications and Limitations: Structure contour maps based on subsurface information are dependent upon accurate elevation and location control as attitude information is rarely available. A comprehensive knowledge and familiarity with probable structures in the area are essential as there is usually very little surface indication of structures at depth.

Method: Most oil companies maintain well card files for the areas in which they are operating. Depths to various formation boundaries as well as surface elevations are recorded on these cards. In some regions service companies provide well cards on a subscription basis. Petroleum Information and Wells Information provide such information in the United States and Canada, respectively. The depths to various subsurface formation boundaries are converted to elevations above or below sea level by subtracting the depth from the surface elevation. There are several types of surface elevation used for oil wells: actual ground elevation, rotary table elevation, and Kelly bushing elevation. The latter is used most frequently, and it is important to refer all depths to this same reference when using data from a number of wells in the same region.

Many wells deviate somewhat from the vertical. This deviation may be either intentional or otherwise. Intentional directional drilling is done most often for reasons of inaccessibility. It is impossible or very expensive to set up derricks in some locations, whereas the desired position at depth can be reached almost as easily by directional drilling from another location.

If a drill hole does deviate from the vertical, then drilling depths will have to be converted to true depths—otherwise errors in subsurface elevations will result. Formation thicknesses will be affected also.

True vertical depth can be computed from the following equation:

$$\text{Cosine Deviation Angle } \gamma = \frac{\text{True Depth}}{\text{Drilled Depth}}$$

Thus,

$$\text{True Depth} = \text{Drilled Depth} \times \text{Cosine } \gamma$$

The deviation angle is not available directly in some cases but can be converted from dips observed in well cores. The conversion is made using the following equation:

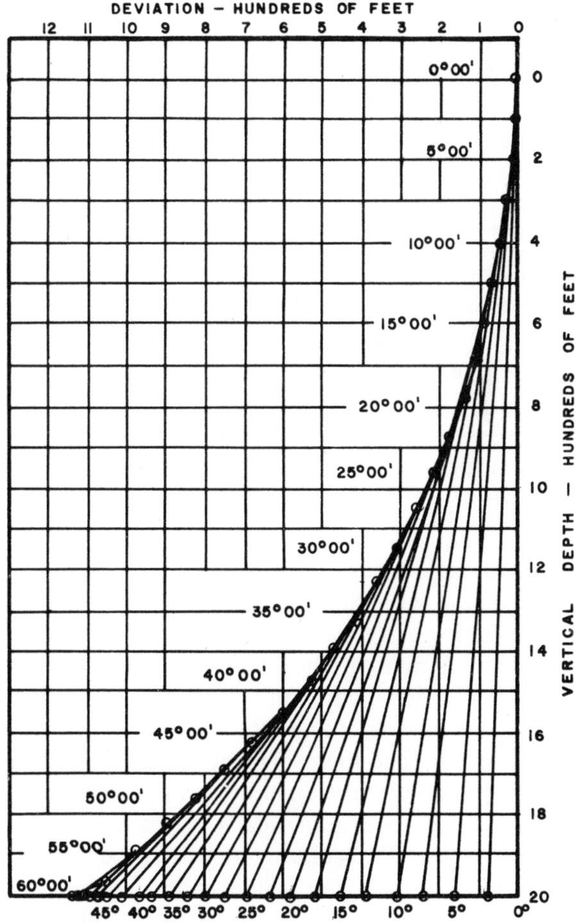

FIGURE 105. True vertical depth can be obtained from drilling depth when the rate of drift is known for numerous drilling depths in the borehole. The chart illustrated is for uniform increase in drift (deviation) of 2° 30′ per 100 feet of hole drilled. (From J. B. Murdoch, Jr. [1951], *Subsurface Geologic Methods*, 2nd. ed., Colorado School of Mines, Fig. 255.)

$$\text{Cos } \theta = \text{Cos } \gamma \times \text{Cos } \phi \pm \text{Sin } \gamma \times \text{Sin } \theta \times \text{Cos } \psi$$

Where θ = Apparent dip in cores.
γ = Drill hole deviation from the vertical.
ϕ = True dip.
ψ = Difference between azimuth of dip and azimuth of drill hole.

Note: Use + when the deviation is up dip.
Use − when the deviation is down dip.

For directionally drilled wells, it is general practice to limit the average increase in drift (from the vertical) to 2° 30′ or 3° 00′ per 100 feet drilled. In such cases a chart like that shown in Figure 105 is usually made up for the well, and the vertical depth can then be read directly off the chart.

Geologists using subsurface information must be familiar with the approved legal methods of describing well locations. In most surveyed areas of North America, the land is divided up into townships (36 square miles) by township lines which run east-west and by range lines which run north-south. The township and range lines often start at state, provincial, or international boundaries and increase numerically away from these starting lines. The subdivions within each township differ in the United States and Canada (Fig. 106). A well location is described in the following order: township, range, section, portion of section (or legal subdivision in Canada). The location within a legal subdivision is in terms of feet measured from one of the corners of the subdivision.

Latitude and longitude descriptions are used for well locations in unsurveyed territory.

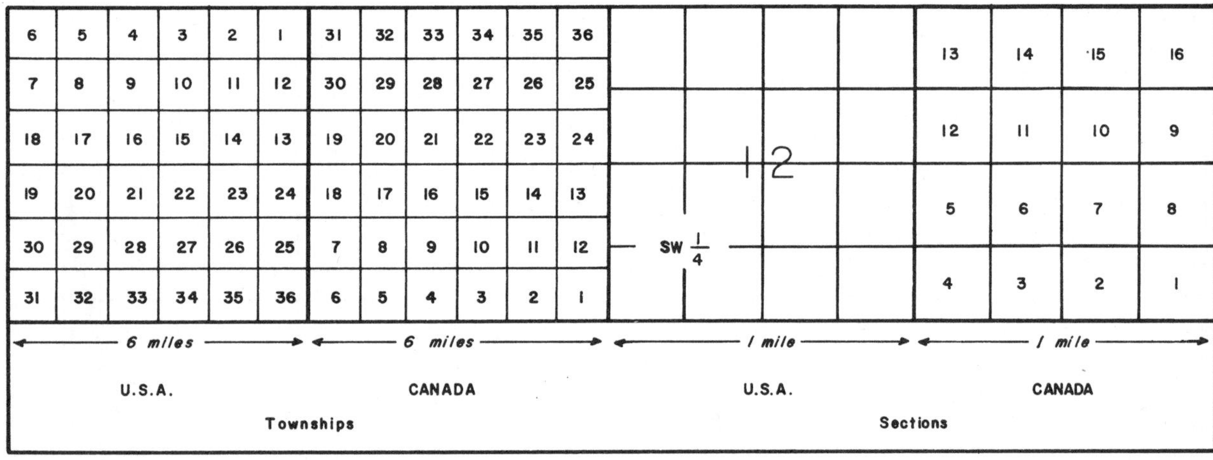

FIGURE 106. Illustrating the legal method of describing well locations in the United States and in Canada.

STRUCTURE CONTOURING IN MULTIFAULTED AREAS

Applications and Limitations: It is commonly necessary to work out the structure contour picture for the multifaulted pattern over salt plugs or similar structures, because of their economic significance.

Prior to establishing such a picture, a certain amount of subsurface information must be available. Each fault surface must be penetrated a sufficient number of times to determine the strike and dip of each fault. Possibly this information might be provided by surface mapping. In addition, drilling density must be sufficient to allow determination of the strike and dip of the contour horizon on adjoining fault blocks and determination of the vertical component of net slip for each fault. The relative ages of each fault must also be known, as the fault intersection patterns can be quite complicated (Fig. 107, lower right). The development of an intersecting fault pattern is shown in Figure 107. The intersection pattern is dependent upon the stage of erosion. Figure 107 (lower left) shows the appearance of the fault pattern after all the faults have been eroded to a common level. *Note that the intersection of the intersected (initial fault) fault with the earth's surface is invariably offset in the direction of its dip in the fault block which is upthrown by the intersecting fault.* The case illustrated is a simple one as the bedding is horizontal. The method described below indicates the

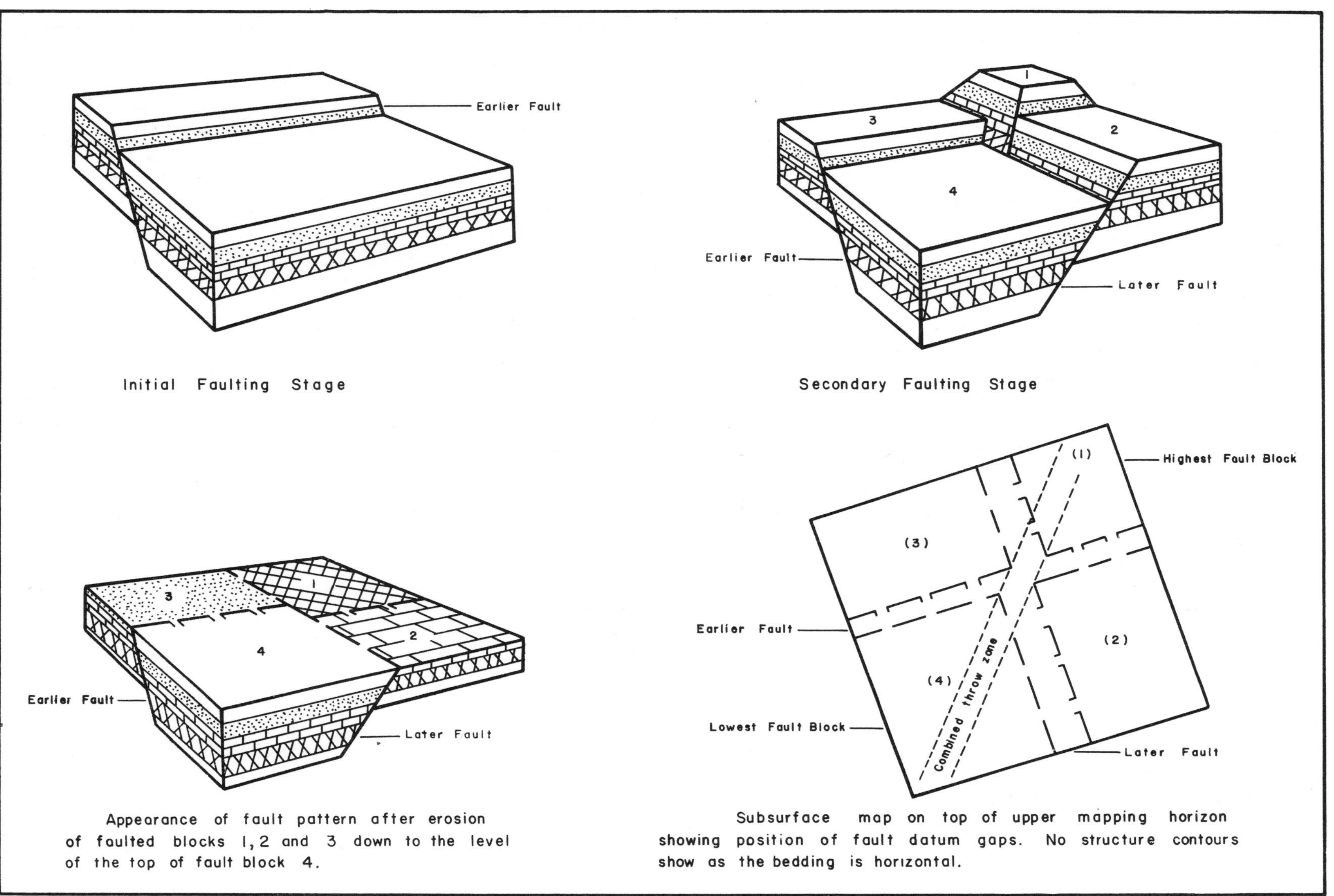

FIGURE 107. **The development of intersecting fault patterns (upper left and right), the appearance of fault patterns after erosion to a horizontal surface (lower left), and the appearance of the same conditions in the subsurface (lower right). Note that the bedding is horizontal. (Redrawn from G. Dickinson [1954], *Bull. Am. Assoc. Petrol. Geol.*, vol. 38.)**

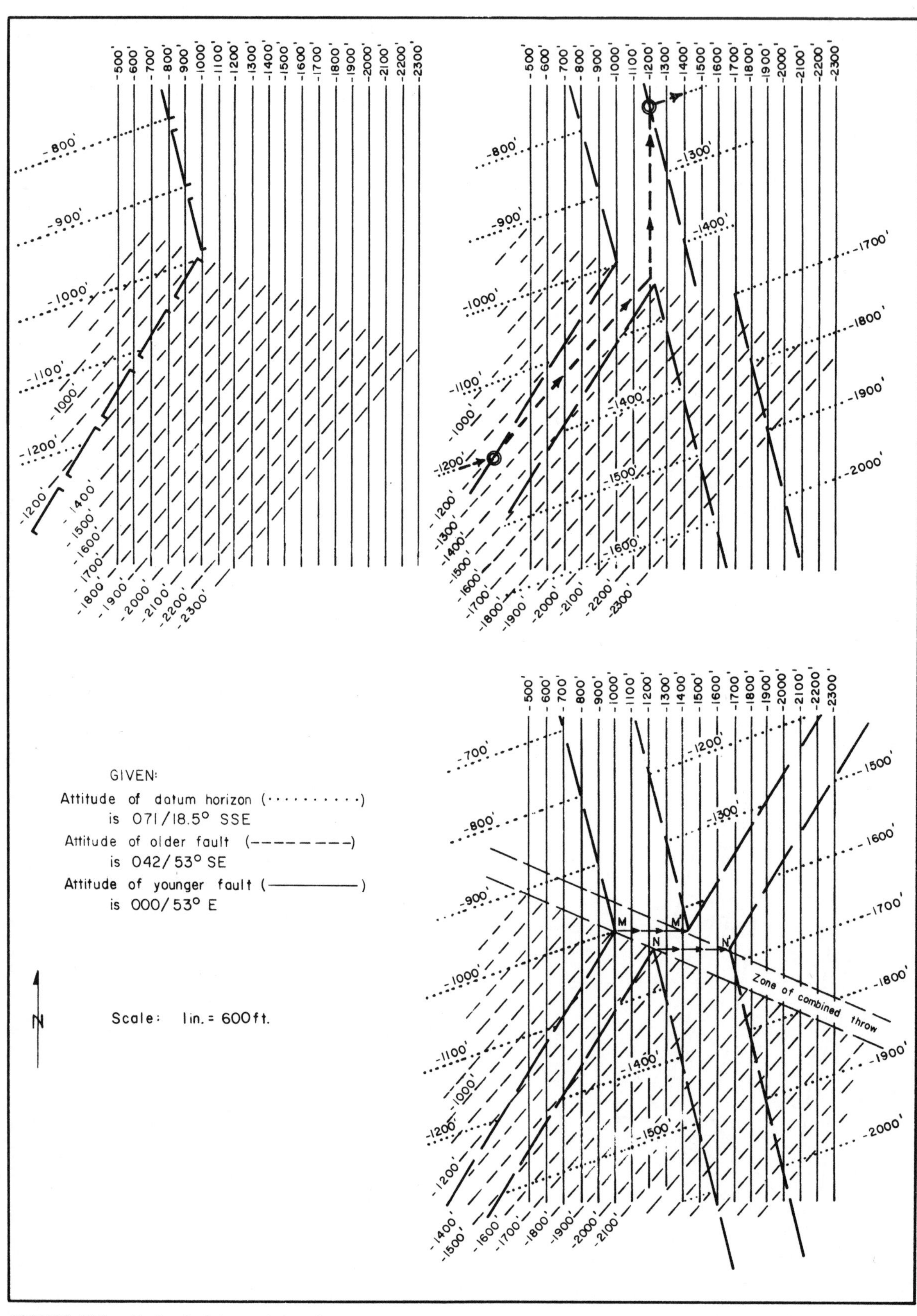

FIGURE 108. Method of determining the structure contour pattern in a multifaulted area. (Modified from G. Dickinson [1954], *Bull. Am. Assoc. Petrol. Geol.,* vol. 38.)

procedure for the more common cases involving dipping strata.

Data Provided: Figure 108 shows the structure contour picture on the highest fault block in an area broken by two periods of faulting. The strike and dip are known for the datum horizon (071°/18.5°SSE) and for each fault (older fault, 042°/53°SE; younger fault, 000/53°E) from surface outcrops. The vertical component of net slip is 200 feet for the older fault and 400 feet for the younger fault. A contour interval of 100 feet is to be used.

Determine: The extent of each datum gap and the structure contour picture for each fault block.

Method: The contour spacing for the datum horizon and for each fault are determined by reference to Figure 108. The contour pattern for the younger fault is drawn in completely (Fig. 108, upper left). The contour pattern for the older fault is drawn in for the upper side (hanging wall) of the younger fault, but the contours for the older fault do not cross the younger fault's contours. The contour pattern for the datum horizon is drawn in for the hanging wall side of each fault (Fig. 108, upper left). By joining the intersection points of the datum contours with the respective contours for each fault (Fig. 108, upper left), the western edges of the datum gaps for each fault are delimited. Because the vertical component of net slip is known for each fault, the projections of the contours on the datum plane are known immediately for the opposite side of each datum gap. Thus the 1300-foot structure contour on the east side of the younger fault's datum gap will lie opposite the 900-foot structure contour on the west side of the same datum gap. However, the width of the datum gap remains to be determined. This can be accomplished by following any datum contour (e.g., the 1200-foot structure contour on the datum horizon) eastward to the western limit of the older fault's datum gap (Fig. 108, upper right). Then the 1200-foot contour on the older fault is followed northeastward until this 1200-foot fault contour intersects the 1200-foot contour of the younger fault. The 1200-foot contour of the younger fault is then followed northward until it intersects the north-northeastern projection of the 800-foot datum contour. This establishes one point on the eastern edge of the datum gap for the younger fault. By repeating this procedure for each datum contour on the original fault block, a series of points are established on the opposite side of each datum gap. Figure 108 (lower right) illustrates the end result of this process.

It is now a simple matter to locate the fourth arm of the intersecting fault system. It is only necessary to determine the displaced position of the datum gap for the older fault. M and N are the nondisplaced intersection points of the older datum gap with the younger fault.

Inasmuch as the movement on the younger fault is directly down dip in this case (as we are dealing with dip slip faults), point M must move along a line perpendicular to the younger fault contours until this line meets the downthrown side of the younger fault's datum gap at point M'. Similarly N moves down to point N' (make $NN' = MM'$ in length). Since the faulting is nonrotational, the displaced position of the older fault's datum gap will be parallel to the nondisplaced portion of its datum gap, and the lines delimiting the displaced portion pass through M' and N' as shown in Figure 108 (lower right).

The *zone of combined throw* is that segment of the intersecting fault (i.e., the younger fault) which lies between the offset limbs of the intersected (older) fault. This zone is delimited by passing lines through M and N, and M' and N', respectively (Fig. 108, lower right). In this zone a drill hole will encounter only one fault when two normal faults intersect, although the drill hole may cross three faults when reverse faults intersect. In this latter case the zone might be referred to as an area of combined overlap.

STRUCTURE CONTOURING OF VEINS AND FRACTURES AS A MEANS OF REVEALING ORE SHOOTS

Applications and Limitations: Most ore deposits, other than the bedded sedimentary ores, the magmatic segregation type, and the disseminated igneous ores of the porphyry copper type, are controlled by openings in rocks created along channels, fractures, breccia zones, shear zones, formation contacts, and so forth, most of which have formed as a result of deformation. The country rock thus is prepared in advance to receive the deposition of ore solutions. Experience has shown that ore deposition is often richer close to irregularities in the fractures, shear zones, and so forth. Irregularities in the fractures, channels, and so

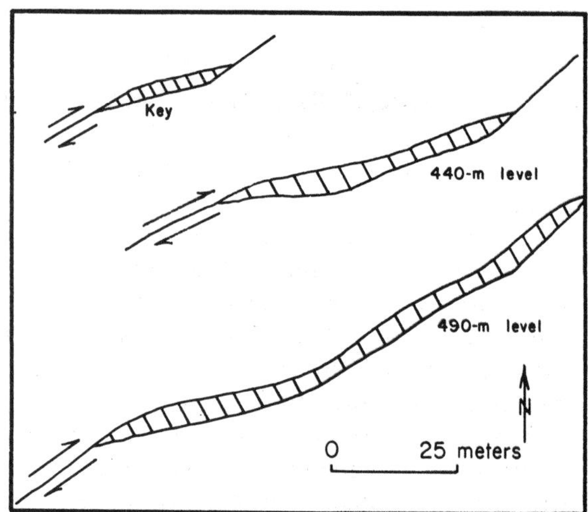

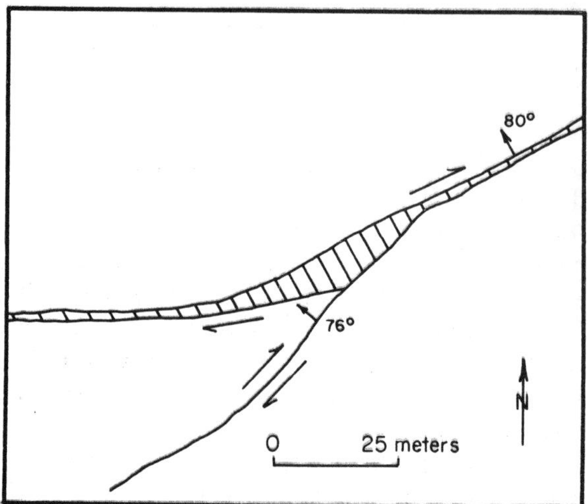

FIGURES 109 (*left*) **and 110** (*right*). **Showing how openings develop along fractures due to strike-slip movement. (From E. Wisser [1942], in W. H. Newhouse *et al.*, *Ore Deposits as Related to Structural Features*, Princeton University Press.)**

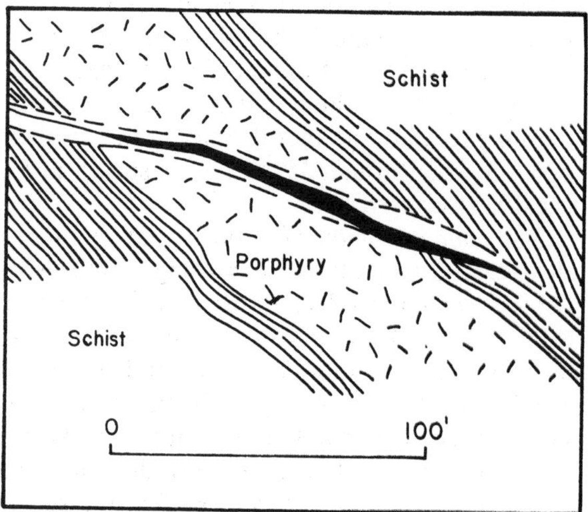

FIGURE 111. Showing how a vein thickens when passing from schist into porphyry. The vein shown is the Main Vein at Silver Plume, Colorado. (From T. S. Lovering [1942], in W. H. Newhouse *et al.*, *Ore Deposits as Related to Structural Features*, Princeton University Press.)

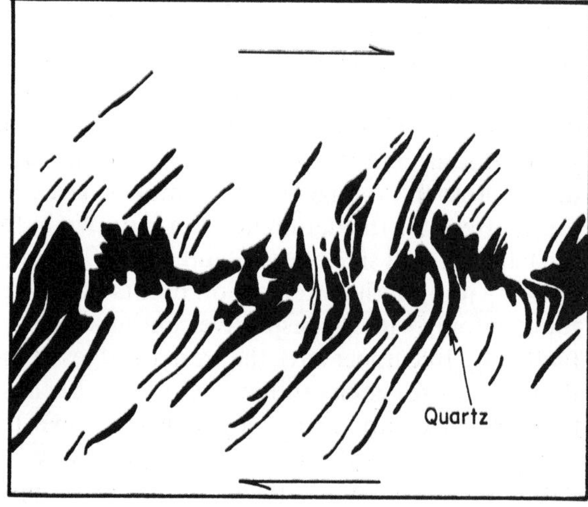

FIGURE 112. Tension gash fractures formed by movement along a fault. The fractures illustrated are gold-bearing quartz veins at the Hollinger mine, Timmins, Ontario, Canada. (From F. Ebbutt [1948], *Structural Geology of Canadian Ore Deposits*, Can. Inst. Min. Met. Symposium Volume.)

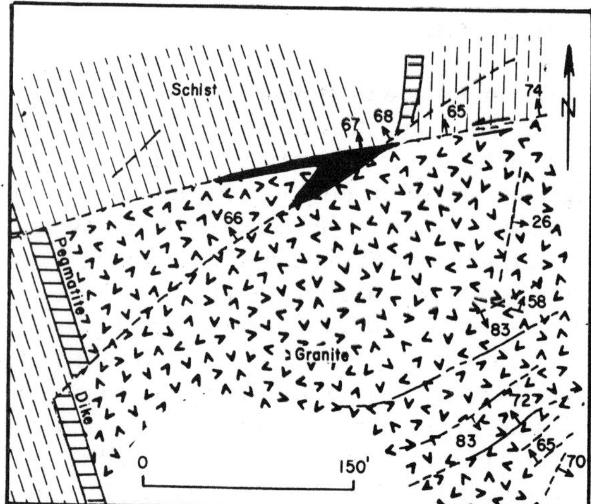

FIGURE 113. Ore shoot localized by the intersection of fractures. Lily tunnel level of the Rakeoff Mine, Nederland, Colorado. (From T. S. Lovering [1950], *U.S. Geol. Surv.*, Prof. Paper 223.)

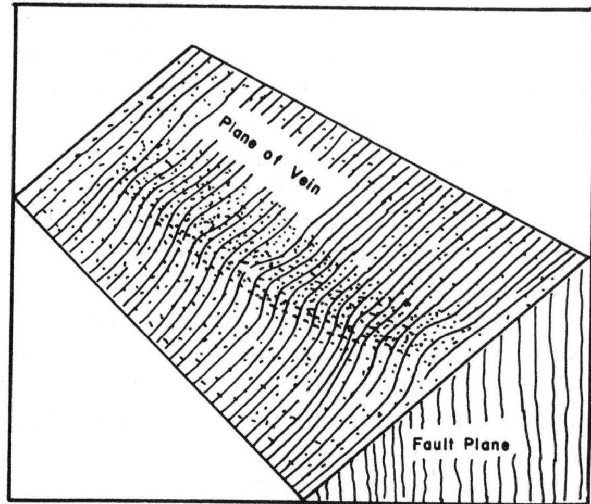

FIGURE 114. Ore shoot related to a "roll" in the plane of a vein. The vein illustrated is the Missouri vein northwest of Grant, Colorado. (From T. S. Lovering [1942], in W. H. Newhouse *et al.* *Ore Deposits as Related to Structural Features*, Princeton University Press.)

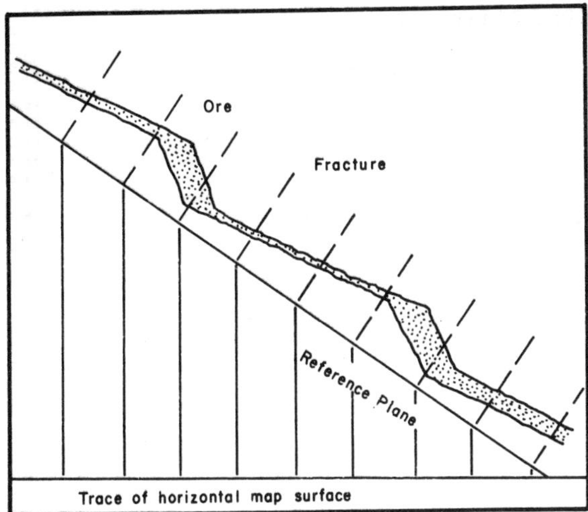

FIGURE 115. Showing how the topographic relief on a fracture may be compared with a reference plane and then projected to a horizontal map surface.

forth can be produced in several ways, the commonest irregularities being related to differences in rock competency or due to differential movement along the fractures. Figures 109 to 114 illustrate some of the fracture patterns which control ore location.

Method: Because of the importance of changes in attitude of fractures, it is desirable to be able to map these irregularities. This is accomplished by noting the differential relief of the opening or fracture surface and comparing it with a reference plane surface drawn parallel to the general attitude of the fracture. This information is then transposed to a horizontal map surface. This method would be difficult to apply to pipelike fracture systems.

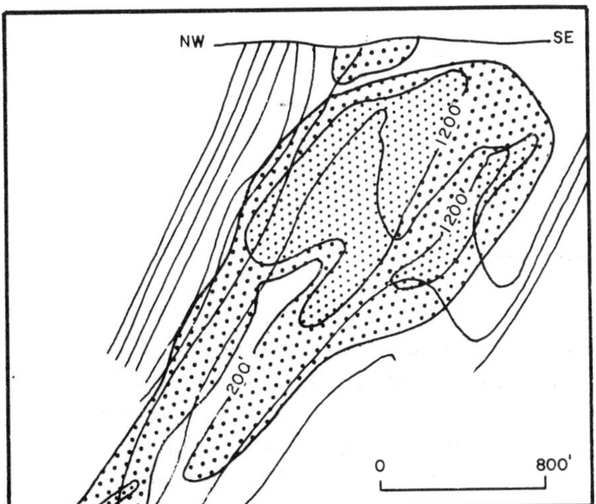

FIGURE 117. Shows the relationship between ore values and the relief of a vein. The light stippling indicates the highest ore values, and the lines represent distance from a reference plane. This is in the Great Fingle Mine, western Australia. (From H. J. C. Conolly [1936], *Econ. Geol.*, vol. 31.)

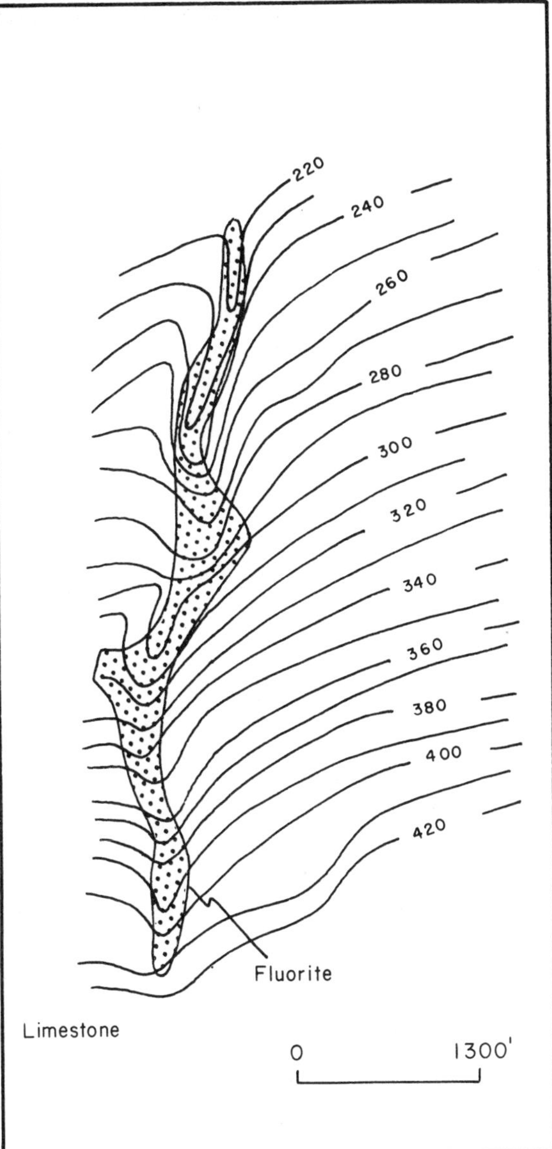

FIGURE 116. Ore shoot related to a topographic low. This is a channel developed on a limestone in the East Green Mine, Illinois. (From R. M. Grogan [1949], *Econ. Geol.*, vol. 44.)

The steps involved in contouring an ore body related to a fracture, bed, shear zone, and so forth, are shown in Figure 115.

Several cross sections through an ore body are required if sufficient contour points are to be obtained for mapping purposes. Figures 116 and 117 show ore bodies related to irregularities on structure contour maps.

PROBLEM 13 (Fig. 118)

FORM LINE CONTOURING FROM STRIKE AND DIP INFORMATION

Data Provided: Figure 118 shows strike and dip information obtained from geological field work in southeast Turkey. Many of the low dips were computed from dip component information and by using the three-point method. This particular structure was probably formed in Miocene-Pliocene time, and being of relatively low structural relief, it has been only slightly stripped by erosion. The Midyat limestone of Eocene age is the only formation exposed at the surface. This formation is believed to be about 700–800 meters thick in this area. The total stratigraphic section exposed on this structure is only about 50 meters, and this portion of the section consists of a monotonous sequence of massive limestone beds, lacking key horizons.

Determine: Form line map of the area, amount of structural closure, and recommended drilling location, if the main reservoir objective in this area is expected at a depth of about 1000 meters. The student must select his own contour interval.

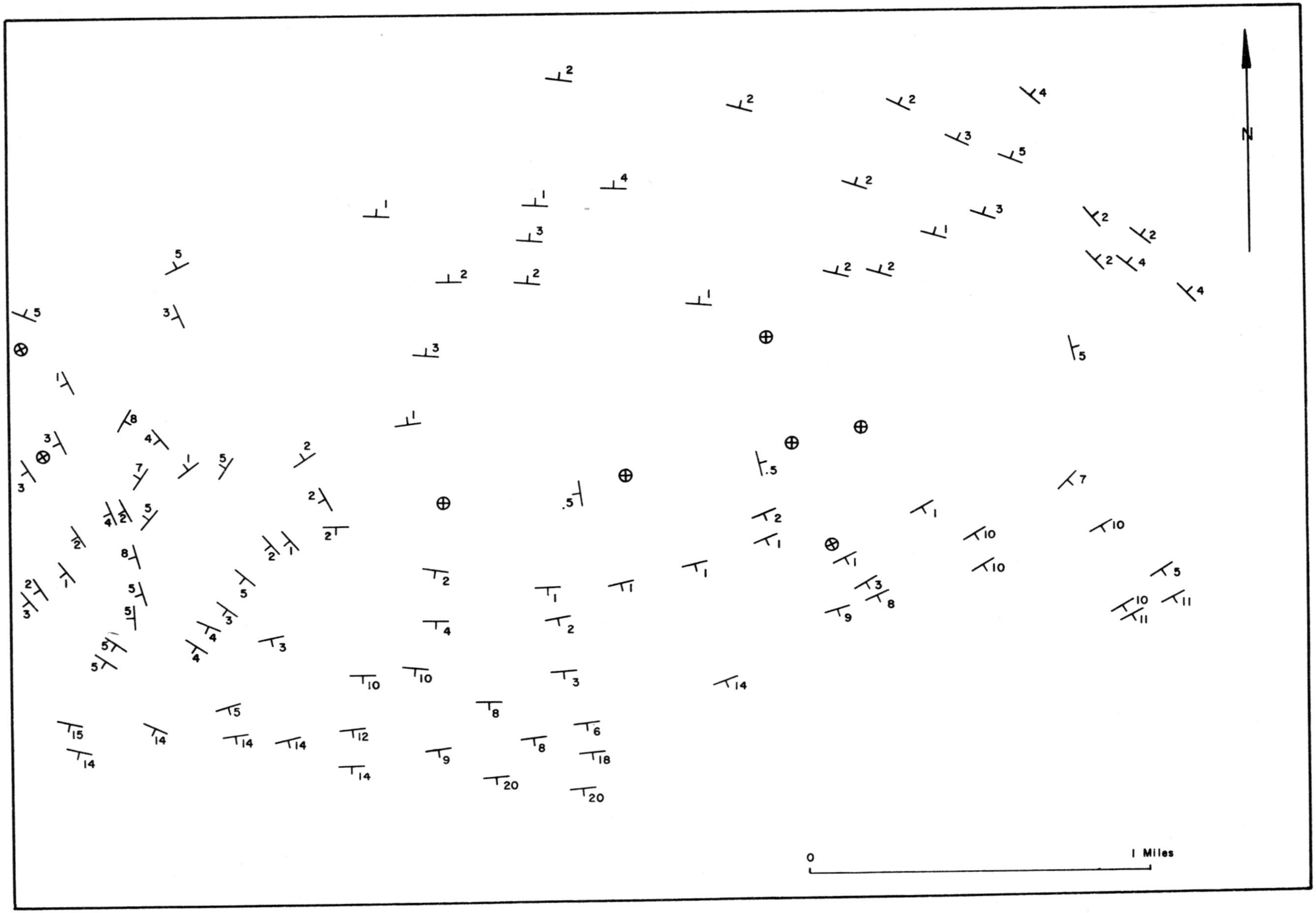

N

0 1 Miles

FIGURE 118.

PROBLEM 14

FORM LINE CONTOURING FROM FORMATION BOUNDARY INFORMATION (AIR PHOTOGRAPHS)

Data Provided: Plate 2 is an uncontrolled mosaic (two air photographs) of the Circle Ridge dome in Wyoming. Plates 3 and 4 show series of overlapping air photographs oriented and spaced for viewing stereoscopically. The Circle Ridge structure is situated on the north flank of the Wind River Basin, south of the Owl Creek Mountain front (Fig. 119). The structure is a tightly folded, partly overturned anticline asymmetric to the southwest. The dome is cut by a thrust fault dipping to the northeast. This fault reaches the surface just northeast of the anticlinal crest—part of the anticline is thus preserved beneath the thrust.

Oil production is found in the Mississippian Madison limestone, in the Pennsylvanian Tensleep sandstone, and in the Permian Phosphoria dolomite. All three reservoirs are productive on the overthrust block whereas only the stratigraphically higher two reservoirs are productive on the subthrust block.

The Phosphoria formation is exposed near the crest of the dome but the Triassic Chugwater siltstone and shale and the Jurassic Sundance and Morrison formations are located on the flanks.

The scale of the air photos is approximately one inch to 2000 feet.

There are commonly no topographic maps available in new exploration provinces, and there is still no published topographic map for this particular region, even though oil production was first obtained here as early as 1923, and there are now nearly 100 producing wells in the Circle Ridge oil field. Plate 2, the uncontrolled mosaic, will be used as a base map for this project. Distance errors do exist in uncontrolled mosaics, but these will not be serious in this case as our geological information is an estimation only and no doubt will also include errors.

Determine: Draw form line maps for both the overthrust and underthrust blocks, using the same datum horizon in each case. Estimate the extent of the datum overlap and indicate the overlap area clearly on your maps. Where would you locate a well to test the top of the Madison reservoir in the subthrust block? How deep would you have to drill in

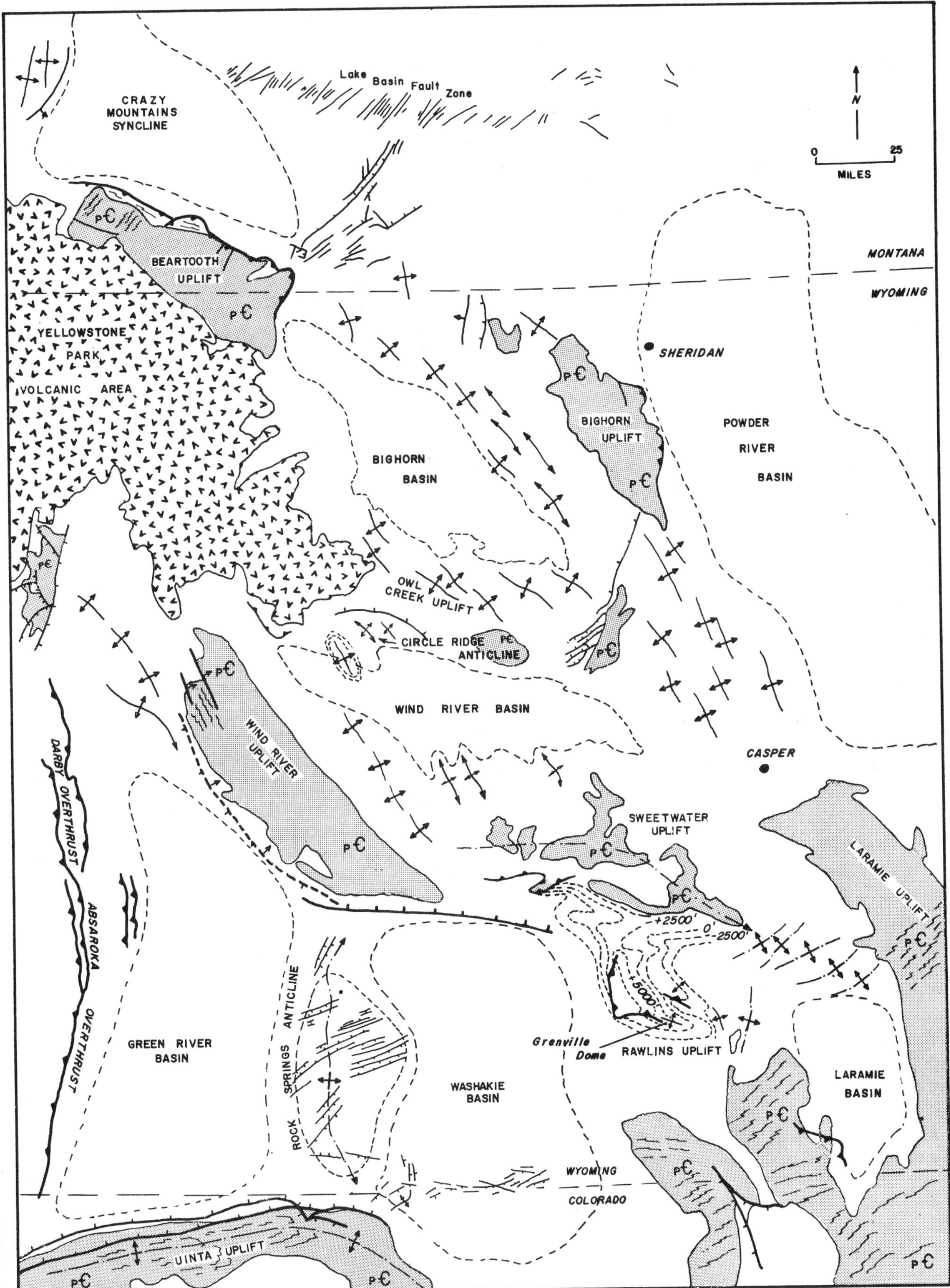

FIGURE 119. Tectonic framework of Wyoming and adjoining areas, showing the location of the Grenville dome and the Circle Ridge anticline (Problems 14 and 16). (Modified from the Tectonic Map of the United States [1944], Am. Assoc. Petrol. Geol.)

this well for the Madison top? Draw a cross section through the structure. Refer to Figure 120 for stratigraphic information.

Procedure: Use Plate 2 as your base map. Plot your attitude and contact information on a transparent sheet of paper (or acetate) placed over this mosaic.

To study the air photos, place your lens-type pocket stereoscope over (and parallel to) the dashed lines joining the small circles. The small circles represent the optical centers of the respective air photos. On the south half of Plate 3, each lens of the stereoscope should be located approximately over one of the two circles. While looking through the lenses, make small adjustments in orientation or lens spacing to obtain perfect fusion of the lines and circles. The stereoscope can now be moved east or west without losing the three-dimensional effect. For viewing the north half of Plate 3, place one lens approximately over each of the northern two circles and adjust as before.

For viewing Plate 4, place the center (nose position) of the stereoscope over the southern circle and align the stereoscope parallel to the dashed lines. Adjust for orientation and spacing of lens distance until perfect fusion of circles and lines occurs. For viewing the north end of Plate 4, place the center of the stereoscope over the northern of the three circles and adjust as before.

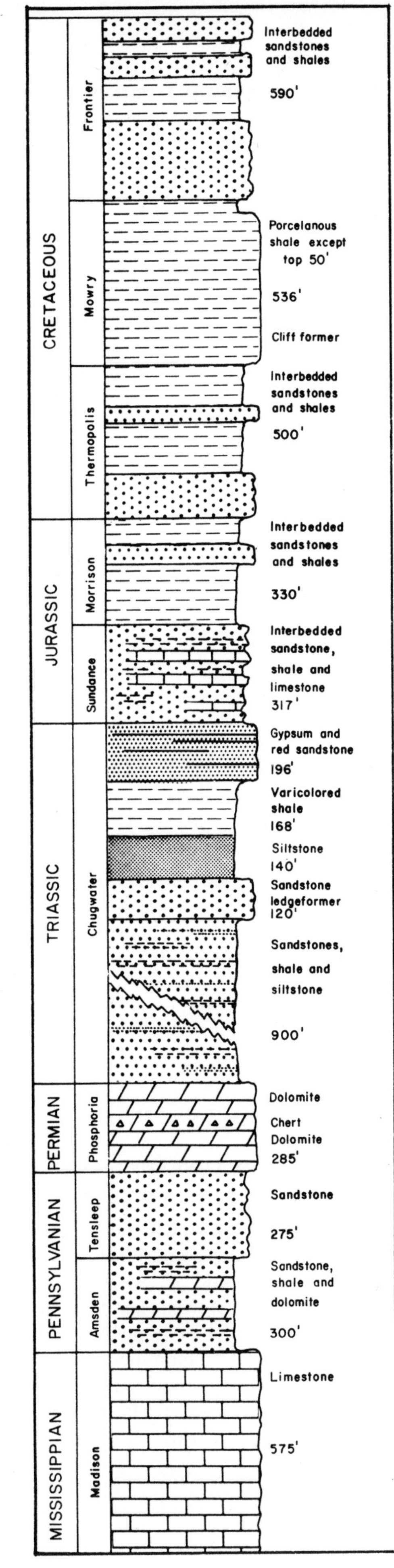

FIGURE 120. Generalized stratigraphic section for the Circle Ridge anticline area, Fremont County, Wyoming.

PROBLEM 15

FORM LINE CONTOURING FROM ATTITUDE AND FORMATION CONTACT INFORMATION

Data Provided: The accompanying map (Fig. 121) shows the results of a photogeologic study for an area in the eastern Rocky Mountain region of Alberta, Canada (see regional maps, Figs. 73 and 85). It was impossible to determine attitudes exactly, but the approximate attitudes shown are believed to be reliable. Only those formation contacts which could be followed clearly on air photographs are shown on the map. The oil and gas rights for this spread of land are available through purchase from the government, but purchase bids must be submitted to the government office within a few weeks. Thus an evaluation of the area is required on short notice. Weather conditions preclude the possibility of a field examination. However, air photographs of the regions and a simple stereoscope are available. It is necessary to determine whether a closed structure exists and, if so, what

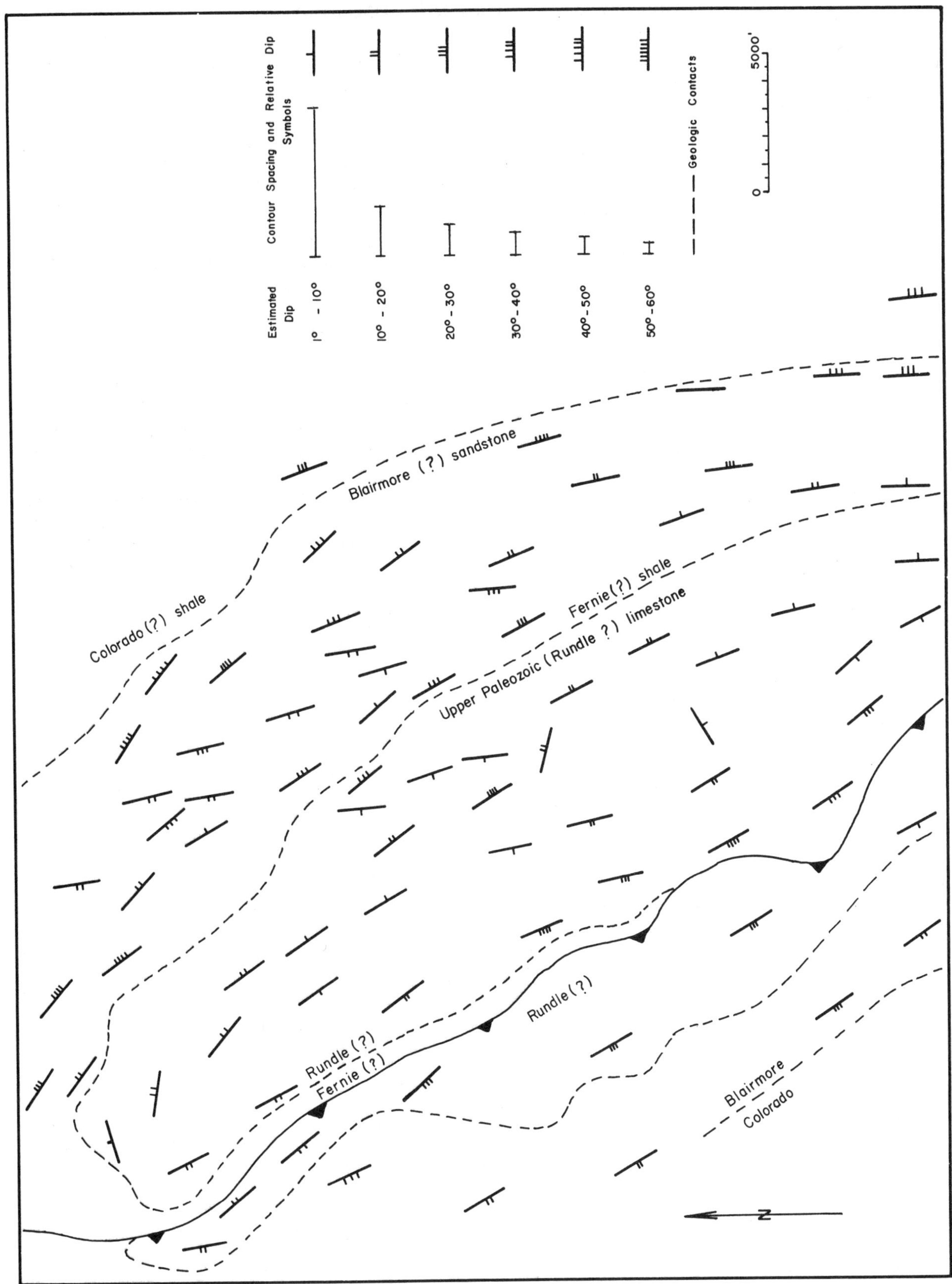

FIGURE 121. Photogeologic data for an area in the foothills belt of southwestern Alberta, Canada. Problem 15 requires a form line map to be drawn from this information.

part of the region appears most promising from the standpoint of discovering oil or gas. The general stratigraphic column for the region is known to be approximately as indicated in Figure 122.

A thrust fault occurs in this area and can be observed on the air photographs. If the form lines can be imagined as being on top of the Fairholme formation, then this thrust will not disturb the structure contour picture as the thrust will only cut the Fairholme formation near the western edge of the map.

Determine: Draw a form line map for this area on some horizon which is below the thrust fault. The attitudes at depth are believed to be similar to those at the surface, although the axial surface is not vertical. The fault is believed to dip westward at about 30°.

Questions Based on Problem No. 15

1. By examining the nomograph on page 71 (Fig. 78) and the spacing symbols (Fig. 121) one can estimate the structure contour interval used. What is it?
2. Where is the most favorable drilling location on the map?
3. Approximately how deep would one have to drill from the most favorable position to the top of the Fairholme formation, assuming that only 1000 feet of Rundle formation has been stripped from the top of this structure?
4. If one's company was the successful bidder in the government sale of these lands, what procedure should be recommended next?

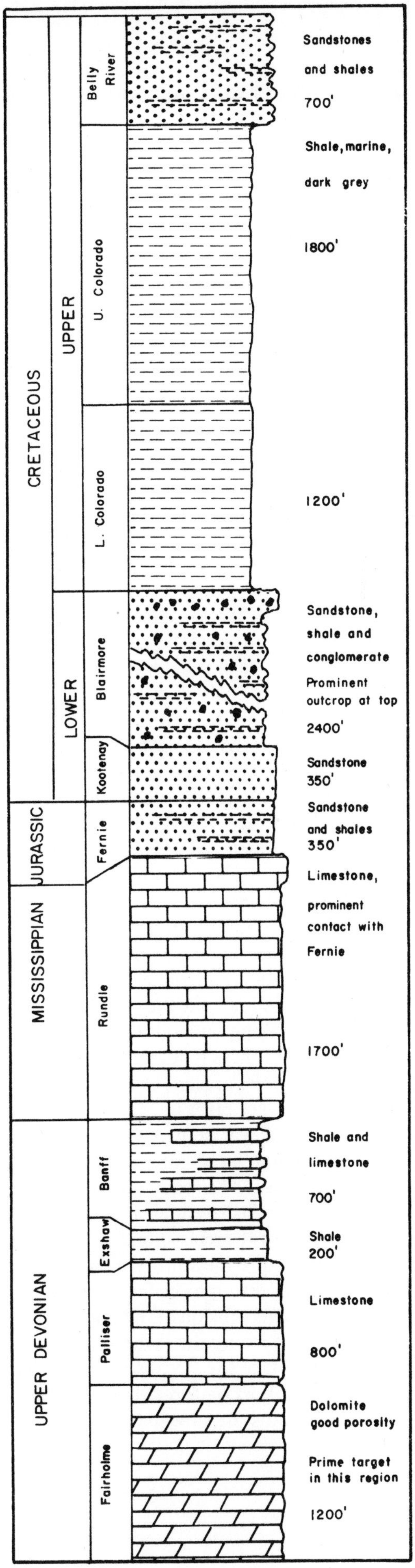

System	Series	Formation	Description
CRETACEOUS	UPPER	Belly River	Sandstones and shales 700'
CRETACEOUS	UPPER	U. Colorado	Shale, marine, dark grey 1800'
CRETACEOUS	UPPER	L. Colorado	1200'
CRETACEOUS	LOWER	Blairmore	Sandstone, shale and conglomerate Prominent outcrop at top 2400'
CRETACEOUS	LOWER	Kootenay	Sandstone 350'
JURASSIC		Fernie	Sandstone and shales 350'
MISSISSIPPIAN		Rundle	Limestone, prominent contact with Fernie 1700'
MISSISSIPPIAN		Banff	Shale and limestone 700'
UPPER DEVONIAN		Exshaw	Shale 200'
UPPER DEVONIAN		Palliser	Limestone 800'
UPPER DEVONIAN		Fairholme	Dolomite good porosity Prime target in this region 1200'

FIGURE 122. Generalized stratigraphic section for the area involved in Problem 15.

PROBLEM 16

STRUCTURE CONTOURING FROM FORMATION BOUNDARIES (AIR PHOTOGRAPHS) AND TOPOGRAPHIC MAPS WITH ONLY LIMITED STRIKE AND DIP INFORMATION

Data Provided: Plate 5 is a series of three overlapping air photos oriented and spaced for viewing stereoscopically. Plates 6 and 7 are enlargements of the same area. Figure 123 is a topographic base map for the same area. The photos show an aerial view of the Grenville dome, just south of the town of Sinclair, Wyoming. This dome is located on the eastern plunge of the Rawlins uplift (Fig. 119) which separates the Washakie Basin on the west from the Hanna Basin on the east. Upper Cretaceous Mowry shale is found in the core of the dome, whereas sands of Frontier formation form the rimrock of the structure. Niobrara shale overlies the Frontier on the flanks of the dome. Remnants of Miocene-Pliocene strata lie unconformably upon the Mesozoic formations near the west end of the structure. The Frontier formation is approximately 800 feet thick in this area. The Grenville dome is believed to have formed during the Laramide mountain-building period. Nine dry holes have been drilled on the structure, and all of these wells encountered water-laden porosity in the Nugget, Tensleep, and Madison reservoirs. The positions of formation contacts are shown at a few spots on the air photos, and a limited amount of strike and dip information is indicated. This latter information was provided through the courtesy of James A. Barlow, consulting geologist, Casper, Wyoming. The student should be able to add map information through dip estimation methods.

Determine: Draw a structure contour map on top of the Dakota sandstone, assuming that the stratigraphic interval between the base of the Frontier and the top of the Dakota is 300 feet. Assume that the dome was formed by flexure folding. There are several north-northeast striking faults in the area and these should be allowed for in contouring. Discuss the origin of these features and their relationship to the regional picture (Fig. 119). After contouring the present structural form of the dome, recontour the structure so as to show its appearance prior to Miocene-Pliocene deposition. The stereographic method described on page 195 will be useful at this point. There are a number of oil-producing structures in this region on apparently less perfect closures. Why is there no oil in this structure?

Procedure: To study the air photos properly, place the pocket-size, lens-type stereoscope over the dashed lines. For viewing the south end of the photo strip (Plate 5), the southern and central circles should appear near the right and left sides of the stereoscopic view. This will require the southern circle to be almost beneath the center of the stereoscope. While looking through the lenses, make slight adjustments in orientation or lens spacing to obtain perfect fusion of the lines and circles. The stereoscope view can be moved east and west without losing the three-dimensional effect. Now, for viewing the north end of the photo strip, place the stereoscope over the northern circle and parallel tc the dashed lines and again adjust for three-dimensional viewing. The circles represent the principal points of the air photos. Be sure to have a very good light source on the photographs when examining them.

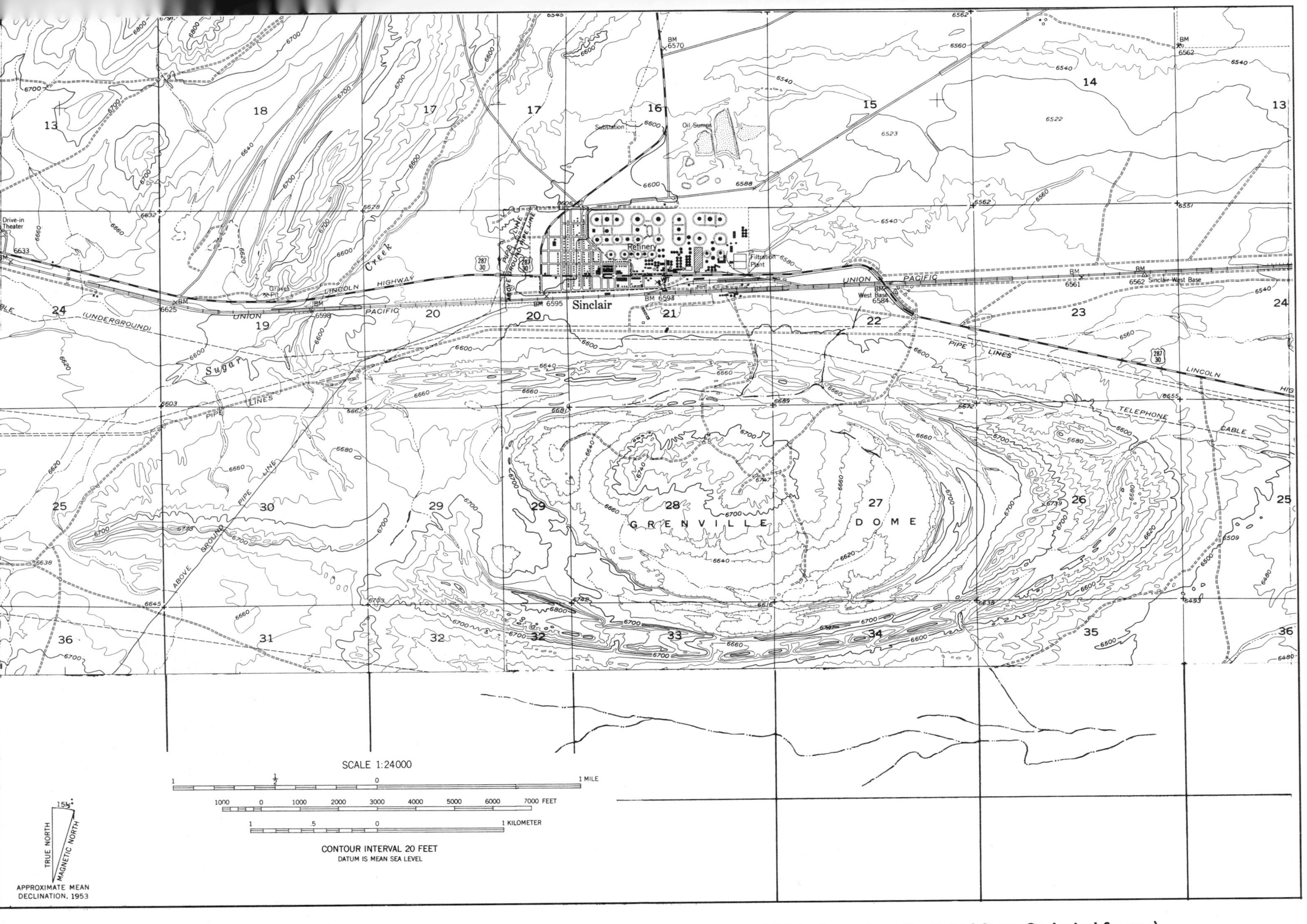

FIGURE 123. Topographic base map for the Grenville dome area, Carbon County, Wyoming. (Original map from the United States Geological Survey.)

PROBLEM 17

STRUCTURE CONTOURING FROM ATTITUDE, FORMATION CONTACT, AND TOPOGRAPHIC INFORMATION

Data Provided: Figure 124 shows attitude, formation contact, and topographic information for an area in the eastern Rocky Mountain Region of Alberta, Canada (see regional maps, Figs. 73 and 85).

Determine: Draw a structure contour map on top of the Fairholme formation for both hanging and footwall blocks. It will be necessary to utilize elevation control along all formation contacts (Rule 11, p. 73), and some interpolation between topographic contours will also be necessary to provide adequate control points. Determine the attitude of the thrust fault, and contour the fault surface by joining points of equal elevation along the trace of the fault. The strike of the fault may not be constant. Locate the positions of the lines of intersection of the top of the Fairholme formation with the thrust fault for both the hanging and footwall blocks.

Procedure: Color in the various formations on the map. This will make contact lines more distinguishable from topographic contour lines.

To complete the Fairholme structure contour map for the footwall block, it will be necessary to estimate, to some extent, the contour picture below the thrust fault. An examination of the strike and dip symbols just east of the thrust will help. Thrust faults normally are steeper than the bedding they traverse, and this is the situation in the region being studied. Thus the contour packing for the Fairholme surface below the thrust will probably be somewhat less than that for the thrust surface, although the packing for both surfaces could be about the same.

The compressive stress which caused the folding in this region has been from the southwest, based on extensive field evidence. Thus most folds in this region are slightly to moderately asymmetric to the northeast. Consequently, the structure contour spacing on the west limb of the anticline should be somewhat less closely packed than on the east limb of the anticline.

The footwall Fairholme intersection with the lower side of the thrust surface should lie southwest of the hanging wall Fairholme intersection with the upper side of the thrust surface, otherwise there would be no thrust faulting.

Bearing in mind the above facts, it should be possible to draw a very reasonable structure contour picture for the faulted anticline. Use different colors for each of the three surfaces contoured in order to avoid confusion.

Questions Based on Problem No. 17

1. Where would be the most favorable location to drill to test the Fairholme formation (allowing for migration of the anticlinal crest)?
2. What would be the estimated depth to the top of the Fairholme for the above location?
3. What is the approximate strike and dip of the thrust fault?
4. Can the extent of the net slip be determined in this map area? If so, what is the minimum net slip and the minimum width of the datum gap (assuming that this is a dip-slip fault)?
5. Is structure reflected by topography in this area?
6. Is lithology reflected by topography in this area? If so, how?

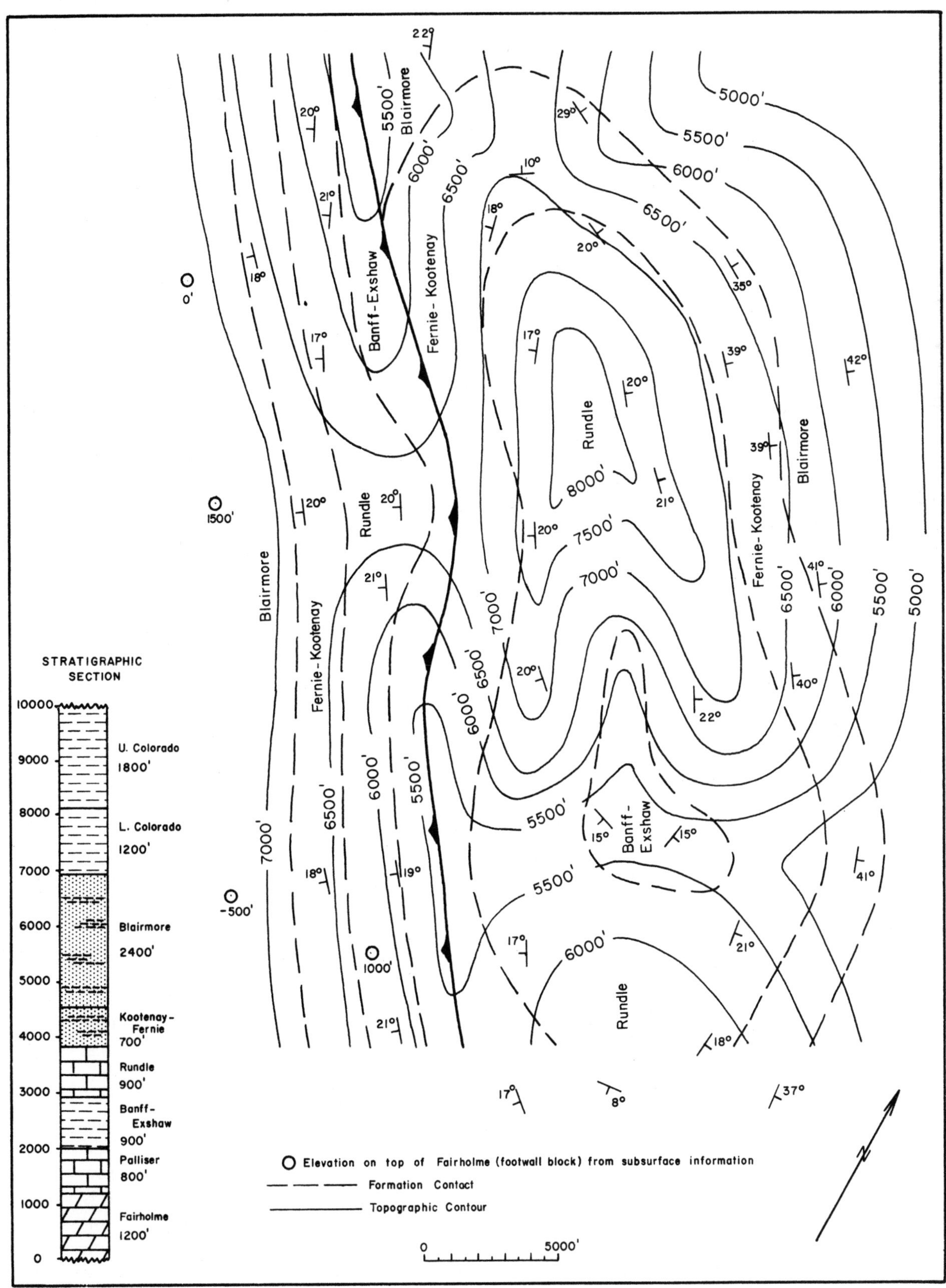

FIGURE 124. Geologic and topographic information for an area in the southern foothills of Alberta, Canada. Problem 17 requires that a structure contour map be drawn for this area.

PROBLEM 18

STRUCTURE CONTOURING FROM SUBSURFACE INFORMATION

Data Provided: The region shown on Figure 126 lies on the unstable shelf of the Western Canada Basin between the Leduc and Stettler reefs (Figs. 73 and 85). The Duhamel, New Norway, and Malmo reefs lie within the map area of this problem. We are required to locate these reefs on the basis of dry hole, off-reef wells only. The stratigraphy of this reef province is shown in Figure 125. We are provided with structural elevations on the base of the Fish Scale zone (Fig. 126), on the top of the Nisku (D_2) member (Fig. 127), and on the top of the Cooking Lake member (Fig. 128). Because of the incompactibility of the Leduc member compared to the off-reef Ireton member, differential compaction is greatest in off-reef areas. On-reef areas are therefore higher structurally. The situation has been complicated by pre-Cretaceous erosion and southwestward tilting, and these factors must also be considered. Structure contour maps on Nisku and Cooking Lake horizons give the best clues for proximity to reefs. Naturally, structural maps on top of the Leduc reef member itself are even better indicators of reef configuration, but we cannot draw Leduc structure maps until reefs have been discovered. The exploration geologist's job is to find the reefs. The Fish Scale horizon is complicated by erosional topography on top of the pre-Cretaceous unconformity, and thus a map at this level will show many high areas which are not related to reefing. A paleogeological map (or subcrop map) of the unconformity surface will help us to decide which high areas are related mainly to differential erosion. The Fish Scale horizon is valuable because it is a uniform marker in

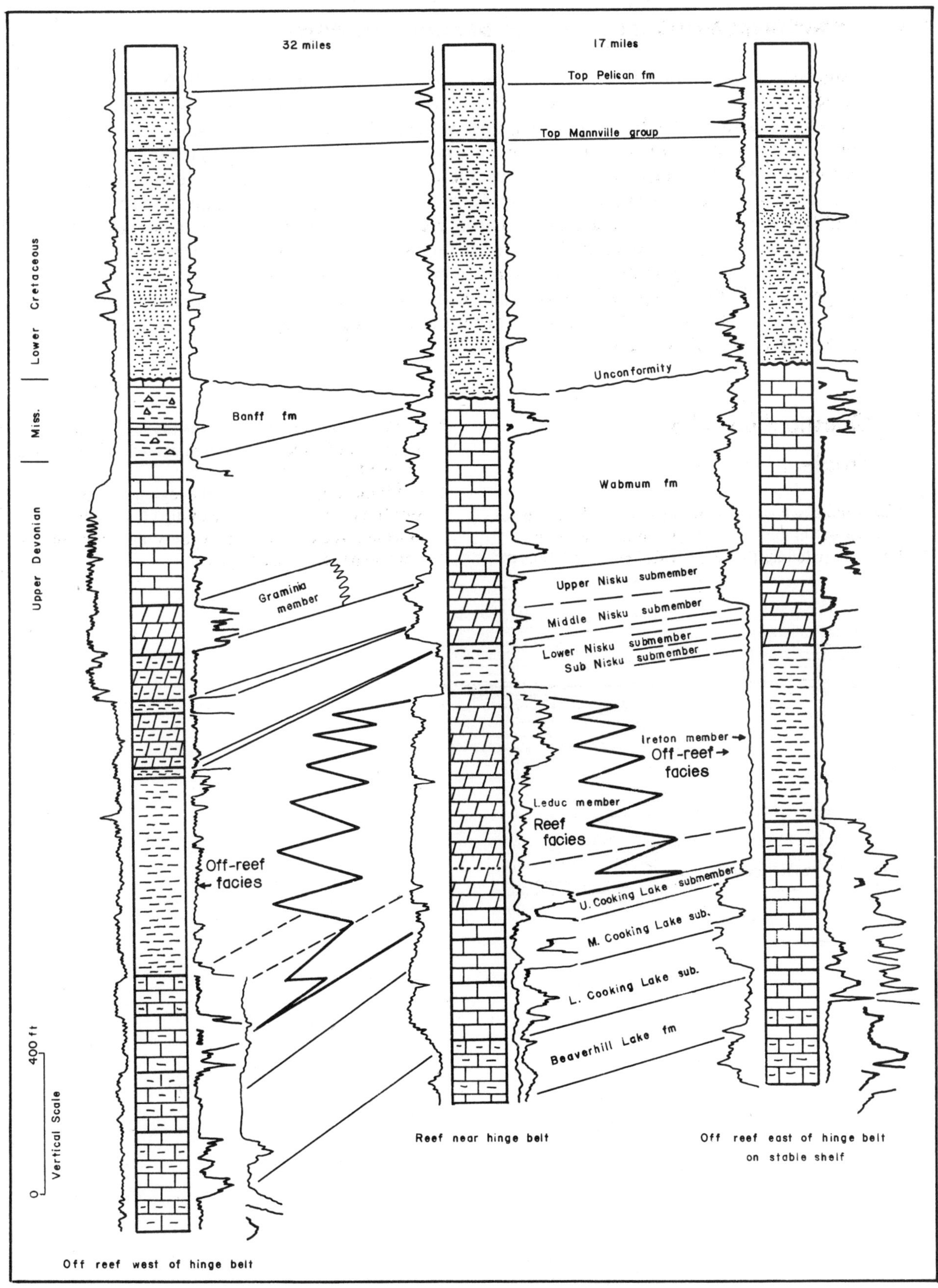

FIGURE 125. Subsurface stratigraphy of the central plains area of Alberta, Canada. *Note:* The base of the Fish Scale zone lies approximately 120 feet above the top of the Pelican formation. The Pelican formation is also known as the Viking sandstone. See page 145 for a written description of the Upper Cretaceous stratigraphy.

contrast to markers on top of the Viking or Mannville. Many more wells have penetrated through the Fish Scale horizon than have reached the Nisku because of the numerous oil and gas fields in the Viking and Mannville sands. The Fish Scale map thus provides information in areas where there are no Nisku wells. Facies maps for the Nisku, Ireton, and Cooking Lake members are useful in locating reefs but require detailed lithological studies in contrast to the more rapid structural method. Isopach maps of the Nisku and Ireton members are also useful in locating reefs and will be discussed in a later chapter. Isopach changes are commonly related to facies changes within these members, however, and these changes must be allowed for in interpreting such maps.

Determine: Outline the probable position of Leduc reefs in this area and recommend wildcat locations. Discuss the differences in structural patterns among the maps. Which map is the best exploration tool in your opinion?

Questions Based on Problem No. 18

1. What would be considered the most favorable areas for oil discovery in the Leduc (D_3) member? Be specific.
2. Which map defines the reef borders most accurately?
3. Are there any anomalous areas that are not due to the presence of Leduc (D_3) biohermal reefs? If so, how can you explain them?
4. Is it important to establish the regional structure contour trend and regional rate of dip? If so, why?
5. In what direction would there be a thickening of post-Devonian sediments? Explain.

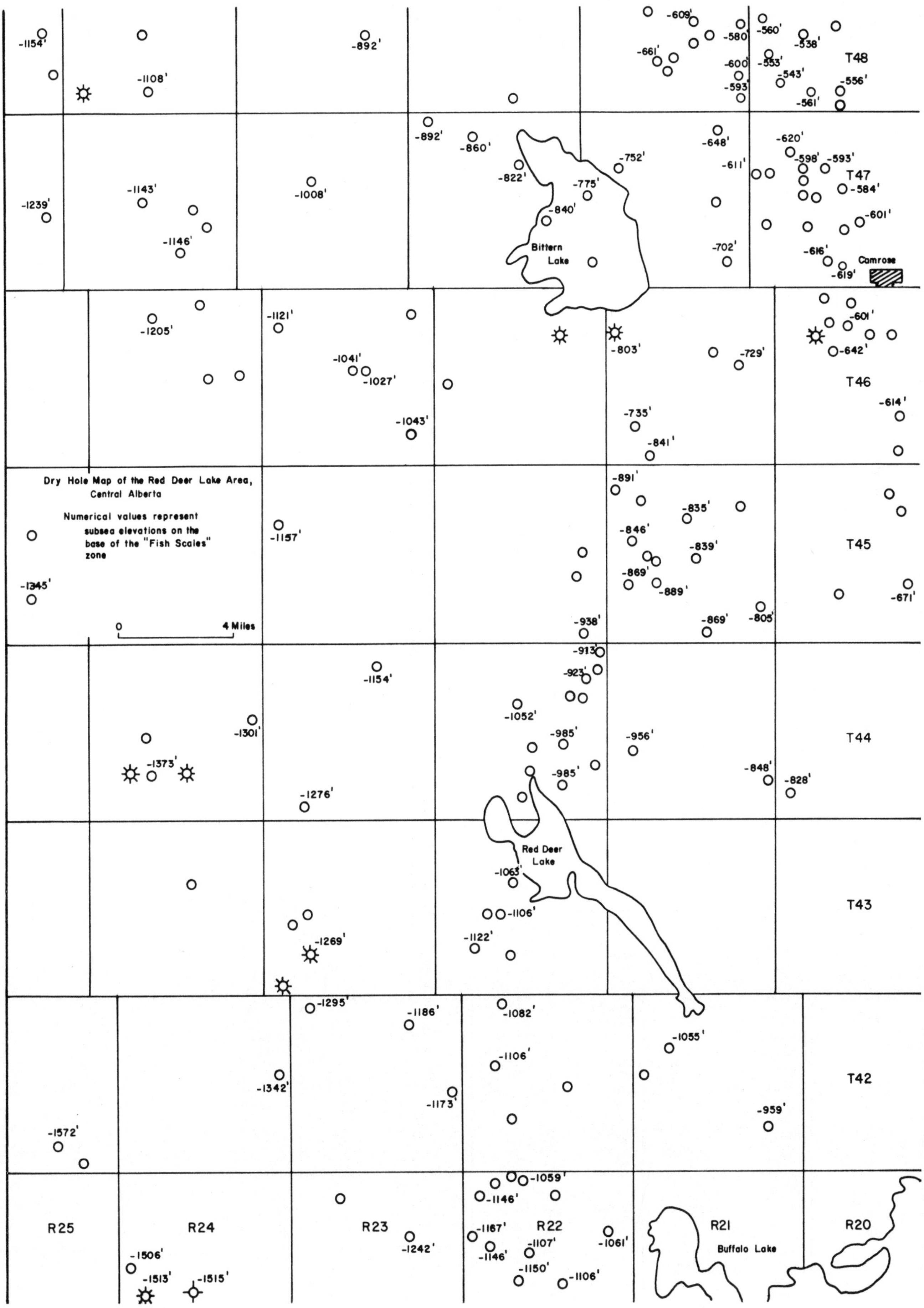

Dry Hole Map of the Red Deer Lake Area, Central Alberta

Numerical values represent subsea elevations on the base of the "Fish Scales" zone

0 4 Miles

Bittern Lake

Camrose

Red Deer Lake

Buffalo Lake

T48

T47

T46

T45

T44

T43

T42

R25 R24 R23 R22 R21 R20

FIGURE 126. For use with Problem 18.

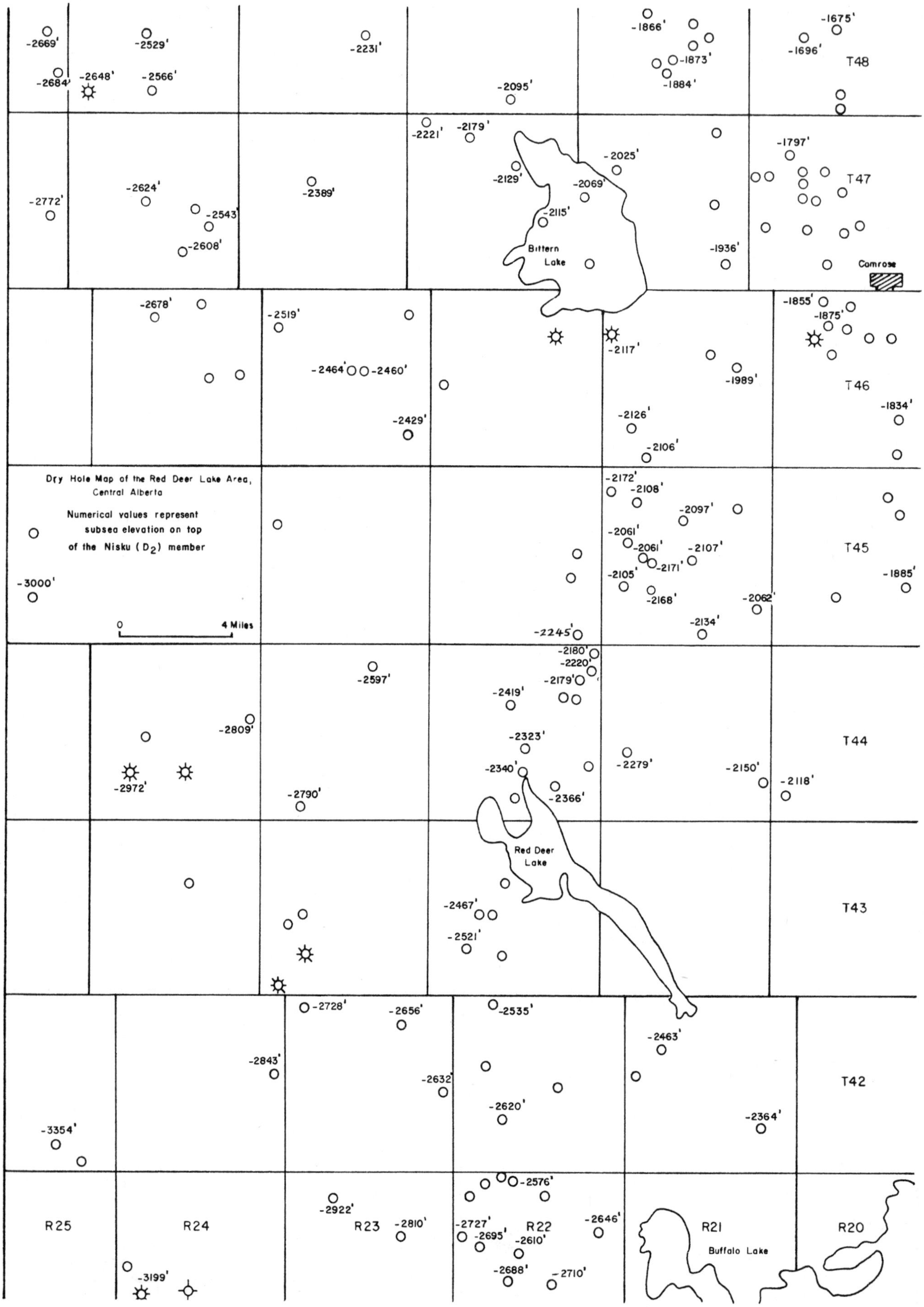

Dry Hole Map of the Red Deer Lake Area, Central Alberta

Numerical values represent subsea elevation on top of the Nisku (D_2) member

0 4 Miles

FIGURE 127. For use with Problem 18.

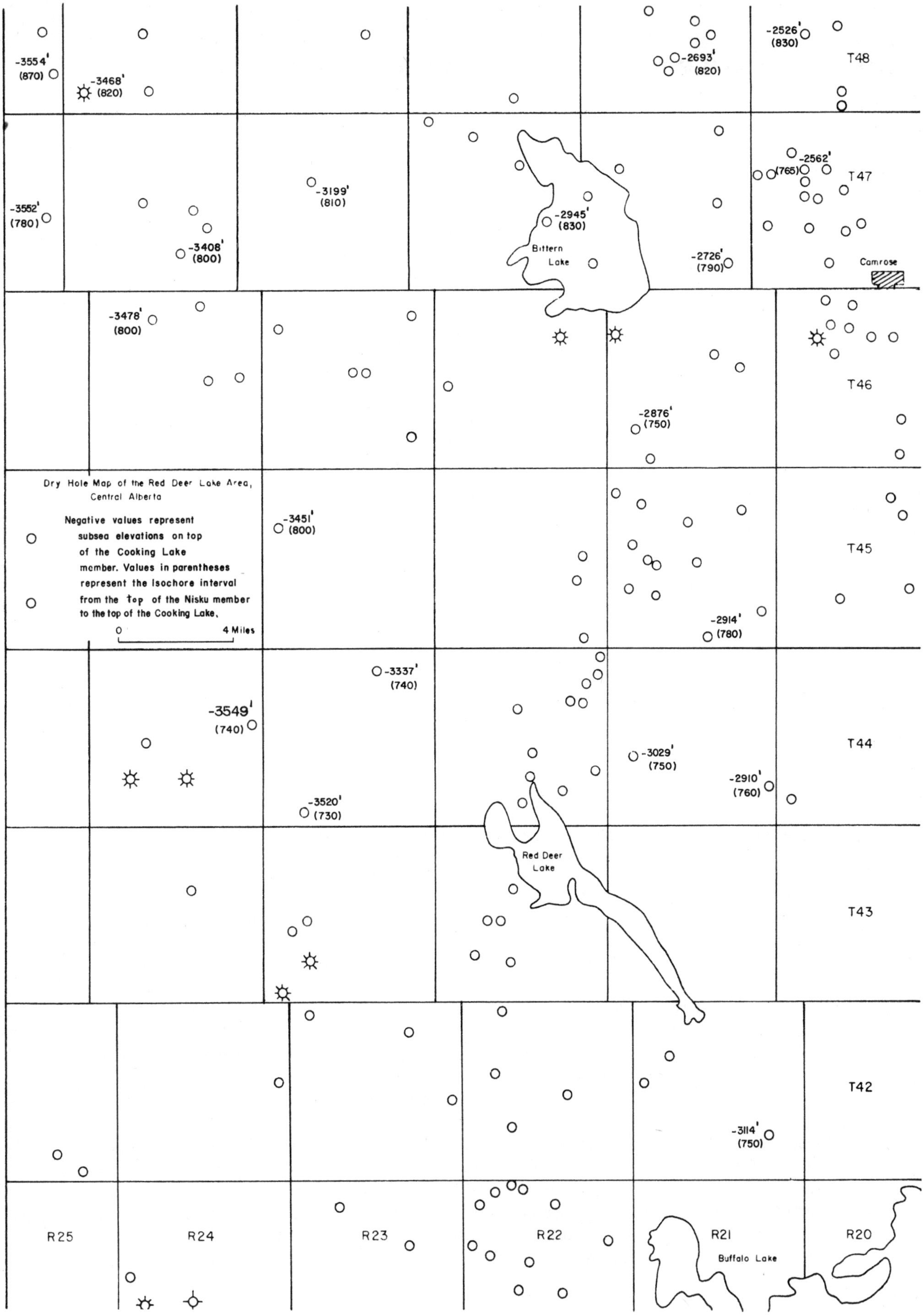
Dry Hole Map of the Red Deer Lake Area, Central Alberta
Negative values represent subsea elevations on top of the Cooking Lake member. Values in parentheses represent the isochore interval from the top of the Nisku member to the top of the Cooking Lake.
0
4 Miles
-3554'
(870)
-3468'
(820)
-2693'
(820)
-2526'
(830)
T48
-3552'
(780)
-3199'
(810)
-3408'
(800)
-2945'
(830)
Bittern Lake
-2726'
(790)
-2562'
(765)
T47
Camrose
-3478'
(800)
-2876'
(750)
T46
-3451'
(800)
-2914'
(780)
T45
-3337'
(740)
-3549'
(740)
-3029'
(750)
-2910'
(760)
-3520'
(730)
T44
Red Deer Lake
T43
-3114'
(750)
T42
R25
R24
R23
R22
R21
Buffalo Lake
R20

FIGURE 128. For use with Problem 18.

PROBLEM 19

STRUCTURE CONTOURING IN MULTIFAULTED AREAS (FAULT AND FORMATION BOUNDARIES AVAILABLE FROM SUBSURFACE OR SURFACE GEOLOGY AND TOPOGRAPHY)

Data Available: Figure 129 shows surface strike, dip, and elevation information for a good mappable horizon over a salt dome in the Gulf Coast area of the United States. The salt dome is cut by two normal faults, and attitude and elevation data are supplied for these also. You will note that the attitudes are not constant for either the mapping horizon or the faults—this is a more common situation than the ideal case described previously on pages 92–95. Because of this added complexity, the displaced portions of the datum gaps may not be perfectly parallel to the nondisplaced portions. One will have to arrive at the best compromise possible. In actual field operations the answer may be decided by subsurface drilling information.

Determine: The complete structure contour picture for the map area and the best spot for an initial test well.

Procedure: Draw the structure contour pattern for the youngest fault completely. Then project the structure contours on the older fault until they intersect the younger fault surface. The contour spacing can be determined by means of the nomograph for converting degrees of dip to structure contours (Fig. 78). Project the structure contours for the datum horizon until they intersect contours of similar elevations on the fault surfaces. By joining these intersection points, determine the extent of the datum gaps.

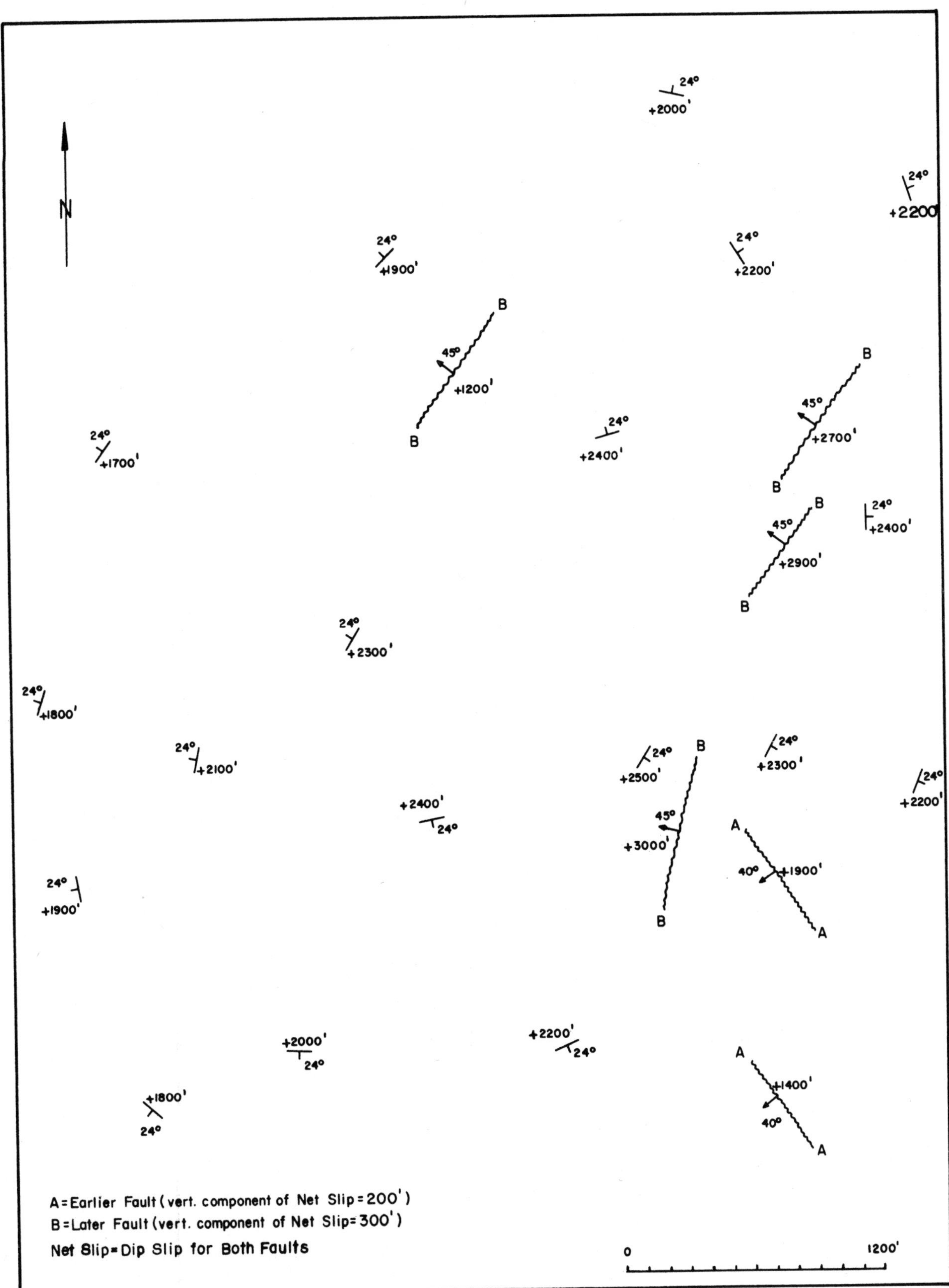

FIGURE 129. For use with Problem 19.

PROBLEM 20

CONTOURING OF FRACTURE SURFACES

Data Provided: A mineralized shear zone, carrying lead values, strikes approximately east-northeast and dips north-northwest. The attitude of the shear zone varies with the competency of the formations traversed (Fig. 130). The country rock consists of alternating limestones and shales striking north-south and dipping west at approximately 60°. A west-northwest striking subsidiary fracture set dips 70° north-northeast. The shear zone has been mined down to the −2300-foot level with access drifts every 200 feet. Figure 130 shows the positions of the shear zone, subsidiary fractures, and formation contacts at the −500-foot level. Lead values obtained during development work and by exploratory diamond drilling have also been projected to the −500-foot level (Fig. 131).

Determine: The structural factors controlling mineralization. The following maps will be required:

1. Structure contours on the upper surface of the major shear zone projected to the 500-foot level.
2. Structure contours on the reference plane, projected to the −500-foot level.
3. Contours showing the differential relief between the shear zone and the reference plane.
4. Isopach map of ore values.

In actual practice a contour map showing the thickness of ore would also be made if a reserve estimate were required.

Procedure: Determine the relief between the two structure contour maps by calculating the elevation difference between the two surfaces at each grid point intersection. Then contour the relief values obtained. Determine the positions of the subsidiary fractures on the shear surface by means of descriptive geometry (intersecting plane method). Compare the differential relief map with the isopach map of ore values. What would be the ore reserves (in the ground) in tons between the −500-foot, and −1500-foot levels if the ore body had an average thickness of 15 feet for ore values greater than 2.0 per cent lead? Values of less than 2.0 per cent lead are not considered commercial in this case. The tonnage factor is 10.5 cubic feet per ton of ore. The volumetric method for computing ore reserves is discussed on pages 167–168.

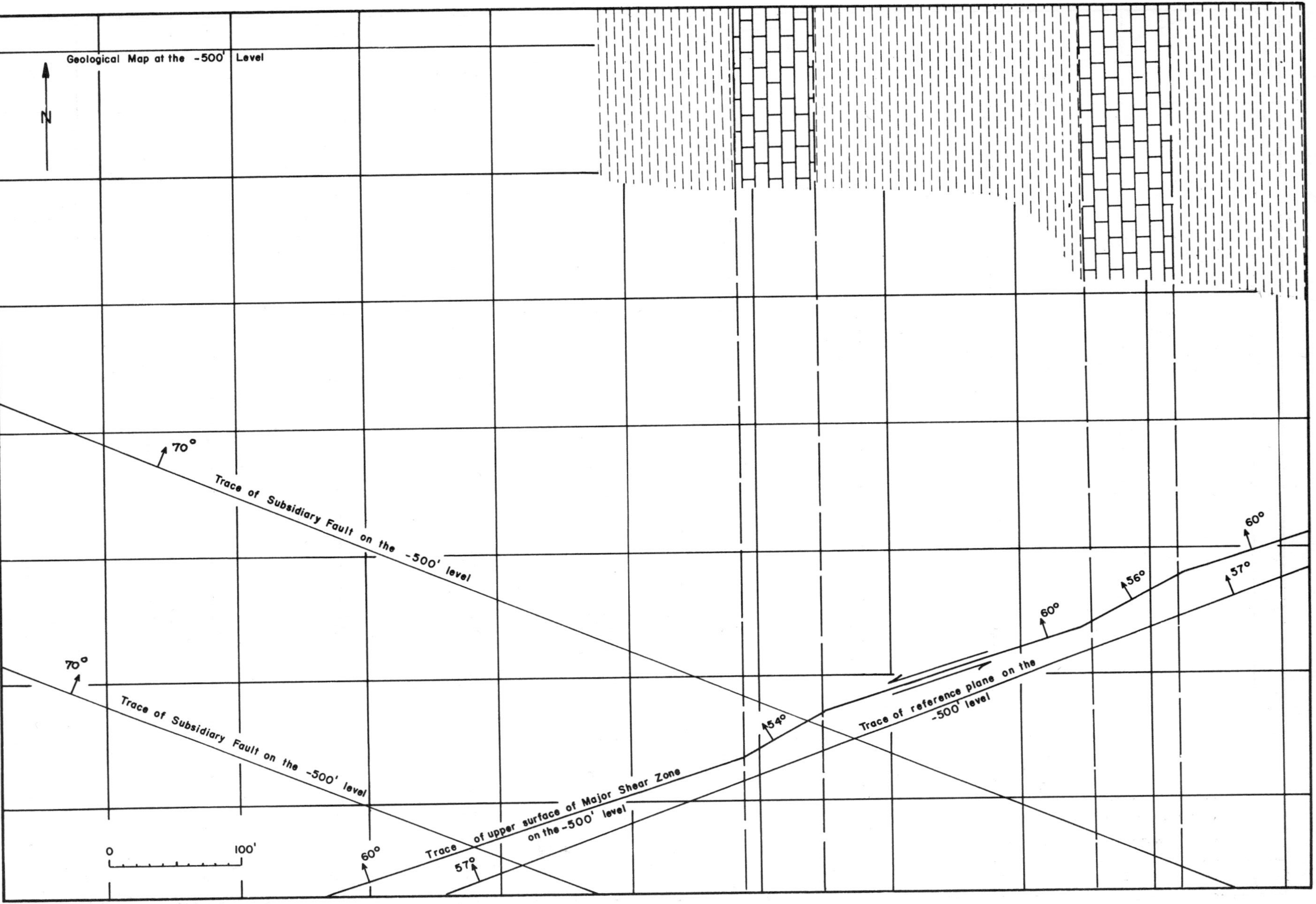

FIGURE 130. For use with Problem 20.

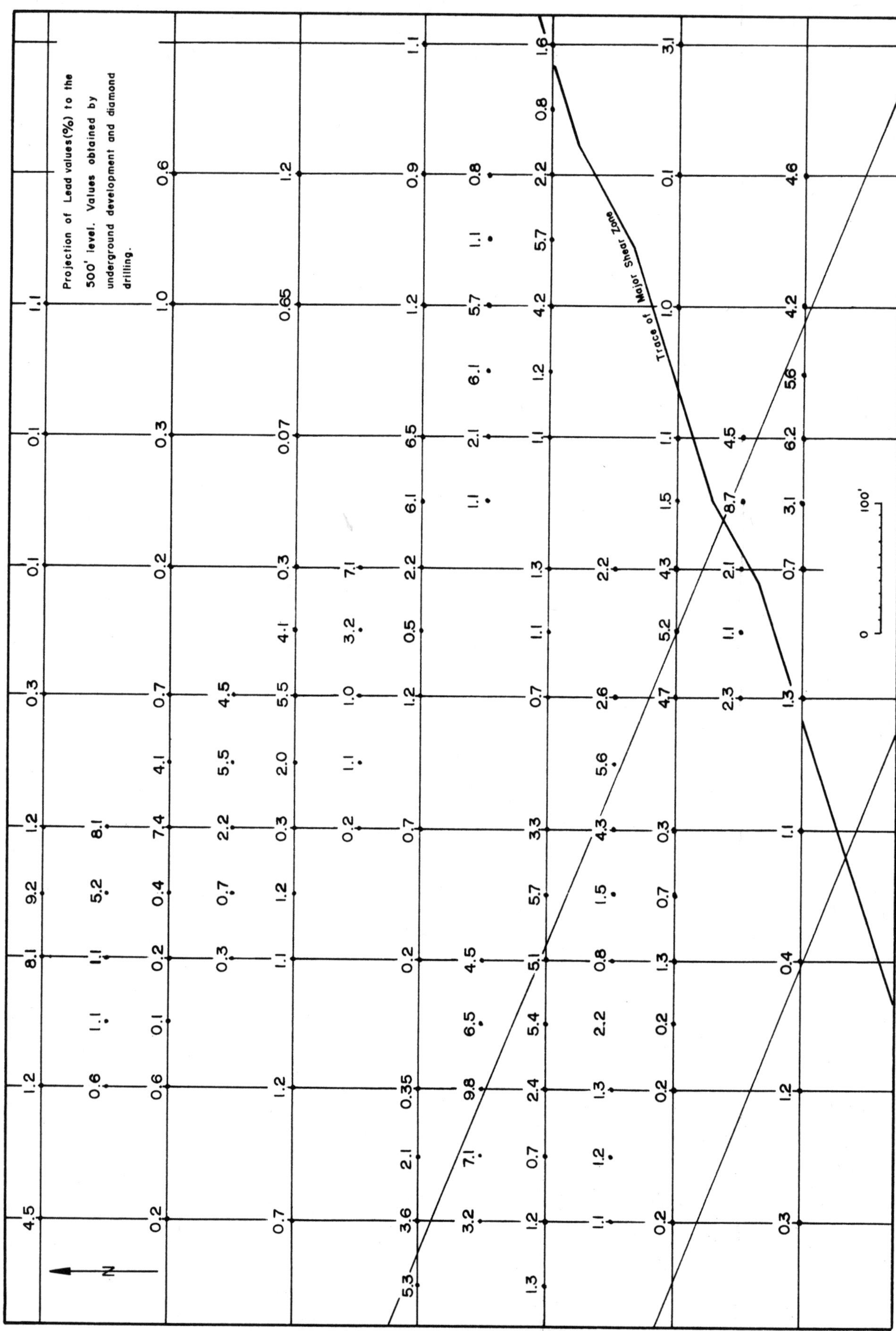

FIGURE 131. For use with Problem 20.

References

Andrews, D. A. (1944), Geologic and Structure Contour Map of the Maverick Springs Area, Fremont County, Wyoming, *U.S. Geol. Surv. Oil and Gas Investigation,* Prel. Map 13.

Atwater, G. (1948), The Discovery History of the University Oil Field, East Baton Rouge Parish, Louisiana, *Geophysical Case Histories,* vol. 1, Am. Assoc. Petrol. Geol., pp. 208–223.

Badgley, P. C. (1952), Notes on the Subsurface Stratigraphy and Oil and Gas Geology of the Lower Cretaceous Series in Central Alberta, *Geol. Surv. Can.,* Paper 52–11.

Barlow, J. A. (1953), Geologic Map of the Rawlins Uplift, Carbon County, Wyoming, University of Wyoming, Thesis.

Bartram, J. G. (1929), Elk Basin Oil and Gas Field, Park County, Wyoming, and Carbon County, Montana, *Structure of Typical American Oil Fields,* vol. II, Am. Assoc. Petrol. Geol., pp. 577–588.

Beebe, L. E. (1953), Wyoming's Circle Ridge Field, *Oil and Gas Jour.,* vol. 52, no. 19, pp. 109–114.

Conolly, H. J. C. (1936), A Contour Method of Revealing Some Ore Structures, *Econ. Geol.,* vol. 31, pp. 259–271.

Coryn, F. R. (1948), Geophysical History of the Apache Pool, Caddo County, Oklahoma, *Geophysical Case Histories,* vol. I, Am. Assoc. Petrol. Geol., pp. 312–318.

Crowell, J. C. (1948), Template for Spacing Structure Contours, *Bull. Am. Assoc. Petrol. Geol.,* vol. 32, pp. 2290–2294.

De Blieux, C. (1949), Photogeology in Gulf Coast Exploration, *Bull. Am. Assoc. Petrol. Geol.,* vol. 33, pp. 1251–59.

Desjardins, L. (1943), Contouring and Elevation Measurement on Vertical Aerial Photographs, *Photogrammetric Engineering,* vol. 9, pp. 214–224.

Desjardins, L. (1943), Measurement of Dip Angles on Aerial Photographs, *Bull. Am. Assoc. Petrol. Geol.,* vol. 27, pp. 1534–1538.

Desjardins, L. (1950), Techniques in Photogeology, *Bull. Am. Assoc. Petrol. Geol.,* vol. 34, pp. 2284–2317.

Desjardins, L., and Hower, S. G. (1939), Geologic, Topographic, and Structural Mapping from Aerial Photographs, *Am. Petrol. Inst. Finding and Producing Oil,* pp. 29–33.

Dickinson, G. (1954), Subsurface Interpretation of Intersecting Faults and Their Effects Upon Stratigraphic Horizons, *Bull. Am. Assoc. Petrol. Geol.,* vol. 38, pp. 854–877.

Dobbin, C. E., Kramer, W. B., and Miller, J. C. (1944), Geologic and Structure Map of the Elk Basin Oil and Gas Field and Vicinity, Park County, Wyoming, and Carbon County, Montana, *U.S. Geol. Surv.,* Map.

Driver, H. L. (1943), Inglewood Oil Field, Calif. *Div. of Mines,* Bull. 118, pp. 306–309.

Eardley, A. J. (1941), *Aerial Photographs, Their Use and Interpretation,* Harper & Brothers, 203 pp.

Ebbutt, F. (1948), Relationships of Minor Structures to Gold Deposition in Canada, *Structural Geology of Canadian Ore Deposits,* Can. Inst. Min. Met., pp. 64–77.

Fitch, A. A., *et al.* (1949), *Aerial Photography in Petroleum and Mineral Prospecting,* 4th Empire Min. & Metal. Cong. (London).

Gill, D. (1932), Aerial Survey in Relation to Economic Geology, *Inst. of Min. and Met.* (London), Prel. Paper, pp. 2–48.

Grogan, R. M. (1949), Structures Due to Volume Shrinkage in the Bedding Replacement Fluorspar Deposits of Southern Illinois, *Econ. Geol.,* vol. 44, pp. 606–616.

Harrington, J. W. (1951), The Elementary Theory of Subsurface Structural Contouring, *Trans. Am. Geophy. Union,* vol. 32, pp. 77–80.

Ireland, H. A. (1955), Pre-Cambrian Surface in Northeastern Oklahoma and Parts of Adjacent States, *Bull. Am. Assoc. Petrol. Geol.,* vol. 39, pp. 468–483.

Jenkins, C. E. (1951), Grenville Dome, Carbon County, Wyoming, *Wyoming Geol. Assoc.* Guide Book, Sixth Annual Field Conference (South Central Wyoming), pp. 58–65.

Jolliffe, A. W. (1942), Structures in the Canadian Shield, *Trans. Am. Geophy. Union,* vol. 23, pp. 699–707.

Levings, W. S. (1944), Aerogeology in Mineral Exploration, *Colo. School of Mines Quart.,* vol. 39, no. 4, 77 pp.

Link, T. A. (1949), Interpretations of Foothills Structures, Alberta, Canada, *Bull. Am. Assoc. Petrol. Geol.,* vol. 33, pp. 1475–1501.

Loel, W. (1941), Use of Aerial Photographs in Geologic Mapping, *Am. Inst. Min. Met. Eng.,* Trans., vol. 144, pp. 356–409.

Longwell, C. R. (ed.) (1944), Tectonic Map of the United States, Am. Assoc. Petrol. Geol.

Lovering, T. S. (1942), The Mineral Belt of the Colorado Front Range, in W. H. Newhouse (ed.), *Ore Deposits as Related to Structural Features,* Princeton University Press, pp. 79–93.

Low, J. W. (1957), *Geologic Field Methods,* Harper & Brothers, 489 pp.

Lowenstam, H. A. (1948), Marine Pool, Madison County, Illinois, Silurian Reef Producer, *Structure of Typical American Oil Fields,* vol. III, pp. 153–188.

McCabe, W. S. (1948), Elk Basin Anticline, Park County, Wyoming, and Carbon County, Montana, *Bull. Am. Assoc. Petrol. Geol.,* vol. 32, pp. 52–67.

McKinstry, H. E. (1948), *Mining Geology,* Prentice-Hall, Inc., 680 pp.

Miller, V. C. (1950), Rapid Dip Estimation in Photo-Geological Reconnaissance, *Bull. Am. Assoc. Petrol. Geol.,* vol. 34, pp. 1739–1743.

Nevin, C. M. (1949), *Principles of Structural Geology,* John Wiley & Sons, Inc., 410 pp.

Nugent, L. W. (1947), Aerial Photographs in Structural Mapping of Sedimentary Formations, *Bull. Am. Assoc. Petrol. Geol.,* vol. 31, pp. 478–494.

Palmer, H. S. (1918), New Graphic Method for Determining the Depth and Thickness of Strata and the Projection of Dip, *U.S. Geol. Surv.,* Prof. Paper 120-G, pp. 123–128.

Parker, T. J., and McDowell, A. N. (1955), Model Studies of Salt-Dome Tectonics, *Bull. Am. Assoc. Petrol. Geol.,* vol. 39, pp. 2384–2470.

Petroleum and Natural Gas Conservation Board of Alberta (Calgary, Alberta, Canada), Schedule of Wells Drilled for Oil and Gas up to 1949, and Schedules for Individual Years Thereafter.

Reiter, W. A. (1947), Contouring Fault Planes, *World Oil,* vol. 126, pp. 34–35.

Rettger, R. E. (1929), On Specifying the Type of Subsurface Structural Contouring, *Bull. Am. Assoc. Petrol. Geol.,* vol. 13, pp. 1559–1561.

Scott, V. C. (1945), Apache Oil Pool, Caddo County, Oklahoma, *Bull. Am. Assoc. Petrol. Geol.,* vol. 29, pp. 100–105.

Shearer, E. M. (1957), Stereo-Structural Contouring, *Bull. Am. Assoc. Petrol. Geol.,* vol. 41, pp. 1694–1703.

Smith, H. T. U. (1943), *Aerial Photographs and Their Applications,* Appleton-Century-Crofts, 372 pp.

Van Nouhuys, J. J. (1937), Geological Interpretations of Aerial Photographs, *Am. Inst. Min. Met. Eng.,* Trans., vol. 126, pp. 607–624.

Vaughan, F. E. (1925), The Five Islands, *Bull. Am. Assoc. Petrol. Geol.,* vol. 9, pp. 761–774.

Wisser, E. (1942), the Pachuca Silver District, in W. H. Newhouse (ed.), *Ore Deposits as Related to Structural Features,* Princeton University Press, pp. 229–235.

World Oil, September, 1951, p. 101.

CHAPTER 5

Isopach, Isochore, and Convergence Maps

Terminology and Principles Involved

An *isopach contour* is an imaginary line connecting points where thickness is equal.

An *isopach map* is one which shows the variations in stratigraphic thickness of formations by means of isopachous contour lines drawn through points where the formations have equal thickness. Isopach maps require two horizons or key beds, one at the top and the other at the bottom of the stratigraphic unit.

An *isochore map* is one that shows by contours the drilled thicknesses of formations without regard to the true stratigraphic thicknesses. Many so-called isopach maps are actually isochore maps. The *difference* between isopach and isochore formations varies with the degree of dip, being insignificant when the dip is low angle.

Surface geological thickness data is usually available in the form of true stratigraphic thickness whereas subsurface thickness data is always obtained as drilled thicknesses. Drilled thickness can be related to a stratigraphic thickness as follows:

$$\text{Stratigraphic Thickness} = \text{Drilled Thickness} \times \text{Cosine of Dip}$$

The derivation of this equation is as follows (Fig. 132):

$$\sin \text{“d”} = \frac{\text{“ST”}}{\text{“O.W.”}} \qquad \text{“ST”} = \text{“O.W.”} \times \sin \text{“d”} \quad (1)$$

$$\tan \text{“d”} = \frac{\text{“D”}}{\text{“O.W.”}} \qquad \text{“O.W.”} = \frac{\text{“D”}}{\tan \text{“d”}} \quad (2)$$

Substitute value of “O.W.” in (1). Then

$$\text{“ST”} = \frac{\text{“D”}}{\tan \text{“d”}} \times \sin \text{“d”} \qquad \text{“ST”} = \text{“D”} \times \cos \text{“d”}$$

The nomograph (Fig. 93) on page 80 is based on this relationship and can be used for converting drilled thickness to stratigraphic thickness.

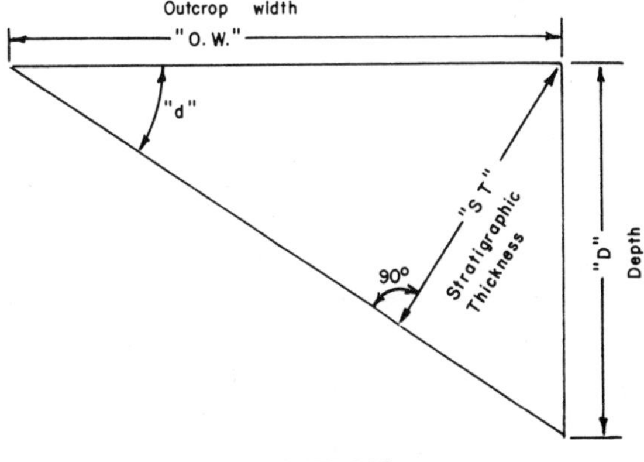

FIGURE 132.

Dips must be available for converting drilled thicknesses to stratigraphic thicknesses as shown by the above relationship. In subsurface work, dips are obtained from cores. Inasmuch as most deep drill holes, and many shallow ones, deviate from the vertical, both the drilled thickness and dip angles will be read in error unless corrected. Deviation surveys are run on many drill holes today.

The true formation dip can be obtained by the following equation:

$$\cos\theta = \cos\gamma \times \cos\phi \pm \sin\gamma \times \sin\theta \times \cos\psi$$

Where ϕ = true dip.
γ = hole deviation from vertical.
ψ = difference between azimuth of dip and azimuth of hole.
θ = apparent core dip.

Note: Use + when the deviation is up dip (see Fig. 104).
Use − when the deviation is down dip (see Fig. 104).

General Usage

1. Isopach data are used to locate buried structures. In many regions deposition was less (thin-

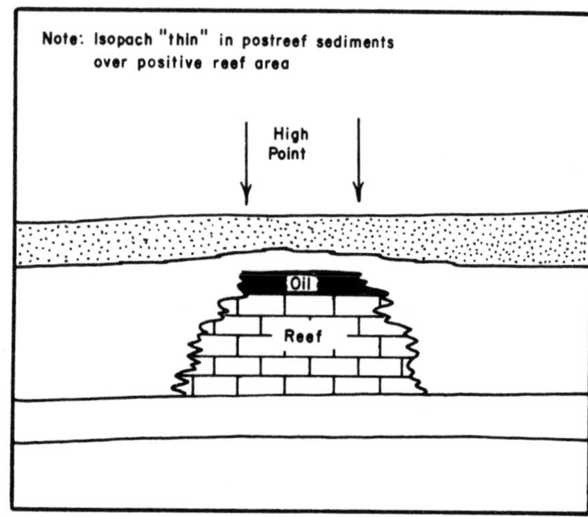

FIGURE 133.

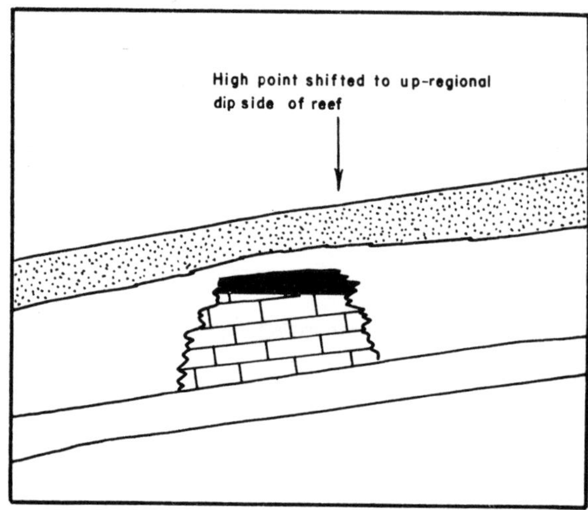

FIGURE 134.

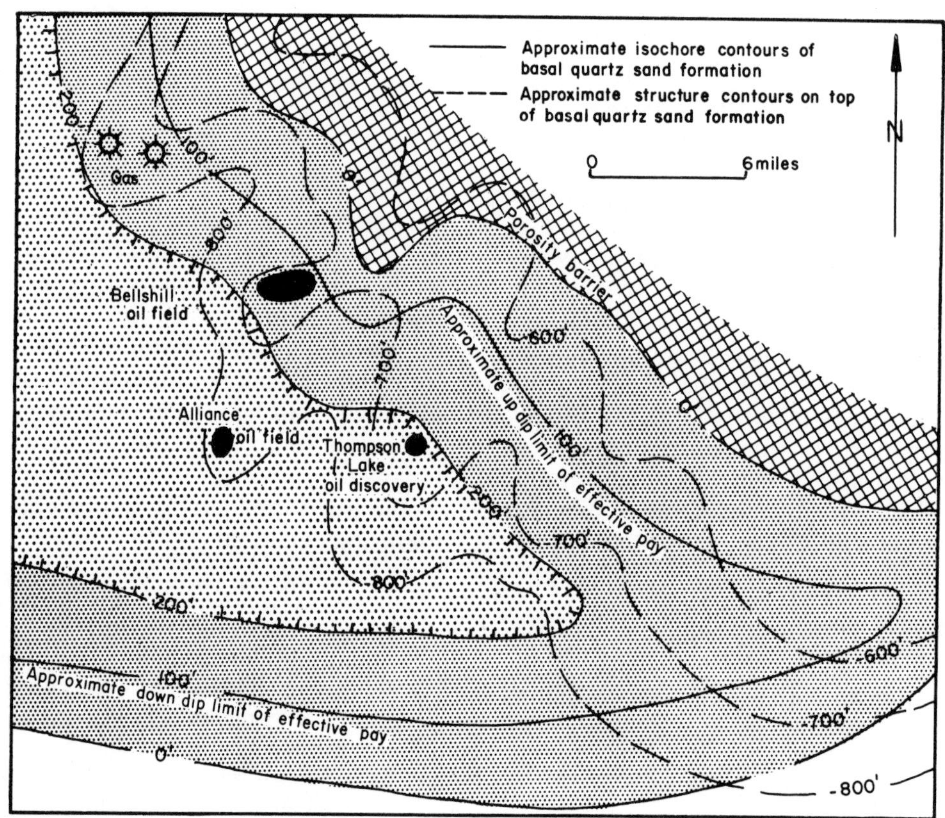

FIGURE 135. Showing the relationship between isochore values, structure contours, and oil discovery in the central plains area of Alberta. The Bellshill oil field was discovered near the up dip edge of the Basal Quartz Sand reservoir.

ner) over structures which were positive at the time of deposition (Fig. 133).

They are also used to locate the highest portions of areas which were positive at the time of original deposition—in many areas, particularly biohermal reef areas, deposition was thinnest (in the immediate post reef sediments) over the top of the ancient structures, but later tilting has caused the crest of the structure to migrate up the regional dip from the original high point (Fig. 134).

2. Many petroleum traps are related to wedge belts of porosity. Isopach maps are used to indicate the direction of probable wedging (or convergence). To determine more accurately the most favorable petroleum prospecting areas, isopach maps are usually combined with isolith maps, lithofacies maps, and often with structure contour maps. Figure 135 shows a wedge of the Basal Quartz Sand reservoir in central Alberta. Several oil discoveries have been made on structural noses located near the up dip edge of the effective pay. Both isochore and structural maps are essential to discovery in this region.

3. Isopach maps are of assistance in drawing up prognoses for wildcat wells by helping to determine the estimated depth to specific formations. This often involves estimating the elevation on deep subsurface mapping horizons when the structural information does not penetrate as deep as the deep mapping horizons. A structure contour map is drawn on a shallow horizon, and an isopach map for the interval between the shallow and deep horizons (same scale as structure map) is laid over the shallow structure contour map. Whenever the isopach and structure contour lines cross, the isopach thickness at the intersection point can be subtracted from the shallow structural elevation to determine the structural elevation on the deep horizon.

4. Isopach data can be used in conjunction with porosity, water saturation, etc., data to calculate the volume of oil or gas in a reservoir (see oil reserve estimate problem).

5. By selecting a series of datum planes and preparing a succession of isopach maps, the structural growth of an area can be developed in detail. The detailed structural history of an area is of basic value in petroleum exploration inasmuch as it sheds light on the possible movements and entrapment of oil in response to structural controls (see Problem 22).

6. Isopach maps help to evaluate the rate of subsidence in an area. Thick isopach contours represent areas of relatively rapid subsidence.

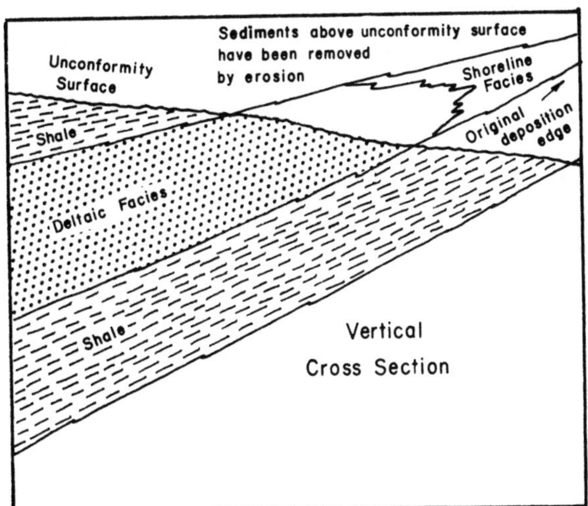

FIGURE 136. Thickness studies can be used to determine the location of original depositional edges.

7. Isopach maps can help in restoring the original depositional edge of a stratigraphic unit. In some cases the present-day zero isopach represents the ancient shoreline, whereas in other cases the shoreward parts of formations have been eroded away (Fig. 136).

Suggestions for Preparations of Isochore–Isopach Maps

1. Isopach maps are prepared by subtracting the elevations of the lower stratigraphic mapping horizon being used from those of the upper map horizon at each control point, and drawing contours of equal thickness between the two surfaces.

2. Closed hachured contours are used for areas of maximum thickness.

3. Contour spacing will depend upon a knowledge and interpretation of sedimentary conditions in the area. Thus the geologist should acquaint himself with the local geological picture.

PROBLEM 21

RELATION BETWEEN REGIONAL ISOCHORE MAPS AND UNDERLYING PALEOGEOLOGY

Data Provided: Figure 137[1] shows the isochore pattern for part of the McMurray formation in central Alberta. The McMurray formation, dominantly a quartzose sand facies, was deposited upon the top of the widespread pre-Cretaceous erosion surface and has filled most of the topographic irregularities which formed during the long erosion interval. For accuracy of correlation in subsurface isochore mapping, the top of the McMurray formation has been taken at the base of the *Metacypris angularis* ostracod zone. This zone occurs at or near the top of the McMurray formation. This formation is referred to as the Basal Quartz Sand by most petroleum geologists. The stratigraphic situation is discussed in more detail by Badgley (1952). The isochore pattern for this formation gives an excellent picture of the paleotopography existing prior to McMurray sedimentation.

Figure 138 indicates the paleogeology immediately below the pre-Cretaceous erosion surface. This type of map is also called a subcrop map by some geologists. It will be noted that older and older formations are progressively exposed to the northeast. This progressive truncation is due to the regional southwest tilt toward the most actively subsiding portion of the basin. The lithological nature of the formations exposed below the erosion surface is depicted in Figures 122, 125, in Table 11, and on page 145. It will be noted that the Banff, Calmar, and Ireton units are softer than the interbedded limestone or dolomite formations (Rundle, Wabamum, Nisku, Leduc, and Cooking Lake). The position of the Calmar siltstone member was not mapped accurately at the time this map was prepared. Only its approximate position is indicated. The positions of Upper Devonian biohermal reef masses are also indicated on Figure 138. These bioherms have been unroofed by the pre-Cretaceous erosion surface only near the northeast portion of Figure 138. They are shown because they seem to have had some effect upon later sedimentation, partially because of their associated differential compaction effects and partially because of their distribution which seems to be linked to regional tectonic trends in the Western Canada Basin. The strongest of these trends are also found in the Laurentian shield to the northeast of the Western Canada sedimentary basin and in the Cordilleras to the southwest.

Determine: Discuss the relationship between the McMurray isochore pattern and the underlying geological and topographic picture. Bear in mind that some of the oil now found in Basal Quartz Sand oil fields may be derived through escape of oil from Mississippian and Devonian oil traps. Can you point out any areas that warrant particular attention for exploration? Figure 135 gives some idea of the type of trap occurring in the Basal Quartz Sand.

[1] NOTE: Figs. 137 and 138 were prepared several years ago and may need revision in some localities.

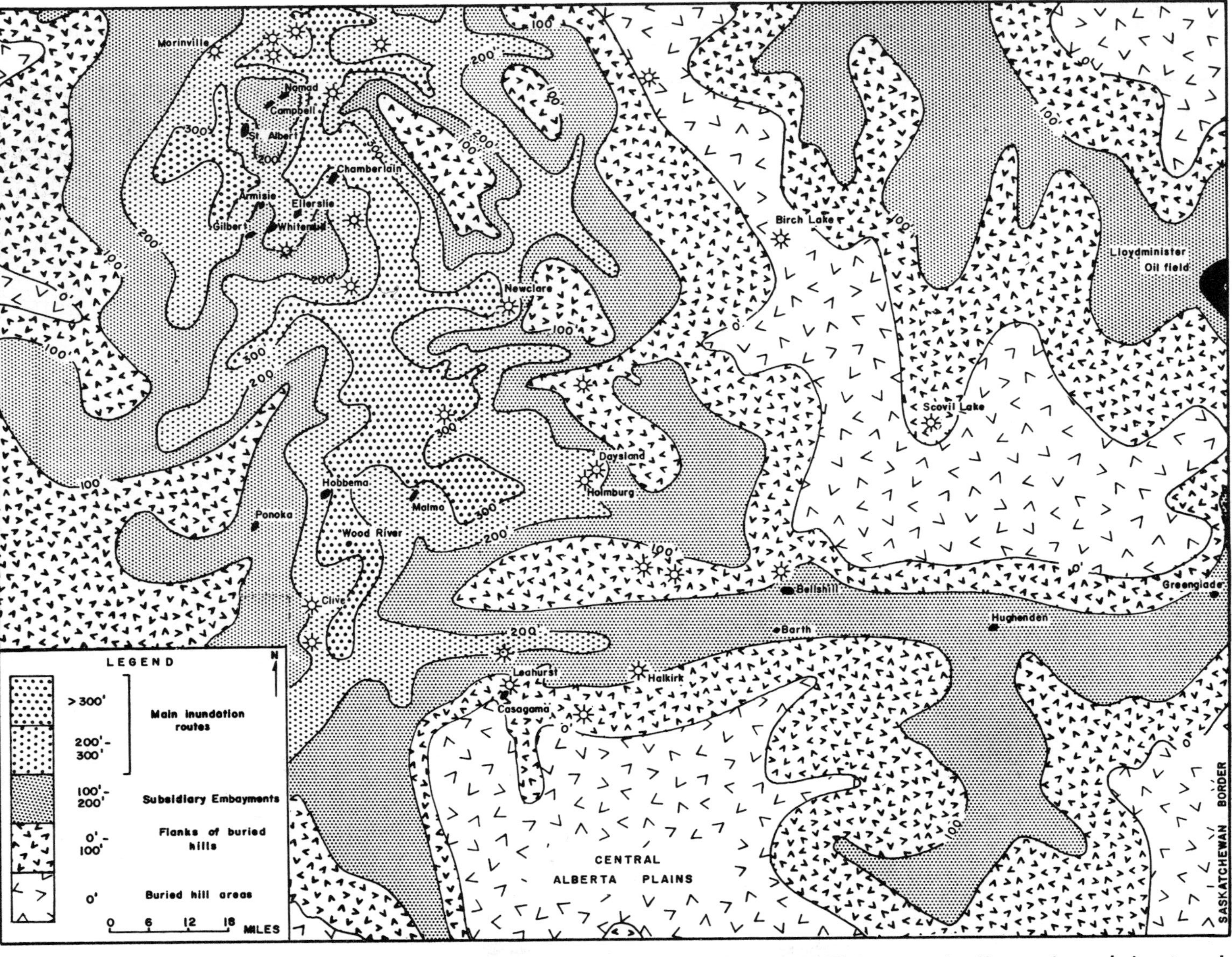

FIGURE 137. Isochore map of that portion of the McMurray formation ("Basal Quartz Sand") between the *Metacypris angularis* ostracod zone and the Paleozoic erosion surface. The positions of oil and gas fields producing from the Basal Quartz Sand are indicated.

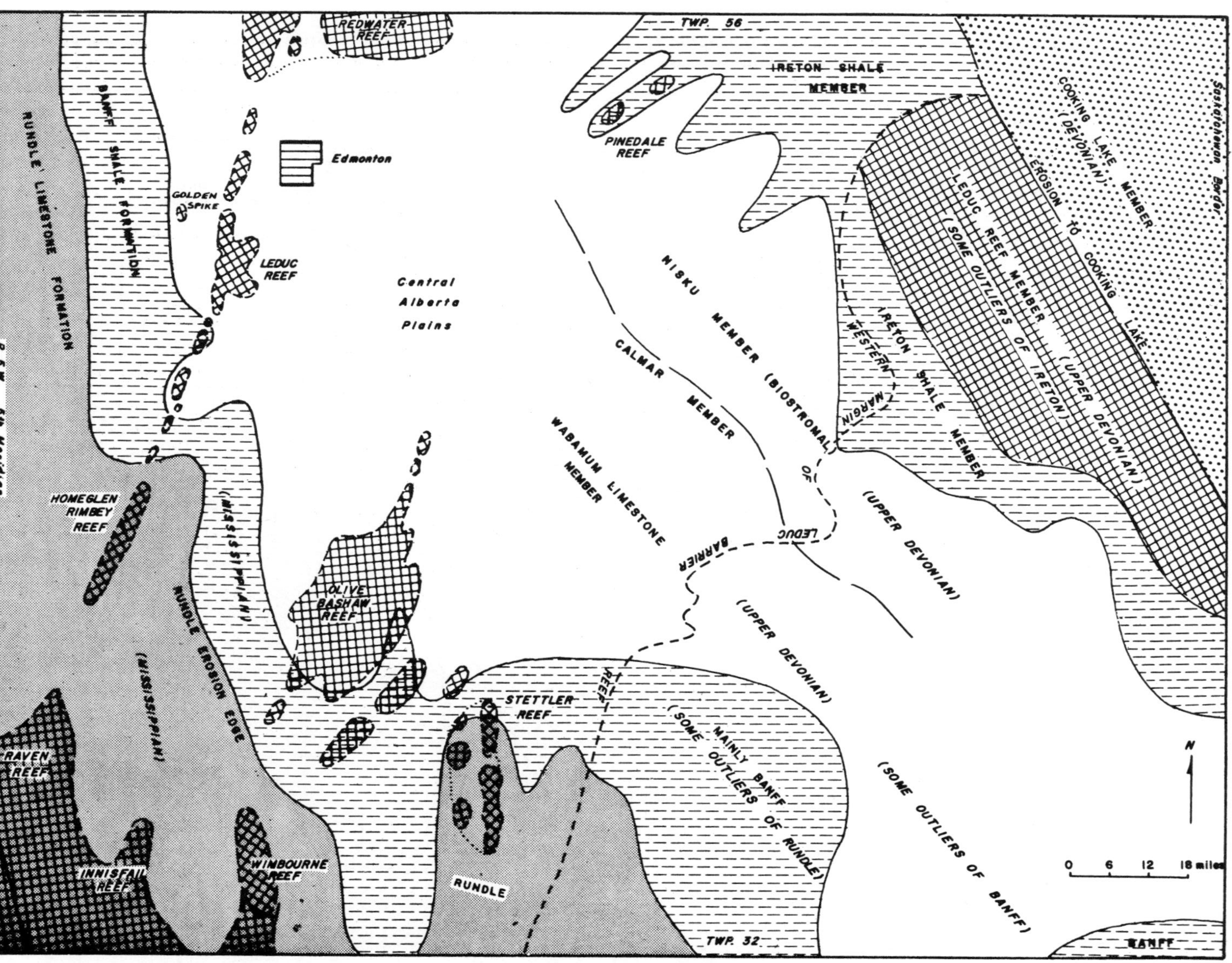

FIGURE 138. Central Alberta plains area, Canada. Illustrating the paleogeologic map at the end of the pre-Cretaceous erosion interval. The positions of upper Devonian biohermal reef areas, which are mainly uneroded by the pre-Cretaceous erosion, are shown also. These reefs are exposed at the erosion surface in the northeastern portion of the map area. This map covers the same area as Figure 137.

PROBLEM 22

THE USE OF ISOCHORE AND STRUCTURE CONTOUR MAPS

Introductory Discussion: This problem deals with the Golden Spike biohermal reef mass located near the western edge of the hinge belt in the Western Canada Basin (Figs. 73 and 138). The regional trend of the structure contours is north-northwest by south-southeast for this part of Alberta. The strata dip so gently to the west-southwest that drilling depths (isochore maps) are not usually converted to stratigraphic thicknesses (isopach maps) in thickness studies.

Figure 125 illustrates the stratigraphic relationships for the Golden Spike area. Note the facies changes in the Woodbend formation between on- and off-reef wells. These facies changes are not confined exclusively to the exact age equivalent of the Leduc facies (on-reef areas), but the reef makes its presence felt both up and down section. We shall be studying these effects by both isochore and structure contour maps. The present chapter deals with isopach maps, but it is almost impossible to solve the problems of an area with one type of map alone. Often facies and paleogeology (or subcrop) maps are needed also.

Bioherms are reefs whose vertical extent is relatively great compared to their horizontal extent. In this area the Leduc biohermal facies reaches a maximum thickness of almost 700 feet and occurs over an area of about 1 square mile. The Nisku (D_2) member, in contrast, is a biostromal blanket type of reef, extending over hundreds of square miles with only slight changes in thickness. The thickness of the Nisku is partly dependent upon internal facies changes and partly dependent upon facies changes in the underlying Woodbend formation.

The Golden Spike field was discovered by seismic prospecting, but the accompanying series of contouring exercises will show that subsurface studies can also pinpoint biohermal reef masses when sufficient off-reef well information is available. Subsurface studies are far cheaper than seismic prospecting and usually give more dependable information. Sometimes, however, the subsurface well density is insufficient to be of great value. Good seismic reflecting horizons in this region are the Blairmore top, the pre-Cretaceous unconformity, the Ireton top, the base of the Cooking Lake member.

The Leduc (D_3) top is usually difficult to detect seismically because of its proximity to the Ireton top, and in reefoid areas the Ireton top is also characterized by lack of clear-cut reflections. Thus it often becomes necessary to rely on seismic isopach (or isotime) maps.

The isotime map bracketing the interval between the pre-Cretaceous surface and the Cooking Lake shows thinning in D_3 bioherm areas due to the greater velocity in dolomite as contrasted to shale. Should erosional highs on the erosion surface coincide with biohermal areas, then a seismic masking effect would make the detection of the bioherm difficult, owing to the greater thickness of limestone which is encountered above the reef in such erosional high areas.

The erosion interval complicates things further as it served to disrupt the differential compaction history of the area. Differentional compaction recommences above the unconformity only after a thickness equivalent to the eroded thickness has accumulated. This fact should be borne in mind when interpreting isochore maps of Cretaceous formations.

Oil production in the Golden Spike field is primarily from the Leduc biohermal reef facies, but minor production is obtained from the highest portions of the Cooking Lake member where it is porous and from the highest portions of the Nisku (D_2) member where it is draped over the underlying bioherm.

Procedure: Subsurface information is provided for several formations on the accompanying maps. The following map sequence is recommended to demonstrate the great amount of information which can be obtained by a comprehensive study of this type:

1. Isochore Map of the Nisku (D_2) Member, Using Off-Reef Information (Fig. 139).
2. Structure Contour Map on Top of the Nisku (D_2) Member, Using Off-Reef Information Only (Fig. 140).
3. Structure Contour Map on Top of the Leduc (D_3) Member Where It Is Present and Elsewhere on Top of the Cooking Lake Porosity (Fig. 141).
4. Isochore Map of the Interval from the Top of the Ireton Member to the Top of the Cooking Lake Porosity, Or to the Top of the Leduc (D_3) Member Where It Is Present (Fig. 142).
5. Isochore Map of the Nisku (D_2) Member, Using All Available Well Information (Fig. 143).
6. Structure Contour Map on Top of the Nisku (D_2) Member, Using All Available Well Information (Fig. 144).
7. Isochore Map of the Interval from the Top of the Wabamum Formation (Eroded) to the Top of the Nisku (D_2) Member (Fig. 145).
8. Topographic Contours on Top of the Eroded Wabamum Limestone (Fig. 146).
9. Isochore Map of the Blairmore Formation (Fig. 147).
10. Structure Contours on Top of the Blairmore Formation (Fig. 148).
11. Isochore Map of the Interval from the Top of the First White Specks to the Top of the Second White Specks (Fig. 149).
12. Structure Contours on Top of the First White Specks Zone (Fig. 150).

Questions Based on Problem No. 22

1. Where was the high point of the reef at time of original deposition?
2. How does the present high point of the reef compare with the original high point of the reef?
3. Has there been any postdepositional regional tilting history in this area as evidenced by the maps?
4. Has there been any differential compaction in this area? If so, discuss its significance.
5. Does the Blairmore isochore map give any indication of the underlying reef? Discuss.
6. Should a seismic isotime (isochore) map between the top of the Wabamum and the top of the Cooking Lake member indicate the presence of the D_3 reef? If so, explain.
7. Can you see any reasons why a seismic isotime (isochore) map between the top of the eroded Wabamum (D_1) formation and the Beaverhill Lake formation might not indicate the presence of the D_3 reef? Explain.
8. Does the isochore map from the top of the First White Specks to the top of the Second White Specks indicate the presence of the underlying reef? Discuss the difference between this isochore map and the Blairmore isochore and the reasons for this difference.
9. Discuss each map briefly, indicating its value as an indicator of underlying reef conditions.
10. Which map gives the largest "halo" effect? In other words, which map shows the possibility of reefing farthest away from the actual reef? This is an area of greater than average off-reef information. Usually there are fewer clues available.
11. Which is the best map for reef exploration? Bear in mind that most wells which miss the reef do not penetrate more than 250–300 feet of Ireton shale before abandonment. Why is this so?

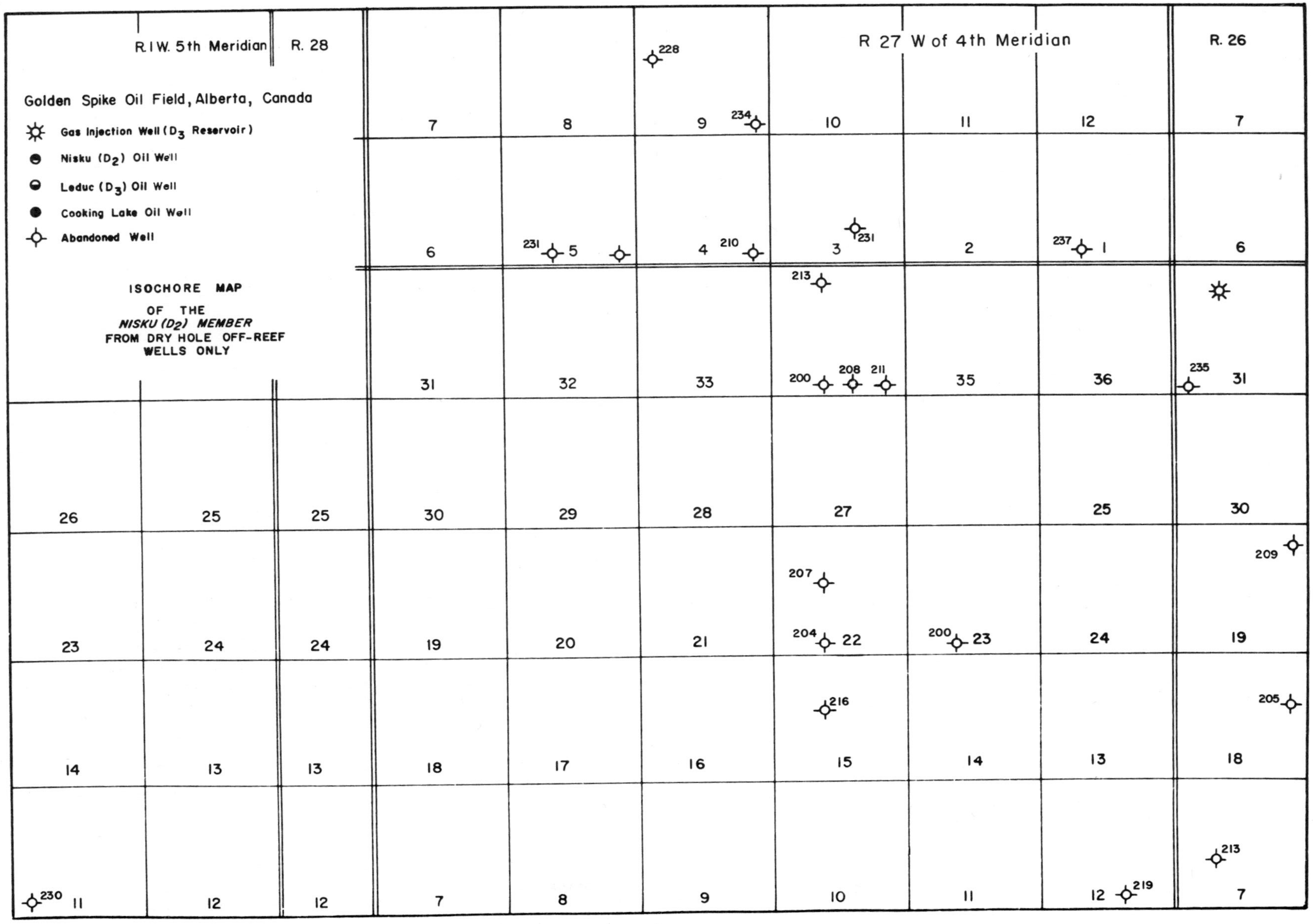

R.I W. 5th Meridian R. 28

R 27 W of 4th Meridian

R. 26

Golden Spike Oil Field, Alberta, Canada

- Gas Injection Well (D_3 Reservoir)
- Nisku (D_2) Oil Well
- Leduc (D_3) Oil Well
- Cooking Lake Oil Well
- Abandoned Well

ISOCHORE MAP
OF THE
NISKU (D_2) MEMBER
FROM DRY HOLE OFF-REEF
WELLS ONLY

FIGURE 139. For use with Problem 22.

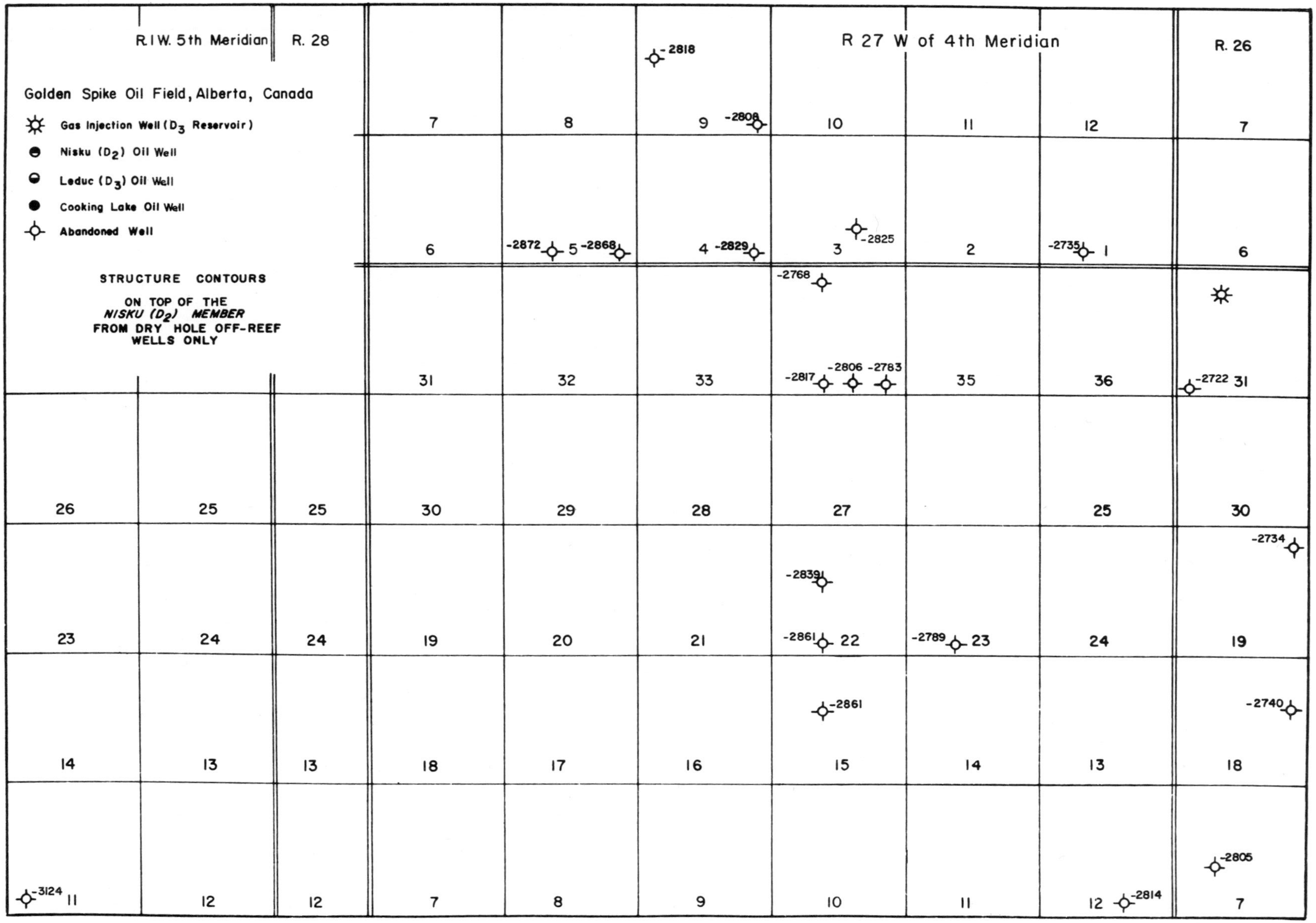

R.I W. 5th Meridian | R. 28

R 27 W of 4th Meridian

R. 26

Golden Spike Oil Field, Alberta, Canada

- Gas Injection Well (D_3 Reservoir)
- Nisku (D_2) Oil Well
- Leduc (D_3) Oil Well
- Cooking Lake Oil Well
- Abandoned Well

STRUCTURE CONTOURS

ON TOP OF THE
NISKU (D_2) MEMBER
FROM DRY HOLE OFF-REEF
WELLS ONLY

-2818
7 8 9 -2808 10 11 12 7
-2825
6 -2872 5 -2868 4 -2829 3 2 -2735 1 6
-2768
-2817 -2806 -2783
31 32 33 35 36 -2722 31
26 25 25 30 29 28 27 25 30
-2734
-2839
23 24 24 19 20 21 -2861 22 -2789 23 24 19
-2861 -2740
14 13 13 18 17 16 15 14 13 18
-2805
-3124 11 12 12 7 8 9 10 11 12 -2814 7

FIGURE 140. For use with Problem 22.

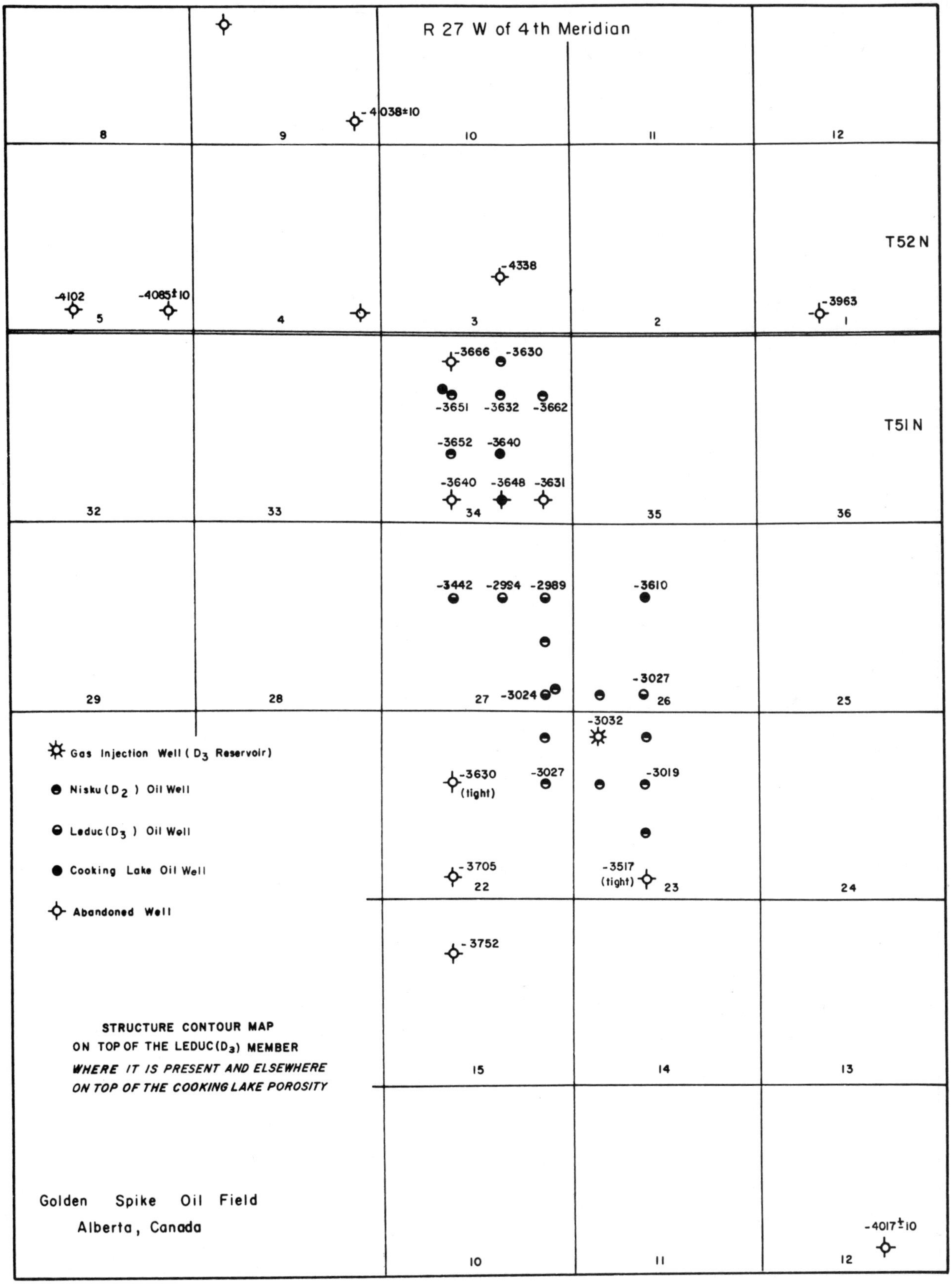
R 27 W of 4th Meridian
T52 N
T51 N
Gas Injection Well (D_3 Reservoir)
Nisku (D_2) Oil Well
Leduc (D_3) Oil Well
Cooking Lake Oil Well
Abandoned Well
STRUCTURE CONTOUR MAP
ON TOP OF THE LEDUC (D_3) MEMBER
WHERE IT IS PRESENT AND ELSEWHERE
ON TOP OF THE COOKING LAKE POROSITY
Golden Spike Oil Field
Alberta, Canada
-4038±10
-4338
-4102
-4085±10
-3963
-3666
-3630
-3651
-3632
-3662
-3652
-3640
-3640
-3648
-3631
-3442
-2984
-2989
-3610
-3027
-3024
-3032
-3630 (tight)
-3027
-3019
-3705
-3517 (tight)
-3752
-4017±10

FIGURE 141. For use with Problem 22.

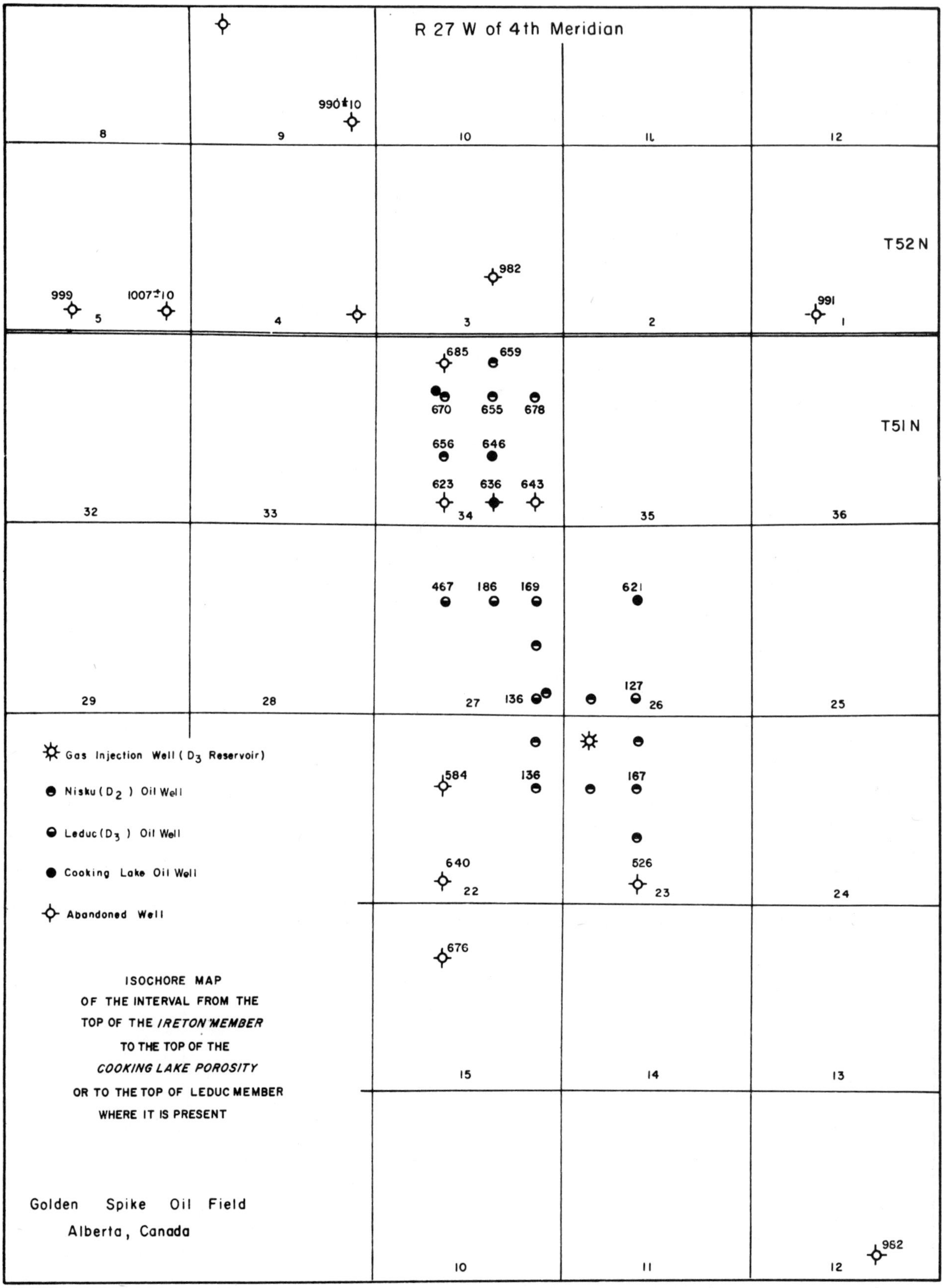
R 27 W of 4th Meridian
T52 N
T51 N
990±10
999
1007±10
982
991
685
659
670
655
678
656
646
623
636
643
467
186
169
621
136
127
584
136
167
640
526
676
962
8
9
10
11
12
5
4
3
2
1
32
33
34
35
36
29
28
27
26
25
22
23
24
15
14
13
10
11
12
Gas Injection Well (D_3 Reservoir)
Nisku (D_2) Oil Well
Leduc (D_3) Oil Well
Cooking Lake Oil Well
Abandoned Well
ISOCHORE MAP
OF THE INTERVAL FROM THE
TOP OF THE IRETON MEMBER
TO THE TOP OF THE
COOKING LAKE POROSITY
OR TO THE TOP OF LEDUC MEMBER
WHERE IT IS PRESENT
Golden Spike Oil Field
Alberta, Canada

FIGURE 142. For use with Problem 22.

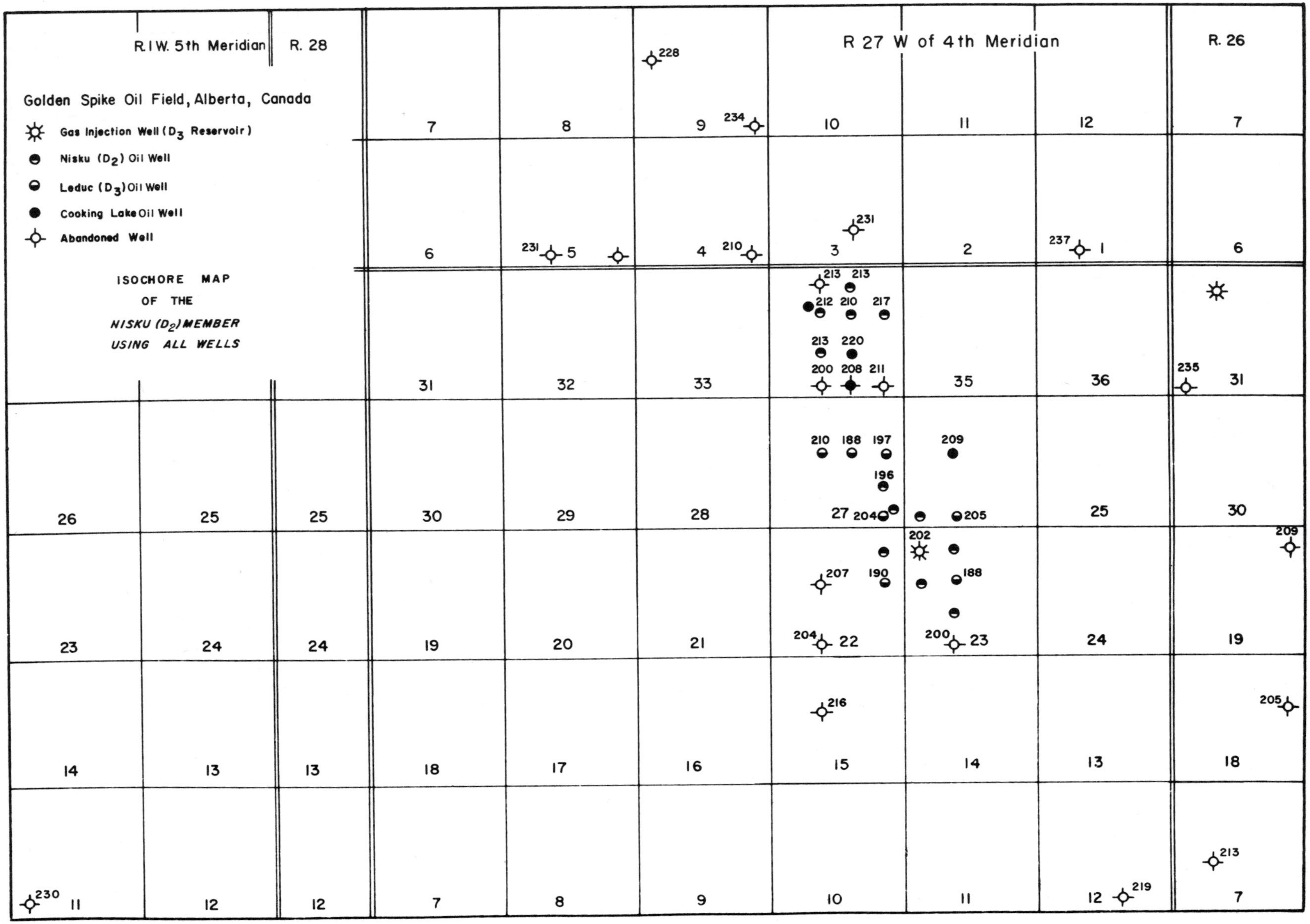

R.1 W. 5th Meridian | R. 28 | R 27 W of 4th Meridian | R. 26

Golden Spike Oil Field, Alberta, Canada

- Gas Injection Well (D_3 Reservoir)
- Nisku (D_2) Oil Well
- Leduc (D_3) Oil Well
- Cooking Lake Oil Well
- Abandoned Well

ISOCHORE MAP
OF THE
NISKU (D_2) MEMBER
USING ALL WELLS

FIGURE 143. **For use with Problem 22.**

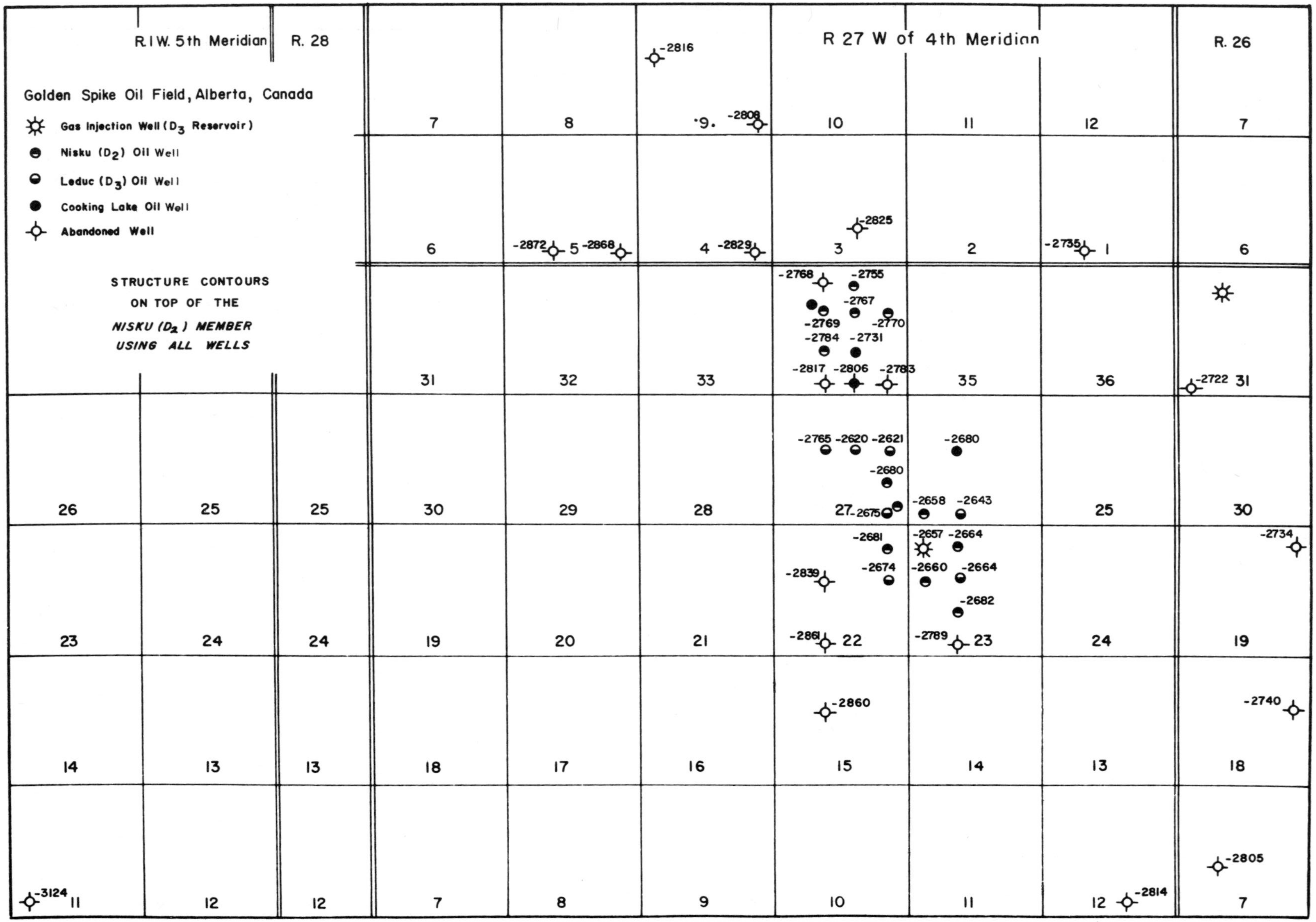
R.1 W. 5th Meridian
R. 28
R 27 W of 4th Meridian
R. 26
Golden Spike Oil Field, Alberta, Canada
Gas Injection Well (D_3 Reservoir)
Nisku (D_2) Oil Well
Leduc (D_3) Oil Well
Cooking Lake Oil Well
Abandoned Well
STRUCTURE CONTOURS
ON TOP OF THE
NISKU (D_2) MEMBER
USING ALL WELLS
-2816
-2808
-2825
-2872
-2868
-2829
-2735
-2768
-2755
-2767
-2769
-2770
-2784
-2731
-2817
-2806
-2783
-2722
-2765
-2620
-2621
-2680
-2680
-2675
-2658
-2643
-2681
-2657
-2664
-2839
-2674
-2660
-2664
-2682
-2861
-2789
-2734
-2860
-2740
-2805
-3124
-2814

FIGURE 144. For use with Problem 22.

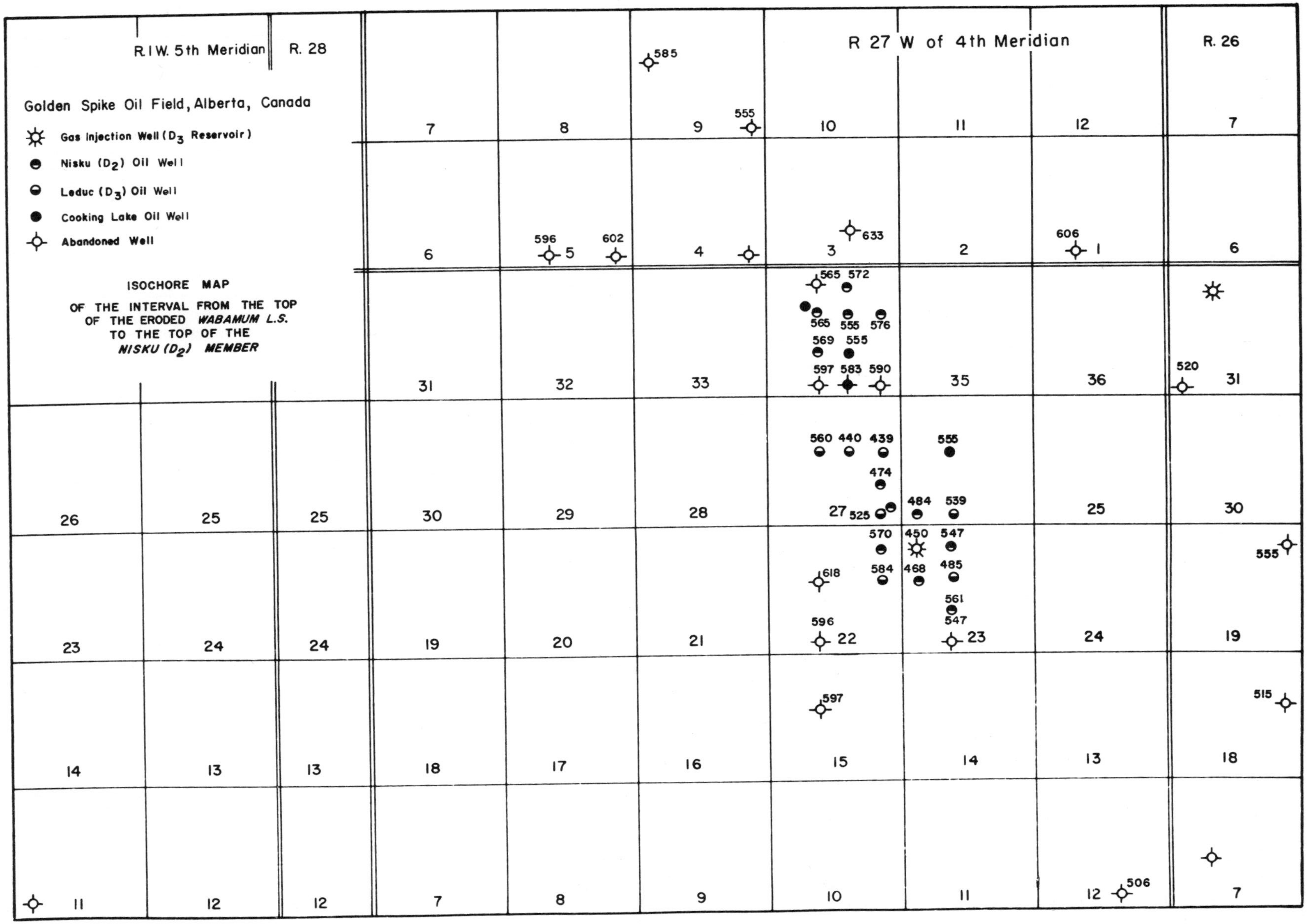

R.1W. 5th Meridian | R. 28 | R 27 W of 4th Meridian | R. 26

Golden Spike Oil Field, Alberta, Canada

- Gas Injection Well (D_3 Reservoir)
- Nisku (D_2) Oil Well
- Leduc (D_3) Oil Well
- Cooking Lake Oil Well
- Abandoned Well

ISOCHORE MAP

OF THE INTERVAL FROM THE TOP OF THE ERODED *WABAMUM L.S.* TO THE TOP OF THE *NISKU (D_2) MEMBER*

FIGURE 145. For use with Problem 22.

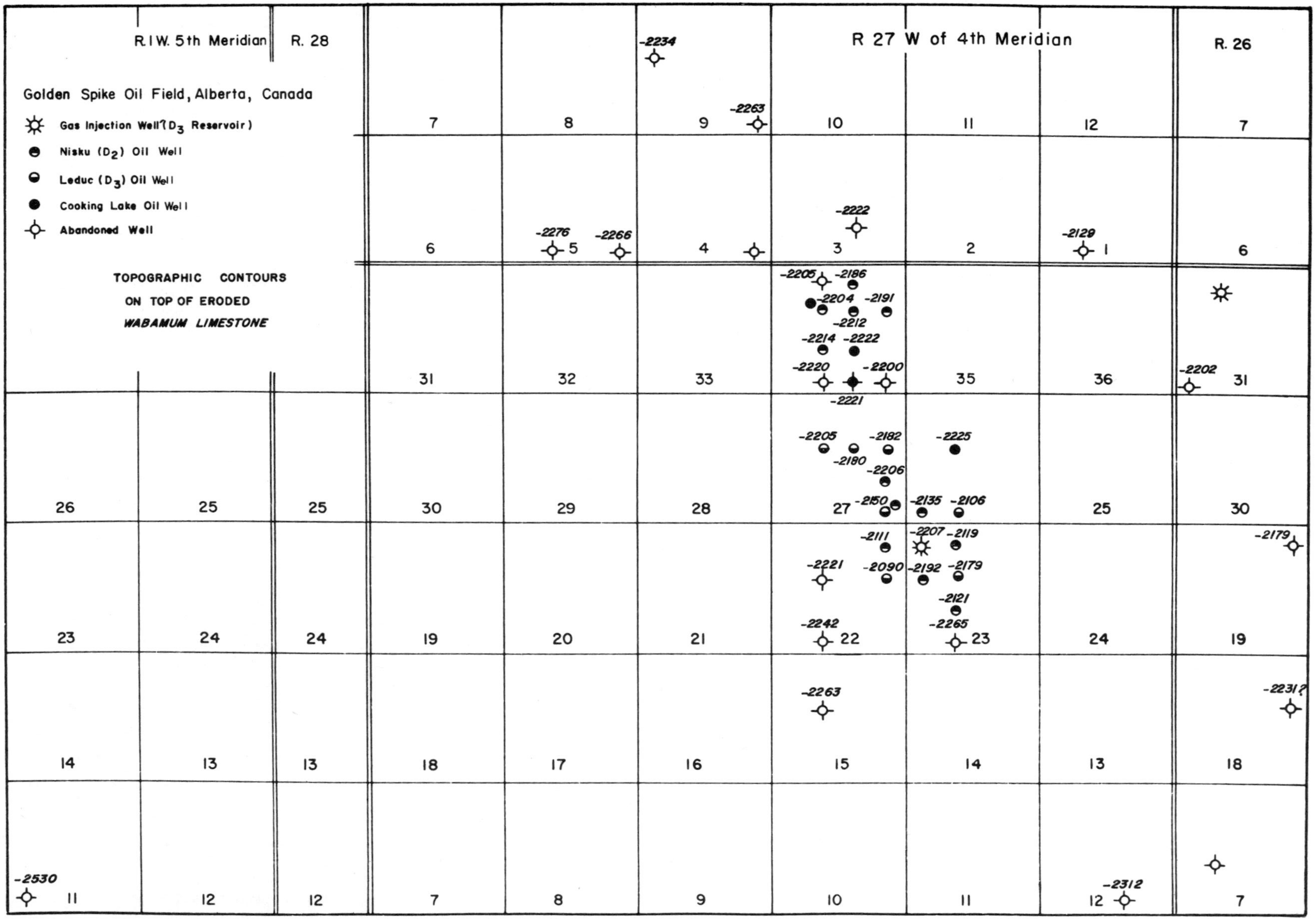

R.1 W. 5th Meridian | R. 28 | R 27 W of 4th Meridian | R. 26

Golden Spike Oil Field, Alberta, Canada

- Gas Injection Well? (D_3 Reservoir)
- Nisku (D_2) Oil Well
- Leduc (D_3) Oil Well
- Cooking Lake Oil Well
- Abandoned Well

TOPOGRAPHIC CONTOURS
ON TOP OF ERODED
WABAMUM LIMESTONE

FIGURE 146. For use with Problem 22.

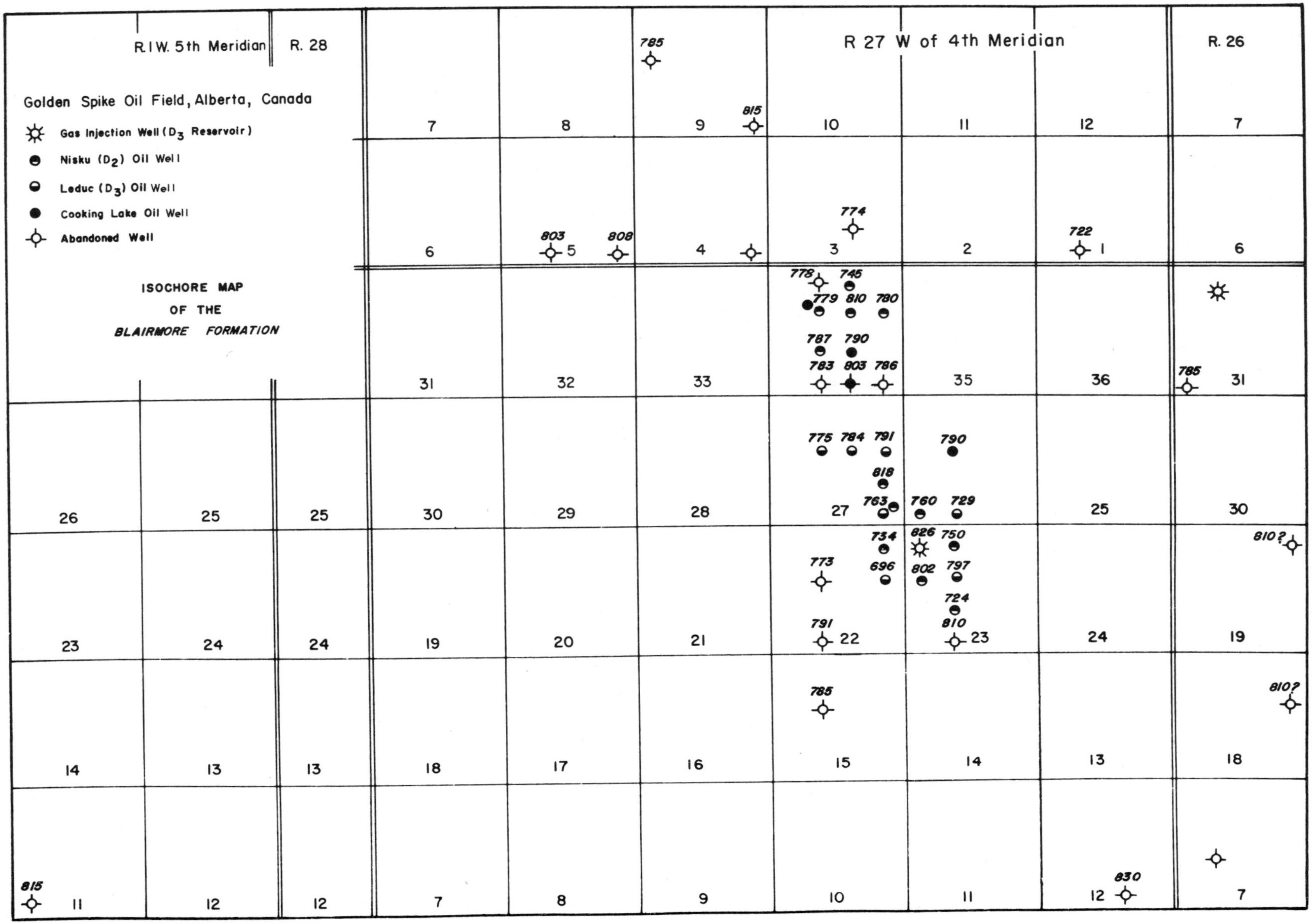

R.I W. 5th Meridian
R. 28
R 27 W of 4th Meridian
R. 26
Golden Spike Oil Field, Alberta, Canada
Gas Injection Well (D3 Reservoir)
Nisku (D2) Oil Well
Leduc (D3) Oil Well
Cooking Lake Oil Well
Abandoned Well
ISOCHORE MAP
OF THE
BLAIRMORE FORMATION
785
815
774
803
808
722
778
745
779
810
780
787
790
783
803
786
785
775
784
791
790
818
763
760
729
734
826
750
773
696
802
797
724
791
810
810?
810?
785
815
830

FIGURE 147. For use with Problem 22.

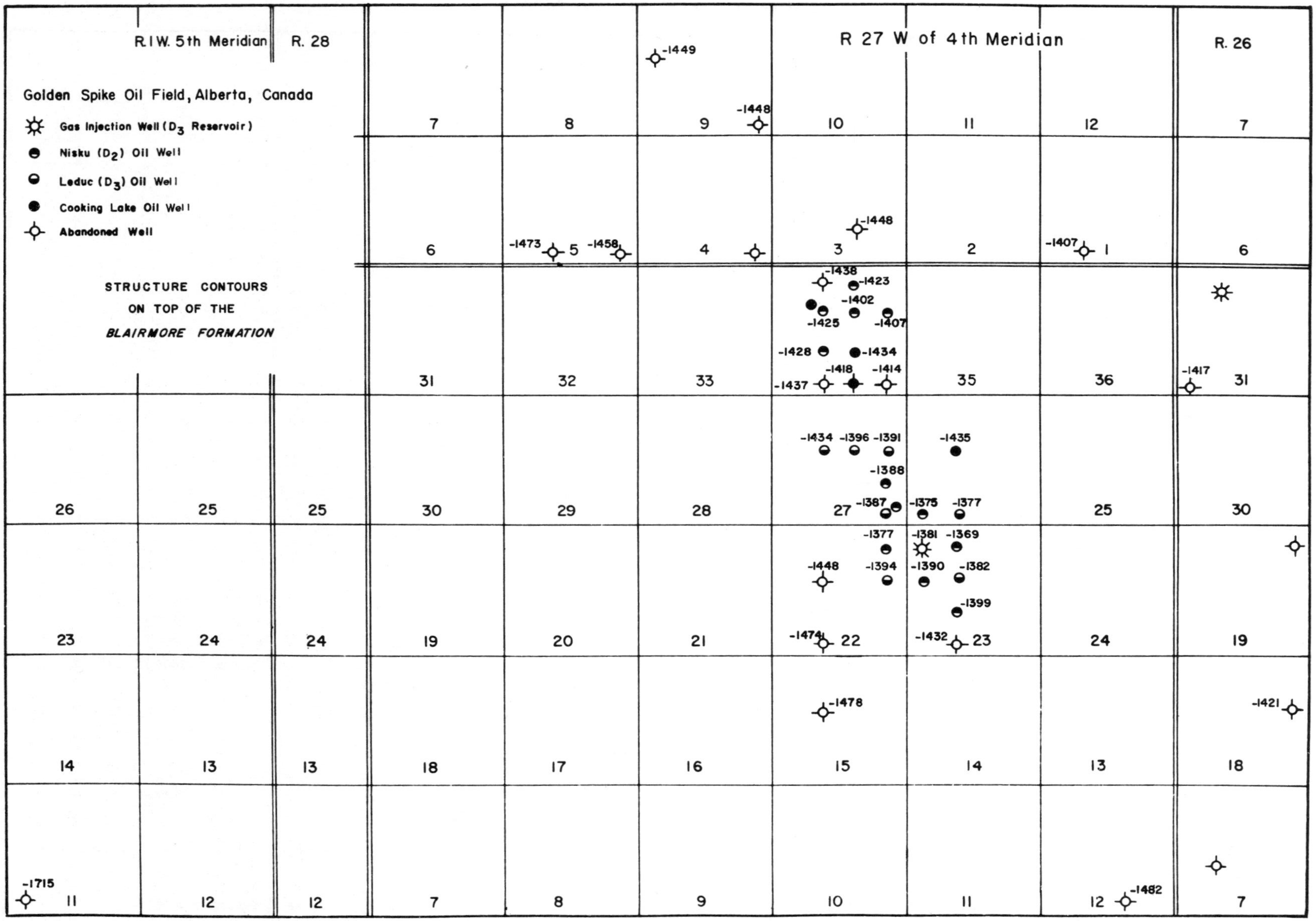

R.1 W. 5th Meridian | R. 28

R 27 W of 4th Meridian

R. 26

Golden Spike Oil Field, Alberta, Canada

- Gas Injection Well (D_3 Reservoir)
- Nisku (D_2) Oil Well
- Leduc (D_3) Oil Well
- Cooking Lake Oil Well
- Abandoned Well

STRUCTURE CONTOURS
ON TOP OF THE
BLAIRMORE FORMATION

FIGURE 148. For use with Problem 22.

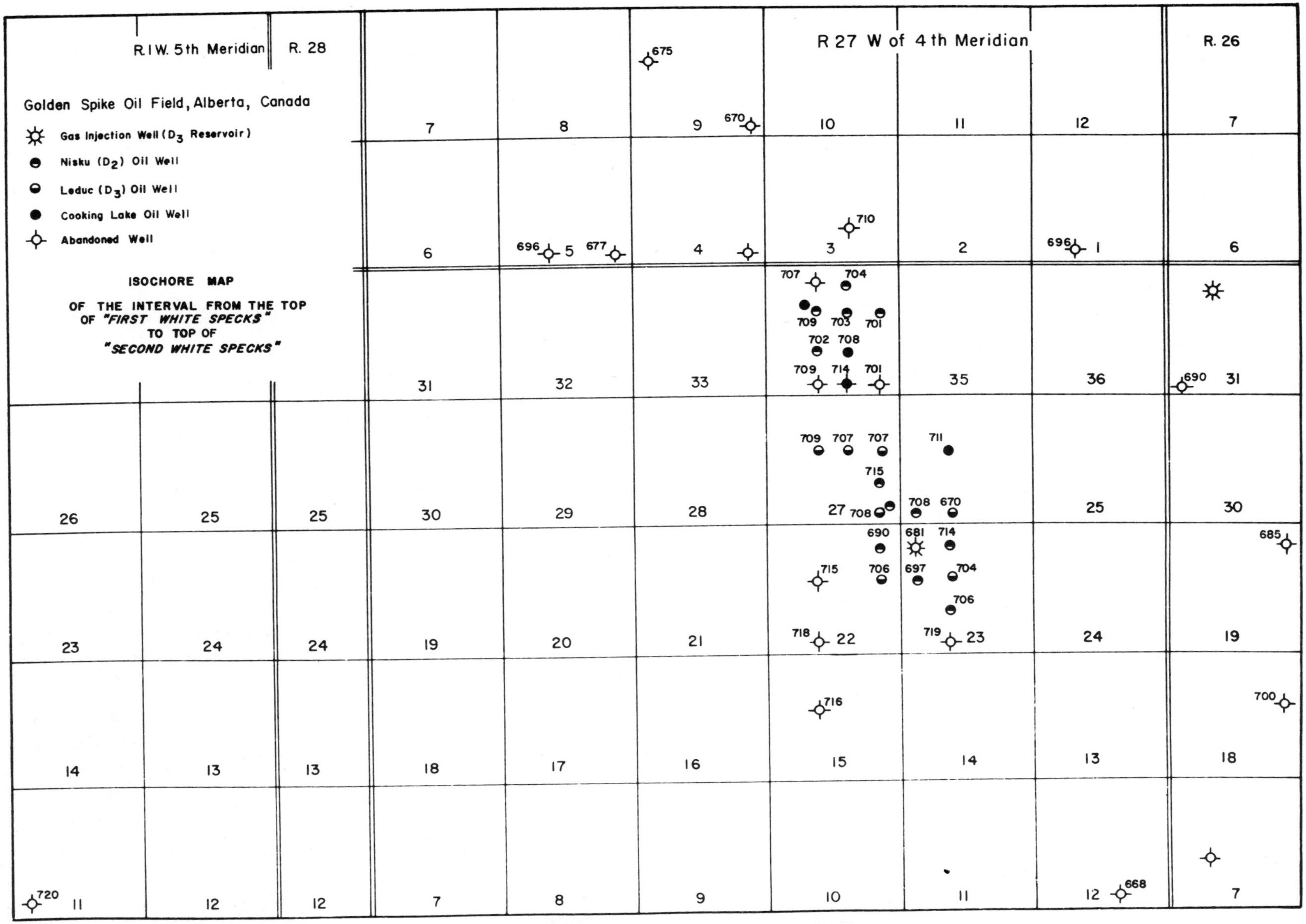

R.1W. 5th Meridian | R. 28 | R 27 W of 4th Meridian | R. 26

Golden Spike Oil Field, Alberta, Canada

- Gas Injection Well (D_3 Reservoir)
- Nisku (D_2) Oil Well
- Leduc (D_3) Oil Well
- Cooking Lake Oil Well
- Abandoned Well

ISOCHORE MAP

OF THE INTERVAL FROM THE TOP OF *"FIRST WHITE SPECKS"* TO TOP OF *"SECOND WHITE SPECKS"*

FIGURE 149. For use with Problem 22.

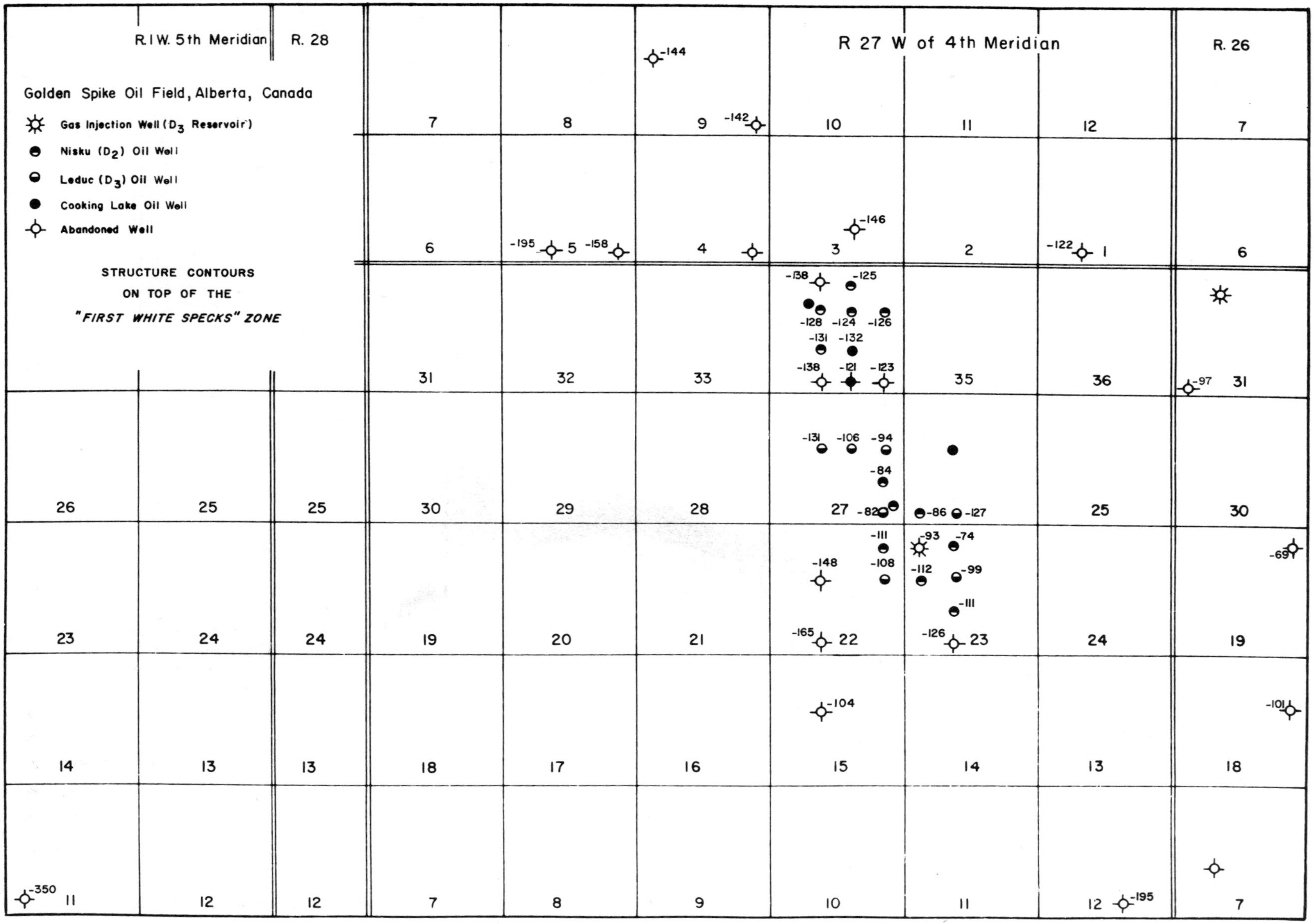

R.I W. 5th Meridian | R. 28

R 27 W of 4th Meridian

R. 26

Golden Spike Oil Field, Alberta, Canada

- Gas Injection Well (D_3 Reservoir)
- Nisku (D_2) Oil Well
- Leduc (D_3) Oil Well
- Cooking Lake Oil Well
- Abandoned Well

STRUCTURE CONTOURS
ON TOP OF THE
"FIRST WHITE SPECKS" ZONE

FIGURE 150. For use with Problem 22.

The stratigraphic section for the Golden Spike area is illustrated by Figure 125, Chapter 4, which shows an on-reef well and two off-reef wells near Golden Spike. This figure illustrated the subsurface geology below the top of the Pelican (Viking sandstone) formation. That portion of the stratigraphic section above the Pelican formation is summarized briefly as follows:

Age	Formation	Approximate Thickness	Lithology
Upper Cretaceous	Belly River formation	1000′	Sandstone (graywacke in nature), gray, nonmarine for the most part; alternating with gray and green shale, for the most part marine.
Upper Cretaceous	Lea Park formation	500′	Shale, gray, marine, locally silty, some iron stone nodules.
Upper Cretaceous	Colorado group	1300′	Shale, dark gray, locally bentonitic, some thin siltstone and sandstone lenses, some iron stone nodules, group is marine. Various members and zones within the Colorado group are: *First White Speckled Shale zone* (80′) *Second White Speckled Shale zone* (180′) *Fish Scale zone (Upper Cretaceous)* (Variable thickness) *Viking Sand Member (Lower Cretaceous)* (Variable thickness) The First White Speckled Shale zone occurs at the top of the Colorado group and the Viking sandstone occurs near the base of the group. The stratigraphic interval from the top of the First White Speckled Shale zone to the top of the Second White Speckled Shale zone is approximately 700′. The stratigraphic interval from the top of the Second White Speckled Shale zone to the base of the Fish Scale zone is approximately 310′. The stratigraphic interval from the base of the Fish Scale zone to the top of the Viking Sand member is 120′.

Because of the regional tilt which has occurred in this area, and because of the lack of well information for Sections 13, 24, 25, 35, 36 of Township 51, Range 27, west of the 4th Meridian, the student may wish to draw the structural maps to show the reef mass as a structural nose, instead of as an isolated high. For this reason each structure contour map is preceded by its equivalent isochore map. A little thought will then indicate whether a structural nose or isolated high should be drawn. The student will thus see that it is impossible to draw good structure contour interpretations without full knowledge of thickness conditions.

PROBLEM 23

OIL RESERVE ESTIMATES

Principles Involved: Many geologists, although well prepared to explore for new oil fields, do not have adequate economic or evaluation perspective. Consequently they may recommend exploration programs in areas where the economic factors do not justify production even after a discovery has been made. Training in reserve estimation and property evaluation gives a geologist the required perspective.

The estimation of the recoverable oil content of a producing property is probably the most important step in the total evaluation of the worth of the property.

Oil reserve estimates may be made by several methods involving the following:

1. The volumetric method.
2. The pressure decline curve method.
3. The material balance method.

The latter two methods give a more realistic determination but can be used ordinarily only when the property's production history is well known and well recorded. The volumetric method can be used early in the productive life of a property provided certain basic reservoir information is available. The volumetric method is based largely upon an estimation of the available pore space in the reservoir, and this estimate is actually made by means of isopaching the net pay thickness of the reservoir. Experience in isopaching is thus invaluable and for this reason an exercise in oil reserve estimation is included at this point. The ensuing problem is a sequel to the isochore-structure contour study of the Golden Spike reef, and the student should be familiar with that area before attacking this problem.

The geologist is usually better qualified than the petroleum engineer to construct isopach or isochore maps because such maps depend upon the intricacies of the geological structures being mapped. Although the remainder of the property evaluation is more or less a mathematical calculation, a high degree of interpretive ability is required at the isopach stage. The geologist is commonly the only man well qualified to distinguish between proven, probable, and possible reserves.

The problem which follows is based mainly upon the isochore map of the Leduc (D_3) section above the original D_3 oil/water interface (Fig. 151). No reserves can be assigned, however, to those wells with a D_3 section above the oil/water interface if these wells were abandoned. It is probable that in these wells where the D_3 reef was developed only partially, the porosity was insufficiently developed for commercial production.

In making a reserve estimate and property evaluation, it is usually desirable to have reservoir information for the property similar to that indicated in Table 13. Not all of the information is always available, and in some cases a part of the information is subject to change. The recovery factor is particularly difficult to determine early in the life of a field and is based commonly upon analogy with other similar fields. The following formula is used in the volumetric determination of oil reserves:

$$Bbls = A \times Th \times por \times OS \times SF \times RF \times 7758$$

$Bbls$ = Recoverable barrels of stock tank oil.
A = Area of proven tract in acres.
Th = Reservoir thickness in net feet.
por = Porosity expressed as a fraction of the rock volume.
OS = Oil saturation expressed as a percentage of the pore space.
SF = Shrinkage factor expressed as a percentage of the volume occupied by the oil in place. It allows for the decrease in volume between oil in the reservoir and

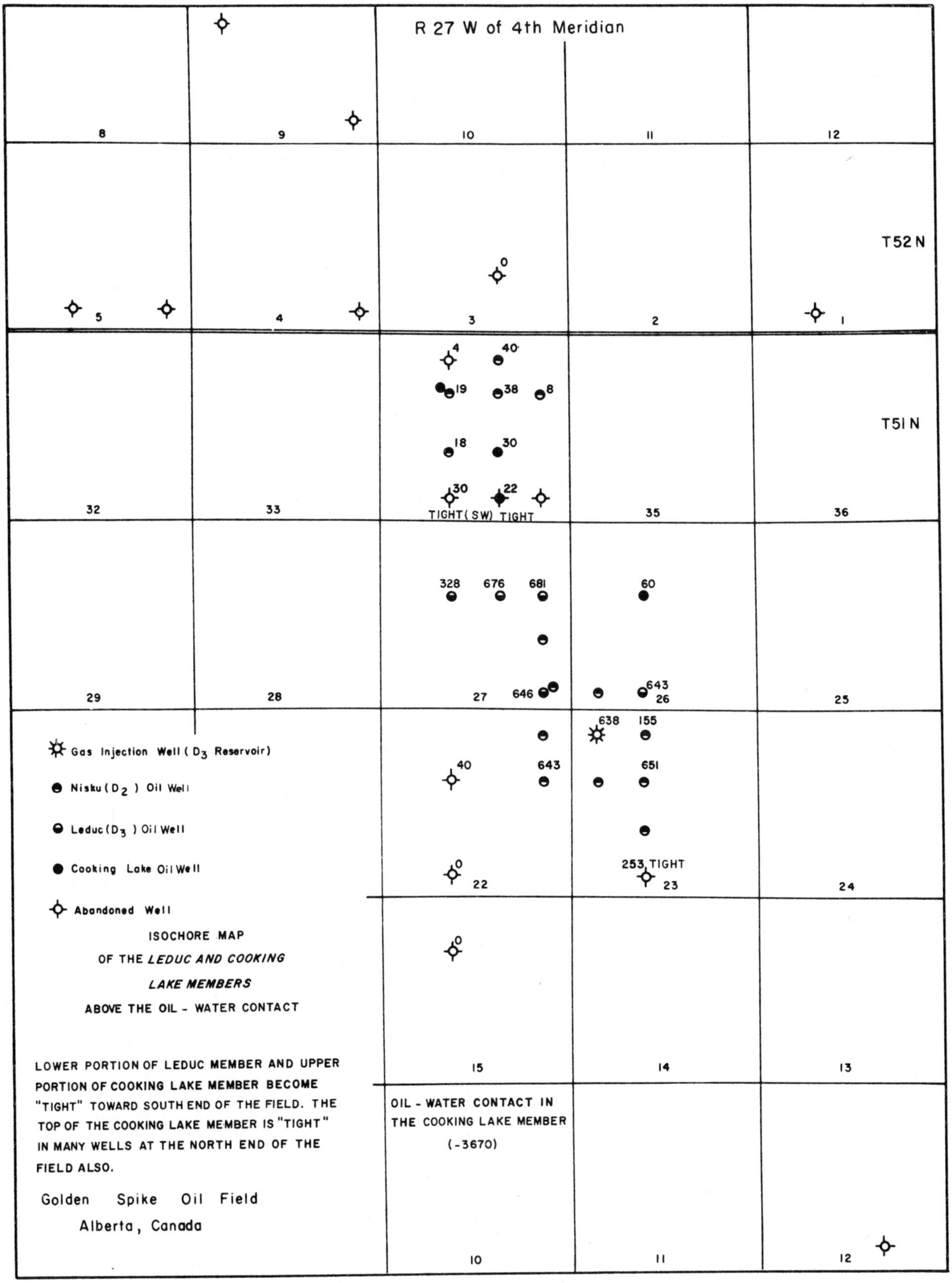

R 27 W of 4th Meridian

T52 N

T51 N

8 9 10 11 12

5 4 3 2 1

32 33 35 36

29 28 27 26 25

22 23 24

15 14 13

10 11 12

0

4 40

19 38 8

18 30

30 22

TIGHT (SW) TIGHT

328 676 681 60

646 643

638 155

40 643 651

0

253 TIGHT

0

Gas Injection Well (D_3 Reservoir)

Nisku (D_2) Oil Well

Leduc (D_3) Oil Well

Cooking Lake Oil Well

Abandoned Well

ISOCHORE MAP

OF THE *LEDUC AND COOKING LAKE MEMBERS*

ABOVE THE OIL - WATER CONTACT

LOWER PORTION OF LEDUC MEMBER AND UPPER PORTION OF COOKING LAKE MEMBER BECOME "TIGHT" TOWARD SOUTH END OF THE FIELD. THE TOP OF THE COOKING LAKE MEMBER IS "TIGHT" IN MANY WELLS AT THE NORTH END OF THE FIELD ALSO.

OIL - WATER CONTACT IN THE COOKING LAKE MEMBER (-3670)

Golden Spike Oil Field
Alberta, Canada

FIGURE 151. For use with Problem 23.

oil in the tank at surface, owing to escape of solution gas which occurs when the oil is brought to the surface.

RF = Recovery factor expressed as a percentage of the total oil reserves in place. The natural reservoir drive mechanism permits the extraction of only a percentage of the total oil in the place.

7758 = Barrels (of 42 gallons each) per acre-foot of volume.

TABLE 13. Golden Spike Oil Field—Leduc (D_3) Reservoir Data

Lithology of reservoir	Limestone
Average porosity	9.16%
Average permeability (radial)	1000 md. (estimated)
Average permeability (vertical)	10 md. (estimated)
Connate water	20%
Shrinkage factor	0.76
Recovery mechanism	Solution gas
Estimated recovery factor (primary)	35 to 50%
Estimated recovery factor (secondary)	65 to 70%
Estimated life in years (primary)	Dependent on proration
Initial gas/oil ratio	400 cu. ft. per bbl. (April, 1949) (14.4 psia and 60°F.)
Current gas/oil ratio	457 cu. ft. per bbl. (Oct., 1957)
Initial water/oil ratio	.001 bbl. per bbl.
Current water/oil ratio	.001 bbl. per bbl. (only sediment)
Initial reservoir pressure	2095 psig (April, 1949)
Saturation pressure	1385 psig
Current reservoir pressure	1657 psig (Sept., 1957)
Reservoir temperature	154° F. — 3300 ft. (subsea)
Average depth to midpoint of producing zone	5600 ft.
Gravity of oil	37.2° API
Pour point	— 5°F.
Sulphur content	0.2%
Wellhead price of crude	$2.50 (at time of field development)
Wellhead price of crude	$2.65 (Dec., 1957)
Average thickness of productive zone	520 feet
Original gas/oil interface	Not present
Original oil/water interface	—3670 (is in Cooking Lake member)
Cost per completed well	$75,000.00 (at time of field development)

The reserve estimate may also be accomplished by using the accompanying alignment diagram (Fig. 152) which is self-explanatory.

Data Provided: Reservoir data for the Golden Spike field is provided in Table 13. Net pay data for the Leduc (D_3) reservoir is provided in Figure 151. The writer is indebted to Imperial Oil Ltd., which kindly provided him with some of the reservoir information and which provided electric-log coverage for all of the wells in the field area. Figure 153 is a reservoir performance chart for the Golden Spike field. This chart is not used in the volumetric method of oil reserve calculation, but it would be essential in the pressure decline method. It is provided to give the student additional background data for this field.

In a reservoir such as the Leduc (D_3) at Golden Spike, which does not have a uniform pay thickness, it is useful to first determine the number of recoverable barrels per foot of pay section for any 40-acre tract. Then, after isopaching the pay section map (Fig. 151), assign an estimated pay thickness to each legal subdivision (40 acres). Multiply this thickness figure by the previously established value of recoverable barrels per foot of pay for

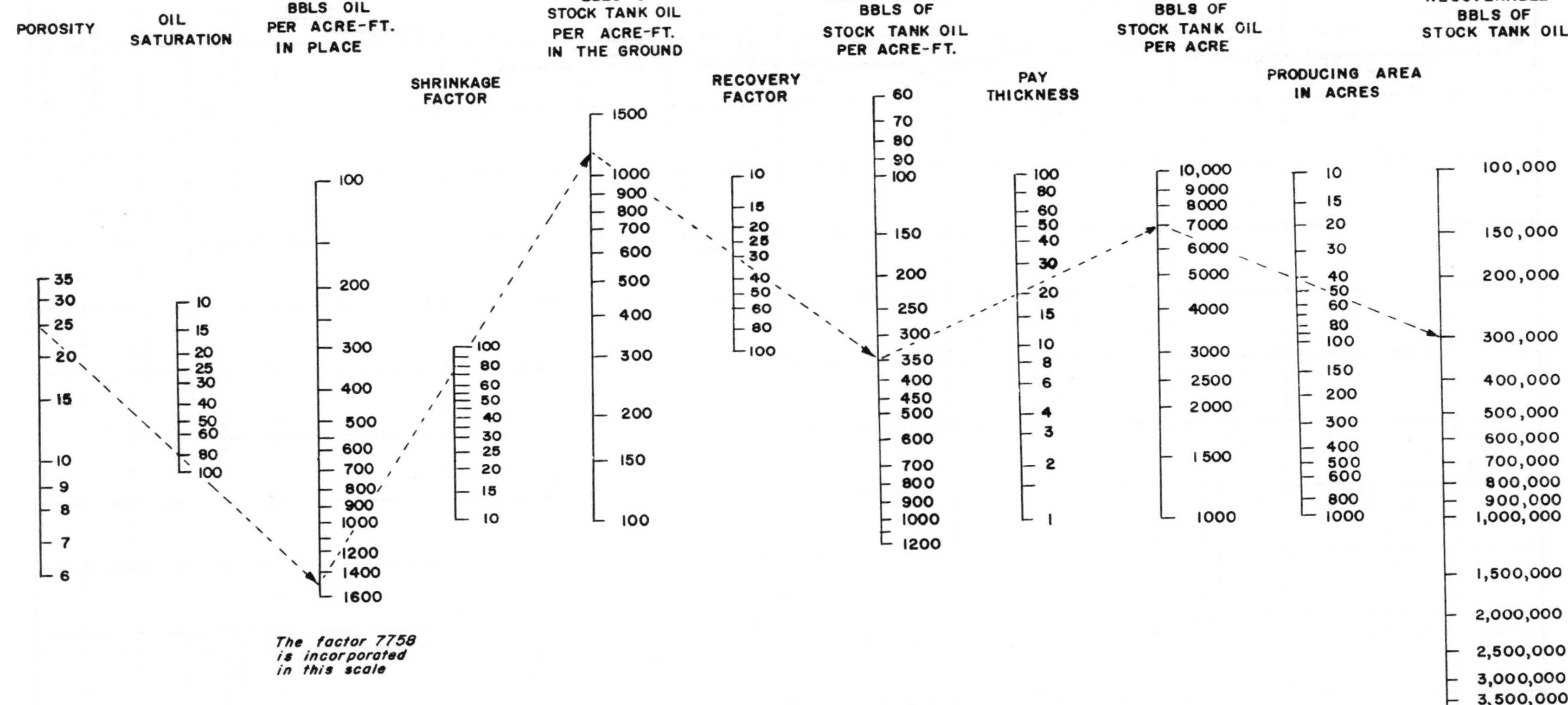

FIGURE 152. Alignment diagram for calculating oil reserves by the volumetric method. The following example (see dashed lines on diagram) will serve to illustrate the use of this diagram: Porosity = 25 per cent, oil saturation = 80 per cent, shrinkage factor = .80, recovery factor = 30 per cent, pay thickness = 20 feet, producing area = 40 acres. Answer = 300,000 bbls. of recoverable stock tank oil.

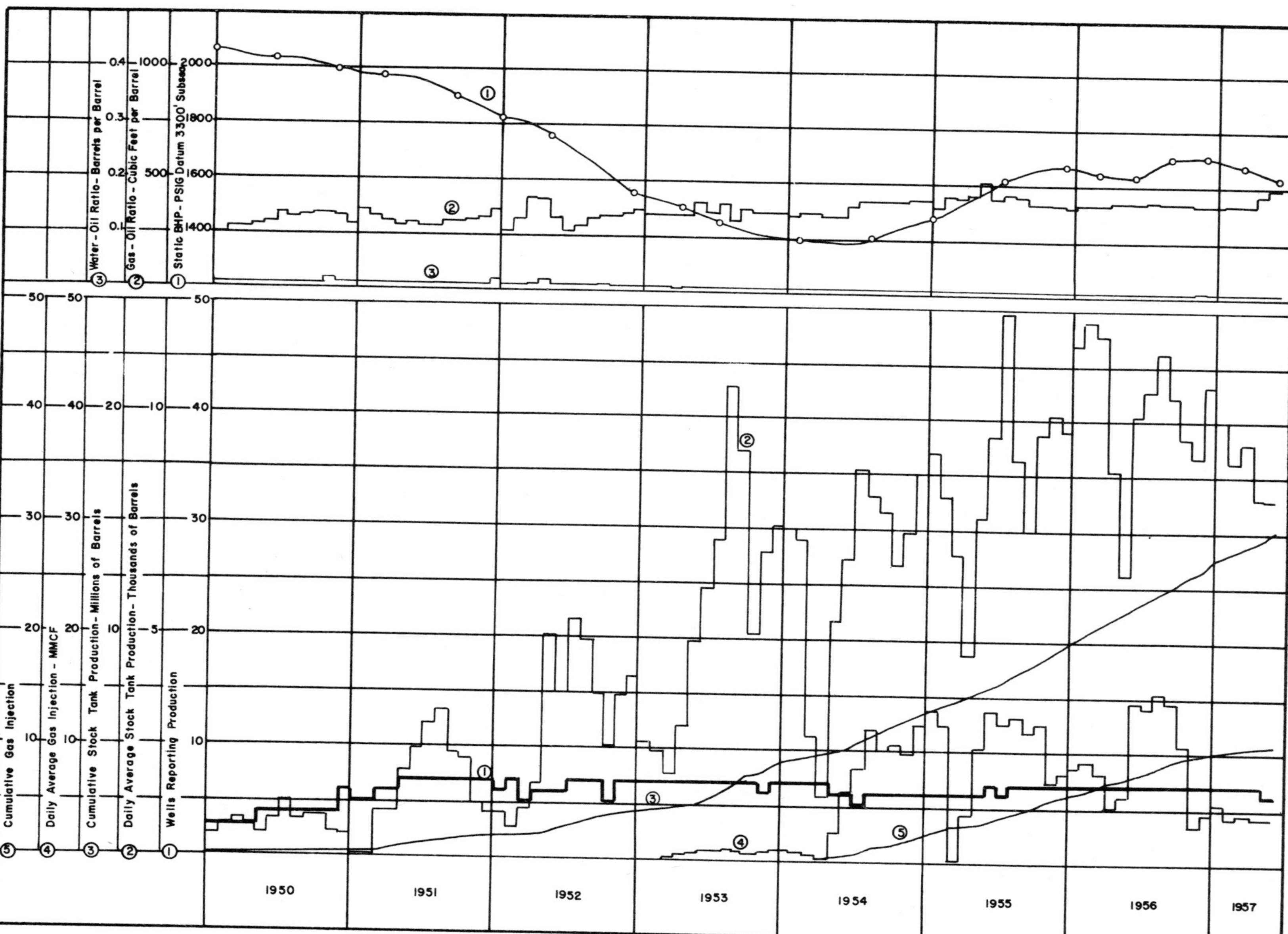

FIGURE 153. **Reservoir performance chart for the Golden Spike Oil field (D_3 reservoir), Alberta, Canada.**

that 40-acre tract. Add up the results for every legal subdivision above the zero isochore line and this will give the total reserve estimate for the reservoir. Not every potential drill site has a well on it, as some drainage of these sites is expected from adjoining wells.

Determine: The total Leduc (D_3) recoverable reserves at Golden Spike (entire area within the zero isochore line) prior to any depletion.

Questions Based on Problem No. 23

1. What is the figure of recoverable barrels per acre-foot in this reservoir?
2. What would be the gross value of the best D_3 well in this field (40-acre drainage)?
3. What would be the value of the D_3 recoverable reserves at Golden Spike after development costs?
4. What would be the minimum D_3 net pay thickness necessary to pay for development costs of one well?

References

Badgley, Peter C. (1952), Notes on the Subsurface Stratigraphy and Oil and Gas Geology of the Lower Cretaceous Series in Central Alberta, *Geol. Surv. Can.*, Paper 52–11.

Paine, P. (1942), *Oil Property Valuation*, John Wiley & Sons, Inc., 204 pp.

CHAPTER 6

Isometric Projections and Ore Reserve Estimations

Principles Involved

A block diagram illustrates the relationship between the surface of the ground and subsurface structure by using an imaginary block cut out of the earth's crust. The top of the block shows an aerial view of the geological and topographical features of the surface; the sides of the block present the underlying structural features. A block diagram thus presents a three-dimensional picture which is easily understood by those not familiar with the area or even with geology.

Before geology and topography can be drawn in block diagram, it is necessary to construct the block diagram itself. This may be done either by means of isometric projection or by perspective drawing. Perspective is the apparent relationship which exists between position and distance. Thus the back of a block diagram appears smaller in a perspective diagram (Fig. 154) than it does in an isometric projection. The area of the front of the block is equal to the area of the back in the latter case.

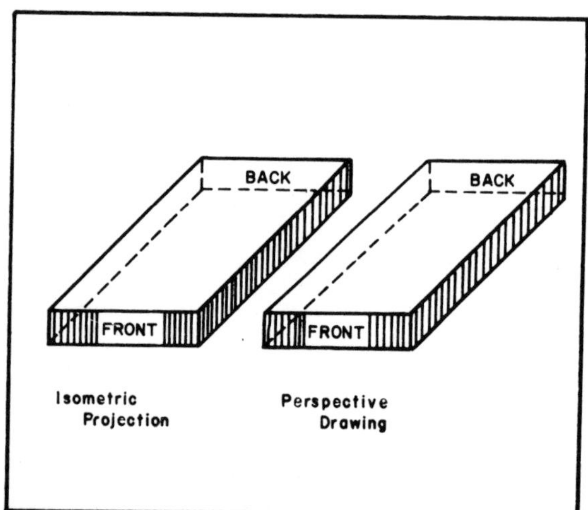

FIGURE 154. Showing the difference between isometric and perspective projections.

Isometric diagrams are favored for ore body illustration as they can be constructed systematically. All of the distances in isometric diagrams are equal to the measurements along the corresponding directions in the maps and cross sections which are being used to make up the block diagram.

To transform a block such as is shown in Figure 155*a* into an isometric projection, it is necessary to draw a lozenge-shaped figure, such as shown in Figure 155*b*. The sides in the lozenge-shaped figure $L'M'$, $M'N'$, $O'N'$, $L'O'$ will have the same length as the equivalent sides LM, MN, ON, LO in the original block, and the opposite sides $L'M'$ and $O'N'$ are still parallel as are $M'N'$ and $L'O'$. The only difference is that the angles $L'M'N'$ and $L'O'N'$ now equal 120° instead of 90° and the angles $M'L'O'$ and $M'N'O'$ now equal 60° instead of 90°. The angles at the corners, 60° and 120°, are chosen for two reasons—they can be drawn conveniently and rapidly with the usual 30°–60° triangles and the 30° projection, as this type is called (because the angle $R'Q'S = 30°$), allows both vertical planes of the projection to be seen equally well.

Once the top of the projection has been constructed, vertical lines $L'P'$, $M'Q'$, and $N'R'$ are dropped equal to LP, MQ, and NR.

The angle $R'Q'S$ need not equal 30° but can be varied to allow one of the sides to be shown to better advantage (Fig. 156).

The following rules, partially after Lobeck (1924), always apply in isometric projections:

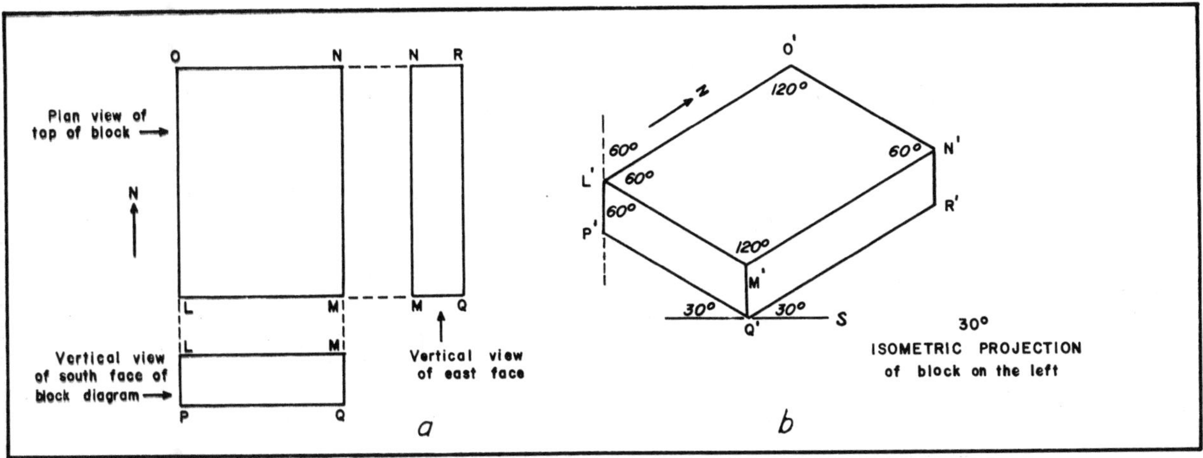

FIGURE 155. The true relations of the isometric projection are shown in *a*, whereas the isometric relations appear in *b*.

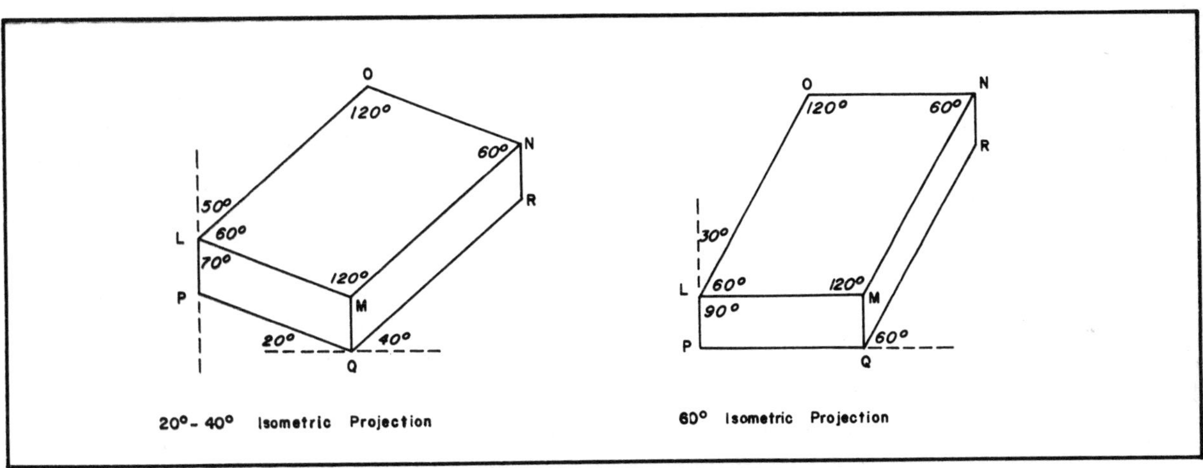

FIGURE 156. Isometric projections can be drawn with a 20°–40° relationship and with 0°–60° relationship as well as with the 30°–30° relationship.

1. Measurements made along any of the three co-ordinate directions of the original block, north-south, east-west, or vertical, can be transferred directly to the isometric projection provided it is on the same scale as the original block. Distances in other directions on the isometric diagram are not commensurate with each other unless measured along lines parallel to each other, and they are not commensurate with distances measured on the sides of the block. In illustrating ore body relationships it is thus important to tie all geological data into a well-organized co-ordinate grid system. When this is done it is a simple matter to transform mine plan and cross-section geological data into an isometric projection. Isometric projections can be of great value in predicting ore body extensions during the development stages at a mine.
2. All lines parallel in the block are parallel in the isometric projection.
3. All lines vertical in the block are vertical in the isometric diagram.
4. If the vertical scale of the diagram is the same as its horizontal scale, then the measurements made in the direction of any of the three co-ordinates are commensurate.
5. All angles in an isometric projection are distorted, and even two angles lying in the same plane cannot be compared with each other unless they lie in exactly similar positions.

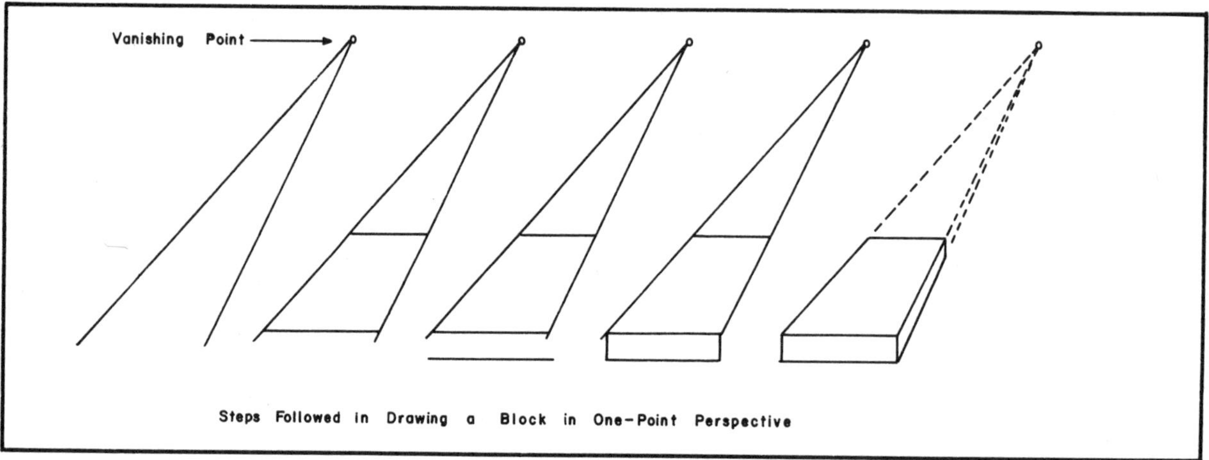

Vanishing Point
Steps Followed in Drawing a Block in One-Point Perspective

FIGURE 157.

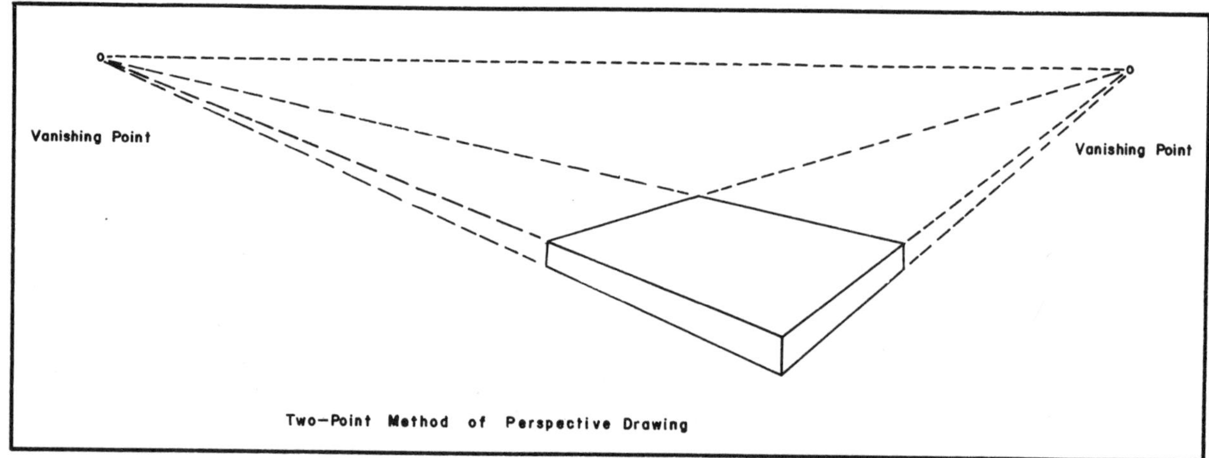

FIGURE 158.

Perspective drawings, although not constructed with dimensional accuracy, give an excellent feeling for the distance involved. They may achieve this feeling of depth and distance by means of one-point perspective or by two-point perspective. A one-point perspective diagram is drawn by selecting some point near the top of the drawing paper (Fig. 157) and drawing radiating lines downward. Two-point perspective is drawn in a similar manner (Fig. 158) but requires two vanishing points instead of one.

General Usage

Isometric projections are particularly valuable in demonstrating the complex relationships of structurally controlled hydrothermal ore deposits.

Areas which appear complex in plan or cross-sectional view appear greatly simplified in block diagrams. Because the simple is more comprehensible than the complex, block diagrams are of tremendous value in showing the detailed and complex relationships of ore bodies. Managements not familiar with the intricacies of geology are readily convinced by good three-dimensional diagrams (Figs. 159–162) whereas maps and cross sections, however well prepared, often do not transmit the desired message. The basic simplicity of block diagrams compels a rapid understanding of the problem involved. It is for this reason that block diagrams are often used in illustrating basic principles in elementary geological texts. Isometric projections are used most commonly with tabular-shaped ore deposits but can also be used for pipelike ore deposits (Fig. 162). It must be pointed out that isometric diagrams can be constructed only after considerable underground information is available. Once such a diagram has been made, it gives the geologist an idea of the three-dimensional trend of the ore body and enables him to lay out an intelligent exploratory drilling program.

Applications

All geological information and underground workings must be tied to a co-ordinate system which is usually laid out in a north-south and east-west pattern. The edges of the isometric projection must be drawn parallel to the directions of the grid lines of the co-ordinate system. It may be necessary to cut out portions of the isometric projection to visualize an inclined and/or plunging ore body on several mine levels. This procedure is shown in Figure 160. The isometric projection should be oriented to show the ore body to best advantage. Thus if an ore body strikes approximately north-south, dips to the east, and rakes

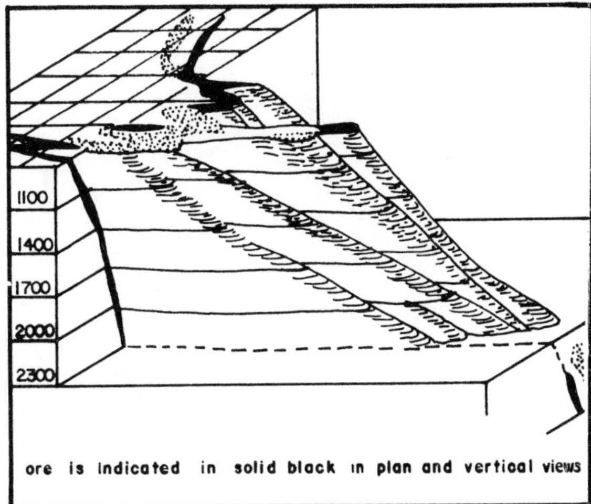

FIGURE 159. Isometric projection of ore bodies of the Homestake Mine, Lead, South Dakota. Note the use of the isometric projection to illustrate the plunging ore bodies. (Modified from D. H. McLaughlin [1933], in *Ore Deposits of the Western States*, Am. Inst. Min. Met. Engineers.)

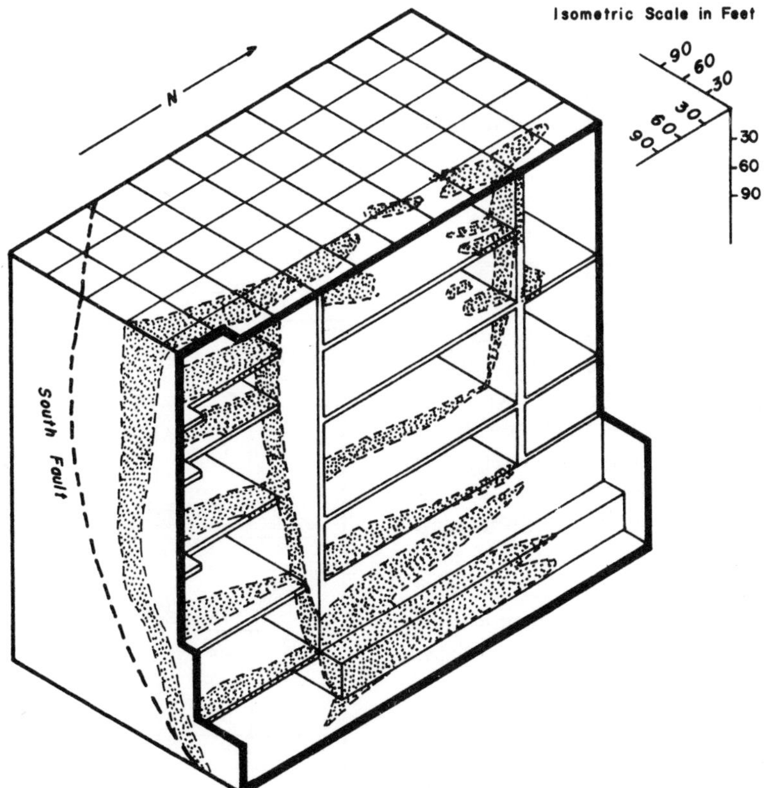

FIGURE 160. Isometric projection of the Blinman Copper Mine. Note the use of "cut outs" to illustrate the ore body to best advantage. (Modified from *Geology of Australian Ore Deposits* [1953], Aust. Inst. Min. Met.)

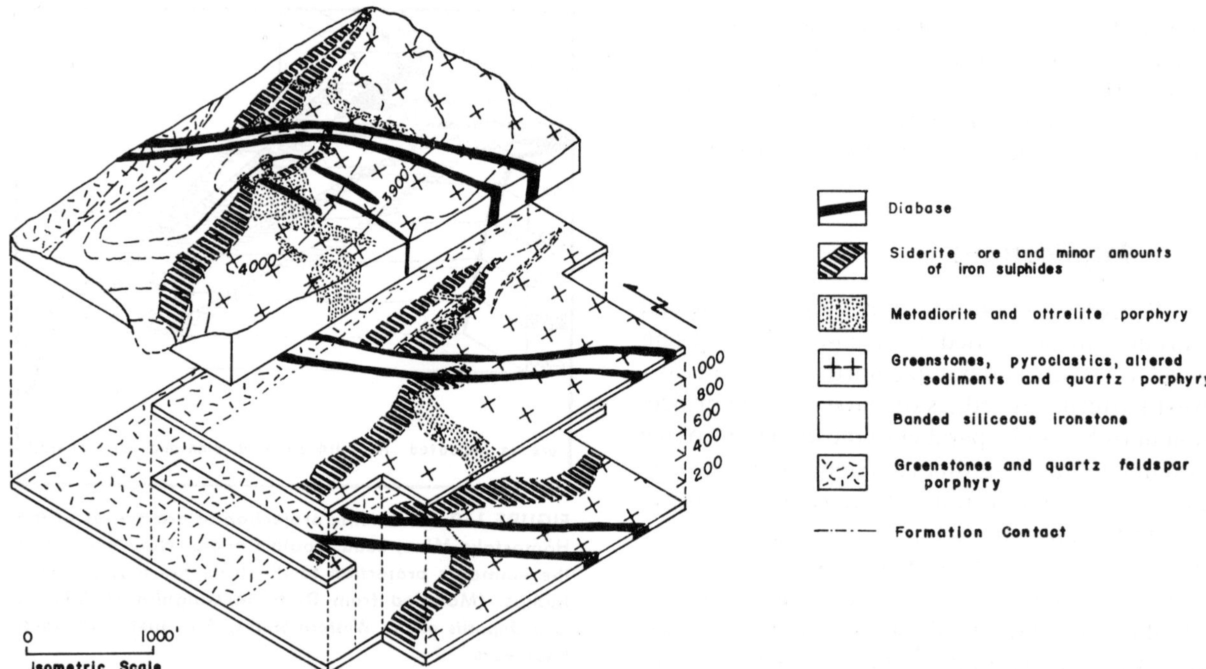

FIGURE 161. Isometric projection of the New Helen Mine, Ontario, Canada. Note the use of topographic relief in addition to the subsurface geologic configuration. (Modified from S. J. Kidder and G. C. McCartney [1948], in *Structural Geology of Canadian Ore Deposits*, Can. Inst. Min. Met.)

northeast, the isometric diagram should be constructed so that the south and east edges of the isometric projection are visible as vertical sections (Fig. 160).

REPRESENTATION OF RELIEF BY ELEVATED CONTOURS IN ISOMETRIC PROJECTIONS

Applications and Limitations: Many ore deposits show some relationship to surface topography so that it may be desirable to combine surface topographic relief with the underground three-dimensional picture (Fig. 161). The following method is modified from that of Lobeck (1924).

Figure 163 (stage 1) shows the topographic map of an area drawn on an isometric base (30° projection). To show the relief of this surface it is necessary to elevate each of the topographic contours to its appropriate distance above the base. The representation of relief is often very desirable to show the correct relationships between structure and topography.

A sheet of tracing paper is laid over the topographic map on the isometric base (Fig. 163, stage 2). An arrow has been drawn on the topographic base map near the edge of the tracing paper to serve as a guide when the tracing paper is moved relative to the underlying map later on. A vertical scale, numbered to correspond with the topographic contours on the underlying map, is drawn on the edge of the tracing paper (Fig. 163, stage 2). This vertical scale may be the same as the horizontal scale of the topographic map or it may be enlarged or decreased, depending upon the

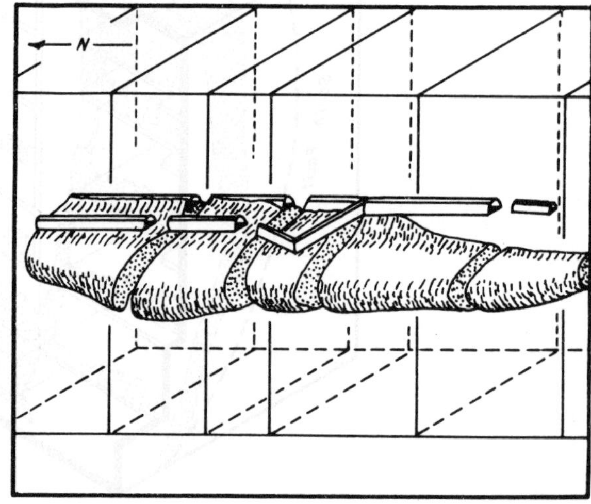

FIGURE 162. Tubular development of a pyrite ore body. Iron King Mine, Australia. (From *Geology of Australian Ore Deposits* [1953], Aust. Inst. Min. Met.)

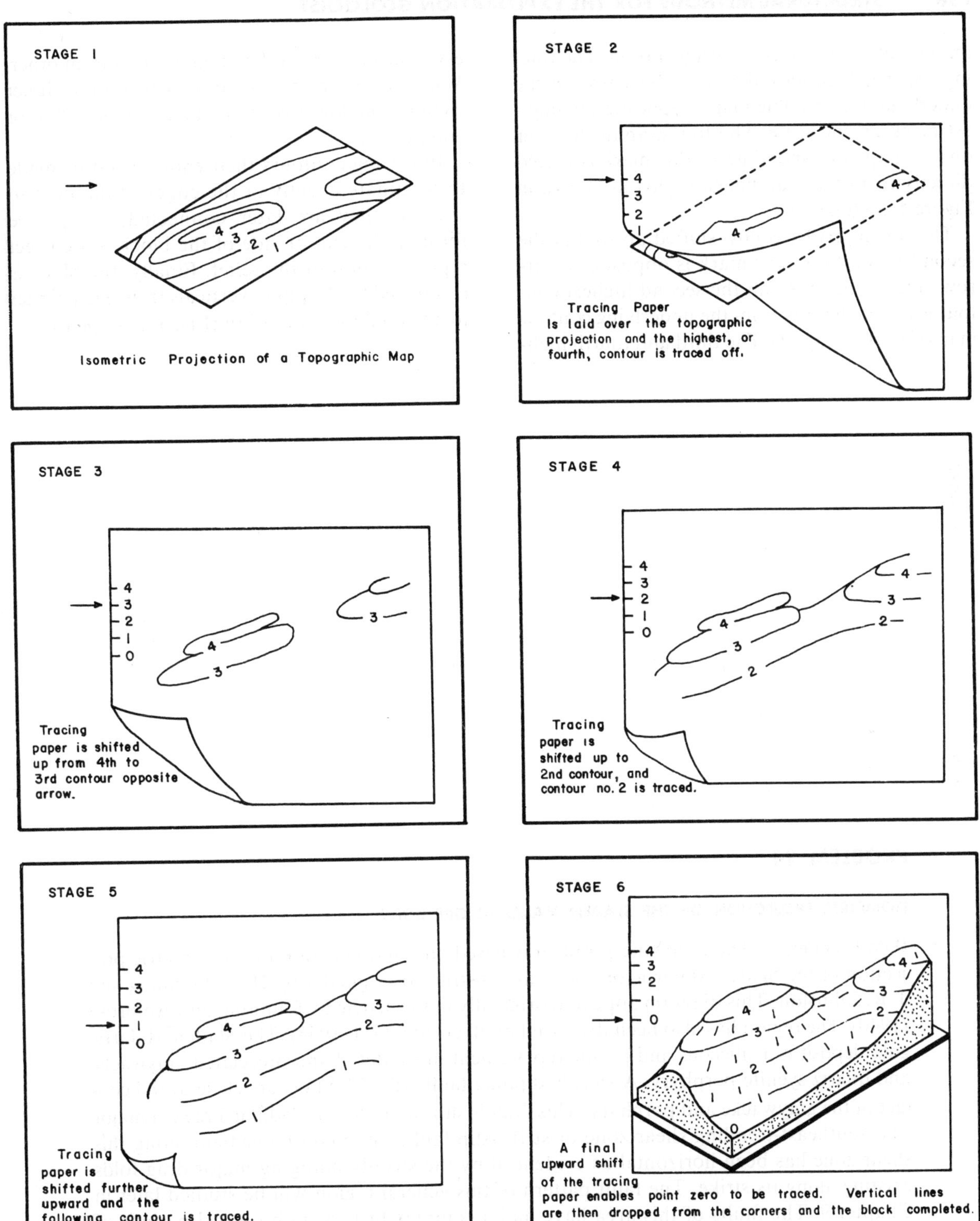
STAGE 1
4
3
2
1
Isometric Projection of a Topographic Map
STAGE 2
4
3
2
1
4
4
Tracing Paper
Is laid over the topographic projection and the highest, or fourth, contour is traced off.
STAGE 3
4
3
2
1
0
4
3
3
Tracing paper is shifted up from 4th to 3rd contour opposite arrow.
STAGE 4
4
3
2
1
0
4
3
2
4
3
2
Tracing paper is shifted up to 2nd contour, and contour no. 2 is traced.
STAGE 5
4
3
2
1
0
4
3
2
1
3
2
1
Tracing paper is shifted further upward and the following contour is traced.
STAGE 6
4
3
2
1
0
4
3
2
1
0
4
3
2
A final upward shift of the tracing paper enables point zero to be traced. Vertical lines are then dropped from the corners and the block completed.

FIGURE 163. Method used in representing relief by elevated contours in isometric projections. (Reprinted in slightly modified form with permission from A. K. Lobeck, *Block Diagrams and Other Graphic Methods Used in Geology and Geography*, 1924, John Wiley & Sons, Inc. and Chapman & Hall, Ltd.)

amount of desired vertical exaggeration. The tracing paper is then moved so that the arrow on the underlying topographic map is opposite the highest mark on the scale. The topographic contour on the map corresponding to this mark is traced directly from the map beneath, just as shown in Figure 163 (stage 2).

The tracing paper is now shifted up so that the second highest contour mark is opposite the arrow, and in this position the second highest contour is traced directly from the underlying contour map (Fig. 163, stage 3). The third and fourth highest contours are located in a similar manner. Where a lower contour passes behind a higher contour, the lower contour should be dotted in or erased.

In tracing contours their ends should be made to terminate exactly at the edges of the map so that, as they are later connected, the profile forming the end or side of the block is a correct representation of the relief. Finally, the block is completed by dropping verticals from each corner to an equal base elevation (Fig. 163, stage 6).

PROBLEM 24

ISOMETRIC PROJECTION OF THE SLADEN MALARTIC ORE BODY

Data Provided: The following problem is based on a modification of an isometric projection of the Sladen Malartic ore body as constructed originally by H. C. Gunning and J. R. Johnston. This diagram appeared originally in the article by Gunning and Ambrose (1940). The region has also been discussed by Byers and Gill (1948). The Sladen Malartic gold deposit is a siliceous and pyritic replacement in shattered and brecciated graywacke and quartz syenite porphyry. A steeply dipping fault (100/57°S) occurs close to the contact of the graywacke and porphyry. This fault is subsidiary to the Cadillac break, a major east-southeast-trending shear zone or strike-slip fault. The main movement along this shear zone has been horizontal as evidenced by the steeply plunging major drag folds existing along its strike. The fault pattern of this general region will be studied later in Chapter 9. The faults of this area have had a complex history with several periods of movement. Brecciation and shattering have resulted particularly in the drag-folded areas which formed as a result of the strike-slip movement. The pattern of minor intrusives has also been fault-controlled to some extent.

Figures 164*a-e* are plan view maps showing the surface and underground geology for a part of the Sladen Malartic mine. The geology is tied into a north-south, east-west co-

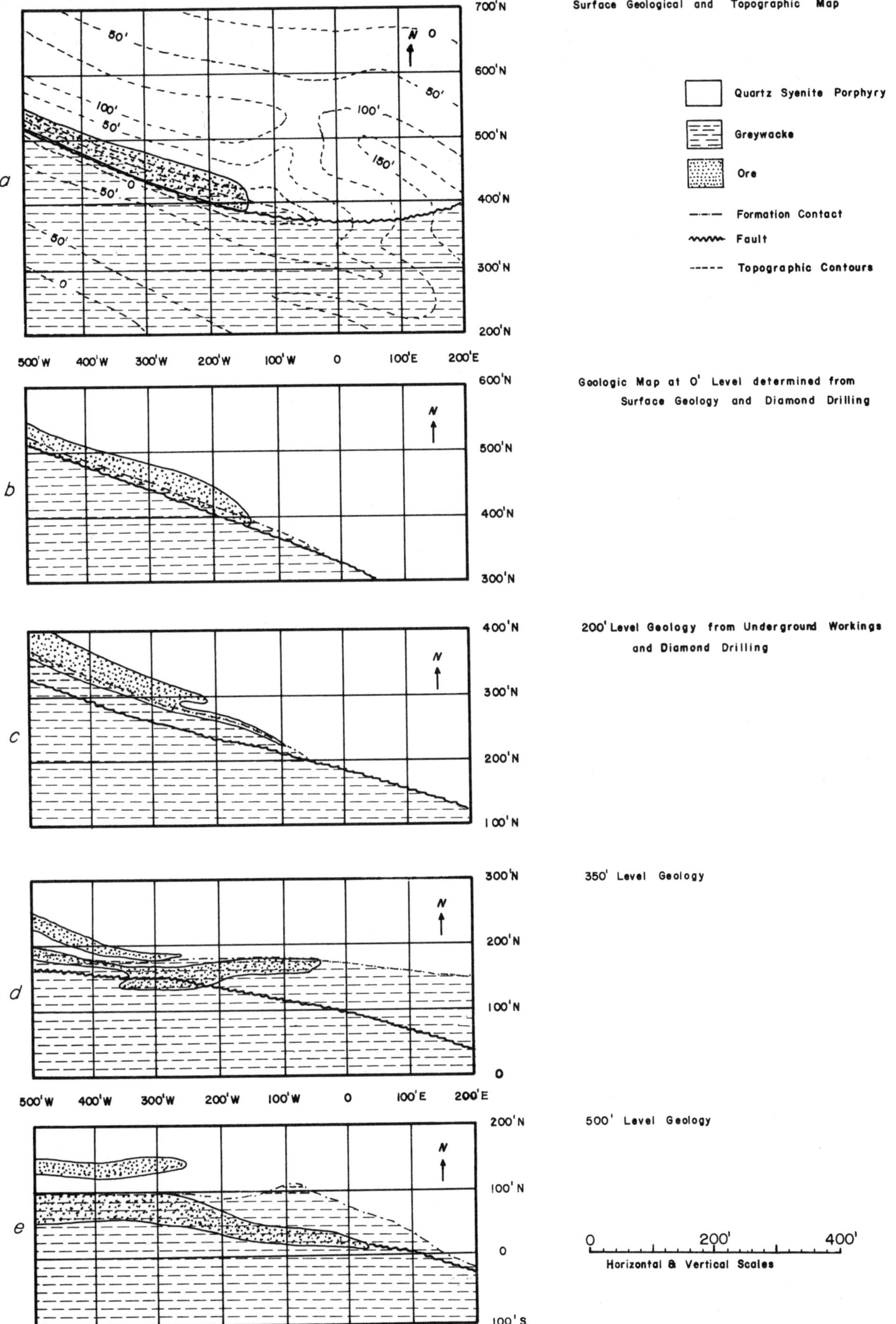

FIGURE 164. Surface and underground geology of the Sladen Malartic Mine, Quebec, Canada. (Modified from H. C. Gunning and J. W. Ambrose [1940], *Geol. Surv. Can.*, Mem. 222.)

ordinate system as shown. Figure 165 is an isometric diagram which the student can use as a base for this problem.

Requirements: Show the shape of the ore body in three-dimensional isometric projection. Reverse "cut outs" may be required to illustrate the ore deposit at all levels.

Questions Based on Problem No. 24

1. Discuss the factors which appear to control the location of the Sladen Malartic ore deposit.
2. Is there a good chance that the Sladen Malartic ore body will persist to the −1000-foot level? This is the type of decision that often confronts geologists. Experienced judgment is a tremendous factor in such decisions. The following assay information combined with the results of the isometric projection should provide a fair amount of information upon which to base a decision.

   Ore grade averages 1.1 ounces of gold per ton on the 0-foot level.
   Ore grade averages 1.2 ounces of gold per ton on the 200-foot level.
   Ore grade averages 1.0 ounces of gold per ton on the 350-foot level.
   Ore grade averages 0.9 ounces of gold per ton on the 500-foot level.
3. What type of exploration program would one recommend for the further extension of this ore body?
4. What is the best way to determine the attitude of the fault on the vertical faces of the isometric projection?
5. What is the rake of the ore body? Would one expect the same direction of rake for other ore bodies in this region? Discuss.

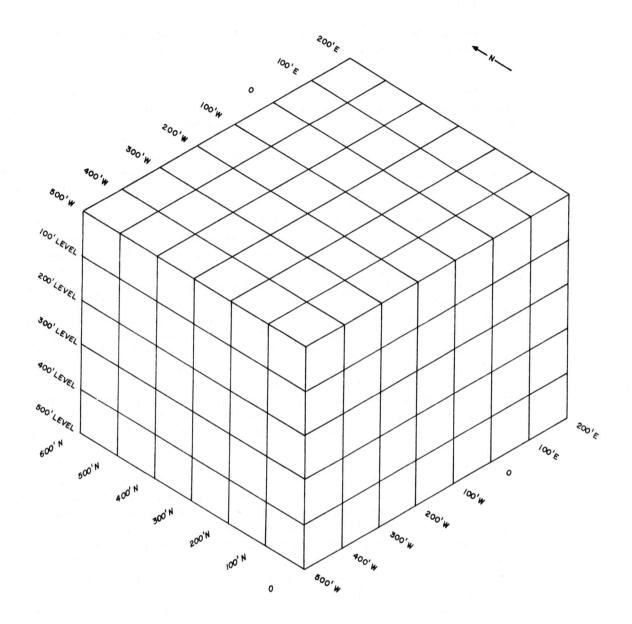

200'E
100'E
0
100'W
200'W
300'W
400'W
500'W
N

100' LEVEL
200' LEVEL
300' LEVEL
400' LEVEL
500' LEVEL

600' N
500' N
400' N
300' N
200' N
100' N
0

500'W
400'W
300'W
200'W
100'W
0
100'E
200'E

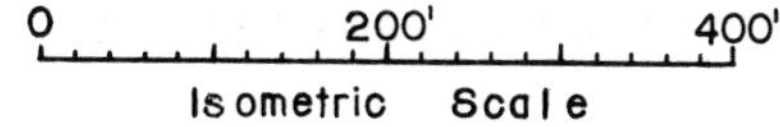

FIGURE 165. Isometric base for use with Problem 24.

PROBLEM 25

ISOMETRIC PROJECTION OF THE FLIN FLON ORE BODY AND AN ANALYSIS OF THE STRUCTURAL FABRIC OF THE FLIN FLON REGION

Regional Discussion: The Flin Flon ore body is a large copper and zinc sulphide replacement deposit located in the Canadian Precambrian shield near the Saskatchewan-Manitoba provincial boundary line. Figure 166 shows the regional geology of the area. Rocks of the Kisseynew complex have apparently been thrust southward over the Amisk series (Kalliokoski, 1952). The Kisseynew lineament is considered to be a major high-angle thrust zone (Harrison, 1951) although granitization has obscured the evidence for faulting in some areas. The trend of fold axes, north of the lineament, is also east-west. The Kisseynew rocks are Archean and of the Grenville type, consisting of sedimentary and amphibolitic gneisses with sheets of granitic gneisses. The Amisk series, also Archean, consists of Keewatin-type volcanic flows and pyroclastics. The Amisk series is overlain unconformably by the Proterozoic Missi sediments. Both Amisk and Missi rocks have been intruded by granites. The relative age of Kisseynew and Amisk rocks is uncertain.

A number of large, approximately north-trending faults occur in this area (Fig. 166). Some of these faults offset the Kisseynew lineament. There is good evidence for strike-slip movement on many of the approximately north-striking faults (Harrison, 1951). These faults may be grouped into two types, those trending north-northwest (Sturgeon-weir river fault, Ross Lake fault, Flin Flon Lake fault, Channing fault, Cliff Lake fault etc.) and those trending north-northeast (Mikanagan Lake fault, Sourdough Bay fault, Vamp Creek fault, Elbow Lake faults, Berry Creek fault, etc.).

The north-northwest faults are dominant in the western portion of the region (Fig. 166), and the north-northeast faults occur mainly in the central and eastern portions of the region. It is difficult to generalize on the movement histories of these faults as the information is still meager. A study of drag folding, cross folding, and second-order faulting (splay faults) as well as offset relations has led to a few preliminary conclusions. The north-northwest faults are probably right-handed. Harrison (1951) reports such a relationship for the Sturgeon-weir river shear zone. The writer has studied second-order, strike-slip fault (splay faults) relationships on the Tramping Lake and Weldon Bay map areas, using fault principles discussed by Anderson (1951), McKinstry (1953), and Moody and Hill (1956). It appears that the north-northeast faults are mainly left-handed.

The main ore occurrences of the region (Fig. 166) are associated geographically with these north-northwest and north-northeast strike-slip faults (Harrison, 1951). The regional geology is thus very similar to that of other North American Precambrian mineralized areas: structurally controlled ore bodies related to right and left-handed strike-slip faults, the strike-slip faults themselves occurring as a conjugate set in front of, and almost perpendicular to, a major thrust-fault direction. These principles will be discussed further in Chapter 9. The student is advised to read Chapter 9 before attempting parts 2 and 3 of this problem.

The Flin Flon ore body is associated with a quartz porphyry sill injected along the contact between competent lava flows to the east and more easily sheared pyroclastics and flow breccias to the west (Figs. 167 and 168). These formations have been tightly folded. The actual ore shoots are associated with drag folds on the east side of the south-southeast plunging Flin Flon Lake anticline (Fig. 167). Shearing along north-northwest trends, probably associated with movement along the north-northwest faults of the area, has affected both the pyroclastics and the intruded quartz porphyry (Fig. 168). The drag folds themselves are thus crumpled and sheared. The ore occurs as shoots along the northeast limbs of these drag folds and plunges south-southeast in harmony with the Flin Flon anticline and the drag folds.

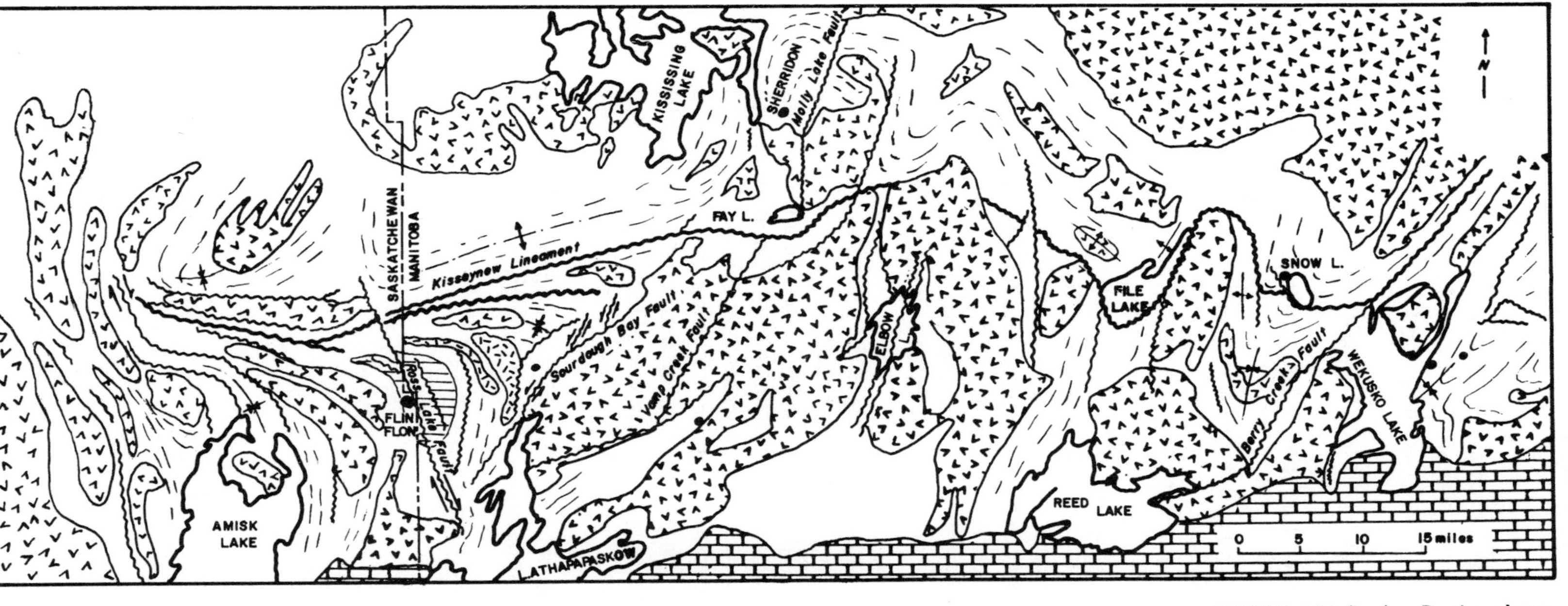

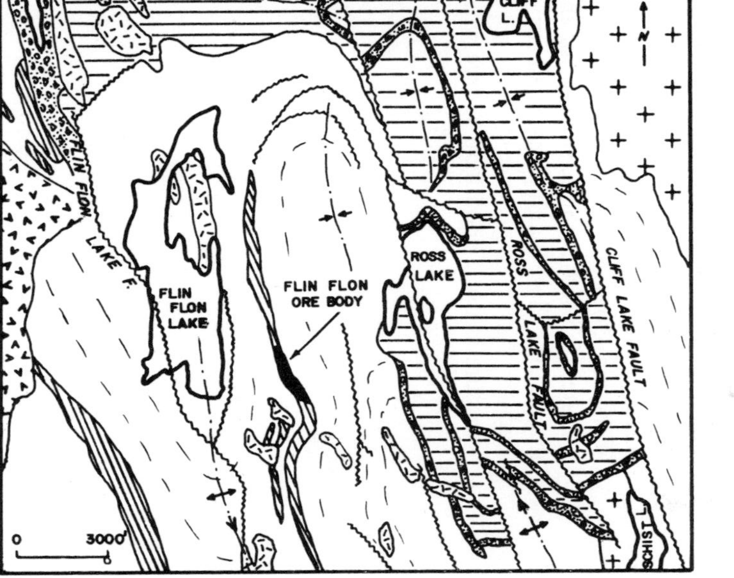

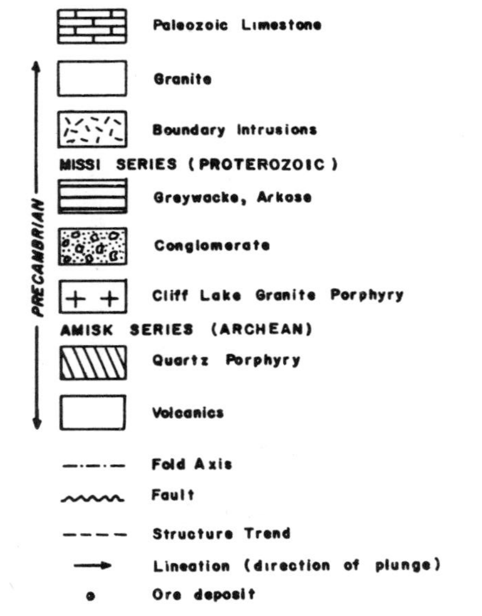

FIGURE 166 (*top*). Regional tectonic setting of the Flin Flon—Sherridon areas, Saskatchewan and Manitoba, Canada. (Modified from maps of the Geological Survey of Canada.)

FIGURE 167 (*left*). Semidetailed map of the area around the Flin Flon ore deposit. (Modified from maps of the Geological Survey of Canada.)

Data Provided: Figure 168 shows the geology of the Flin Flon ore body on the 700-, 1200-, 1700-, and 2200-foot levels. Figure 169 is a 10°–50° isometric diagram which can be used as a base diagram for this ore body. Plate 8 is a series of three overlapping air photos oriented and spaced for stereoscopic viewing. Plate 9 is an uncontrolled air photo mosaic of the Flin Flon area.

Determine: Each of the following requirements can be met independently of the other two.

1. Draw up an isometric projection of the Flin Flon ore body, using cutouts to assist in the illustration.
2. Map all fractures and other apparent structures visible on Plates 8 and 9 and discuss their origin and economic significance.
3. Study the detailed map sheets of northern Manitoba and Saskatchewan referred to in the list of references (pages 172–173) with particular attention to fault directions, movement histories, and offset relations. Study the angular relationships of major folds, drag folds, and cross folds to fault directions. Be sure to note the plunge directions of folds before interpreting the directions of anticlinal and synclinal axes, as many of the folds of this area are tilted recumbent folds whose axes are not easily recognized (Kalliokoski, 1953). Study the relationship of intrusive rocks to folds, faults, and foliation both from the spatial and time point of view. Then give a comprehensive review of the structural development of this region.

Procedure for Examining Plates 8 and 9: To study Plate 8, place the pocket-size lens-type stereoscope over and parallel to the dashed lines. For viewing the south end of the photo strip, the southern and central *X*'s should appear approximately under the left and right lenses. While looking through the lenses, make slight adjustments in orientation or lens spacing to obtain perfect fusion of the lines and *X*'s. The stereoscope now can be moved east and west without losing the three-dimensional effect. For viewing the north end of the photo strip, place the center of the stereoscope over the northern circle and parallel to the dashed lines and make slight adjustments in orientation or lens spacing so that perfect fusion of lines and circles is obtained. The circles represent the principal points of the air photos.

Plate 9 is used as the base map for this problem. Lay a sheet of transparent drafting acetate over Plate 9 and transfer all structural features observed on Plate 8 onto the acetate.

Be sure to use a good light source when studying Plate 8.

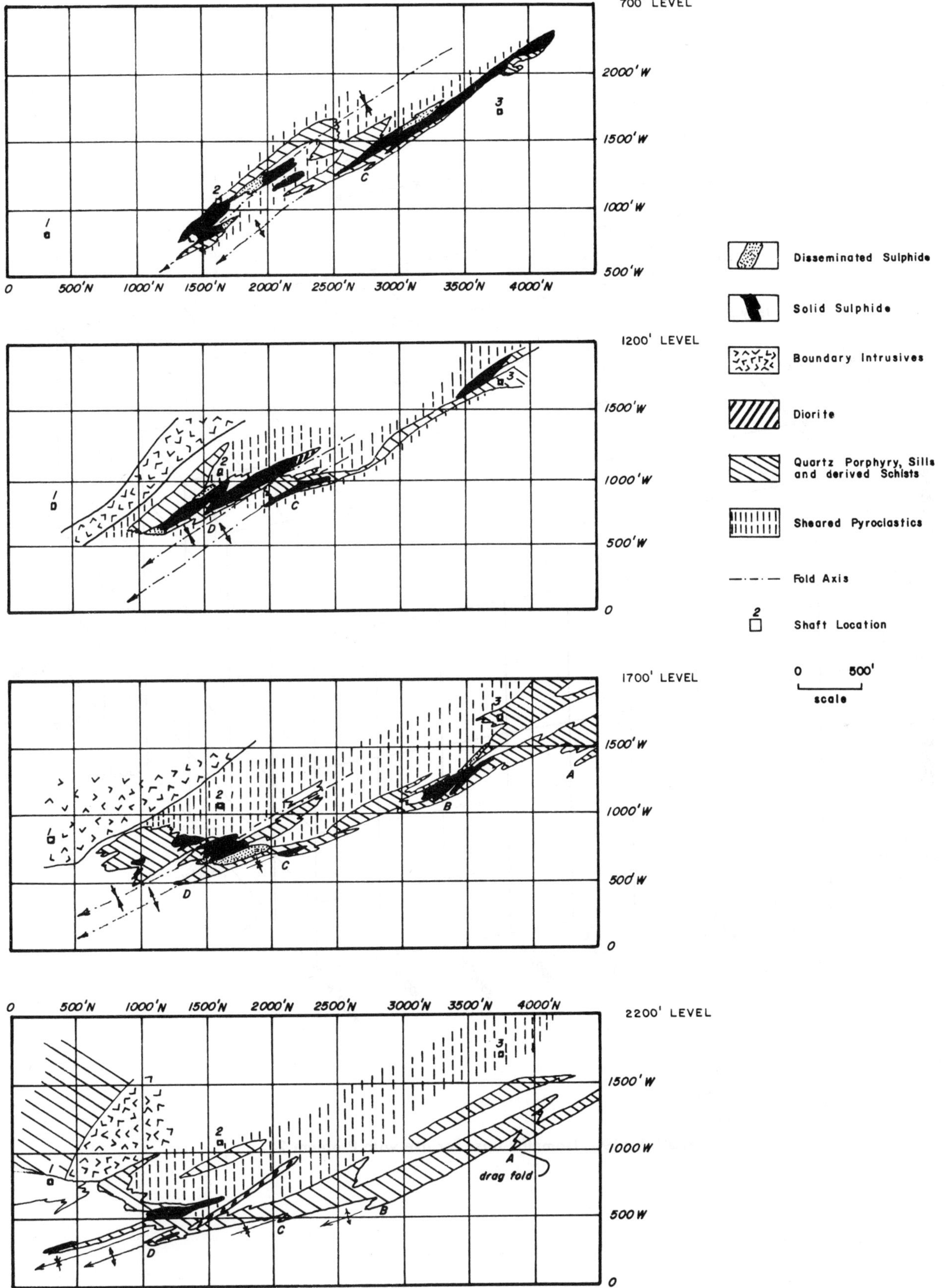

FIGURE 168. Underground geology for the Flin Flon ore body. (Modified from C. H. Stockwell *et al.* [1948], in *Structural Geology of Canadian Ore Deposits*, Can. Inst. Min. Met.)

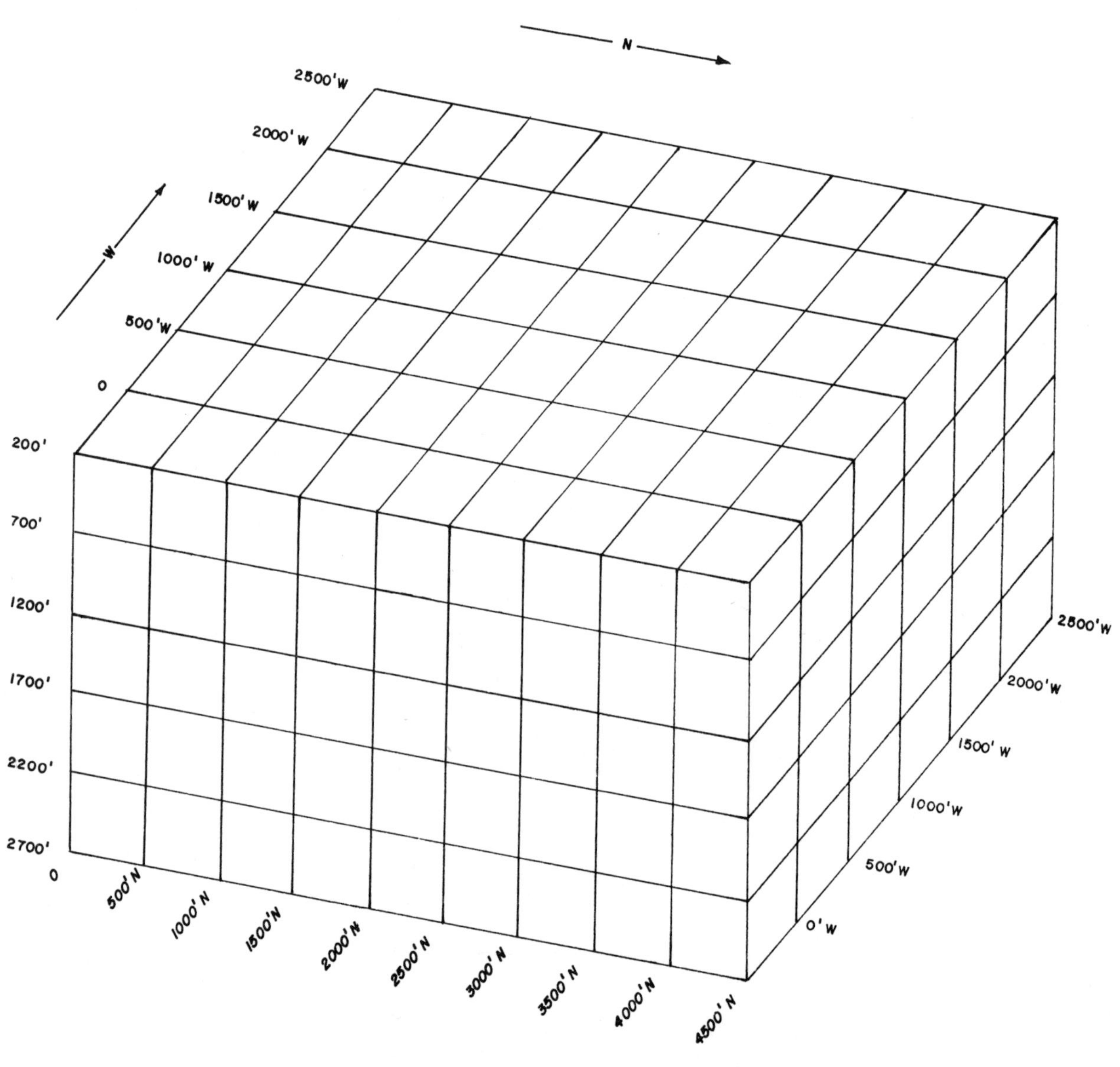

FIGURE 169. Isometric base for use with Problem 25.

PROBLEM 26

ORE RESERVE ESTIMATION

Principles Involved: Ore reserve estimation depends upon many factors, probably the most important of which is the accurate estimation of the volume of rock of ore grade. Because this volume is usually highly dependent upon the intricacies of the structures controlling the ore occurrences, the task of estimating this volume is best performed by a geologist with a good structural geology background.

The calculation of rock volume depends upon the shape of the ore body. Irregular-shaped ore deposits are handled most easily with isopach maps and a polar planimeter. The area between adjoining isopach contours is determined by means of the planimeter and this is then multiplied by the average thickness for this area to give the volume. The average thickness will be the half-way point between the two adjoining contours.

Dipping tabular (or nearly tabular) ore bodies are usually treated by means of longitudinal vertical sections drawn parallel to the strike of the ore body. Consideration of Figure 170 shows that area X = area Y.

Proof:

It is observed that angle bac = angle cbd because angle $bac + \theta = 90°$ and angle $cbd + \theta = 90°$ also. Consequently, $\frac{V.H.}{\cos \alpha} \times H.W. \cos \alpha$ = area X. The cos α's cancel out leaving $V.H. \times H.W.$ = area X, but $V.H. \times H.W.$ also = area Y. Therefore, area X = area Y.

Assay widths are usually obtained along drifts or cross cuts on the various levels in a mine. These assay widths need not be converted to true widths provided the slant height is projected into a vertical longitudinal section.

Ore reserve estimation is simple for dipping tabular ore bodies when the assay width (horizontal width) and length of sampling interval are both uniform. The assay width × ore body length × height between adjoining levels = rock volume.

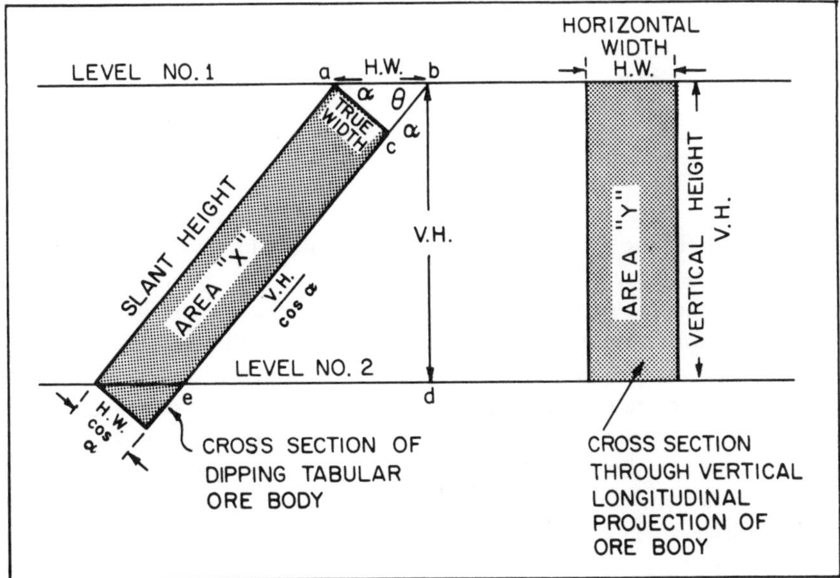

FIGURE 170. Cross sectional diagram through a dipping tabular ore body, showing the relationship between true and horizontal (or assay) width and between slant height and vertical height.

Then:

$$\text{Ore Reserves (Tons in the Ground)} = \frac{\text{Rock Volume}}{\text{Tonnage Factor}}$$

If the assay width varies but the sampling interval remains constant, then it is necessary to weight each sample as follows:

Sample Number	*Width in Feet*	*Assay Value (Per Cent of Copper)*	*Width × Assay*
1	8.2	3.1	25.4
2	7.1	2.7	19.2
3	6.9	4.3	29.65
4	7.4	3.4	35.15
5	8.3	2.4	19.9
	37.9		129.30

Average width = 37.9 ÷ 5 = 7.58 feet
Average ore grade = 129.30 ÷ 37.9 = 3.42% of copper

If both assay width and sampling interval are variable, then it is necessary to weight each sample further:

Sample Number	*Width in Feet*	*Sample Interval*	*Width × Interval*	*Assay Value (Per Cent of Copper)*	*Width × Interval × Assay Value*
1	8.2	6.1	50.0	3.1	155.0
2	7.1	7.4	52.5	2.7	141.8
3	6.9	5.9	40.7	4.3	174.8
4	7.4	8.2	60.6	3.4	206.0
5	8.3	6.7	55.6	2.4	133.7
	37.9	34.3	259.4		811.3

$$\text{Average width} = \frac{259.4}{34.3} = 75.7$$

$$\text{Average grade} = \frac{811.3}{259.4} = 3.13\% \text{ of copper}$$

Gross metal content (in the ground) may then be calculated by multiplying the ore reserve estimate by the average ore grade.

Most ore bodies include some narrow stretches where the ore width is less than the stope width so that dilution in the gross metal content must be allowed for. This is taken care of by lowering the average grade in proportion to the dilution.

It is impossible to mine out the ore body completely because of inaccessibility, pillars that must be left to support the roof, or other reasons. Consequently, this *mining loss* must be allowed for by subtracting the mining loss percentage from the computed tonnage factor before multiplying by the average grade. Thus the recoverable ore reserves can be computed as follows:

$$RMT = \frac{RV}{TF} \times (100 - ML) \times \left(\frac{100\%}{100\% + DF\%}\right) \times G$$

Where RMT = recoverable metal content.
RV = rock volume in cubic feet.
TF = tonnage factor in cubic feet of ore per ton, which is dependent upon

the specific gravity of the ore, the porosity of the rock, and the moisture content of the rock.

DF = dilution factor percentage.

ML = mining loss percentage.

G = average ore grade.

The tonnage factor may be determined as follows:

$$\text{Tonnage Factor (Cubic Feet Per Long Ton of Ore)} = \frac{2240}{\text{lbs./cu. ft.}}$$

when pounds per cubic foot of ore = specific gravity × 62.5.[1]

The specific gravity can be determined in the field by means of scales:

$$\text{Specific Gravity} = \frac{\text{Dry Weight}}{\text{Dry Weight} - \text{Weight When Suspended in Water}}$$

The specific gravity may be estimated by referring to Table 14A and Table 14B also.

TABLE 14A. Average Specific Gravity of Common Rocks

Rock	Sp. Gr.	Rock	Sp. Gr.
Andesite	2.66	Limestone	2.60
Basalt, dense	2.90	Marble	2.78
Basalt, scoriaceous	2.15	Quartz porphyry	2.63
Clay	2.20	Rhyolite	2.50
Diabase	2.94	Sand, dry	1.69
Diorite	2.86	Sand, wet	2.25
Dolomite	2.80	Sandstone	2.60
Gabbro	2.98	Shale	2.70
Gneiss	2.65–2.80	Schist	2.69
Granite	2.65	Slate	2.75
Gravel, dry	1.55	Syenite	2.74
Gravel, wet	2.00	Trachyte	2.58

TABLE 14B. Specific Gravity of Some Common Ore Minerals

Mineral	Sp. Gr.	Mineral	Sp. Gr.	Mineral	Sp. Gr.
Barite	4.5	Cuprite	6.0	Realgar	3.48
Bornite	5.07	Enargite	4.44	Siderite	3.83–3.88
Bournonite	5.85	Galena	7.5	Silver (native)	10.5
Carnotite	4.1	Gold	15.0–19.3	Smithsonite	4.35–4.40
Cassiterite	6.8–7.1	Gypsum	2.32	Sphalerite	3.9–4.1
Cerargyrite	5.5±	Magnetite	5.18	Stibnite	4.52–4.62
Chalcocite	5.5–5.8	Malachite	3.9–4.03	Tennantite	4.6–5.1
Chalcopyrite	4.2	Marcasite	4.89	Tetrahedrite	4.6–5.1
Chromite	4.6	Mercury	13.6	Tin	7.3
Cinnabar	8.10	Molybdenite	4.62–4.73	Uraninite	9.0–9.7
Cobaltite	6.33	Pyrargyrite	5.85	Vanadinite	6.7–7.1
Copper (native)	8.9	Pyrrhotite	4.58–4.65	Wolframite	7.0–7.5

Actually, the matter of specific gravity determination as it affects tonnage factors is more complicated, as the porosity and moisture content should be allowed for. There are thus several definitions of specific gravity:

1. Mineral specific gravity involves the specific gravity of the rock alone and does not allow for pores in rocks or moisture content.

[1] One cubic foot of water weighs 62.5 pounds.

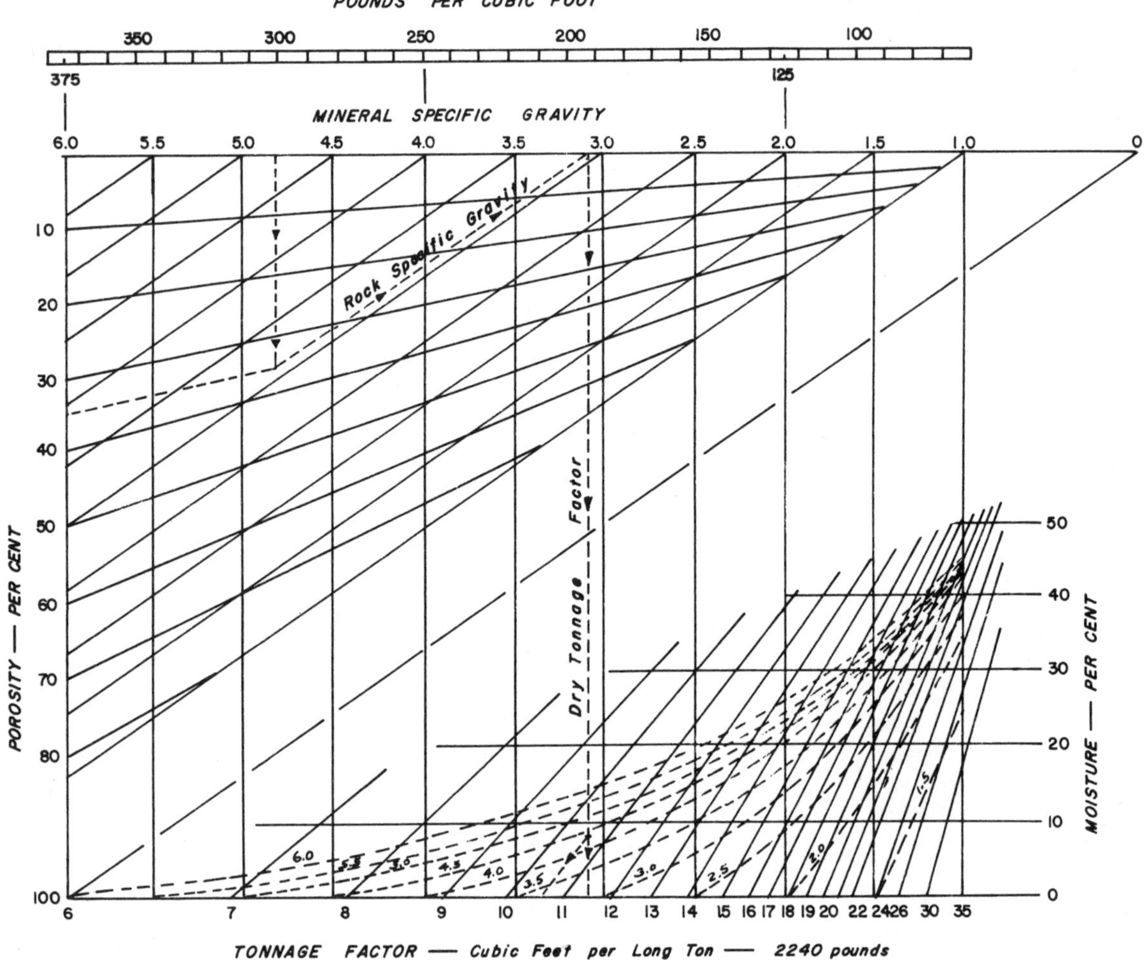

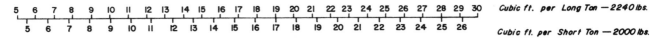

TONNAGE FACTOR CONVERSION CHART

5 6 7 8 9 10 11 12 13 14 15 16 17 18 19 20 21 22 23 24 25 26 27 28 29 30 *Cubic ft. per Long Ton — 2240 lbs.*

5 6 7 8 9 10 11 12 13 14 15 16 17 18 19 20 21 22 23 24 25 26 *Cubic ft. per Short Ton — 2000 lbs.*

EXAMPLE:

A mineral with specific gravity 4.8 and rock porosity 35% has a rock specific gravity of (3.1) and a dry tonnage factor of (11.5 cu. ft/long ton). Assuming a moisture content of 8% the sample has an equivalent dry tonnage factor of (10.6).

FIGURE 171. Calculation of tonnage factor allowing for porosity and moisture content. (Modified from R. D. Parks [1949], *Examination and Valuation of Mineral Property,* Addison-Wesley Publishing Co., Inc.)

2. Rock specific gravity (dried) is mineral specific gravity corrected for porosity (in which case the pore space is included but not the moisture content).
3. Rock specific gravity (natural) is mineral specific gravity corrected for both porosity and moisture content.

Figure 171 shows how the tonnage factor can be determined, allowing for both porosity and moisture content.

To convert the gross metal content into *gross ore value,* it is simply necessary to multiply the gross metal content by the current market price for the metal. Usually it is preferable to estimate what the average market price will be over the life of the mining operation.

To estimate the net value of the property, it is necessary to allow for the *metallurgical recovery factor*. Then costs of production, extraction, amortization, and so forth, are estimated and deducted from the gross ore value. The value of this future income must then be reduced to *present worth*. This present worth reduction is a lengthy subject which can be handled in several ways. Students who are interested should refer to Parks (1949).

In making ore reserve estimates, as with oil reserve estimates, it is tremendously important to distinguish clearly between:

Developed ore (or proven ore)
Probable ore
Possible ore

There are many definitions of these types (C. K. Leith, H. Hoover, U.S.G.S., etc.) and to avoid confusion each evaluator should clearly state what is meant by his designations. In general, the following meanings are implied:

Developed ore: So completely exposed as to tons and tenor (blocked out by mine workings on all sides) as to be certain and immediately available for withdrawal by mining operations.

Probable ore: Ore whose occurrence is reasonably assured (e.g., blocked out by levels both above and below) but not absolutely certain. Not immediately available for withdrawal but could be available soon.

Possible ore: Its existence is a reasonable possibility based on knowledge of the structural and mineralogical persistence of the proven and probable ore already delineated (blocked out by one level and favorable geological relationships). No grade can be assigned to this ore.

Data Provided: The ore body (proven ore) at the Sladen Malartic mine was illustrated in isometric projection in Problem 24. It is assumed that the following factors are effective for this ore body and for the Sladen Malartic mining operation.

Mineral specific gravity of the ore = 3.90, moisture content = 11 per cent, and porosity = 31 per cent.
Ore grade averages 1.1 ounces of gold per short ton for 0-foot level.
Ore grade averages 1.2 ounces of gold per short ton for 200-foot level.
Ore grade averages 1.0 ounces of gold per short ton for 350-foot level.
Ore grade averages 0.9 ounce of gold per short ton for 500-foot level.
Dilution factor = 15 per cent.
Mining loss = 10 per cent.
Market price for the ore = $32.00 per ounce (price to the producer).
Metallurgical recovery factor = 90 per cent.
Total mining and extraction costs = $8.00 per ton.

Determine:

1. Total rock volume betwen the 0- and 500-foot levels.
2. The tonnage factor.
3. Ore reserves in the ground between 0- and 500-foot levels (in short tons).
4. Recoverable metal content, assuming ore grade is given for short tons.
5. Gross ore value.
6. Net ore value after costs but before reduction to present worth value.

References

Anderson, E. M. (1942), *The Dynamics of Faulting and Dyke Formation,* Oliver & Boyd, London, 206 pp.

Bruce, E. L. (1942), The Mineral Deposits of Thunder Bay District, Ontario, in W. H. Newhouse (ed.), *Ore Deposits as Related to Structural Features,* Princeton University Press, pp. 101–106.

Byers, A. R., and Gill, J. E. (1948), Sladen Malartic Area, Structural Geology of Canadian Ore Deposits, *Can. Inst. Min. Met.,* pp. 858–864.

Dickinson, S. B. (1953), Copper Deposits of the Northern Flinders Ranges, Geology of Australian Ore Deposits, *Aust. Inst. Min. Met.,* pp. 505–516.

Ellis, H. A. (1953), Norseman Gold Mines, N. L., Geology of Australian Ore Deposits, *Aust. Inst. Min. Met.,* pp. 150–158.

Forrester, J. D. (1946), *Principles of Field and Mining Geology,* John Wiley & Sons, Inc., chapter 12 entitled "Library and Laboratory Research and the Preparation of Maps, Models, and Illustrations."

Gunning, H. C., and Ambrose, J. W. (1938), Cadillac-Malartic Area, Quebec, *Can. Inst. Min. Met.,* Trans., vol. 40, pp. 341–362.

Gunning, H. C., and Ambrose, J. W. (1940), Malartic Area, Quebec, *Geol. Surv. Can.,* Mem. 222.

Herness, S. K. (1951), Subsurface and Office Representation in Mining Geology, *Subsurface Geologic Methods,* (2nd ed.), chap. 13, Colorado School of Mines.

Ives, R. I. (1939), Shades and Screens for Isometric Block Diagrams, *Econ. Geol.,* vol. 34, pp. 419–436.

Ives, R. I. (1939), Measurements in Block Diagrams, *Econ. Geol.,* vol. 34, pp. 561–572.

Johnson, W. D., and Nolan, T. B. (1937), Isometric Block Diagrams in Mining Geology, *Econ. Geol.,* vol. 32, pp. 550–569.

Kuhn, T. H. (1949), Subsurface Methods as Applied in Mining Geology, *Subsurface Geologic Methods,* Quarterly of the Colorado School of Mines, vol. 44, no. 3, chap. 10.

Lobeck, A. K. (1924), *Block Diagrams, and Other Methods Used in Geology and Geography,* John Wiley & Sons, Inc., 206 pp.

McKinstry, H. E. (1948), *Mining Geology,* Prentice-Hall, Inc., chap. 18 entitled "Valuing Mining Properties."

McKinstry, H. E. (1955), Structure of Hydrothermal Ore Deposits, *Econ. Geol.,* 50th Anniv. vol., pp. 170–225.

McLaughlin, D. H. (1933), Geologic Work at the Homestake Mine, Lead, S. D., Ore Deposits of the Western States, *Am. Inst. Min. Eng.,* Lindgren Volume, pp. 722–729.

Moody, J. D., and Hill, M. J. (1956), Wrench Fault Tectonics, *Bull. Geol. Soc. Am.,* vol. 67, pp. 1207–1246.

Norman, G. W. H. (1940), Thrust Faulting of Grenville Gneisses Northwestward Against the Mistassini Series of Mistassini Lake, Quebec, *Jour. Geol.,* vol. 48, pp. 512–525.

Norman, G. W. H. (1942), The Cadillac Synclinal Belt of Northwestern Quebec, *Royal Soc. Can.,* Trans., vol. 37, sec. 4, pp. 89–97.

Norman, G. W. H. (1948), Major Faults, Abitibi Region, Structural Geology of Canadian Ore Deposits, *Can. Inst. Min. Met.,* pp. 822–839.

Parks, R. D. (1949), *Examination and Valuation of Mineral Property,* 3rd ed. Addison-Wesley Publishing Co., Inc., 504 pp.

Sales, R. H. (1941), Mine Geologic Maps and Models, sec. 19, *Mining Engineer's Handbook,* 3rd ed., John Wiley & Sons, Inc., pp. 1–12.

Secrist, M. H. (1936), Perspective Block Diagrams, *Econ. Geol.,* vol. 31, pp. 867–880.

Tanton, T. L. (1948), New Helen Mine, Structural Geology of Canadian Ore Deposits, *Can. Inst. Min. Met.,* pp. 422–428.

Wilson, J. T. (1949), Some Major Structures of the Canadian Shield, *Can. Inst. Min. Met.,* Trans., vol. 52, pp. 231–242.

Wright, J. F. (1932), Amisk Lake Area, Saskatchewan, *Geol. Surv. Can.,* Sum. Rept., Pt. C, pp. 73–110.

References for the Flin Flon Region

Alcock, F. J. (1920), Reed-Wekusko Map-Area, Northern Manitoba, *Geol. Surv. Can.,* Mem. 119.

Alcock, F. J. (1922), The Flin Flon Map-Area, Manitoba and Saskatchewan, *Geol. Surv. Can.,* Sum. Rept., Pt. C.

Ambrose, J. W. (1936), Structures in the Missi Series Near Flin Flon, Manitoba, *Royal Soc. Can.,* Trans., vol. XXX, sec. IV, pp. 81–98.

Ambrose, J. W. (1936), Progressive Kinetic Metamorphism in the Missi Series near Flin Flon, Manitoba, *Am. Jour. Sci.,* vol. 32, pp. 257–286.

Armstrong, J. E. (1941), Wekusko, Manitoba, *Geol. Surv. Can.,* Map 665A, with descriptive notes.

Bateman, J. D. (1942), Geology and Metamorphism in the McVeigh Lake Area, Northern Manitoba, *Am. Jour. Sci.,* vol. 240, pp. 789–808.

Bateman, J. D., and Harrison, J. M. (1945), Mikanagan Lake, Manitoba, *Geol. Surv. Can.,* Map 832A, with descriptive notes.

Brownell, G. M., and Kinkel, A. R. (1935), The Flin Flon Mine: Geology and Paragenesis of the Ore Deposit, *Can. Inst. Min. Met.,* Trans., vol. 38, pp. 261–286.

Bruce, E. L. (1918), Amisk-Athapapuskow Lake District, *Geol. Surv. Can.,* Mem. 105.

Bruce, E. L. (1933), *Mineral Deposits of the Canadian*

Shield, The Macmillan Company of Canada Limited, Toronto, 428 pp.

Buckham, A. F. (1944), Athapapuskow Lake, Manitoba, *Geol. Surv. Can.,* Map 807A, with descriptive notes.

Dawson, A. S. (1941), Assean-Split Lakes Area, *Manitoba Mines Br.,* Geol. Rept. 39–1.

Eastwood, G. E. P. (1949), Snake Rapids, Saskatchewan, *Geol. Surv. Can.,* Paper 49–18.

Farley, W. J. (1949), Geology of the Sherritt Gordon Orebody, *Can. Inst. Min. Met. Bull.,* vol. 42, pp. 25–30.

Frarey, M. J. (1950), Crowduck Bay, Manitoba, *Geol. Surv. Can.,* Map 987A, with descriptive notes.

Harrison, J. M. (1949), Geology and Mineral Deposits of File-Tramping Lakes Area, Manitoba, *Geol. Surv. Can.,* Mem. 250.

Harrison, J. M. (1949), Kississing, Saskatchewan and Manitoba, *Geol. Surv. Can.,* Map 970A, with descriptive notes.

Harrison, J. M. (1951), Possible Major Structural Control of Ore Deposits in the Flin Flon-Snow Lake Mineral Belt, Manitoba, *Can. Inst. Min. Met.,* Trans., vol. 44, pp. 4–8.

Harrison, J. M. (1951), Precambrian Correlations and Nomenclature, and Problems of the Kisseynew Gneisses, in Manitoba, *Geol. Surv. Can.,* Bull. 20.

Kalliokoski, J. (1952), Interpretations of the Structural Geology of the Sherridon-Flin Flon Region, Manitoba, *Geol. Surv. Can.,* Bull. 25.

Kalliokoski, J. (1952), Weldon Bay Map-Area, Manitoba, *Geol. Surv. Can.,* Mem. 270.

Kerr, F. A. (1936), Flin Flon Map-Area, Manitoba, unpublished report.

Podolsky, T. (1951), Cranberry Portage, East Half, Manitoba, *Geol. Surv. Can.,* Paper 51–17.

Robertson, D. S. (1950), Elbow Lake, Manitoba, *Geol. Surv. Can.,* Paper 50–1.

Robertson, D. S. (1951), Batty Lake, Manitoba, *Geol. Surv. Can.,* Map. 1006A, with descriptive notes.

Robertson, D. S. (1951), The Kisseynew Lineament, Northern Manitoba, *The Precambrian,* vol. 24, no. 5, pp. 8–11, 13, 23.

Stanton, M. S. (1947), Tramping Lake, Manitoba, *Geol. Surv. Can.,* Map 906A, with descriptive notes.

Stockwell, C. H. (1935), Gold Deposits of Elbow-Morton Area, Manitoba, *Geol. Surv. Can.,* Mem. 186.

Stockwell, C. H. (1937), Gold Deposits of Herb Lake, Northern Manitoba, *Geol. Surv. Can.,* Mem. 208.

Stockwell, C. H. (1946), Flin Flon-Mandy Area, Manitoba and Saskatchewan, *Geol. Surv. Can.,* Paper 46–14.

Stockwell, C. H., and Geology Staff of the Hudson Bay Mining and Smelting Co. Ltd. (1948), Flin Flon Mine, *Structural Geology of Canadian Ore Deposits,* Can. Inst. Min. Met., pp. 295–301.

Stockwell, C. H., and Harrison, J. M. (1948), Structural Control of Ore Deposits in Northern Manitoba, *Structural Geology of Canadian Ore Deposits,* Can. Inst. Min. Met., pp. 284–295.

Stockwell, C. H. (1950), The Use of Plunge in the Construction of Cross-sections of Folds, *Proc. Geol. Assoc. Can.,* vol. 3, pp. 97–121.

Tanton, T. L. (1941), Flin Flon, Saskatchewan and Manitoba, *Geol. Surv. Can.,* Map 632A, with descriptive notes.

Wright, J. F. (1929), Kississing Lake Area, Manitoba, *Geol. Surv. Can.,* Sum. Rept. (1928), Pt. B, pp. 73–104.

CHAPTER 7

Solution of Inclined Fault Problems by Descriptive Geometry

Terminology and Principles Involved

There are numerous ways by which faults may be classified. The classification based on mechanics of origin (thrusting, gravity, wrenching, or tearing) was discussed in Chapter 3. In the present chapter classifications based on the nature and direction of movement are more important, as the current problem is to determine the relative positions of disrupted strata or veins on opposite sides of faults.

The nature of the fault movement may be translational (straight line, see Fig. 172) or rotational (circular movement, see Fig. 173).

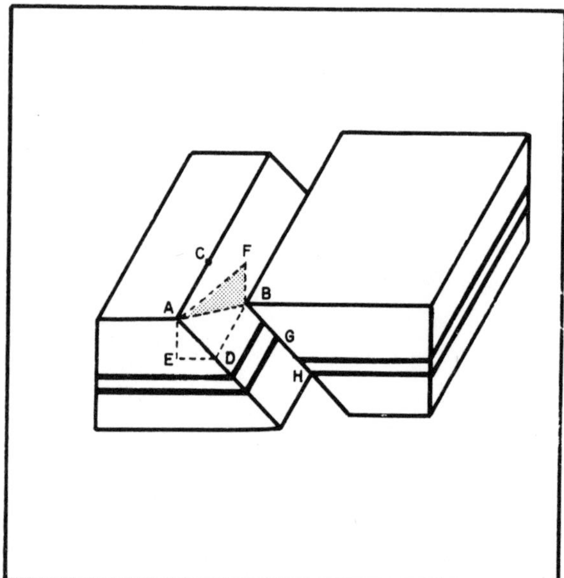

FIGURE 172. An oblique-slip fault with translational movement. *AB* = net slip; *AF* = horizontal component of net slip; *FB* = vertical component of net slip; *AD* = dip slip; angle *CAB* = rake and is measured in the plane of the fault (is known as pitch also); angle *FAB* = plunge of net slip and is measured in a vertical plane.

The direction of movement may be parallel to the strike of the fault (strike-slip fault, see Fig. 174), directly down the dip of the fault (dip-slip fault, see Fig. 175), or diagonally down the dip of the fault (oblique-slip fault, see Fig. 172).

The main problem involved in this chapter is the determination of the position of ore shoots, veins, coal seams, and so forth, which have been displaced by faulting. All of the methods described are limited by the assumption that the faults, veins, beds, and so forth, are plane surfaces in the problem areas.

The first step is to determine the net slip, rake, and movement direction of the fault. This requires knowledge of the location of points on opposite

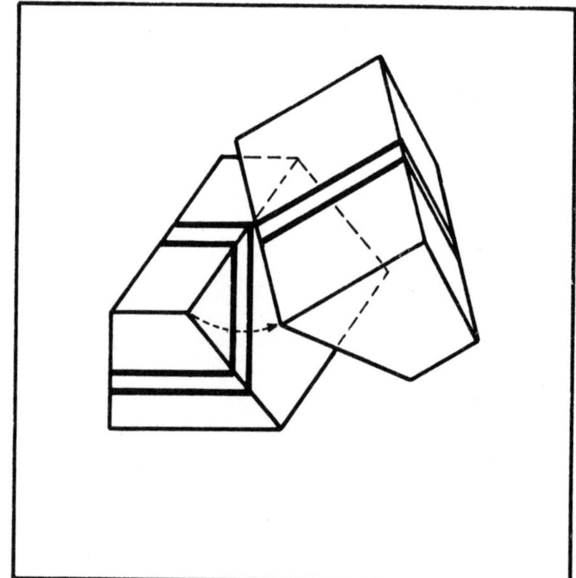

FIGURE 173. Rotational fault movement.

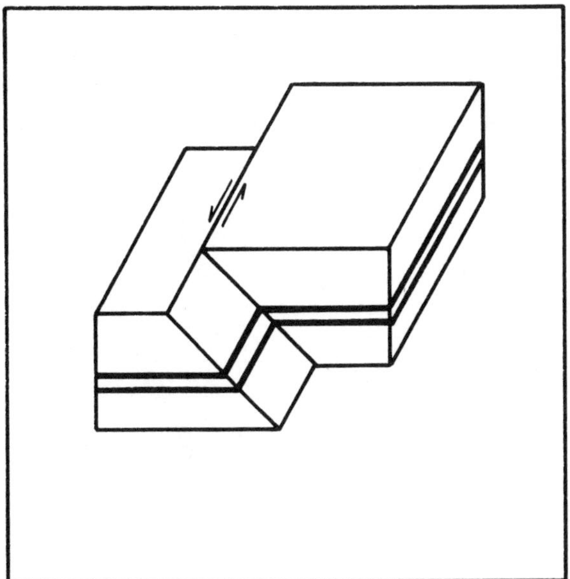

FIGURE 174. Fault movement parallel to the strike of the fault (strike-slip fault).

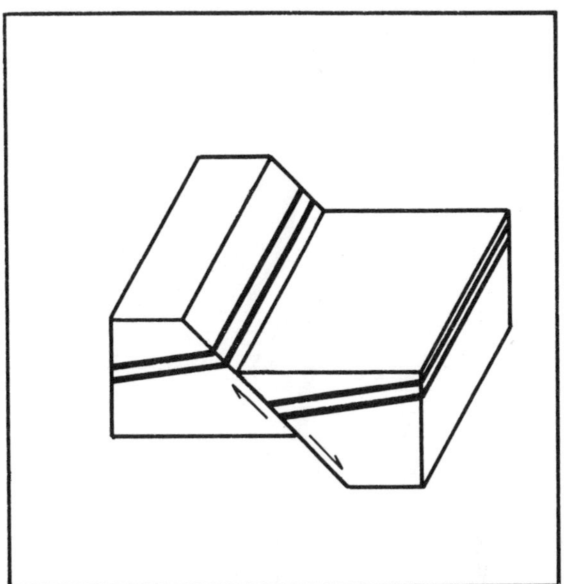

FIGURE 175. Fault movement directly down the dip of the fault (dip-slip fault).

sides of the fault which were in juxtaposition prior to faulting. The intersection of two recognizable plane surfaces such as dikes, coal seams, or veins (Fig. 176) provides a line of intersection (line XY in Fig. 176). The intersection of this line on a fault surface provides a point (point X in Fig. 176) which can be recognized on the opposite side of the fault after displacement has ocurred (point X' in Fig. 177). The distance between points which

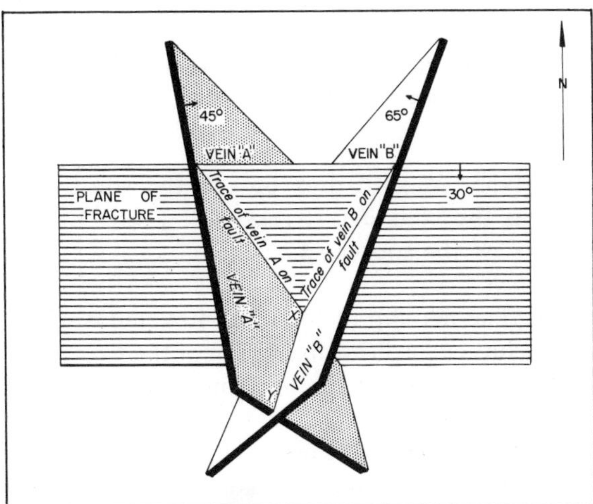

FIGURE 176. Three-dimensional view of veins *A* and *B* cut by a fracture striking east-west and dipping south at 30°.

were previously in juxtaposition (distance XX' in Fig. 177) gives the length of the net slip as seen in the plane of the fault. Thus the problem consists mainly of locating the traces on the fault plane of two veins, beds, dikes, and so forth, which intersect to form a line which penetrates the fault surface. The method used for the determination of the line of intersection of two plane surfaces (e.g., the trace of vein A on the fault, Fig. 176) has been described previously in Chapter 1.

Once the net slip has been determined in the plane of the fault, the fault surface is rotated up to the horizontal by using the strike of the fault as an axis of rotation. This allows the full length of the net slip to be measured ($N'S'$ in Fig. 178) rather than just the horizontal projection of the net slip (NS of Fig. 178).

After the length of the net slip and its rake have been determined (Fig. 177), this information can be used to determine the displaced positions of beds, veins, and so forth which do not intersect other recognizable beds, veins, and so forth. Thus the position of vein C (Fig. 177) and its trace on the lower side of the fault are determined, and the net slip is applied directly to this trace so as to locate the position of this trace on the upper side of the fault also.

The steps involved in the solution of such problems are described in the following example.

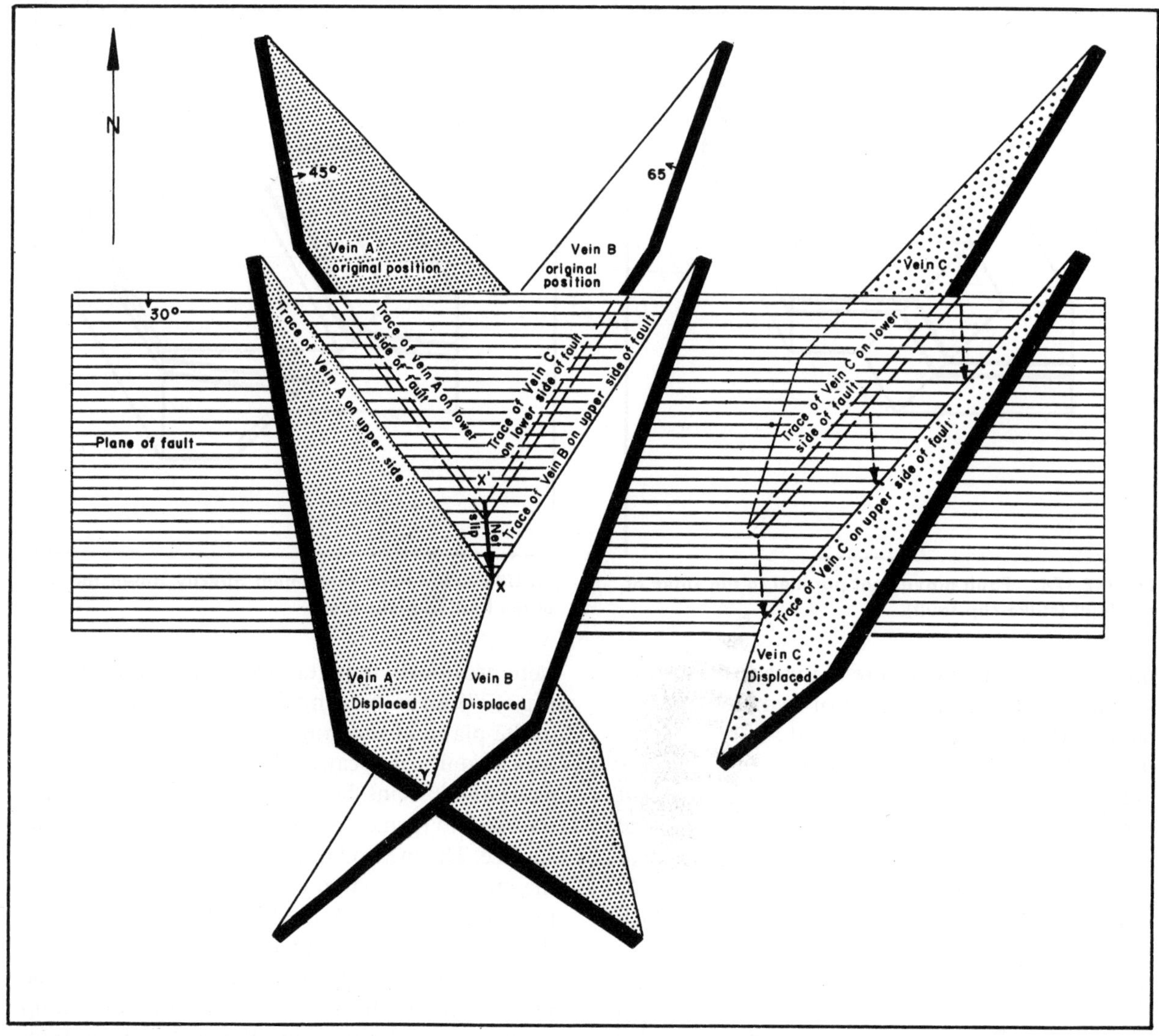

FIGURE 177. Three-dimensional view of veins *A*, *B*, and *C* which have been displaced in a south-southeast direction by oblique slip translational movement on a normal fault striking east-west and dipping south at 30°.

APPLICATION OF DESCRIPTIVE GEOMETRY TO THE SOLUTION OF AN OBLIQUE SLIP-THRUST FAULT PROBLEM INVOLVING TRANSLATIONAL MOVEMENT (Fig. 178)

Data Provided: Thrust fault *TT′* striking 090 (N90°E) and dipping 30°S. Veins BB_1 and AA_1 have formed in fractures which originally were strike-slip faults (= shear zones). These veins are disrupted by thrust fault *TT′* and the disruption has caused the veins BB_1 and AA_1 to be displaced from positions $A'A_1'$ and $B'B_1'$. The vein AA_1 strikes 325° (N35°W) and dips 65° to the southwest, whereas the vein BB_1 strikes 040° (N40°E) and dips 60° to the southeast.

Determine:

1. The net slip of the fault movement which has caused the disruption of the two veins.
2. The strike of the horizontal projection of the net slip.
3. The plunge of the net slip.
4. The rake of the net slip.
5. The relative direction of fault movement.

Method: Draw folding lines (FL, F_1L_1, F_2L_2) at right angles to BB_1, AA_1, and TT', and about these

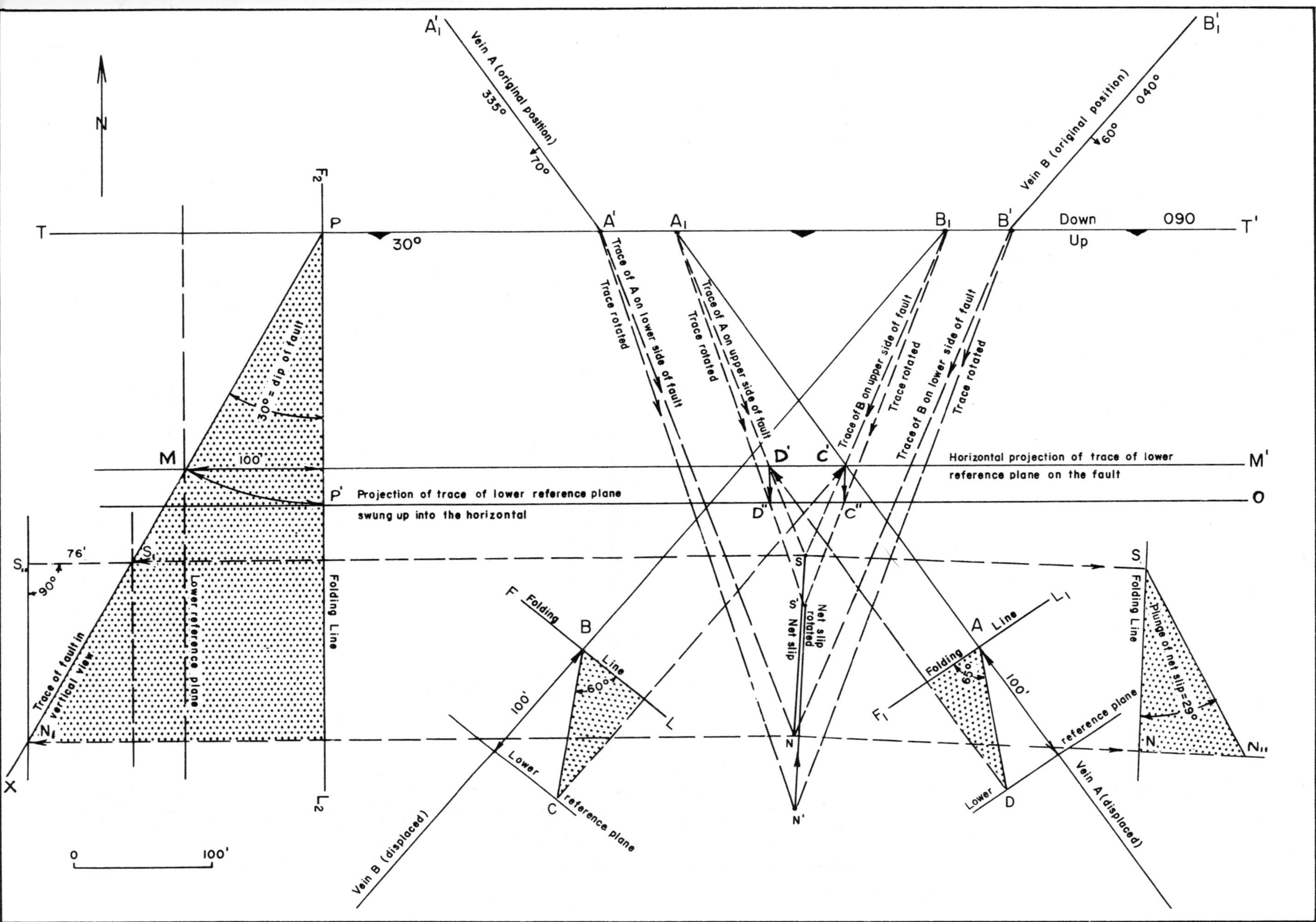

FIGURE 178. Steps involved in the solution of an inclined fault problem (translational movement) by descriptive geometry.

lines construct vertical cross sections to show the traces of the two veins and of the fault in vertical cross section.

Construct lower reference planes 100 feet below each of the folding lines. The traces of the fault and veins intersect the lower reference plane at M, C, and D, respectively.

From M draw in MM' parallel to TT'. MM' represents the horizontal projection of the intersection of the thrust fault with the lower reference plane.

Lines CC' and DD' are drawn parallel to BB, and AA,. The points C' and D' represent the points of intersection of the two veins with the fault at the elevation of the lower reference plane. Inasmuch as the determination of net slip is required, it is necessary to rotate the plane of the fault up into the horizontal, as the full length of the net slip can be measured only in the plane of the fault.

Using PM as a radius and P as the center, draw an arc to intersect F_2L_2 at P'. Now PP' is the true slope distance in the fault plane between the surface plane and the lower reference plane.

From P' draw $P'O$ parallel to TT'. $T'PP'O$ is now a section in the plane of the fault, this plane having been rotated into the horizontal.

From D' and C' drop perpendiculars to $P'O$ so as to intersect $P'O$ at D'' and C'', respectively. D'' and C'' now represent the intersection of the veins with the lower reference plane *as viewed in the fault plane,* this fault plane having been rotated into the horizontal.

Now project A,D'' and B,C'' to an intersection point at S'. A,S' and B,S' represent the trace of the two veins on the south wall of the fault. S' represents their intersection on the south wall (as seen in the plane of the fault which has been rotated up to the horizontal).

Then draw $A'N'$ and $B'N'$ parallel to A,S' and to B,S'. N' represents the intersection of the trace of the two veins on the north wall of the thrust fault.

$N'S'$ then represents the *net slip,* and the angle which the projection of $N'S'$ makes with TT' represents *the rake of the net slip.*

Draw A,D' and B,C' to an intersection at S. A,S is the horizontal projection of the intersection of vein AA, with the fault, and B,S is the horizontal projection of the intersection of vein BB, with the fault. S is the horizontal projection of the intersection of the two veins on the south wall of the fault plane.

Now draw $A'N$ and $B'N$ parallel to A,S and B,S, respectively. NS is then the *horizontal projection* of the net slip.

To determine the plunge of the net slip, the elevation of the points for which N and S are horizontal projections must be calculated. This is accomplished by drawing lines westward from N and S parallel to TT' so as to intersect PX at S, and $N_{,,}$ respectively. The distance $S,S_{,,}$ is then equivalent to the difference in elevation between N and S.

Now the distance NS is laid off on a separate part of the map sheet and a perpendicular is dropped from N to $N_{,,}$ so that $NN_{,,}$ is equal to $S,S_{,,}$. Then complete the triangle by drawing in $SN_{,,}$. The vertical angle $NSN_{,,}$ is the *plunge of the net slip.*

Because the intersection point of the two veins on the south side of the fault with the fault planes (S') is at a higher elevation and to the north-northeast of the corresponding intersection on the north side of the fault (N'), it must be concluded that the *south side of the fault has moved up and to the north-northeast, relative to the north side of the fault.*

Principles Involved for Fault Problems That Have Rotational Movement

Many faults are characterized by rotational movement. The pole about which rotation takes place is usually perpendicular to the fault plane; otherwise a crushing action would result on one side of the fault and a gap would result on the other side. The actual position of the pole of rotation may be located above the ground level of the area being studied, owing to the erosion which has occurred since faulting.

The main problem in rotational faulting is to locate the pole of the fault. This requires the location of two points on opposite sides of the fault which were in juxtaposition before faulting (points C and C' in Fig. 180). Two intersecting dikes, veins, or similar features are required to provide

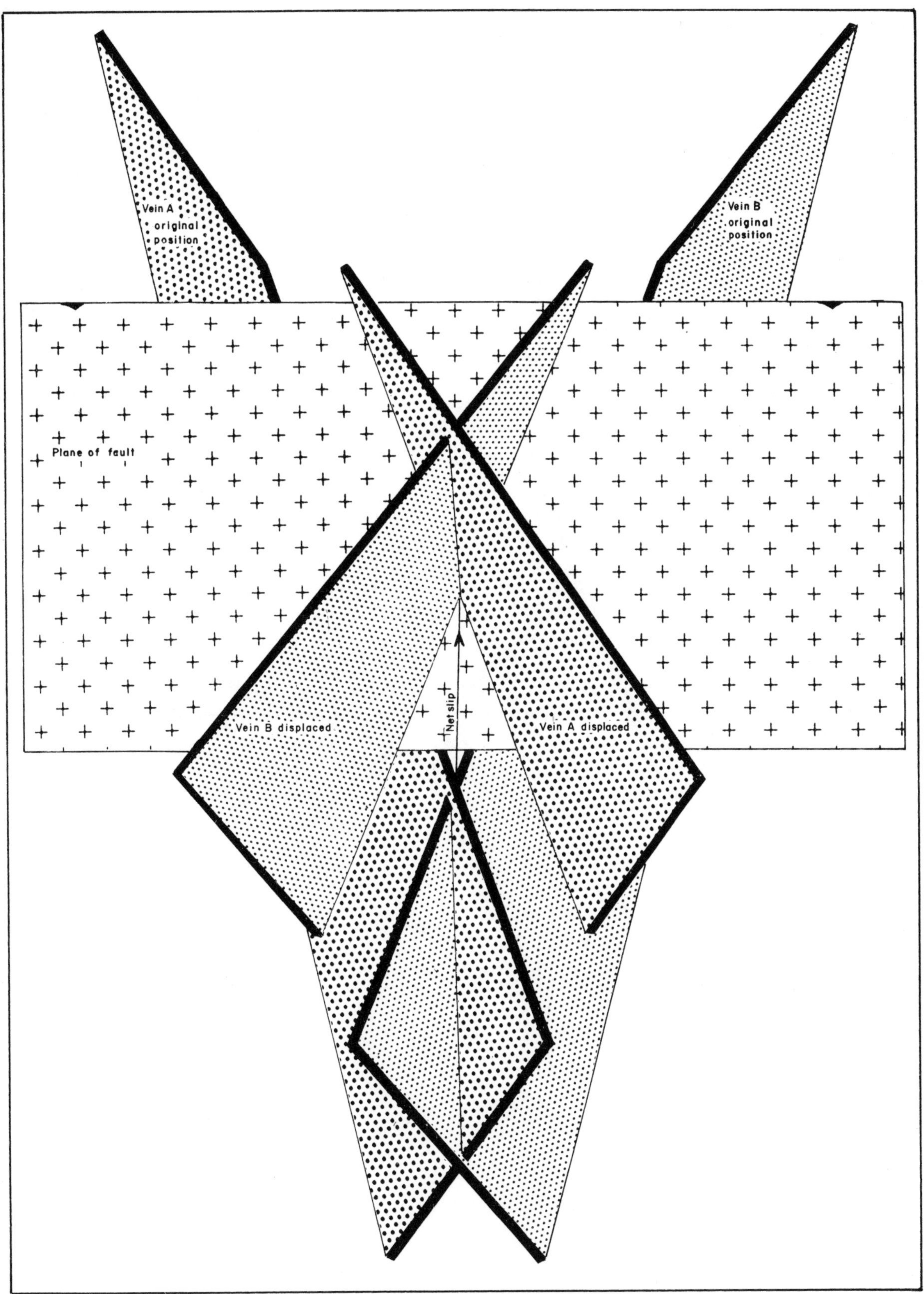

FIGURE 179. Three-dimensional view of the faulted veins shown in Figure 178.

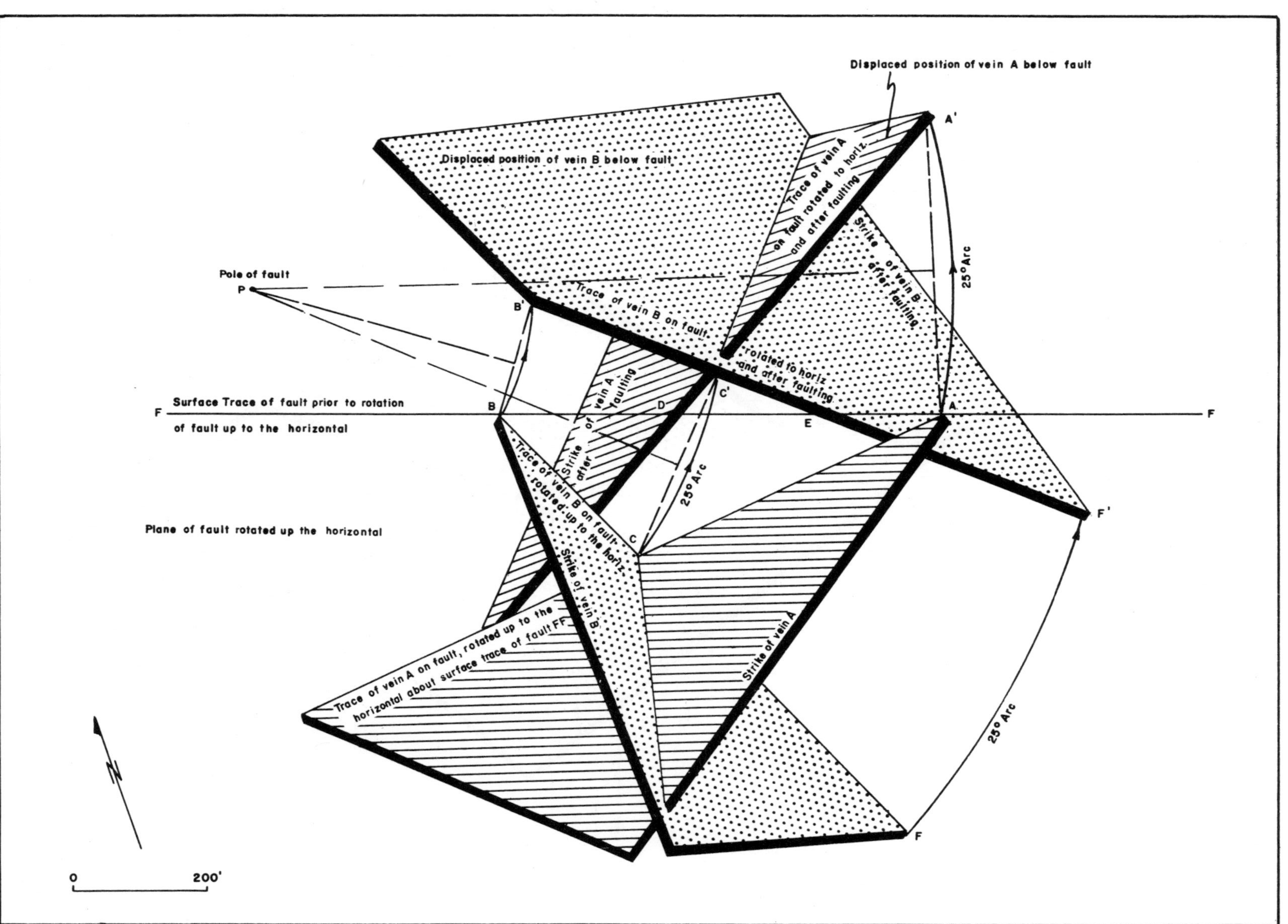

FIGURE 180. Three-dimensional view of veins *A* and *B* which are displaced by fault *FF*. Fault movement is 25° counterclockwise rotation about pole *P*. Pole *P* is located 200 feet above the surface of the ground.

recognizable intersection lines. And these intersecting lines must be in the plane of the fault. In Figure 180, the strike and dip of two intersecting veins are known for both sides of vertical fault *FF* (235/30° NW for vein *A* on south side of fault, 180°/50° E for vein *B* on south side of fault, 044/63° NW for vein *A* on north side of fault, 345°/26° ENE for vein *B* on north side of fault), and the points where the veins intersect the fault are known (*A, B, D, E*). Strike of the fault: 110°.

The first step is to determine the trace of each vein on the fault for points *A, B, D,* and *E*. Then these traces are rotated up to the horizontal about *FF* as an axis of rotation (Fig. 180).

Figure 180, being a section in the plane of the fault, is the plane which contains the pole of the fault. It will be noted that the rotated traces of veins *A* and *B* intersect at point *C* on the upper side of the fault, at point *C′* on the lower side.

CC′ must be on the arc of a circle whose center point is the pole of the fault. If a perpendicular is drawn from the midpoint of line *CC′*, then the pole of the fault must be on this line. The exact position of the pole may be determined by drawing perpendiculars from the midpoints of lines BB′, *AA′*, and *FF′*. It will be seen that these perpendiculars intersect at *P* which is the pole of the fault (Fig. 180).

If the pole of the fault and the amount of angular rotation are known, then almost any rotational fault problem can be solved. The following example will illustrate the principles involved.

APPLICATION OF DESCRIPTIVE GEOMETRY TO THE SOLUTION OF ROTATIONAL FAULTING

Data Provided: Vertical fault *FF* striking N 70° W is shown on the −200-foot level of a mine (Fig. 181). An ore-bearing vein *XX* is terminated by the fault. *XX* strikes north-south and dips 50°E. The movement on the fault is believed to be entirely rotational (25° counterclockwise), and the original position of the rotational pole *P* was at 0 feet elevation.

Determine: Disrupted continuation of ore-bearing vein *XX* on the north side of vertical fault.

Method: The first step is to determine the position of the trace of vein *XX* on fault *FF* and to rotate this trace up to the horizontal. This is accomplished by constructing folding line *hh* perpendicular to *XX* and drawing the dip of 50°E on this vertical section. The line *h,h,* represents the −300-foot level for this vertical section. The line *h,h* is then projected through to intersect *FF* at *h,,*. A perpendicular *h,,h,,,* is dropped from *FF* to the −300-foot level, and the angle *FXt* then equals the apparent dip of *XX* on the vertical fault *FF*. Before rotating the trace *Xh,,,* up to the horizontal, it is necessary to digress for a moment: Draw an auxiliary vertical plane *ff* parallel to *FF* at any convenient distance from *FF*. *FF* and *ff* thus represent the traces of two parallel vertical planes on the −200-foot level. The reason for this auxiliary vertical plane will become apparent later.

Now rotate the −300 levels (i.e., the −300-foot structure contours for vertical planes *FF* and *ff*) for vertical planes *FF* and *ff* up to the horizontal, using *FF* and *ff* as axes of rotation. During this upward rotation, the pole *P* (originally at the 0-foot elevation in vertical fault *FF*) would rotate down to the −200-foot level at point *P′* (Fig. 181), and the trace of *XX* on *FF* would rotate up to the horizontal at *Xt*. The purpose of this rotation is to bring the plane of the fault into the horizontal plane of the paper, so that the rotational fault movement can be applied directly on Figure 181.

It is now possible to revolve *Xt* about *P′* through 25° in a counterclockwise direction. This gives the displaced position of the trace *xt,*. The point *X′* is the position where *xt,* intersects the north side of the fault on the −200-foot level.

It will be noted that *X* moved through 25° to *x* and that *t* also moved through 25° to *t,*. And yet the distances *Xx* and *tt* are not equal. This is always true for rotational faulting. This is why the auxiliary plane *ff* is required. The position of *XX* on *ff* would then be closer to the pole of faulting. *P″* is the pole of the fault for auxiliary vertical section *ff*. It will be noted that the projection of *XX* onto *ff* is *x,*. Now rotate *P″x,* through 25° counterclockwise to *P″x,′*. Then draw *x,′t,′* parallel to *xt,*. It will be noted that *x,′t,′* intersects *ff* at *X,′*. *X′X,′* then equals the strike of the ore vein at the −200-foot level after being displaced by rotational faulting.

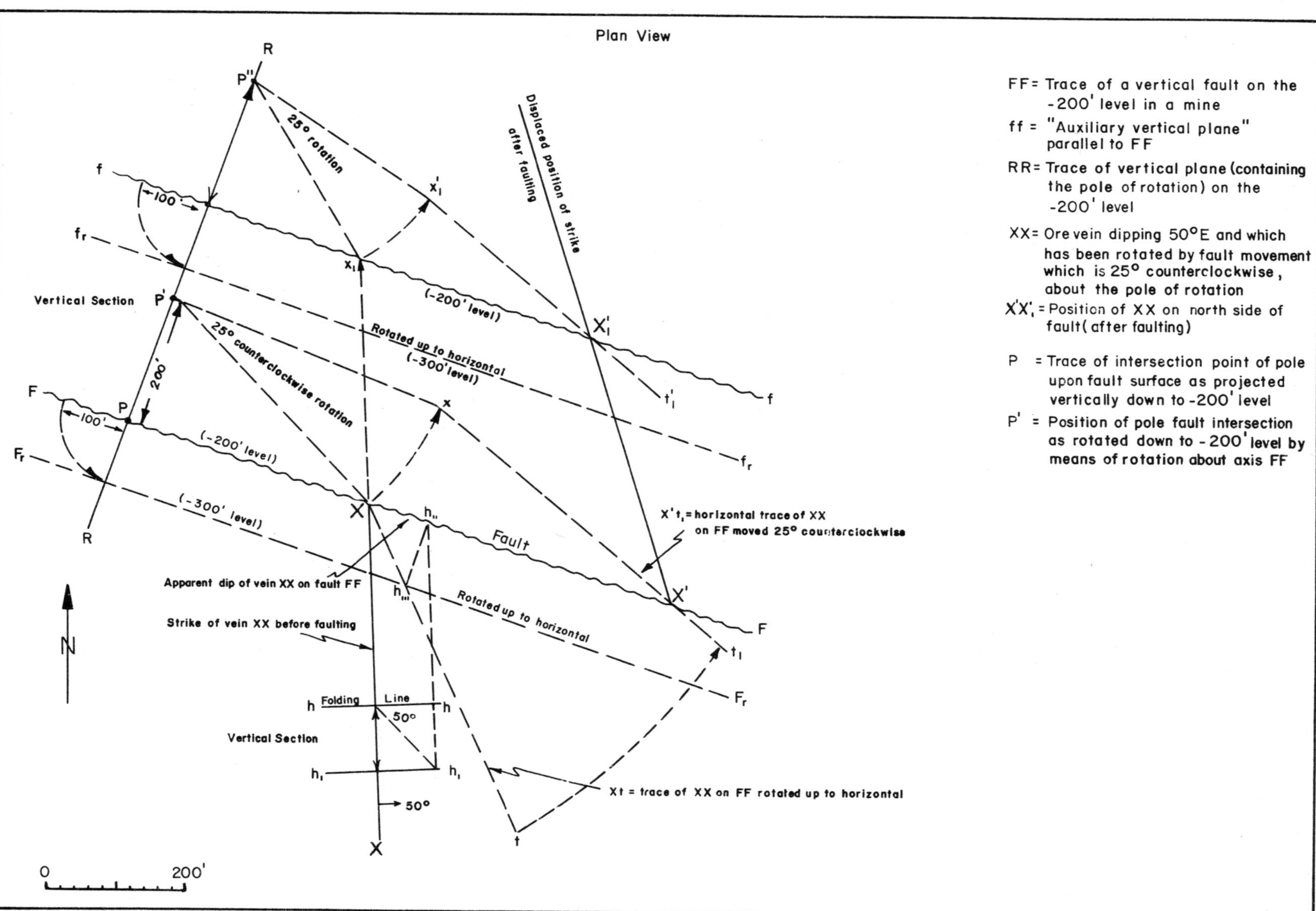

FIGURE 181. Steps involved in the solution of a rotational fault problem. Figure 180 is a three-dimensional view of the fault situation shown in Figure 181.

PROBLEM 27

DETERMINATION OF VEIN AND FAULT PATTERNS (FIG. 182)

Data Provided: Faults and a vein have been mapped at the locations and elevations shown below. The normal fault is older than the thrust fault. The hanging wall of the normal fault moved down and to the south-southeast. The net slip is 250 feet and the rake of the net slip = 80°. The hanging wall of the thrust fault moved up to the east-northeast. Its net slip = 220 feet. Rake of the net slip = 60°. Vein *A* is older than either fault.

Determine: The complete pattern of veins and faults after extending the faults and veins to intersection points and after applying the fault movements. Draw the map on the 1500-foot level. Draw a vertical north-south section through outcrop *C* to show all fault and vein relationships. Draw a three-dimensional diagram of the area (along the lines of Figs. 177 and 179) to show all of the vein-fault relationships.

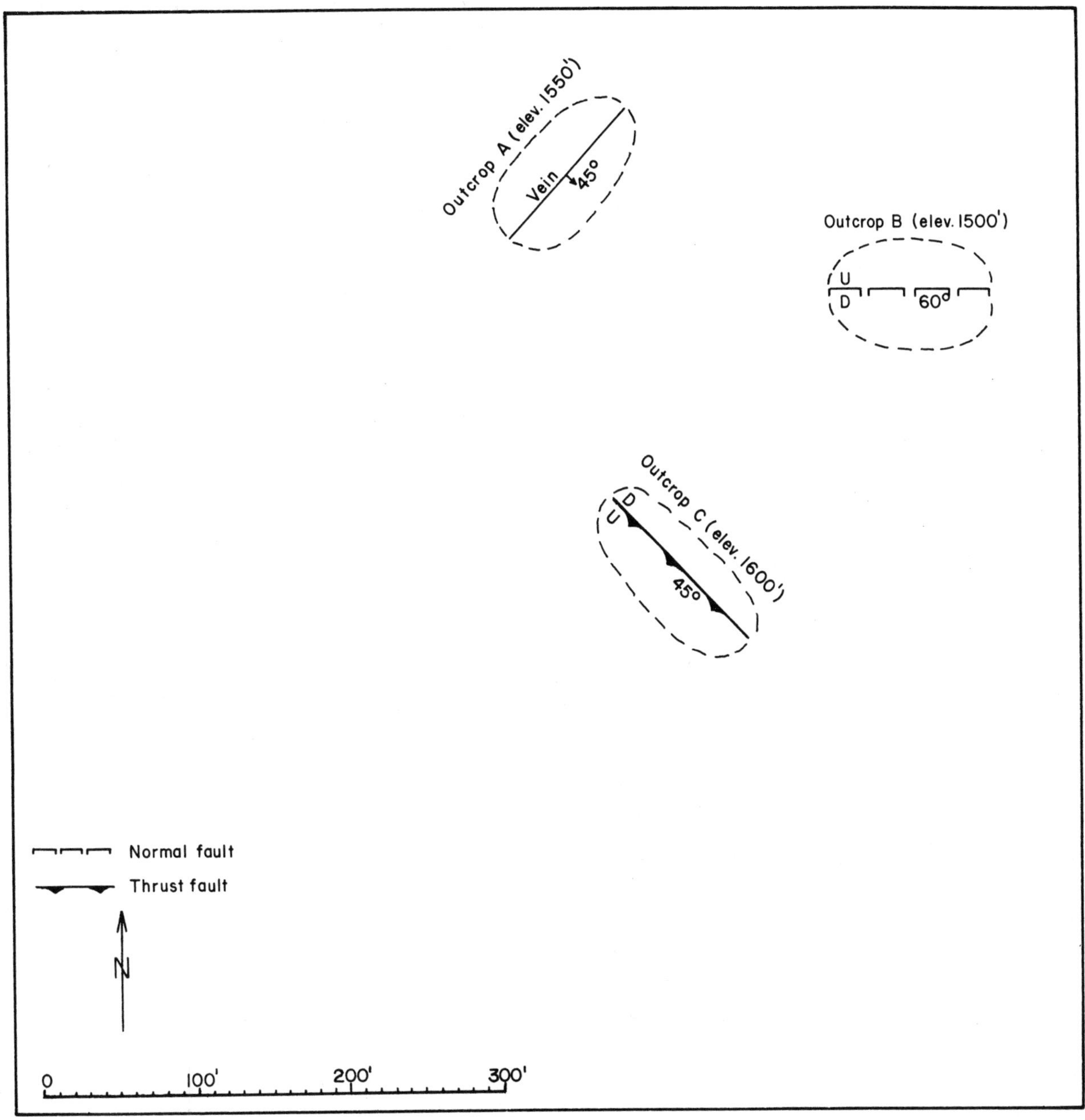

FIGURE 182. For use with Problem 27.

PROBLEM 28

TRANSLATIONAL FAULT PROBLEM

Data Provided: The vein, dike, fault pattern shown in Figure 183 was mapped on the −500-foot level in a mine. The bearing (horizontal) of slickensides on the fault was mapped as 330°.

Determine: What type of fault is this (genetic and geometrical classification)? What is the net slip, horizontal and vertical component of net slip, plunge of net slip, rake of net slip? Discuss the stress distribution which has caused this vein, dike, fault pattern. Has there been any regional tilting in this area (see Figs. 206–225, pp. 194–196)? If so, from what direction? Draw a three-dimensional view of this vein, dike, fault pattern.

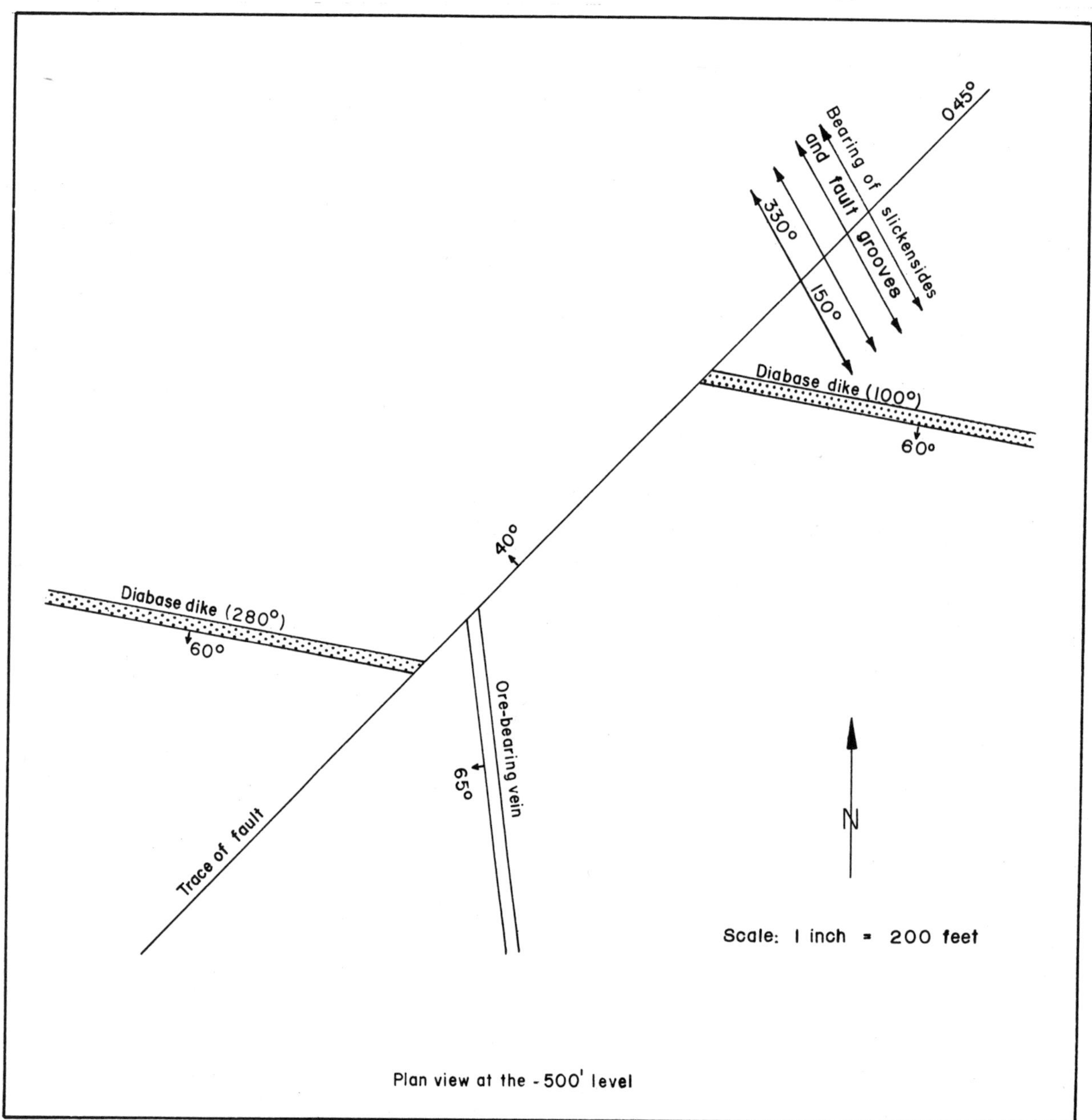

FIGURE 183. For use with Problem 28.

PROBLEM 29

ROTATIONAL FAULT PROBLEM

Data Provided: The vein, dike, fault pattern shown in Figure 184 was mapped on the +1000-foot level of a mine. The fault movement was rotational.
Determine: Locate the pole of the fault and describe its location in terms of co-ordinates and elevation. Describe the fault movement in terms of direction and amount of rotation. Where would the ore vein occur on the north side of the fault and what is its attitude there? Draw a three-dimensional view of this disrupted vein and dike pattern.

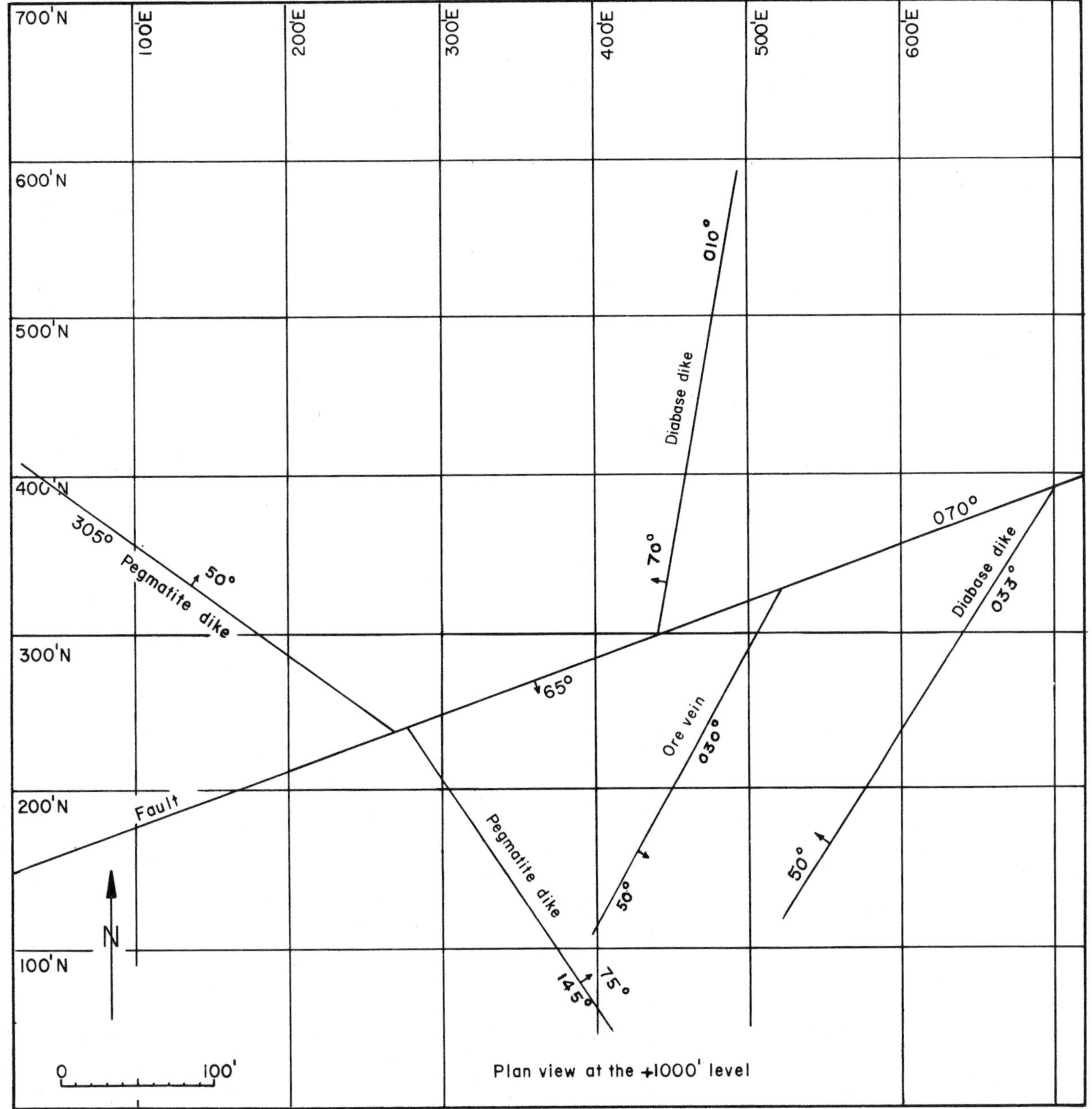

FIGURE 184. For use with Problem 29.

References

Beckwith, R. H. (1947), Fault Problems in Fault Planes, *Bull. Geol. Soc. Am.,* vol. 58, pp. 79–108.

Billings, M. P. (1954), *Structural Geology,* 2nd ed., Prentice-Hall, Inc., 514 pp.

Donn, W. L., and Shimer, J. A. (1958), *Graphic Methods in Structural Geology,* Appleton-Century-Crofts, Inc., 180 pp.

Emmons, S. E. (1892), Faulted Veins, *Eng. and Min. Jour.,* vol. 53, no. 21, p. 548.

Fisher, D. J. (1943), Measuring Linear Structures on Steep-dipping Surfaces, *Am. Miner.,* vol. 28, pp. 204–208.

Forrester, J. D. (1946), *Principles of Field and Mining Geology,* John Wiley & Sons, Inc., 647 pp.

Haddock, M. H. (1926), *Location of Mineral Fields,* Crosby Lockwood & Son, 295 pp.

Haddock, M. H. (1938), *Disrupted Strata,* The Technical Press Ltd., London, 104 pp.

Ingerson, E. (1942), Apparatus for Direct Measurement of Linear Structures, *Am. Miner.,* vol. 27, pp. 721–725.

Lowe, K. E. (1946), A Graphic Solution for Certain Problems of Linear Structure, *Am. Miner.,* vol. 31, pp. 425–434.

Ludlum, J. C., and Dennison, J. M. (1957), *Structural Geology Laboratory Manual,* Edward Brothers Inc., 108 pp.

Morishita, M. (1938), On the Graphic Method of Representing Faults and Strata, *Jap. Jour. Geol. Geogr.,* vol. 15, pp. 207–239.

Nevin, C. M. (1953), *Principles of Structural Geology,* 4th ed., John Wiley & Sons, Inc., 410 pp.

Reid, H. F. (1909), Geometry of Faults, *Bull. Geol. Soc. Am.* vol. 20, pp. 171–196.

Tolman, C. F., Jr. (1911), *Graphical Solution of Fault Problems,* Mining and Scientific Press, 43 pp.

CHAPTER 8

The Use of Stereographic Projections in Solving Structural Problems

Terminology and Principles Involved

Normal, orthographic, perspective, and isometric projections have been discussed previously. It was seen that geological structures, such as beds, veins, dikes, and so forth, could be represented in both vertical and plan view on these projections (Fig. 185). In actuality, geologic structures are mapped on the spherical surface of the earth, and it is frequently desirable to study structures in their true spherical relationship. The spherical nature of structures becomes better appreciated when the great lineaments of the earth's surface are examined. Some of them appear as curved lines on conical projections and as straight lines on mercator projections.

Spherical projections of geologic structures may be used for illustration purposes (Fig. 186) but are difficult to construct. If a sphere is drawn about a structural plane so that the center of the sphere lies on this structural plane, then the plane will intersect the surface of this sphere along a *great circle,* and this circle of intersection constitutes the *spherical projection* of the structural plane. A great circle is defined as the intersection of a sphere by any plane passing through the center of the sphere.

Stereographic projections are used to represent spherical projections on a plane surface. They are geometric projections of spherical co-ordinates onto a horizontal plane. The problem of representing a spherical projection on a two-dimensional horizontal surface is analogous to the problem of the astronomer producing a two-dimensional map of the solar system.

In structural geology the lower hemisphere of spherical projections is usually projected into the horizontal as most problems are concerned with information below the plane of our maps.

The lower half of the great circle formed by the intersection of the above-mentioned structural

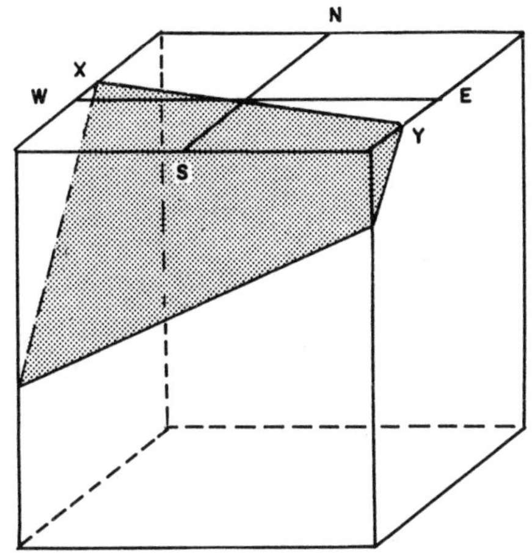

FIGURE 185. A structural plane as visualized in orthographic projection.

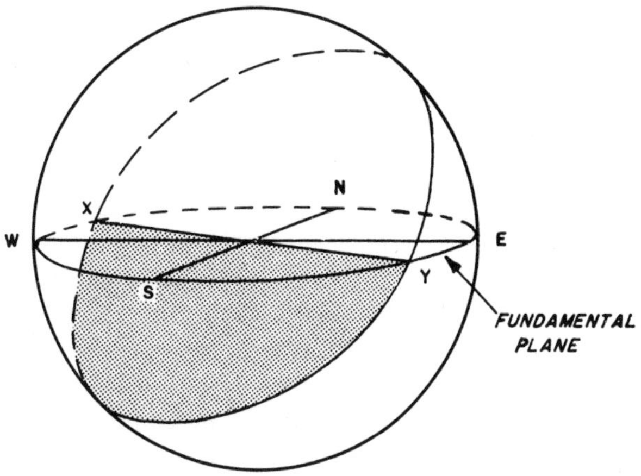

FIGURE 186. The same structural plane as seen in Figure 185,visualized in spherical projection.

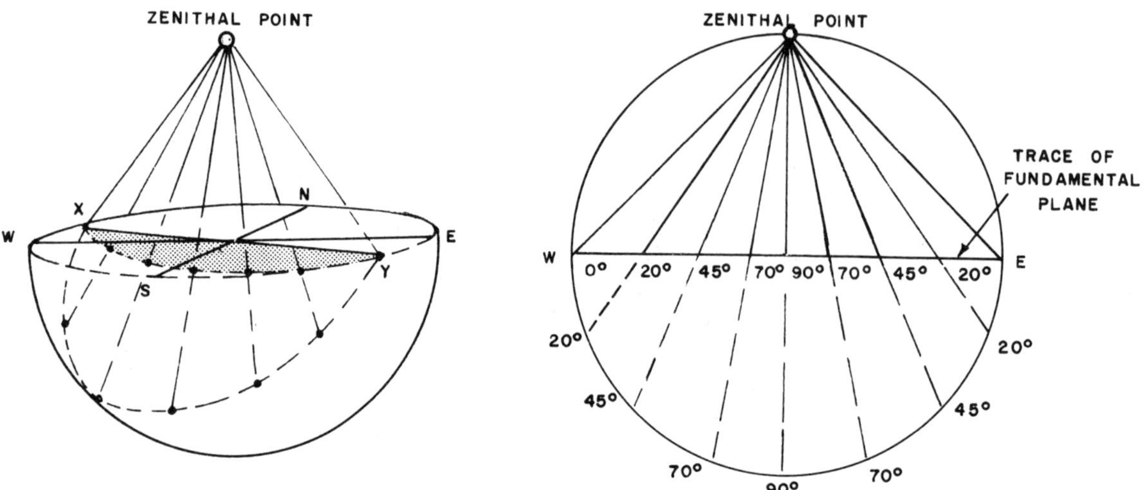

FIGURE 187 (*left*). Illustrating the conversion of a sperical projection into a stereographic projection. The original structural plane is now seen only in the fundamental plane of the stereographic projection.

FIGURE 188 (*right*). Vertical east-west section through a spherical projection to show that the angular relations of the spherical projection are preserved in the stereographic projection but that the linear distance corresponding to a degree of arc is less toward the center of the sphere.

plane with the sphere is projected into a stereographic diagram by joining various points on the great circle (Fig. 187) to the *zenithal point* of the sphere. The intersections of these lines with the horizontal plane of the sphere are noted, and these intersection points are joined together to give a *stereogram* which is the stereographic projection of the lower half of the great circle upon the horizontal plane of the sphere. Thus the structural plane originally shown in spherical projection (Fig. 186) is represented now in stereographic projection (Fig. 187).

Study of Figures 185–188 and Figure 189 indicates that when a great circle is projected onto the equatorial plane, the resultant curve or *stereogram* is still an arc of a circle. By projection in this manner of a series of planes striking north-south and dipping east or west at various angles, it is possible to construct a net of meridional (great circular) curves in which the planes are drawn for every 10° dip between vertical and horizontal. It is thus apparent that any angle on the stereographic projection is equal to the corresponding angle on the surface of the sphere (Fig. 188).

A *small circle* is the intersection of a sphere by any plane not passing through the center of the sphere. If we use north and south as centers on the original spherical projection and construct a series of small circles of increasing radius (Fig. 189), then the stereographic projection of these small circles yields a number of *small circular arcs* on the horizontal or *fundamental plane.* The intersection of these small circular arcs (or parallels) with the meridional arcs gives a *meridional stereographic net* (or stereonet) as shown in Figure 189.

General Usage and Limitations

Stereographic projections may be used for many of the problems which have been solved already by descriptive geometry (orthographic projections) earlier in this book, such as apparent dip-true dip problems, intersecting planes, rotational fault problems, and so forth. The stereographic method is actually quicker and simpler in many cases, but the three-dimensional picture may be grasped more easily in the step-by-step procedure of orthographic projections. This is one reason why stereographic projections are introduced later than orthographic, perspective, and isometric projections. In addition, there is one serious weakness of stereographic projections which applies particularly to fault problems—the amount of translational movement cannot be determined. However, by combining the stereographic and orthographic methods both amount of rotation and translation can be determined. The structural features handled on stereographic projections must be plane surfaces. This limitation applies to orthographic

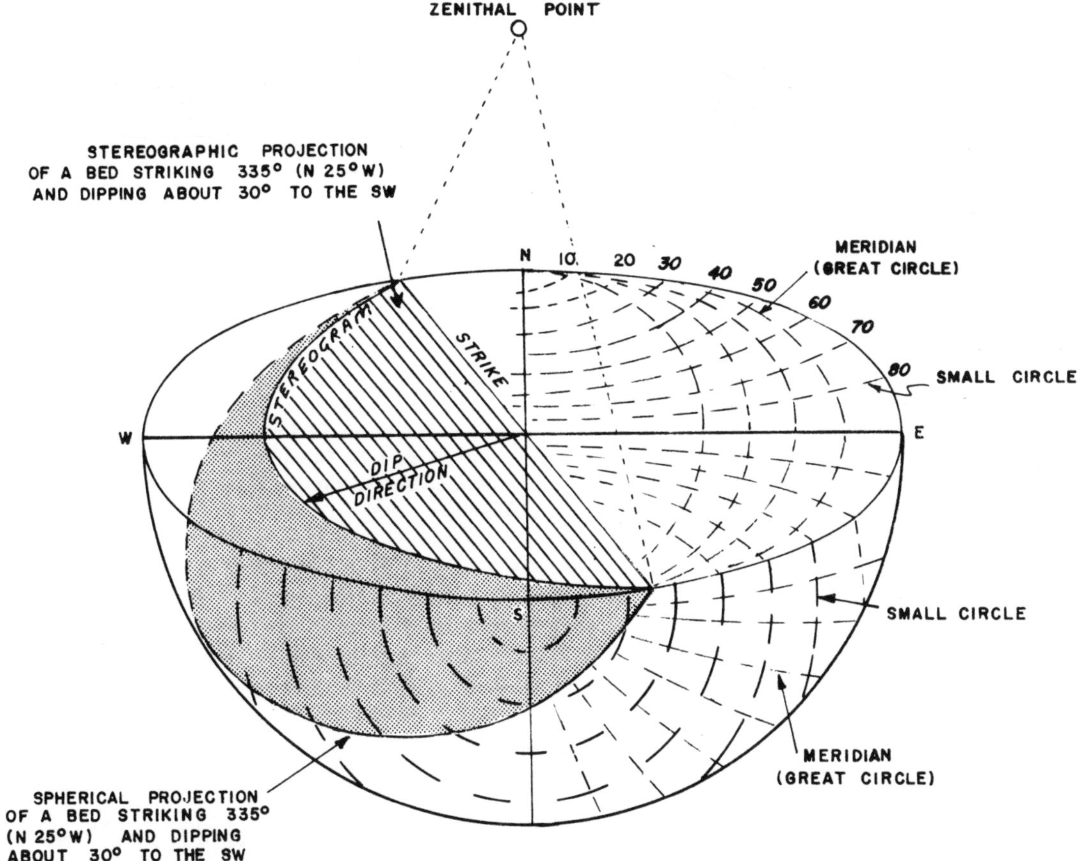

FIGURE 189. Three-dimensional view of a bed striking 335° (N25°W) and dipping about 30° to the southwest. This illustration shows the relationship between spherical and stereographic projections. Study of this diagram shows why all dip angles on stereographic projection should be measured only when the dip direction (plotted on overlay tracing paper) is oriented east-west. Similarly the stereographic curve can only be drawn in accurately when the strike direction on overlay paper is oriented parallel to the north-south line on the underlying stereonet.

projection methods also, but it can be resolved on isometric projections.

The following examples illustrate the use of stereographic methods in solving a variety of structural problems.

DETERMINATION OF STRIKE AND DIP BY STEREOGRAPHIC PROJECTION, GIVEN TWO APPARENT DIPS

Data Provided: Apparent dips for a marker bed have been measured at two different points. At one outcrop the dip appeared to be 25° in a vertical section striking 010°. In the second outcrop the dip appeared to be 34° in a vertical section whose line of strike was 110°.

Determine: The true dip and strike of the formation.

Method: Draw the dip direction lines $OX = 010°$ and $OY = 110°$ on a piece of tracing paper placed over a stereonet. Both dip direction lines must radiate out from the center of the stereonet (Fig. 190).

Now revolve the tracing paper about the center of the net as an axis until the 010° direction lies in the west-east direction of the stereonet (Fig. 191). Draw in the apparent dip of 25° and thus locate point *A*. Similarly locate point *B* (Fig. 192).

Then revolve the tracing paper until a meridian line is found which will pass through both points *A* and *B* (Fig. 193). Draw in this meridional arc.

Now connect the ends of the arc with a straight line *CD*. This is the strike line of the plane *CABD*

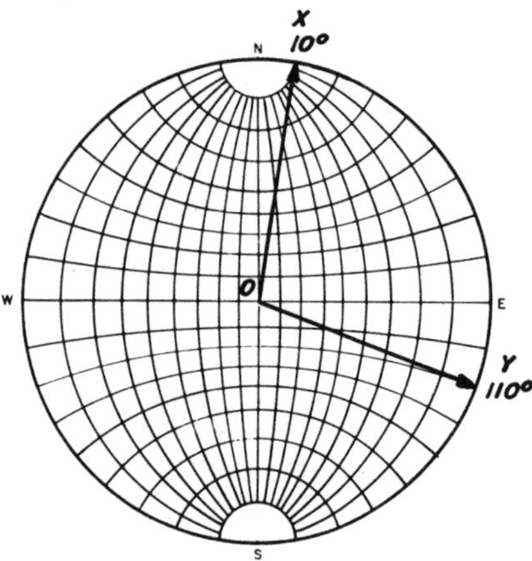

FIGURE 190. Apparent dip directions *OX* and *OY* are plotted in such a manner that they radiate out from the center of the stereonet at 010° and 110°, respectively. These values are not plotted on the net directly but on a sheet of transparent paper placed over the stereonet.

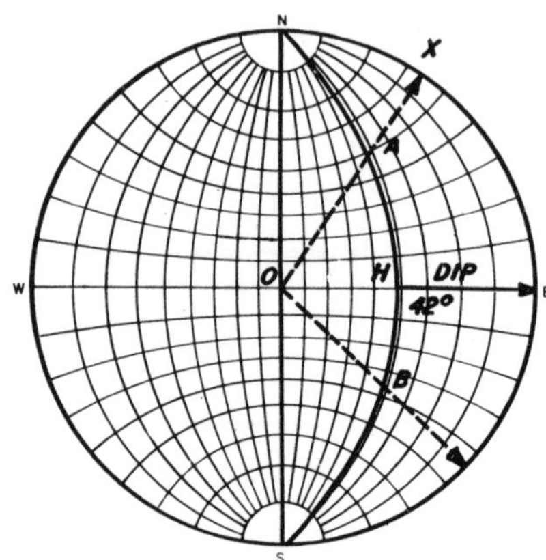

FIGURE 193. The tracing paper is now revolved around until a meridian is found which is common to both points *A* and *B*. The line *OH*, being the only possible perpendicular to the meridian found, is thus the true dip direction.

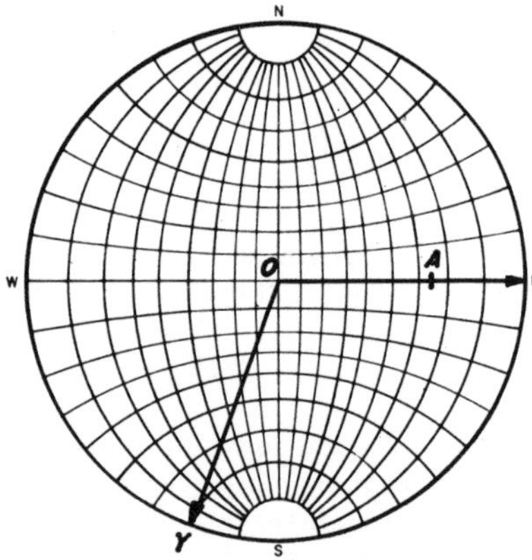

FIGURE 191. The tracing paper is now revolved about the center of the stereonet until the 010° direction lies in the west-east direction of the underlying stereonet. The apparent dip of 25° is then scaled off to give point *A*.

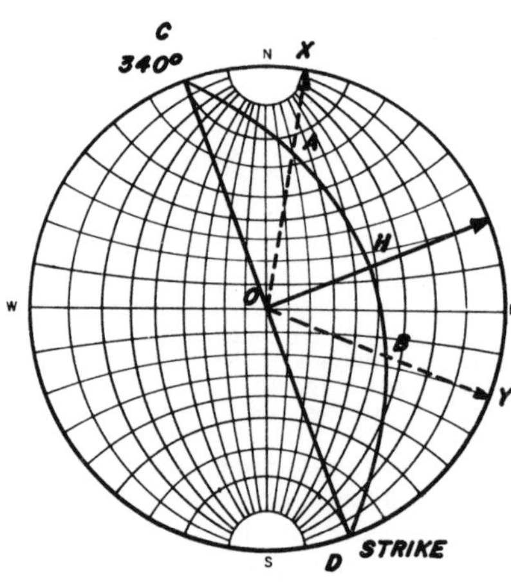

FIGURE 194. The strike direction may be located now by revolving the tracing paper back to its original position where *OX* occupies a strike of 010°.

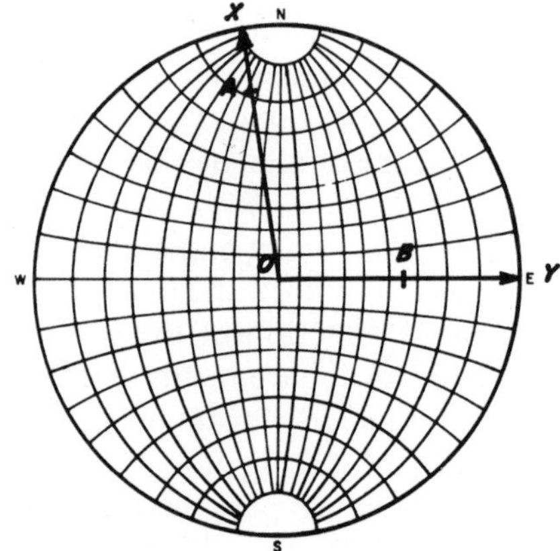

FIGURE 192. Point *B* is located in a similar manner to point *A*, by revolving the tracing paper around until *OY* occupies a west-east position on the underlying stereonet.

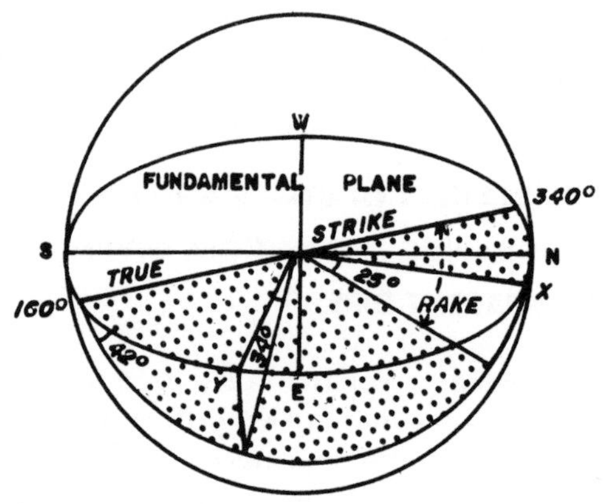

FIGURE 195. Three-dimensional view of Figure 194, facing west.

Determination of strike and dip by stereographic projection, given two apparent dips.

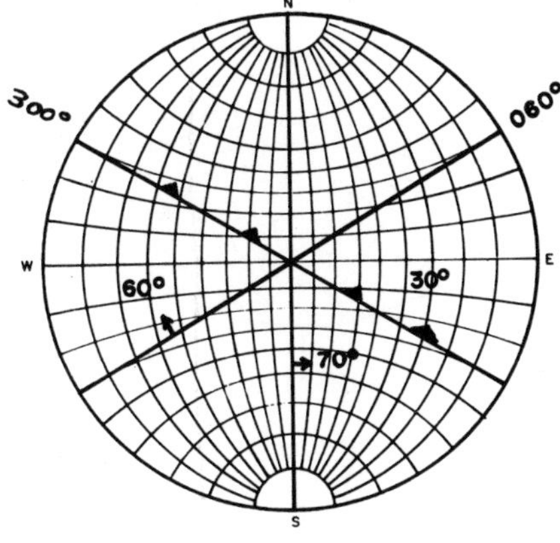

FIGURE 196.

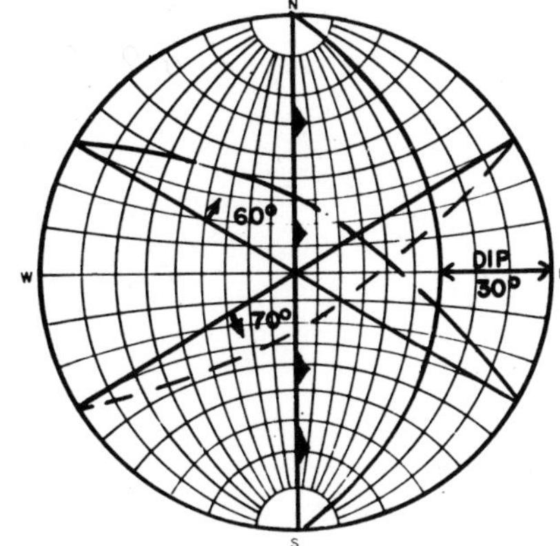

FIGURE 197.

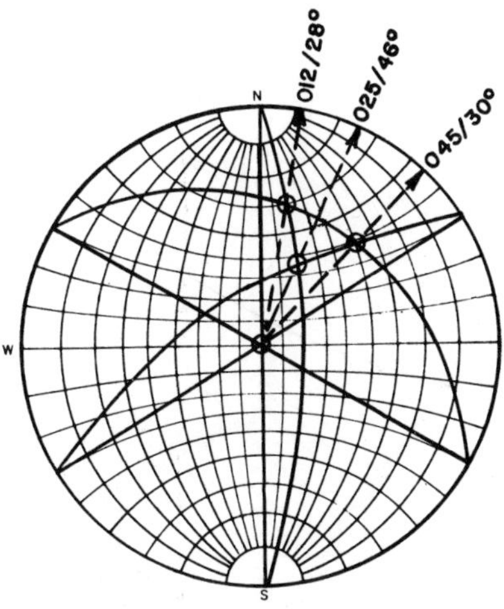

FIGURE 198.

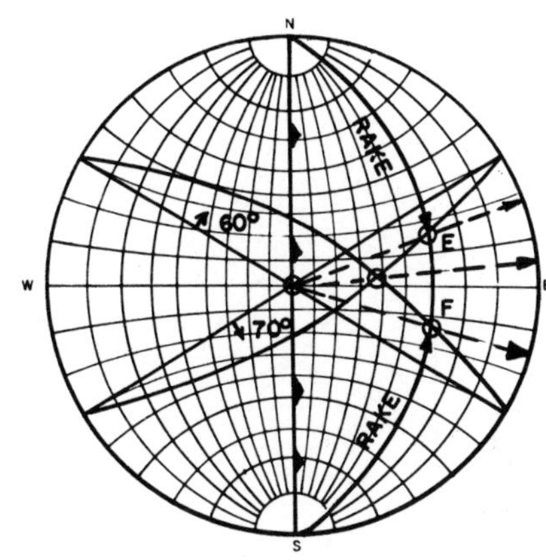

FIGURE 199.

Determination of the attitude of the lines of intersection of plane surfaces by stereographic methods.

at *H*. The true dip angle for the plane *CABD* may then be read off at point *H*, after revolving the tracing paper until *OH* lies in the 090° direction (Fig. 193). The true dip is observed to be 42°.

If the true attitude were known (strike = 340° and dip of 42°ENE), then the apparent dip could be determined for any line of section by simply drawing in the required line of section, noting the points where this section line crossed the meridional arc of the plane *CABD,* and then revolving the tracing paper[1] about the center of the net until this line of section coincided with the west-east line of the underlying stereonet. The apparent dip in such a line of section could then be read off directly. Thus, in a north-south section the apparent dip for plane *CABD* = 18° (Fig. 194).

[1] The use of tracing paper applies to almost all of the methods described. The stereonet itself is usually attached firmly to a table, and a transparent overlay is placed over the net. The overlay is held by a pin or pencil point stuck through the center of the net so that the paper rotates freely.

DETERMINATION OF THE ATTITUDE OF THE LINES OF INTERSECTION OF INTERSECTING PLANE SURFACES

Data Provided: A thrust fault striking 300° and dipping 30°NE. Two veins are disrupted by the thrust fault. One vein strikes 060° and dips 60°NW. The other vein strikes 000° and dips 70° due east.

Determine: The attitude (bearing, inclination, rake) of the intersection of each vein with the thrust fault and the attitude of intersection of the two veins.

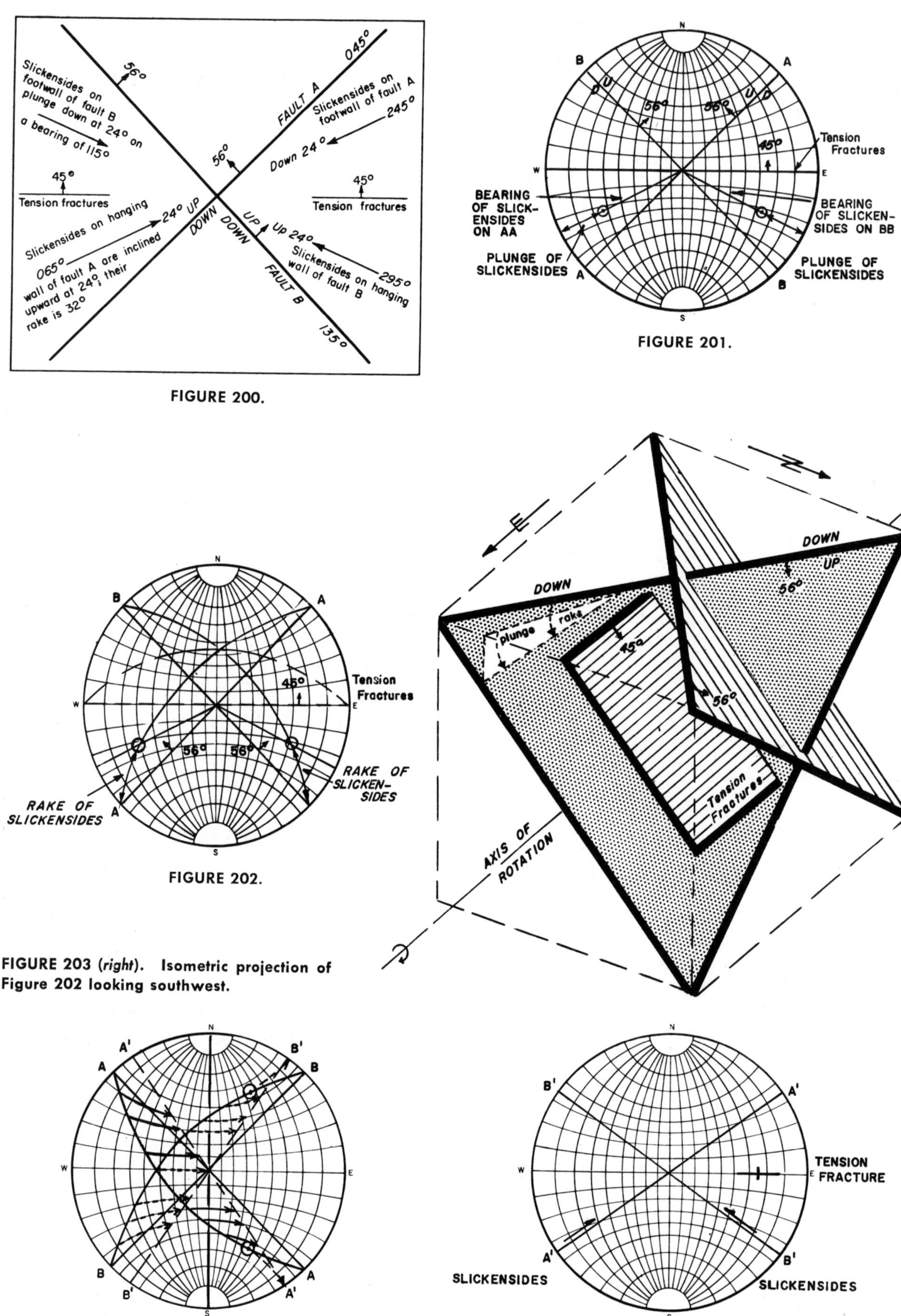

FIGURE 200.

FIGURE 201.

FIGURE 202.

FIGURE 203 (*right*). **Isometric projection of Figure 202 looking southwest.**

FIGURE 204.

FIGURE 205.

Determination of original angular relationships of faults in areas which have been subjected to tilting after the original faulting.

Method: Plot the strikes for the thrust fault and the two veins on a sheet of tracing paper laid over a stereonet diagram (Fig. 196). Revolve the tracing paper until the strike of the thrust fault occupies the polar (north-south) position of the underlying stereonet, and then draw in the 30° meridional arc for the thrust fault as its dip is 30° (Fig. 197). Similarly rotate the strike lines for each of the veins into the polar position and draw in their respective meridional arcs (60° and 70°).

Now it will be observed that the arc of the thrust intersects each of the vein arcs and the two vein arcs also intersect. Connect the center of the stereonet to these intersection points, and project these three lines to the fundamental circle which delimits the area of the net (Fig. 198).

Then revolve the tracing paper until the strike lines for the thrust and each of the veins occupy their original positions (Fig. 198). The bearing of the intersection lines for each set of planes can then be read off directly, (= 012°, 025°, and 045°, respectively). To determine the inclination of each of the intersection lines, it is necessary to revolve each of these lines into the east-west direction of the stereonet. The inclinations can then be read off directly as they equal the distances between the intersection points and the outside of the stereonet (= −28°, −46°, −30°, respectively).

The rake angles, which the traces of the two veins make on the plane of the thrust fault, may be measured by revolving the tracing paper (Fig. 199) until the strike of the thrust fault is north-south. The angular distance from north to point E (Fig. 199) is 75°. This is the rake angle for the trace of the 70° vein on the thrust plane. Similarly the angle between south and point F (76°) is the rake of the trace of the 60° vein on the thrust plane.

Limitations: It is apparent from Figures 196–199 that all strike lines were drawn through the center of the stereonet. It is impossible thus to show the surface distance along the fault between the points where each vein intersects the fault.

DETERMINATION OF THE ORIGINAL ANGULAR RELATIONSHIPS OF FAULTS IN AREAS WHICH HAVE BEEN SUBJECTED TO TILTING AFTER THE FAULTING

Application: The original angular relationships of faults give geologists a good indication of the stress distribution at the time of faulting. Knowledge of stress distribution is very valuable in the exploration of mining districts, as the position, attitude, and time of generation of fracture patterns can be predicted with some confidence in poorly exposed areas after the relationship between stress and fractures becomes apparent in well-exposed adjoining regions. The establishment of stress-fracture relations leads to a better understanding of the structural development of the district. This understanding is essential to the best exploration effort in the area.

Data Provided: Figure 200 shows a fault pattern which was mapped in a mining district.

Determine: The original distribution of maximum, intermediate, and minimum stress axes, the type of faulting, original attitude of the faults and slickensides, and original movement directions on the faults.

Method: It will be necessary to assume that the tension fractures and the stress axes were originally either horizontal or vertical. These matters were discussed in Chapter 3 (Figs. 35, 36, 37). It is seen (Fig. 200) that the tension fractures strike east-west and dip 45° to the north. Tension fractures of this parallel type are developed most commonly with an original vertical attitude, so it will be assumed for the moment that this region has been subjected to a 45° regional tilt to the south (north side up 45°). The problem then will be to restore this fault pattern to its original position, and the method involved is the main concern of this example.

The structural information in Figure 200 is transferred to a tracing paper placed over a stereonet (Fig. 201). The stereograms for faults A and B and for the tension fractures are then drawn on the tracing paper (Fig. 202). Figure 203 is an isometric projection of Figure 202 looking southwest. The tracing paper is then revolved counterclockwise until the strike of the tension fractures occupy the north-south direction on the underlying stereonet. Then the tension fractures are rotated down to a vertical position. Faults A and B are affected by this rotation also. Points on their stereographic curves move eastward through 45° along the small circles to give the new stereograms $A'A'$ and $B'B'$ (Fig. 204). The rake-plunge points on the stereographic curves also move through 45° to the circumference of the stereonet.

The tracing paper is now revolved clockwise

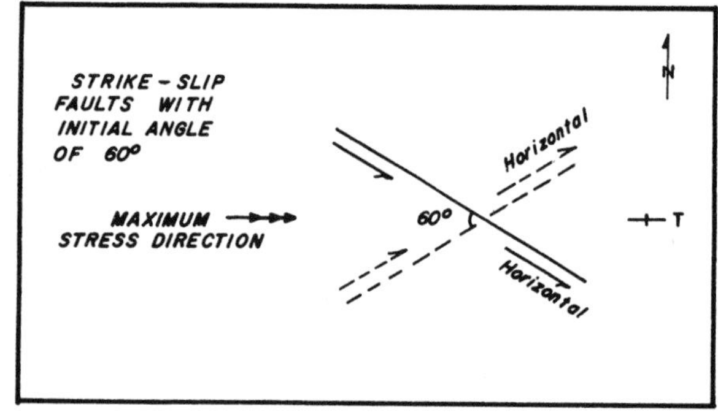

FIGURE 206.

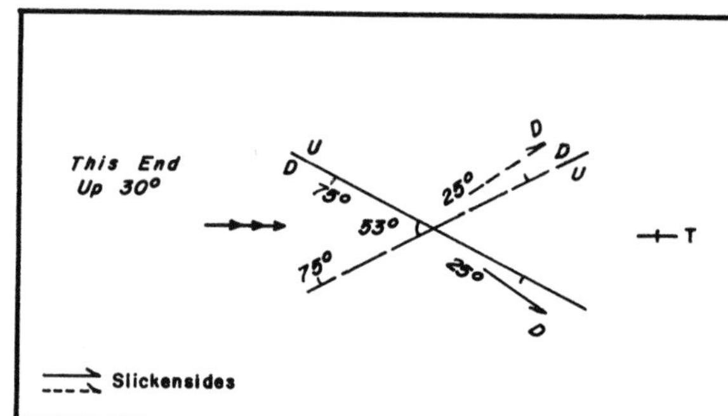

FIGURE 207.

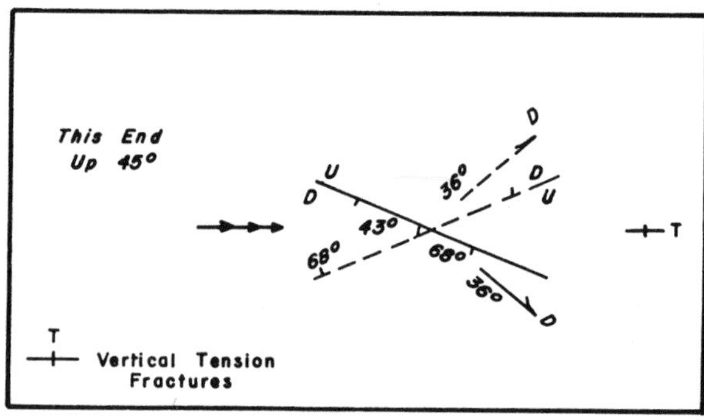

FIGURE 208.

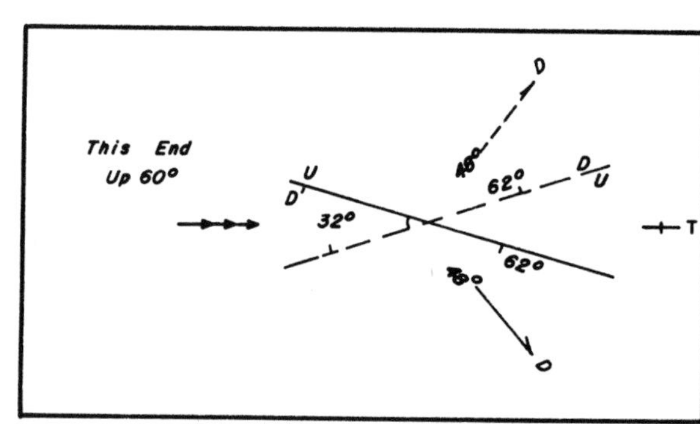

FIGURE 209.

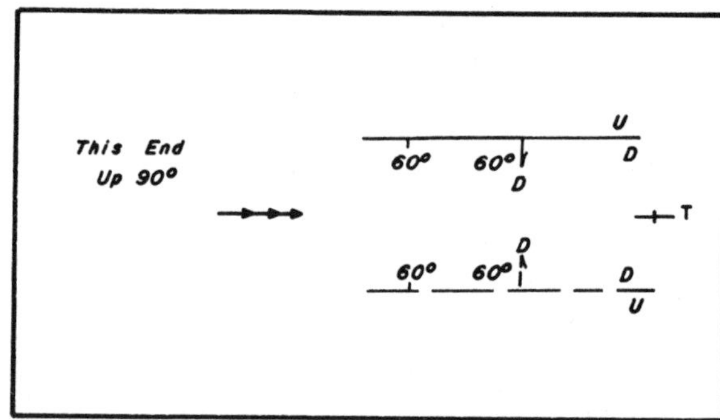

FIGURE 210.

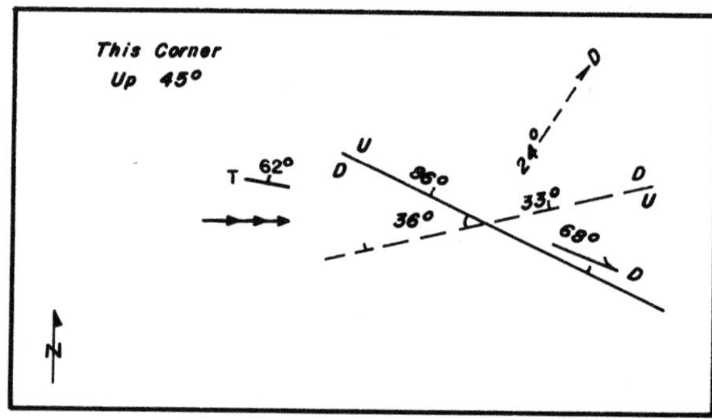

FIGURE 211.

Strike-slip faulting affected by regional tilting from the west in Figures 207–210. Figure 211 shows the results of regional tilting from the northwest applied to Figure 208.

back to its original position so that the tensional direction is east-west (Fig. 205). The faults now strike 055° and 125°, respectively, and are vertical. The rake and plunge of the slickensides are zero. If the original assumption that the tension fractures originated with vertical dips was correct, then these are strike-slip faults.

Figures 206–211, 212–215 show strike-slip and thrust-fault patterns which have been affected by regional tilting. The new angular relations, movement directions, slickenside bearings, and inclinations were computed by stereographic methods similar to those just described. The same type of analysis could be applied to normal faulting also. Study of these figures indicates that the faults shown in Figure 200 are interpreted best as being of a strike-slip nature at their time of origin.

The type of analysis illustrated by Figures 216–225 is very helpful in analyzing complex structural districts.

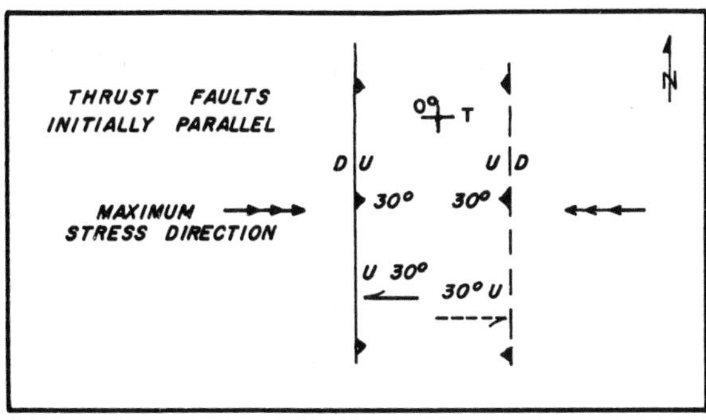

FIGURE 212.

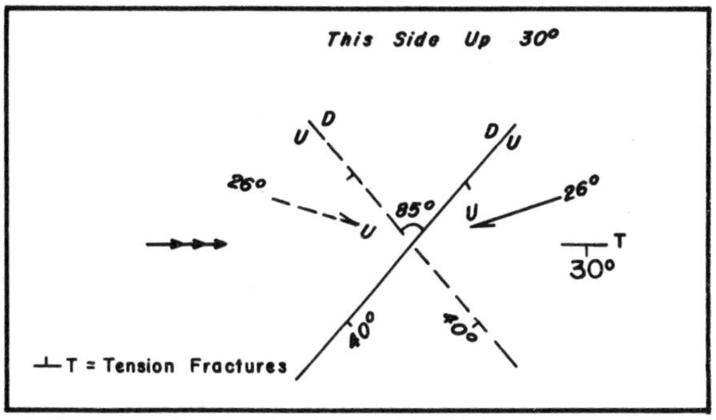

This Side Up 30°
85°
26°
40°
30°
T
⊥T = Tension Fractures

FIGURE 213.

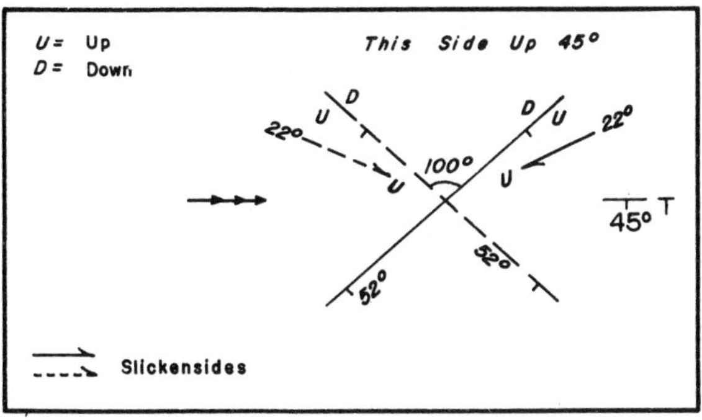

FIGURE 214.

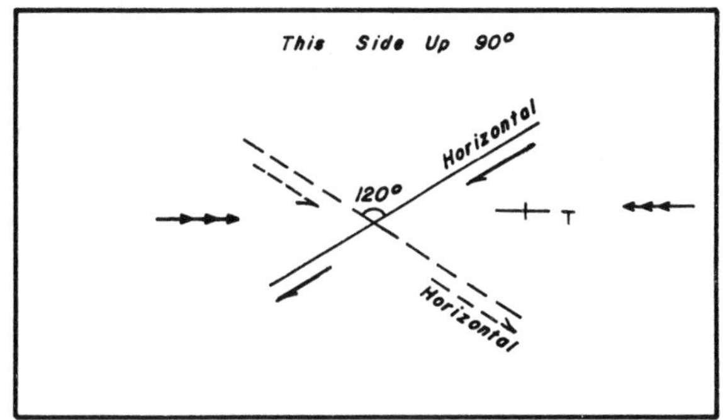

FIGURE 215.

Thrust faults affected by regional tilting from the north.

DETERMINATION OF THE CONFIGURATION OF GEOLOGIC STRUCTURES PRIOR TO TILTING

Application: This type of problem is often met in petroleum exploration. Whenever a potential structural trap has been affected by later tilting, it may be desirable to restore the structure to its original position to evaluate its closure prior to tilting. This is particularly important if there is reason to believe that oil migration occurred prior to tilting.

Data Provided: In Figure 226 a series of beds *AA* striking 290° and dipping 60° SSW are overlain unconformably by beds *BB* striking 220° and dipping 30° SE. The younger beds *BB* were deposited in a horizontal position.

Determine: What was the attitude of *AA* at the time *BB* was deposited?

Method: To solve this problem it is necessary to revolve *BB* (Fig. 228) into the north-south (Fig. 229) position and then to rotate *BB* up 30° into the horizontal (Fig. 230). This rotation will affect beds *AA* also (Fig. 230). Points on *AA* will move upward along the small circle lines. The arrows in Figure 230 show the amount of rotation undergone by *AA* (= 30°). It will be noted at the right-hand side of the stereonet (Fig. 230) that it is impossible to move the arrows a full 30° as this would take the arrows out of the stereonet. As soon as the arrows reach the edge of the stereonet, the remaining angular movement is applied to the reciprocal. Thus 15° of angular movement still remains at point *X* in Figure 230. This remaining 15° is applied at point *Y* (the reciprocal of point *X*). This operation is better understood if the student will bear in mind that only the lower hemisphere of the equivalent spherical projection is being used. Thus if one end of a line is rotated up beyond the horizontal (principal) plane, then the reciprocal end of the line begins to pierce the surface of the lower hemisphere. *A'A'* in Figure 230 shows the position of beds *AA* after rotation. If *BB* and *AA* are now revolved back to their original positions of 220°/30° SE and 290°/60° SSW, respectively, then the pretilt attitude of *AA* (i.e., the attitude of *A'A'*) can be determined (Fig. 231). It works out to be 310°/50° SW. This method could be applied to the Grenville Dome structure contour problem (Problem 16) of Chapter 4.

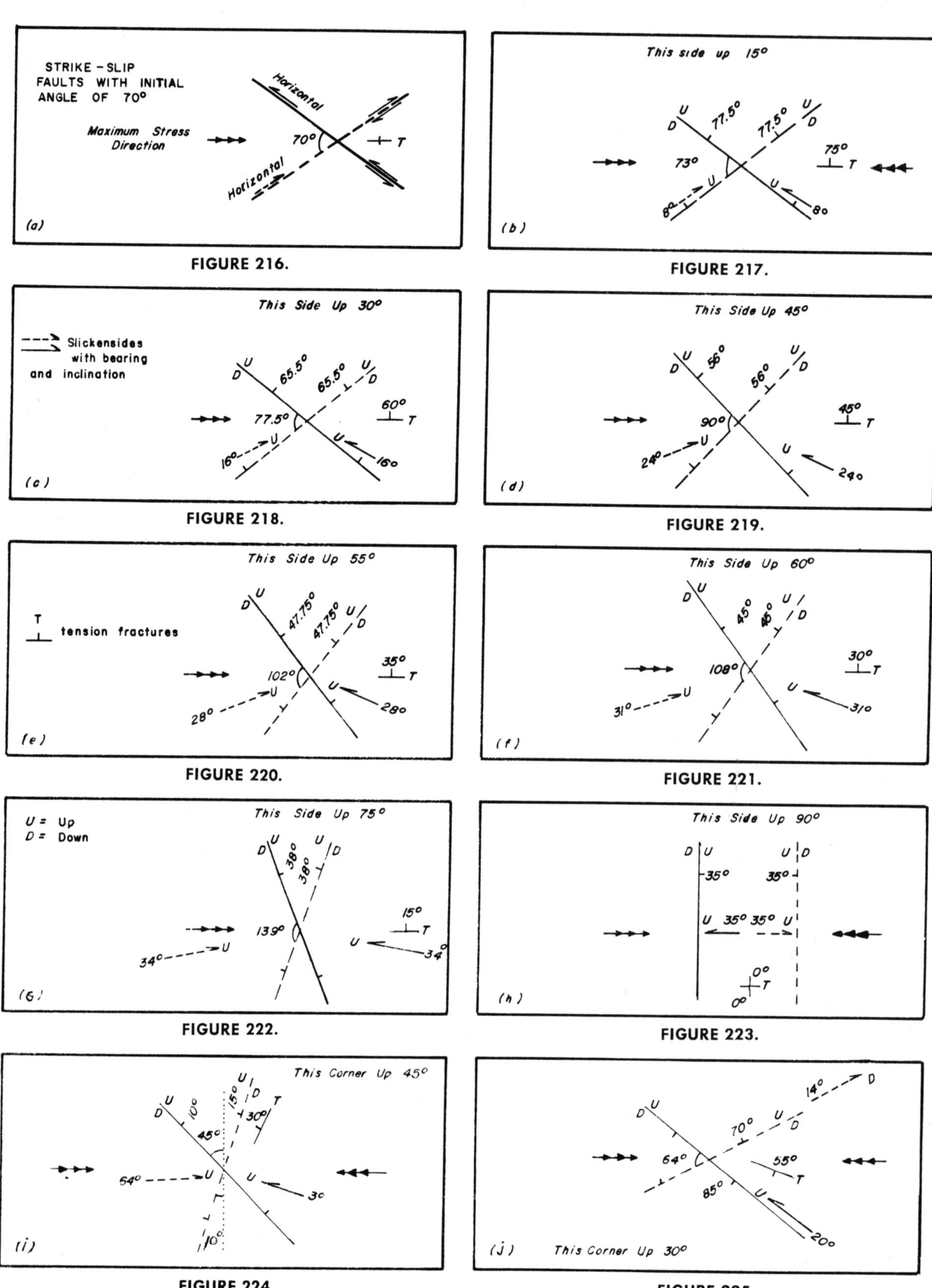

Strike-slip faults affected by regional tilting. The north side has been raised up in Figures 217–220. Figure 224 shows the results of northeast tilting applied to Figure 219. Figure 225 shows the results of southwest tilting applied to Figure 218.

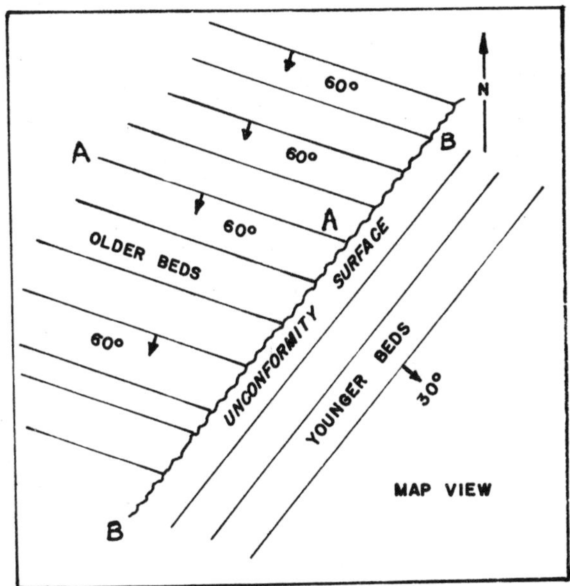

FIGURE 226.

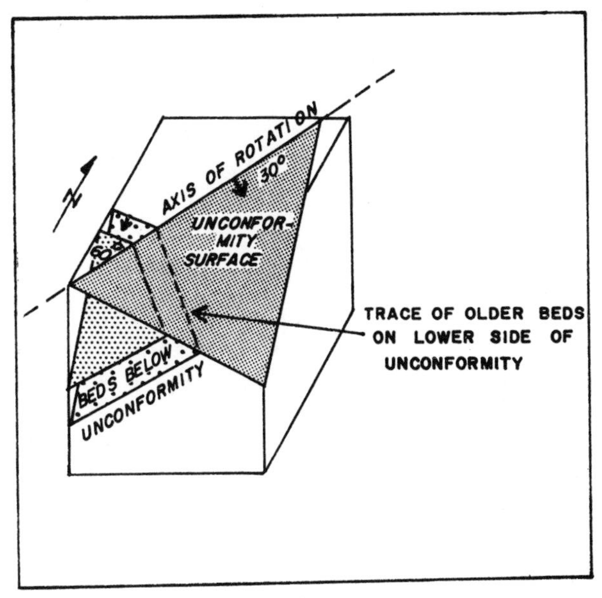

FIGURE 227. Three-dimensional view of Figure 226.

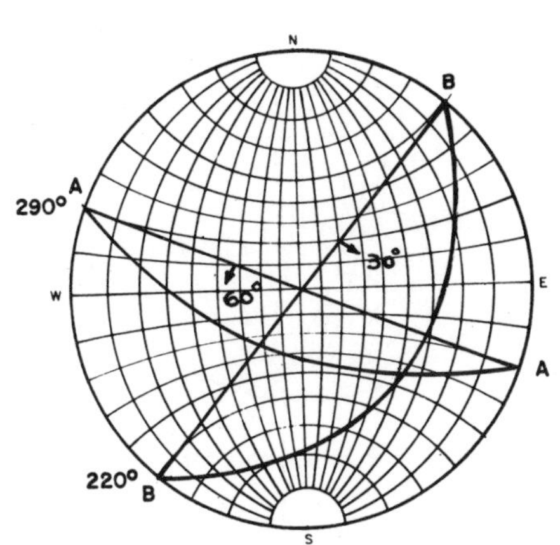

FIGURE 228.

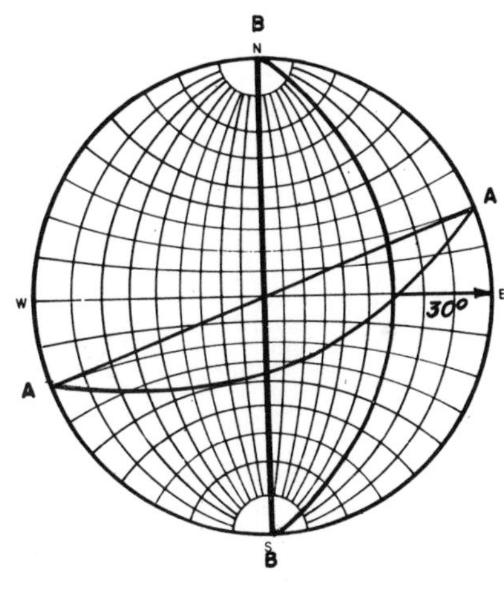

FIGURE 229.

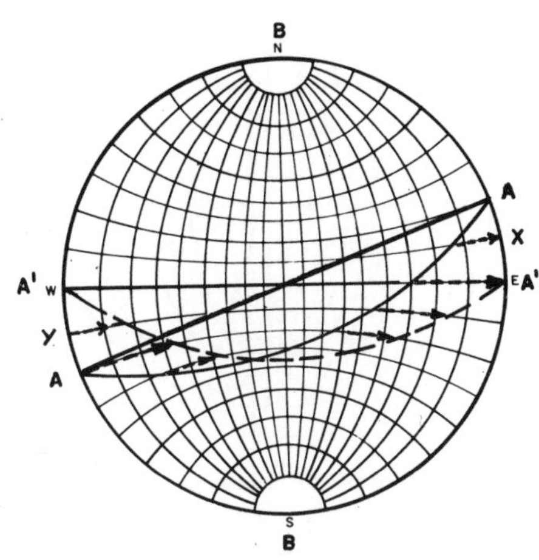

FIGURE 230.

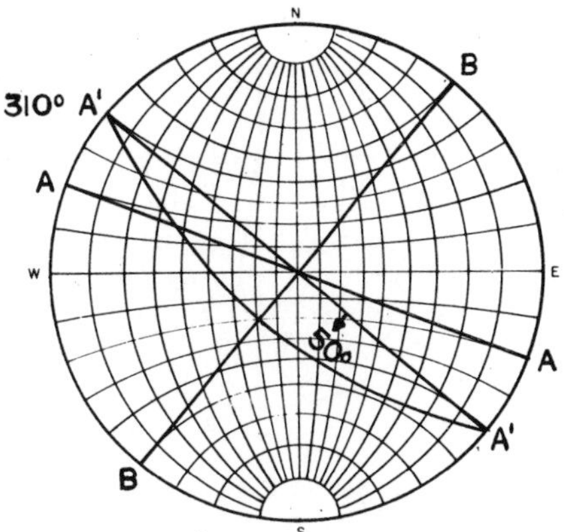

FIGURE 231.

Determination of the configuration of geologic structures prior to regional tilting.

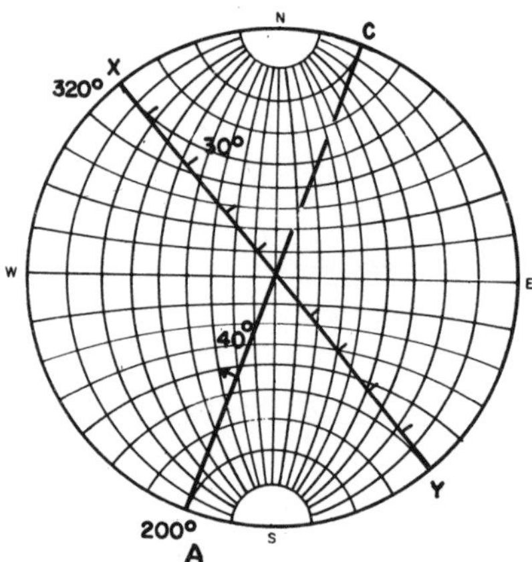

FIGURE 232. Original position of fault *XY* and disrupted bed *AC* on southwest side of fault.

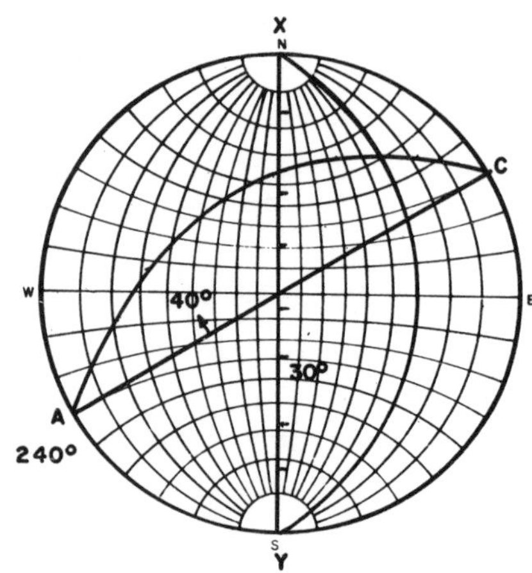

FIGURE 233. Position of fault and disrupted bed after fault has been revolved to a north-south position and after meridional arcs have been drawn in.

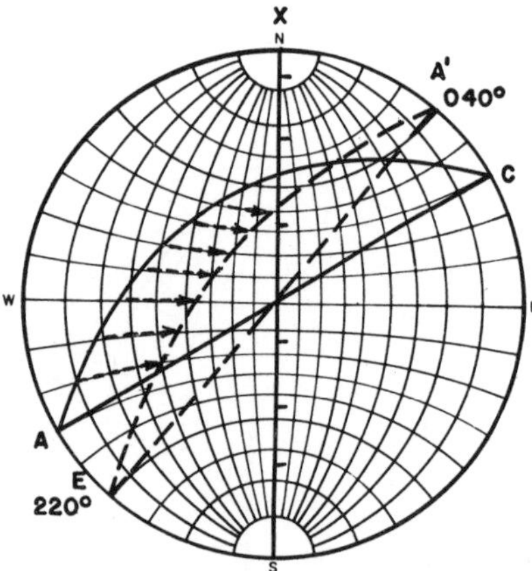

FIGURE 234. Position of disrupted bed *AC* after fault has been rotated into the horizontal.

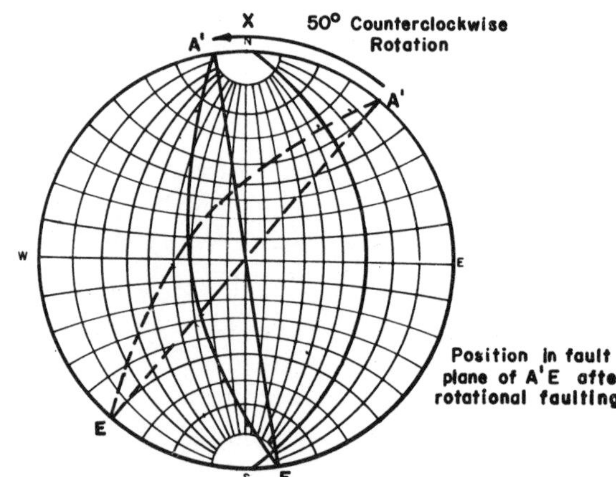

FIGURE 235. Bed *A'E* is shifted 50° counterclockwise in the plane of the fault.

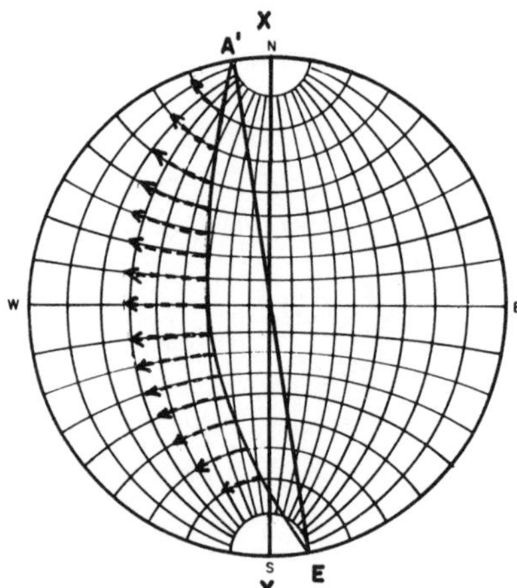

FIGURE 236. The bed *A'E* shifts westward along the small circle lines as the fault is rotated down to −30°E dip along rotation axis *XY*.

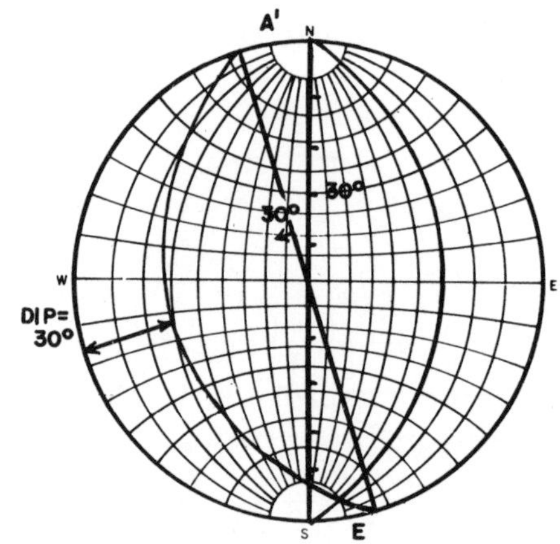

FIGURE 237. Position of stereograms after fault *XY* has been rotated down to −30° of dip.

DETERMINATION OF THE AMOUNT OF DISPLACEMENT DURING ROTATIONAL FAULTING BY STEREOGRAPHIC PROJECTION COMBINED WITH ORTHOGRAPHIC PROJECTION

Application: This method is applicable to any type of fault that has rotational movement. The first example will show how to find the disrupted attitude of beds affected by rotational faulting, provided the position of the pole of rotation and the angle and direction of rotation are known. The second example, which will be a continuation of the first one, shows how to locate the position of the pole of rotation provided the displaced positions of beds, veins, and so forth are known on opposite sides of a fault. The main value of the stereonet in this case, as compared with orthographic methods (Chapter 7), is the ease with which information may be rotated up to the horizontal plane.

These methods are particularly valuable in locating the positions of disrupted ore bodies.

Data Provided: Fault *XY* strikes 320° and dips 30° to the northeast. Key bed *AC*, striking 200° and dipping 40° west northwest, occurs on the southwest side of the fault and has been disrupted by the fault. Rotational movement (50° counterclockwise) occurred in the fault plane during the disruption of the key bed.

Determine: The attitude of the disrupted bed *AC* on the northeast side of the fault *XY*.

Method: (See accompanying Figs. 232–238.) Plot the attitudes of the fault and the disrupted key bed on tracing paper placed over a stereonet (Fig. 232). Then revolve the tracing paper about the center of the stereonet until the strike of the fault occupies a north-south position on the stereonet, and then draw in the dip (meridional arc) for the fault (Fig. 233). The meridional arc representing the dip for the key bed may be drawn in by revolving the strike of the key bed into the north-south position also.

With the fault striking in a north-south position, rotate the fault plane 30° upwards about the north-south axis to bring the fault plane into the plane of the stereonet (Fig. 234). During the rotation of the fault plane up to the horizontal, the position of the disrupted bed is also shifted up 30°. The position of the disrupted strata can be determined by

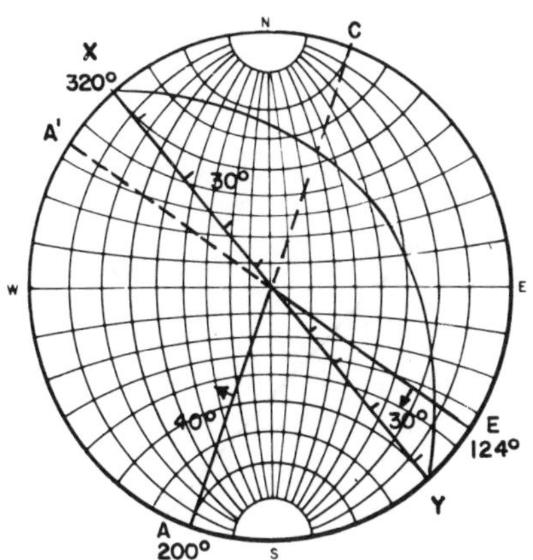

FIGURE 238. Position of disrupted bed on both sides of fault after fault has been revolved back to original position of 320°.

moving the position of the bed 30° to the right. The movement path is parallel to the directions of the small circles on the stereonet (Fig. 234).

Since the plane of the fault has been rotated up to the horizontal about axis *XY*, it is now possible to apply the rotational fault movement directly on the stereonet diagram. This is accomplished by rotating the tracing paper, by means of a rotation pole or axis, perpendicular to the stereonet and passing through the center of the net. The amount of counterclockwise rotation is 50° (Fig. 235).

The next step is to rotate the fault and the new position of the disrupted bed back down to the 30° dip position which the fault really occupies (Fig. 236). The dip of the disrupted bed on the northeast side of the fault can now be read by revolving the newly found strike *AE* into a north-south position and noting the meridional arc which represents the dip. It appears to be 30° (Fig. 237).

The final step is to revolve the thrust fault back to its original strike position of 320° (Fig. 238). The strike of the disrupted bed on the northeast side of the fault can then be measured. It equals 124° (Fig. 238). The attitude of the disrupted bed *AE* on the northeast side of the fault is thus 124°/30°SW.

The next example will show how to locate the position of the pole of rotation and how to determine the amount of angular rotation.

Data Provided: Plan view of fault *XY* (320°/30°NE) and of disrupted beds *AC* (200°/40°NW) and *BD* (270°/45°S) on the south side of fault *XY* and the positions of $A'E$ (124°/30° SW) and $B'F$ (043°/70° SE) on the north side of the fault (Fig. 239).

Determine: The amount of displacement and rotation involved during faulting and the position of the pole of rotation.

Method: Transfer the information shown by plan view map (Fig. 239) to a stereonet (Fig. 240). Then determine the positions which the traces of beds AC, BD, $A'E$, $B'F$ occupy in the plane of the fault. These positions are defined by the rakes of these traces. The rake (or pitch angle, as it called by some authors) is, of course, the angle which a line in a plane makes with a horizontal line in the same plane. These angles are determined by the method described on page 193. These rake angles work out to 40° (AC), 37° (BD), 10° ($A'E$), and 87° ($B'F$), as shown in Figure 241. The various determined rake angles are then drawn in at the appropriate points C, D, E, and F and are shown as they would appear in the plane of the fault (Fig. 242). It will be noted (Fig. 242) that $A'E$ and $B'F$ intersect at M and that AC and BD intersect at L. The points L and M were at the same spot before faulting. Consequently, the line ML represents the net slip, and MN and NL represent the dip slip and horizontal component of net slip, respectively. Further, it will be noted that a counterclockwise rotation of AC and DB through 50° would make these two lines parallel to $A'E$ and FB', respectively (Fig. 243). Figure 243 is a three-dimensional analysis of the situation. Once the displacement and amount of rotation in a fault plane have been determined between two points such as L and M in Figure 243, then it is possible to use this information to locate the position of other disrupted beds which have been affected by the fault, provided their position is known on one side of the fault. In order to find such disrupted strata or ore bodies, it is necessary to locate the pole of rotation for the fault. This can be located by finding the midpoint on the net slip distance and erecting a perpendicular to the net slip at this point. In the problem illustrated in Figure 243, the rotation angle was discovered to be 50°; the net slip distance thus subtends an angle of 50°. The net slip distance is one side of a triangle whose opposite angle is 50°, and the apex of the other two sides of the triangle intersect to make this 50° (see Fig. 244). Their intersection point is the pole of rotation for the fault. Knowing one side of a triangle and the opposite angle, it is a simple matter to determine the other sides and angles of the triangle which then give the location of the pole of rotation. This is accomplished by means of the following equation:

$$\frac{\text{Sin Rotation Angle}}{2} = \frac{\frac{1}{2}\text{ of Net Slip}}{\text{Radius of Rotation}}$$

And in this case,

$$\text{Sin } 25° = \frac{200 \text{ feet}}{\text{Radius of Rotation}}$$

$$\text{Radius of Rotation} = 465 \text{ feet}$$

The position of the pole of rotation may also be determined by constructing the angles MLO and LMO each = 65° and noting their intersection point. This construction is based on the simple geometrical principle that the three angles of a triangle must sum to 180°. In this case two of the angles of the triangle LQO (Fig. 244) are known to be 25° and 90°. Thus the third angle OLQ must be 65°. The pole of rotation can be located, of course, on only one side of the net slip. By examining the distribution of the known disruption from AC to $A'E$ and knowing that the rotation angle = 50°, it is readily apparent that the pole must be on the north-northwest side of the net slip, for only in this location could the disruption from AC to $A'E$ be accomplished with a 50° rotation. There is a possibility that the rotation angle is 310° clockwise rather than 50° counterclockwise, but the pole would still be at point O. Now if an ore shoot is known to intersect the upper surface of the fault plane at point R (Fig. 244), it is a simple matter to determine its position R' on the lower side of the fault by using pole O as center, OR as radius, and swinging through an arc of 50° counterclockwise. The new attitude of the ore shoot will be determined by the method described on pages 191, 193.

Note: The rotation angle in the example illustrated (Fig. 243) was taken to be 50° with the pole of the fault located on the north side of the fault trace. However, the rotation angle could have been the supplementary 130° angle if the pole was located on the south side of the fault trace. Frequently it is difficult to determine which alternative is correct, although the minimum alternative is normally selected when other information is not

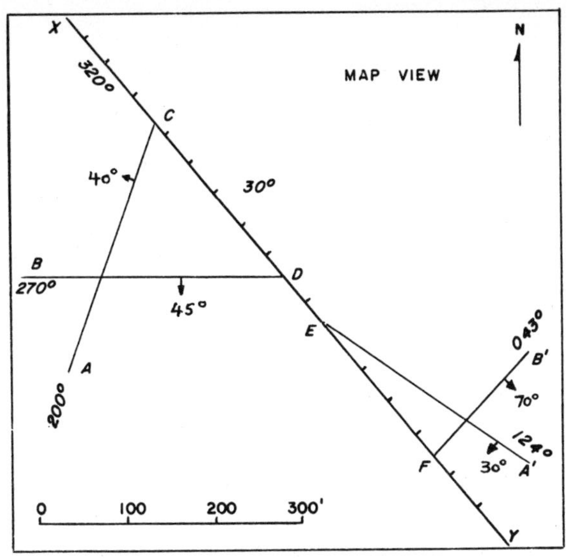

FIGURE 239.

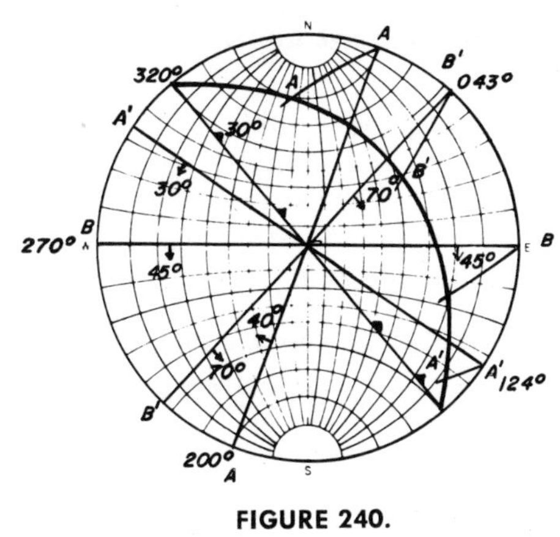

FIGURE 240.

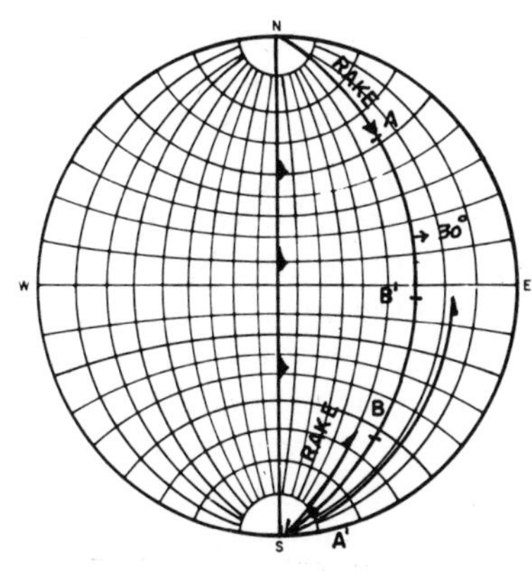

FIGURE 241.

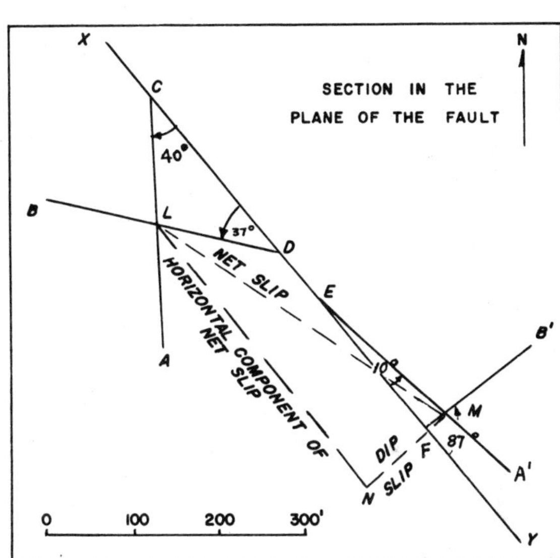

FIGURE 242.

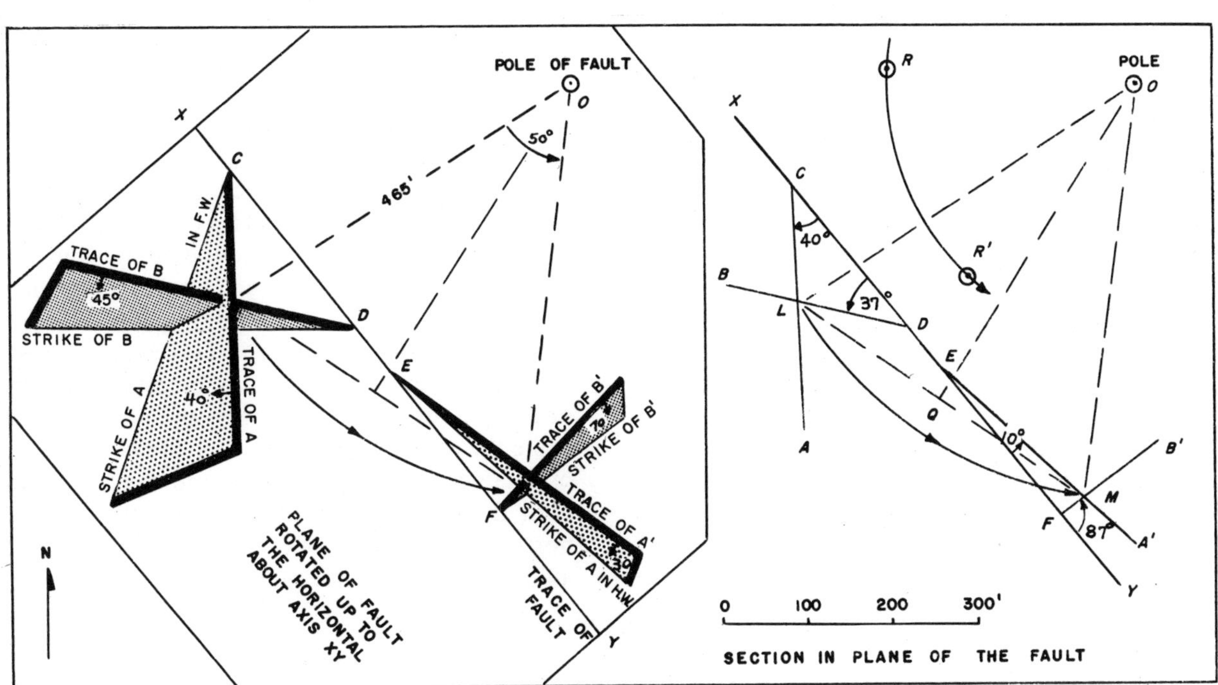

FIGURE 243.

FIGURE 244.

Determination of the amount of angular rotation and the position of the pole of the fault.

available. It may be possible to resolve this perplexity by careful examination of slickensides on the fault surface. The use of additional disrupted plane surfaces should permit the elimination of one of the alternatives also.

DETERMINATION OF DIP AND STRIKE FROM AIR PHOTOGRAPHS, USING STEREOGRAPHIC METHODS

Applications and Limitations: Structural mapping from air photographs is of considerable importance as time, inaccessibility, and weather conditions frequently make it difficult to study the outcrops in the field. This subject was discussed earlier in Chapter 4. The matter of accurate attitude determination from air photographs is a difficult problem but can be resolved in part by several methods. A stereographic method, originally developed by Wallace (1950), is described herewith. The method requires very clear air photographs and knowledge of the focal length of the photographing camera. The present writer has found the method to be practical only when the flight line of the photographing aircraft moved across the strike direction of the strata—flight lines almost parallel to the strata involved make the method difficult to use.

Principles Involved: The outcrop of a bedding plane on a hillside is a line. The bearing and inclination of such rake lines appear to vary as the viewpoint of the observer changes (Figs. 245, 246). It has been demonstrated previously that two dip component lines for the same plane can be combined to yield the attitude of the bedding plane. The present method employs an analogous principle.

Data Provided: Plate 10 shows two overlapping air photographs oriented and spaced for viewing stereoscopically. The principal point for the southern photo is indicated by the circle at *A,* whereas the principal point for the northern photo is indicated by the circle at *C*. The focal length for the camera is 6.0 inches, and the scale of the photos is approximately 1:23,600 (representative fraction). The flight altitude is approximately 11,800 feet. The photographs were taken near the north rim of the Wind River Basin in Wyoming. The bedding can be observed clearly on opposite sides of a northwest-trending stream at point *D*. Point *D′* is the equivalent position for the southern photograph.

Determine: The attitude of the bedding at point *D*.

Method: Place a sheet of tracing paper (Fig. 247) over Plate 10 and mark the principal points *A* and *C,* the points *D* and *D′*, and the apparent plunges of the bedding at points *D* and *D′*. Then draw a north line through both points *D* and *D′*. It may be observed that the apparent rake lines do not have the same attitude at both points. This is because point *D* is being observed from an aircraft immediately above principal point *C,* whereas point *D′* is being observed from an aircraft immediately above principal point *A*. The principal point of the air photograph is the point at which the optical axis of the camera hits the photograph.

It is now necessary to transfer the information on Plate 10 and Figure 247 to stereographic projection. The relation between air photographs and stereographic projection is illustrated by Figure 252. Note that the upper hemisphere of the sphere is used rather than the lower hemisphere as in most stereographic projections. Figure 253 shows how the plunge of the line of sight from an aircraft (above the principal point) down to any point on the air photograph (e.g., points *D* and *D′* in Plate 10) may be determined. The plunge down to point *D* may be determined as 73° from Figure 253 whereas the plunge down to point *D′* is 62°.

The next step is to plot the plunges for the lines of sight (73° and 62°) on a stereonet. For simplicity, all information on the southern photograph will be plotted initially. After plotting the 62° plunge point (Fig. 249), a plane at right angles to this plunge line is added to the stereonet as this is the plane in which the rake lines of the bedding at *D′* are being observed. The dip of this plane, 28°, is thus complementary to the plunge line *AD′* of Plate 10. It is necessary to have a reference plane intersecting the 28° dipping plane to which the rake lines for the outcrop may be compared.

Such a reference plane may be established by drawing a great circle through the plunge point while the original orientation for the north line is maintained. This reference plane thus contains both the original line of sight and the original north line of Figure 247. The 28° dipping plane intersects the reference plane at point *M*.

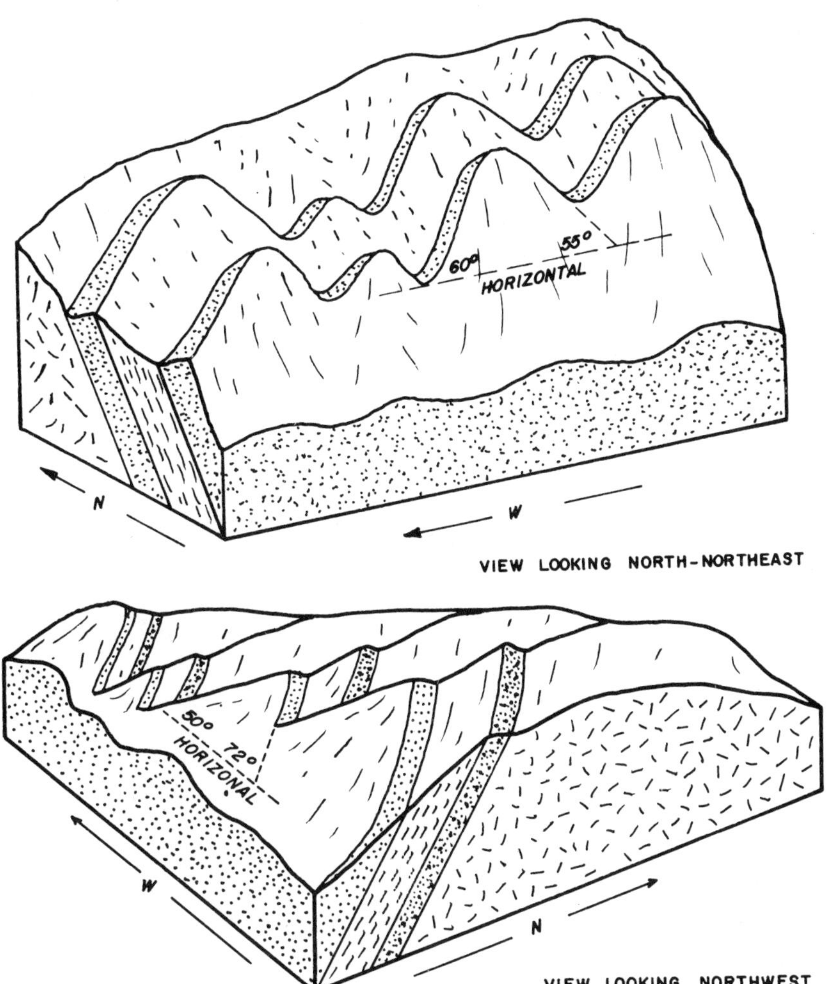

FIGURES 245 (*above*) and 246 (*below*). Illustrating the apparent change in attitude of beds which are observed from different viewpoints. This apparent difference may be used to determine the attitude of such beds from air photograph observations.

The angles between the rake lines and the north reference line at point *D′* of Figure 247 are now plotted on the stereographic projection (Fig. 249). The angle for the west outcrop (52°) is plotted on the left side of point *M* and the angle for the right outcrop (20°) is plotted on the right side of point *M* (Fig. 249). To plot these angles (52°, 20°) it is necessary to rotate the stereonet so that the 28° dipping plane (which is at right angles to the line of sight) occupies a north-south orientation. This is because the angles (52°, 20°) are plotted in this 28° plane on either side of the reference point *M*. In actuality, the reference plane containing the north line could be omitted, and the angles (52°, 20°) could be plotted to the left and right of point *N*, the point where the line of sight crosses the 28° stereogram. The 28° plane would then be the reference plane. This gives satisfactory results so long as the plunge of the line of sight is not too steep.

As the line of sight becomes more nearly vertical, the plane at right angles to it (in which the rake of bedding planes on sloping outcrops are measured) becomes less useful as a reference plane. For greater accuracy the reference plane containing the north line is used in this method.

The next step is to draw a great circle (meridional arc) through point *L* and the plunge point and a great circle through point *P* and the plunge point (Fig. 249). This gives a great circle for the west outcrop at point *D′* and a great circle for the east outcrop at point *D′*.

The entire procedure is now repeated for point

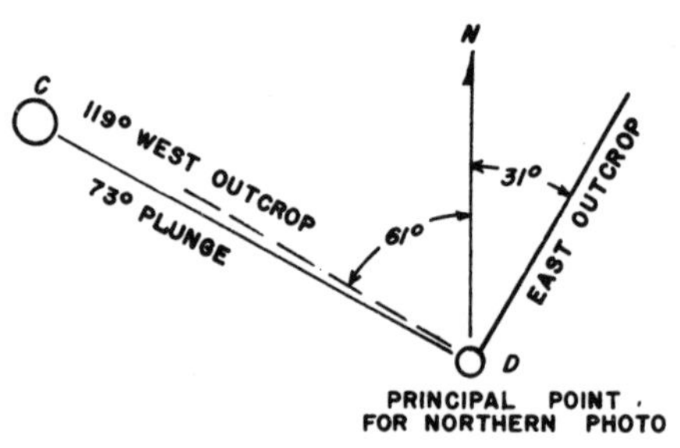

Information from Northern Air Photograph

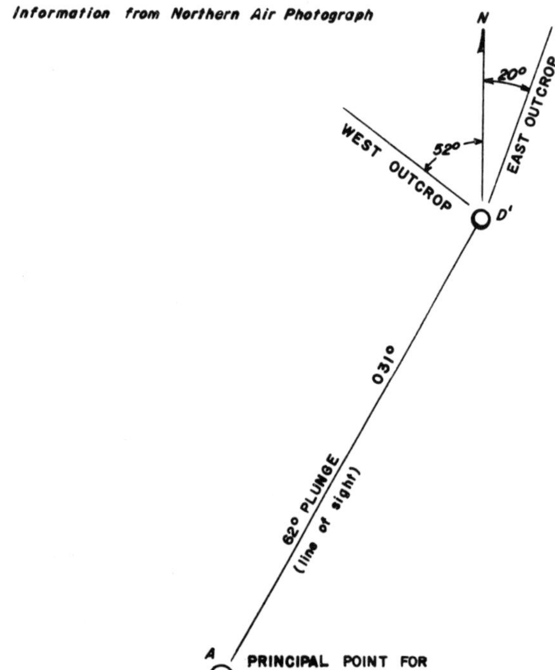

Information from Southern Air Photograph

FIGURE 247.

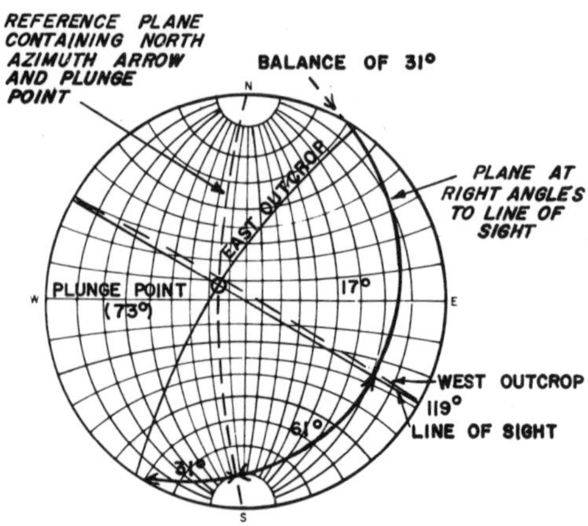

FIGURE 248.

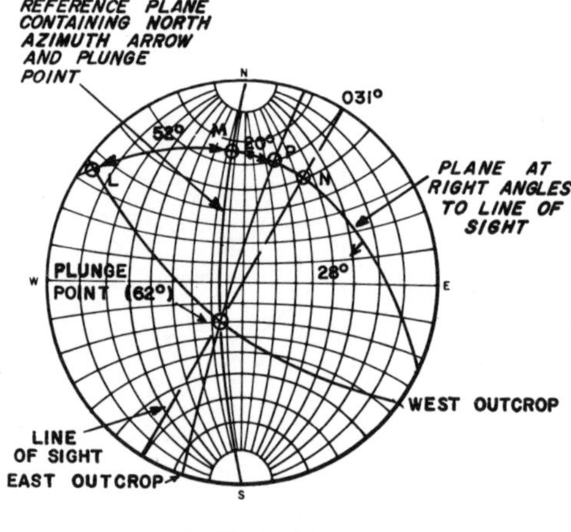

FIGURE 249.

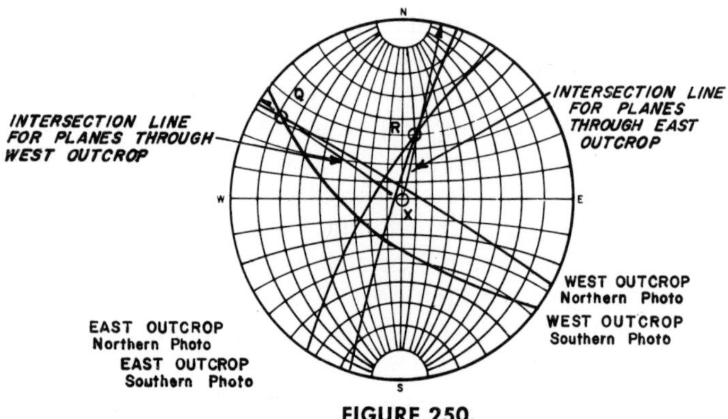

FIGURE 250.

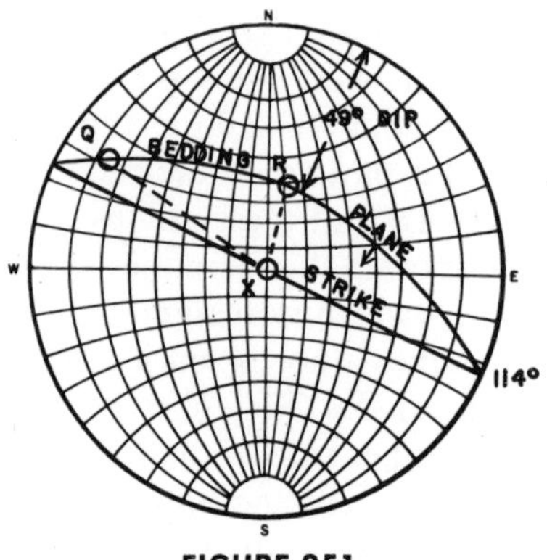

FIGURE 251.

Steps involved in determining attitude of bedding from air photographs by the stereographic method. The upper hemisphere of the stereomat is used in each case.

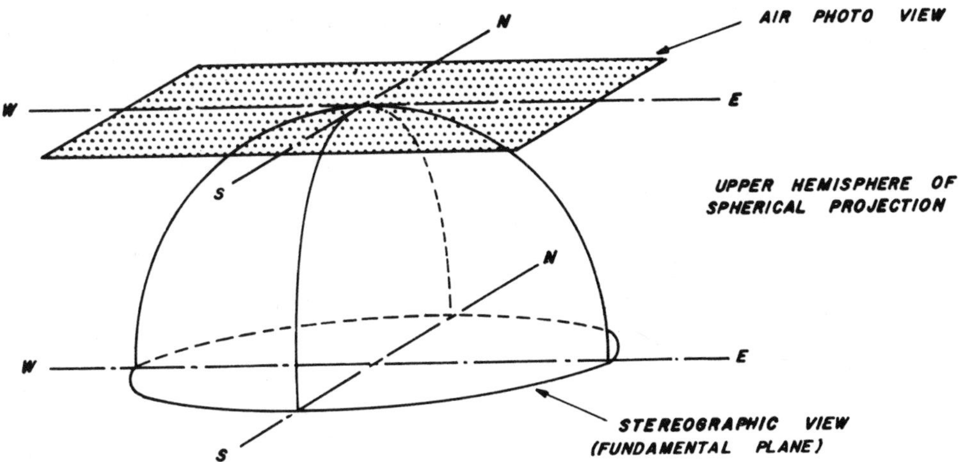

FIGURE 252. An air photographic view may be related to stereographic projection by means of the upper hemisphere of an equivalent spherical projection.

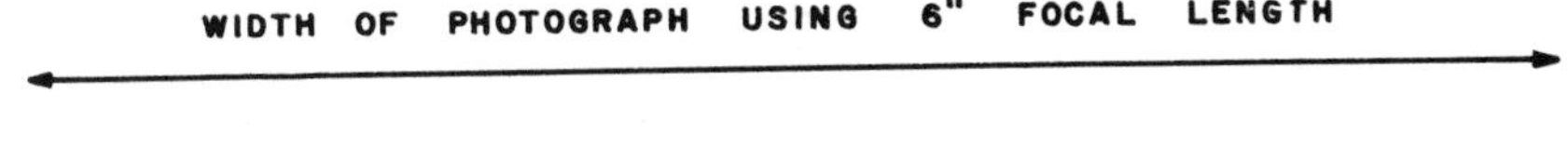

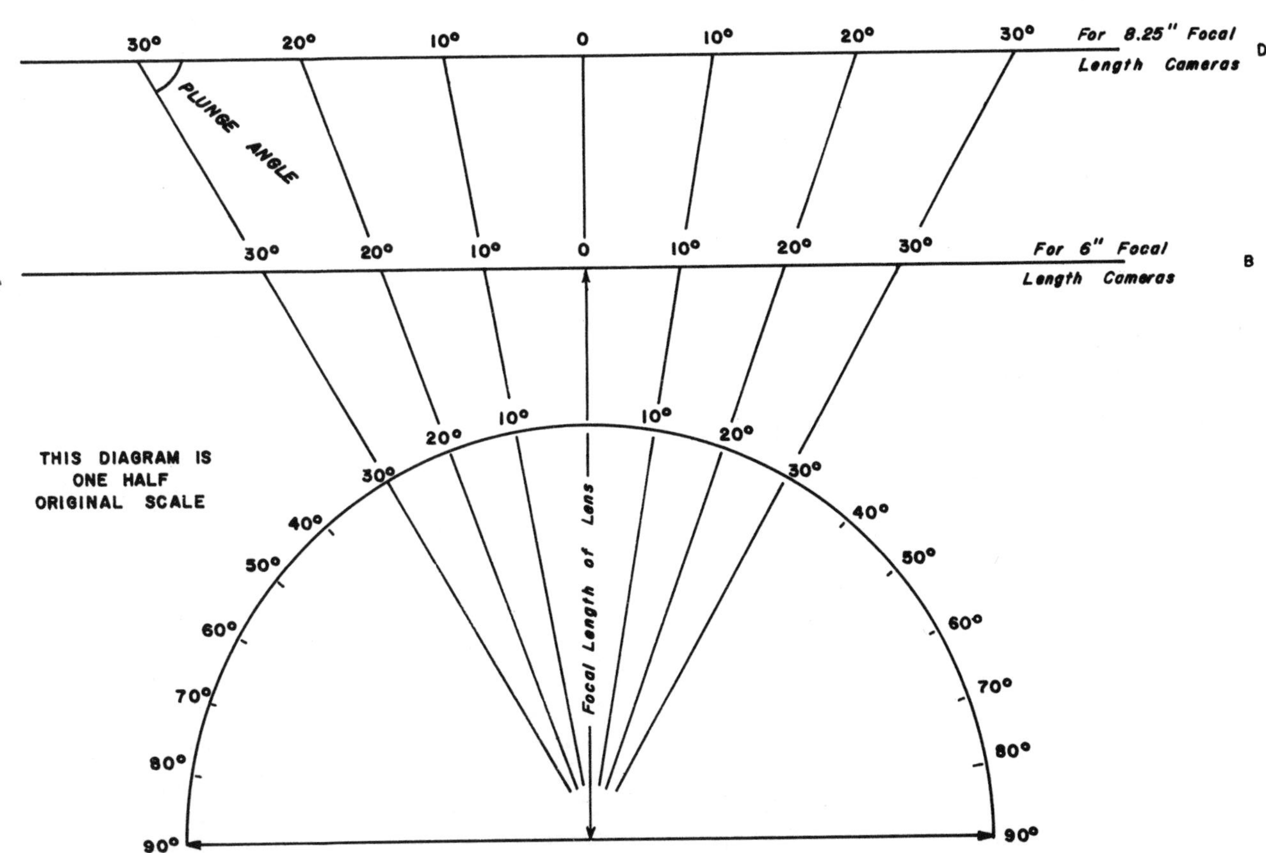

FIGURE 253. Illustrating the relation of angular scale in air photographs to focal length of camera lens. The plunge from the principal point down to any point on the air photograph may be determined by scaling off one-half the distance outward from the 0° point on line *AB* (or use line *CD* for 8.25 inches focal length cameras) to the appropriate point on the air photograph. Only one-half the air photo distance is used, as this diagram is one-half original scale. The angle read off this diagram gives the complement of the plunge angle. For example, the distance *CD* (Fig. 247) laid off on line *AB* (Fig. 253) equals 17°. The plunge angle is thus 73°.

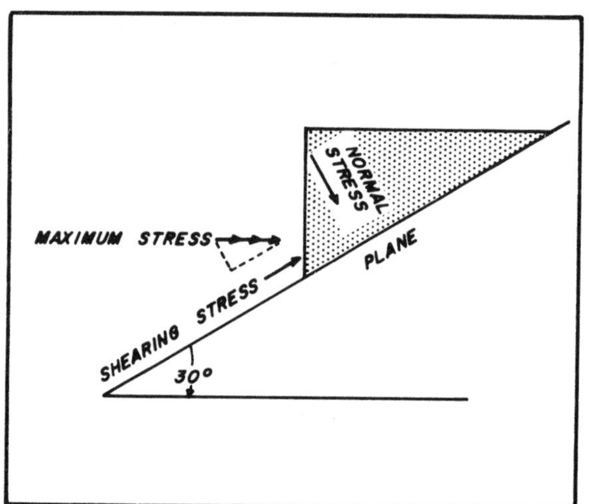

FIGURE 254. The maximum stress may be broken down into components of normal and shearing stress.

D in the northern air photo to give a great circle for the west outcrop at point *D* and a great circle for the east outcrop at point *D* (Fig. 248). The information from both points *D* and *D′* (Figs. 248 and 249) is now combined in Figure 250. Point *Q* then represents the intersection of two planes passing through the west outcrop, and point *R* represents the intersection of two planes passing through the east outcrop. The line *XQ* then represents the true position of the west outcrop, and the line *XR* represents the true position of the east outcrop. The great circle which contains both points *Q* and *R* (Fig. 251) represents the true attitude of the bedding planes at points *D* and *D′*. This attitude is 114/49°SSW.

DETERMINATION OF STRESS ORIENTATION BY STEREOGRAPHIC METHODS

Principle Involved: The subject of stress orientation relative to fault patterns was discussed briefly in Chapter 3. It was pointed out that the compressive stress, in homogeneous isotropic materials under compression, could be expressed in terms of a set of three mutually perpendicular axes. The total resultant stress on any plane in a stress system can be broken into two components, one normal to the plane and the other parallel to the plane (Fig. 254). The normal stress is zero when the plane is parallel to the maximum compression direction and increases to a maximum when the plane is perpendicular to the maximum compression.

As the normal stress varies from zero to a maximum, the shearing stress changes from zero and reaches a maximum when the plane is oriented at 45° to the maximum compression. The shearing stress decreases to zero as the plane becomes oriented perpendicular to the maximum compressive stress. If the normal stress were constant throughout the 90° arc, then shear faults should develop at the orientation of maximum shearing stress. The tendency is for shear faults to develop at an angle of approximately 30° to the maximum compressive stress, which is a compromise between low normal stress and high shearing stress. A mathematical treatment of these principles has been described by Hubbert (1951). Stereographic treatment of these principles was reviewed by Wallace (1950).

The shearing stress intensity can be related to a cone whose apex angle approximates 60° and whose axis is the maximum compressive stress. Shear faults will tend to concentrate at orientations tangent to this cone. If the intermediate and minimum stresses are equal, then the faults can have any attitude so long as they are tangent to the cone. If the intermediate stress axis is actually greater than the minimum stress, and if the minimum stress is vertical (Fig. 255), then thrust faults will form. Their strikes will be perpendicular to the maximum stress direction. If the intermediate stress is vertical, then strike-slip faults will result. Their dips will be vertical. Both the thrust faults and the strike-slip faults are tangent to the cone of maximum rupture potential. In each case, the shear faults are also tangent to a cone drawn about the minimum stress axis (Fig. 257). This relationship between fault patterns and the cone of maximum rupture potential has been illustrated because the trace of the cone can be drawn in stereographic projection and can be used as a means of determining the position of the various stress axes.

Applications and Limitations: If the fault plane orientations and net slip orientations (from slickensides) for a fault system are known, it is possible to determine the orientation and nature of the stress system which produced the faults. The method is limited by the assumption that all the

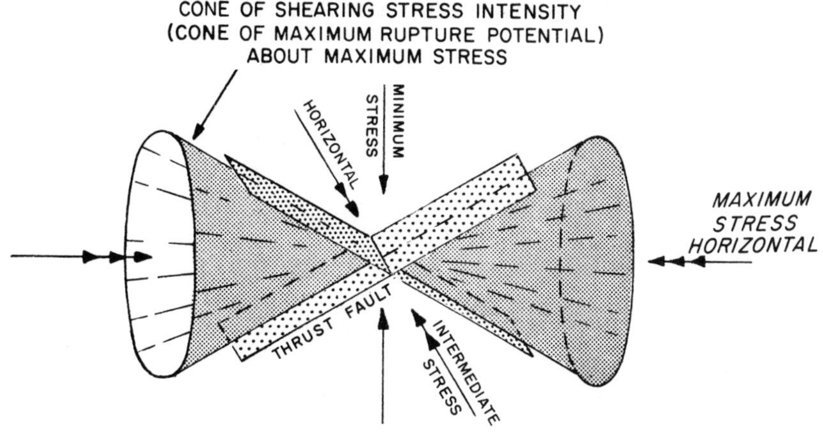

FIGURE 255.

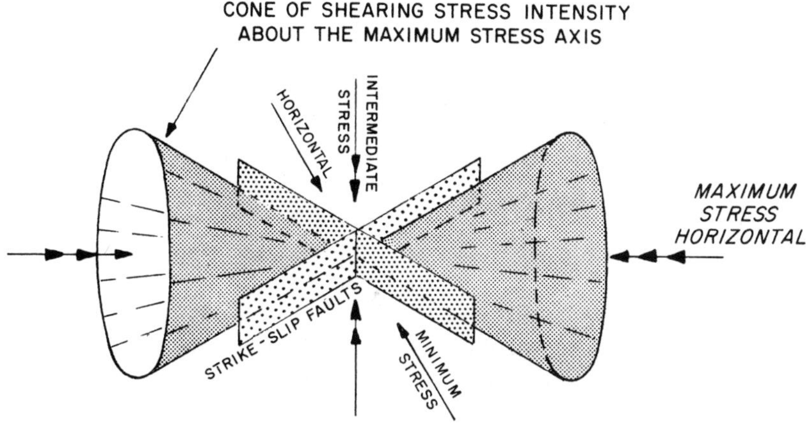

FIGURE 256.

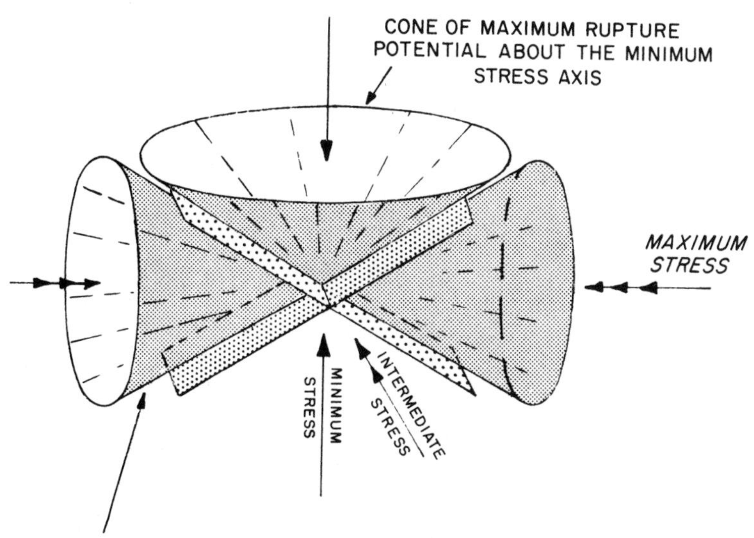

FIGURE 257.

Illustrating the cones of maximum rupture potential and minimum rupture potential which exist around the maximum and minimum stress axes.

faults resulted from the same stress system and that continuity was maintained in the stress system after initial rupture. These assumptions are not always valid. The establishment of a relationship between faulting and stress in any district is fundamental to the understanding of the dynamic development of the district. The angular relations of faults and their time of origin are important considerations in the economic evaluation of mineral districts. These aspects will be discussed further in Chapter 9. The example which follows is modified from Wallace (1951).

Data Provided: The fault pattern illustrated in Figure 258. The arrows indicate the bearing and inclination of net slip for each fault. All of the faults are believed to have resulted from the same stress application.

Determine: The orientation of the maximum stress axis for the stress system causing the fault pattern.

Method: Plot the position of each fault and slickenside arrow on stereographic projection (Fig. 259). Then, by trial and error, locate a circular trace tangent to all three faults. This circle represents the cone of maximum rupture potential for these three faults. Either the maximum stress axis or the minimum stress axis must pass through the center point of this cone. The axis is inclined 30° on a north bearing. Thus the apex angle of the cone is 60° and this is a maximum stress axis. It will be noted that the center of the cone is not located at the center of the circle on the stereonet but is located at the 30° point, which is half of the 60° apex angle of the cone. This is because the distance per degree decreases toward the center of the stereonet.

DETERMINATION OF ATTITUDE BY DRILL HOLES IN FORMATIONS LACKING MARKER BEDS

Applications and Limitations: Mining geologists are frequently called upon to determine the attitude of structural units from diamond drilling. This is not difficult when correlatable units extend from one drill hole to the next. Key beds are often lacking in mining areas, however, because of the metamorphism and disruption which such areas have endured. Nevertheless, the angles between bedding planes and the core axes can usually still be measured, and if this information is combined from several holes, the attitude of the formations penetrated can be obtained, providing no folding occurs between drill holes.

It would be a simple matter to measure attitude from a single core if cores could be withdrawn from drill holes without losing their original orientation. Determinations of original orientation by residual magnetism have been made, but the procedure is elaborate and costly, and errors can make the result unreliable.

Data Provided: Three diamond drill holes have been drilled quite close together in a mining district. The bearings and inclinations of these drill holes are:

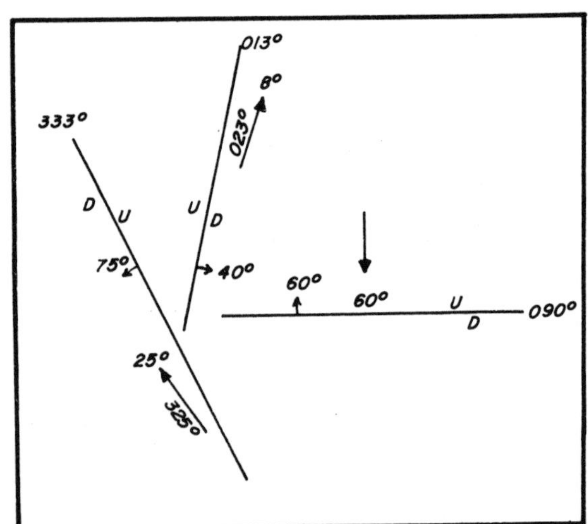

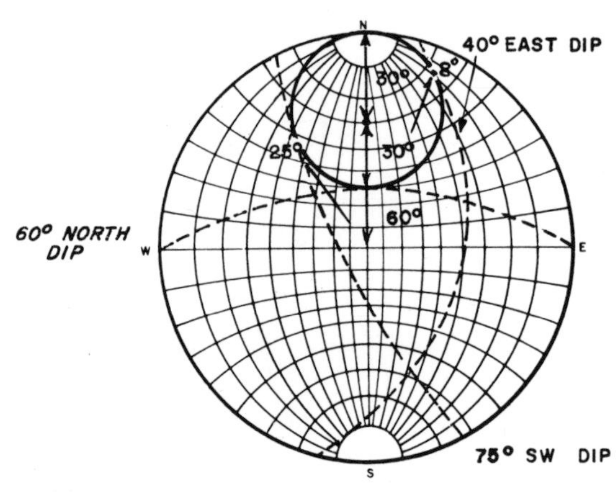

FIGURES 258 (*left*) and 259 (*right*). Steps involved in determining the orientation of the stress system responsible for a fault pattern.

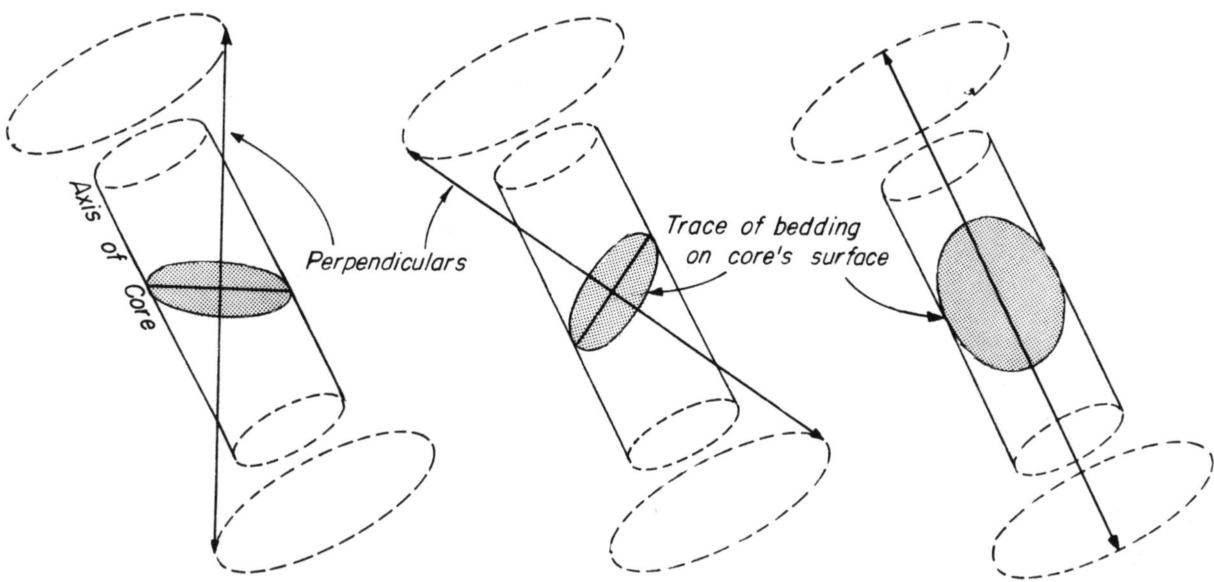

FIGURE 260. Trace of bedding on cone when dip is to the right.

FIGURE 261. Trace of bedding on cone when dip is to the left.

FIGURE 262. Trace of bedding on cone when dip is away from the observer.

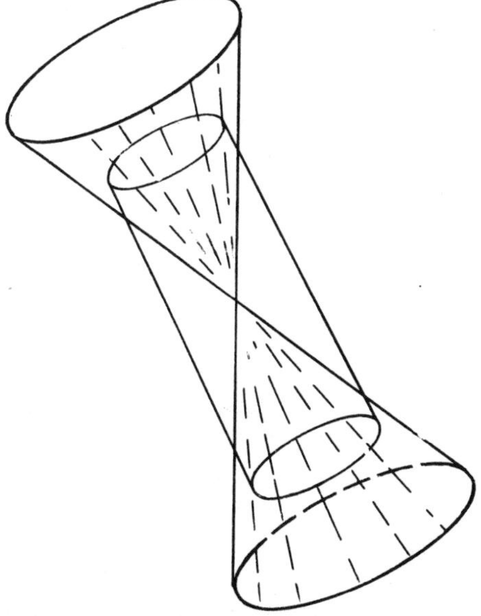

FIGURE 263. Double cone defined by perpendiculars to the dips.

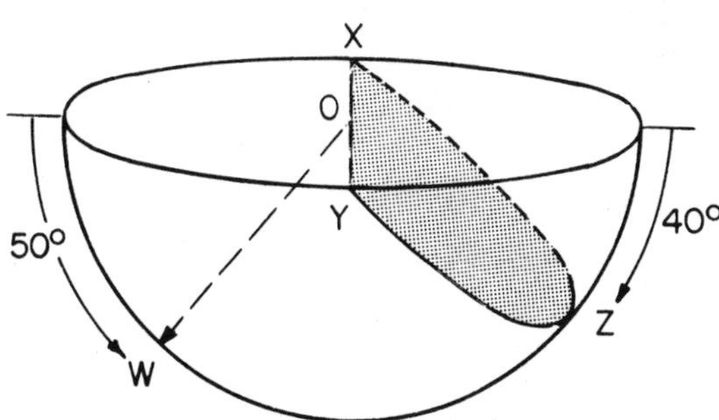

FIGURE 264. OW is the "normal" to the dipping plane XYZ. W is the "pole" of the plane XYZ. The pole W will be represented as a point on the stereonet.

Hole $A = 225°/50°$
Hole $B = 120°/65°$
Hole $C = 343°/37°$

The angles between the normals to the bedding planes and the axes of the cores are:

Hole $A = 35°$
Hole $B = 50°$
Hole $C = 76°$

Determine: Attitude of the formations being penetrated by the drill holes, assuming uniform strike and dip for beds in the region drilled.

Method: The normal, or perpendicular, to a bedding plane appears as a point in stereonet (Fig. 265). The method used is based on the principle that the normal to any bedding plane observed in a drill core must lie somewhere on the

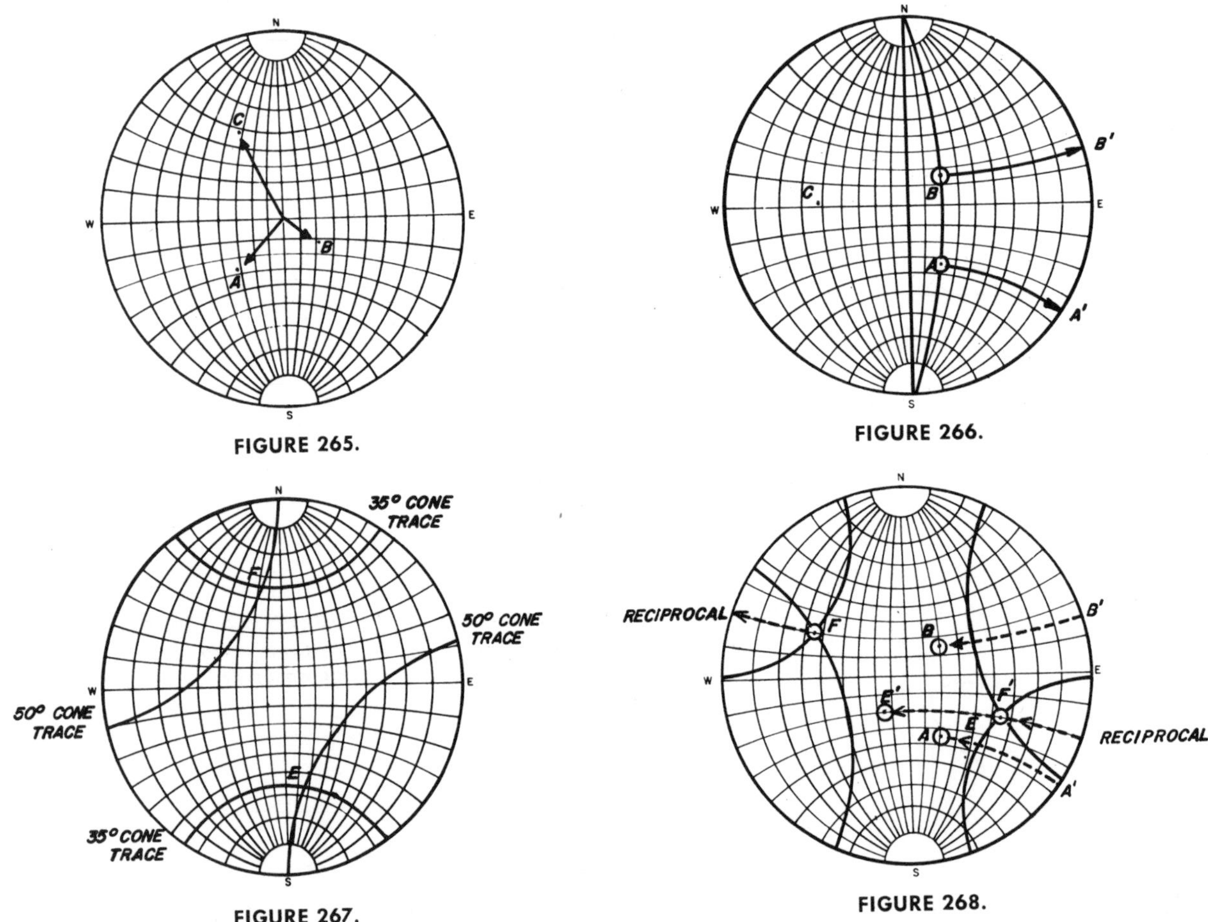

FIGURE 265.

FIGURE 266.

FIGURE 267.

FIGURE 268.

Steps involved in the determination of attitude by drill holes in formations lacking marker beds.

base of a cone, or double cone, whose axial half angle equals the angle between the core axis and the bedding plane normal. Figures 260–262 show three possible orientations of bedding dips in a drill hole which dips 64° to the east. In each diagram the bedding planes form an angle of 60° with the core axes. It will be noted that the perpendiculars or normals to the bedding planes fall on the base of a cone. Figure 263 shows the double cone outline which results from all possible positions of the normals for bedding planes having a 60° relationship with the core axis.

The first step is to locate the orientation of the drill holes on stereographic projection by plotting their respective plunges and bearings (Fig. 265). After the drill hole orientations for holes *A* and *B* have been plotted on a stereonet, the stereographic projections of the points where these drill holes would penetrate the lower hemisphere (points *A* and *B* of Fig. 265) are rotated until they both lie on the same great circle (Fig. 266). This circle common to both points is then rotated up into the horizontal plane of the stereonet, giving points *A′* and *B′*. This is done so that the traces of the cones about each drill hole axis can be drawn in and shown on the horizontal plane of the stereonet. To facilitate the drawing of the cone traces, each drill hole axis point is in turn revolved into a polar position on the stereonet (Fig. 267), and the corresponding cone traces are drawn in by making use of the small circle arcs of the stereonet. As soon as double cone traces for both drill holes have been constructed, the intersection points of the cone traces can be noted (points *F* and *E*). Points *A* and *B* are now revolved back so that they both fall on a common circle (Fig. 268). *A′* and *B′* are then revolved back down to the original position occupied by the great circle

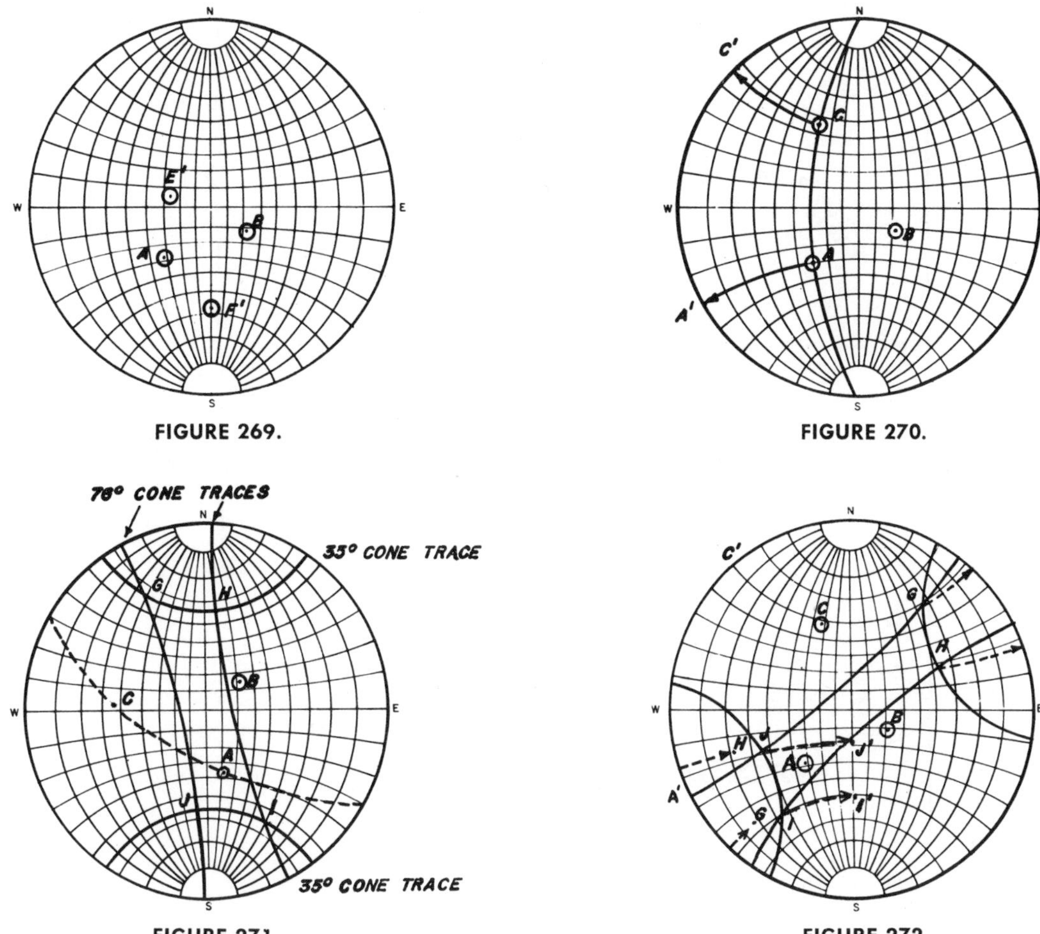

FIGURE 269.

FIGURE 270.

FIGURE 271.

FIGURE 272.

Steps involved in the determination of attitude by drill holes in formations lacking marker beds.

(Fig. 268). This also causes a downward rotation of the cone intersection points *E* and *F* to points *E*′ and *F*′. The tracing paper is now revolved back so that *A* and *B* are in their original positions (Fig. 269). One of these revolved and rotated intersections (*E*′ or *F*′) will represent the actual bedding normal for the formation penetrated. There can be only one such perpendicular, of course, so that the excess intersection point must be eliminated. This is accomplished by plotting the bearing and plunge for the third drill hole *C* (Fig. 270) and noting where the cone traces for *A* and *C* intersect (Fig. 271). It will be noted that only one of the new intersection points (*I*′) from the *A* and *C* cone traces, after being revolved and rotated (Fig. 272), will fall close to the rotated and revolved *A* and *B* intersection (*F*′). This point, which is common to the cone of the bedding plane normals for three different drill holes, will be the actual bedding plane normal in its original orientation (180/36°). The strike and dip of the formation (090/54°N) will, of course, be perpendicular to this normal.

DETERMINATION OF ATTITUDE OF BEDDING IN BOREHOLES BY DIPMETER SURVEYING AND STEREOGRAPHIC PROJECTIONS

Principles Involved: Attitude determination for the formations penetrated in wildcat drilling is essential. This is particularly true in structurally complex regions. This method is used also in directionally drilled off-shore wells.

When a borehole transects a dipping bedding plane, the strike and dip may be determined by finding three points *A, B,* and *C* at different elevations on this plane (Fig. 273). The problem is

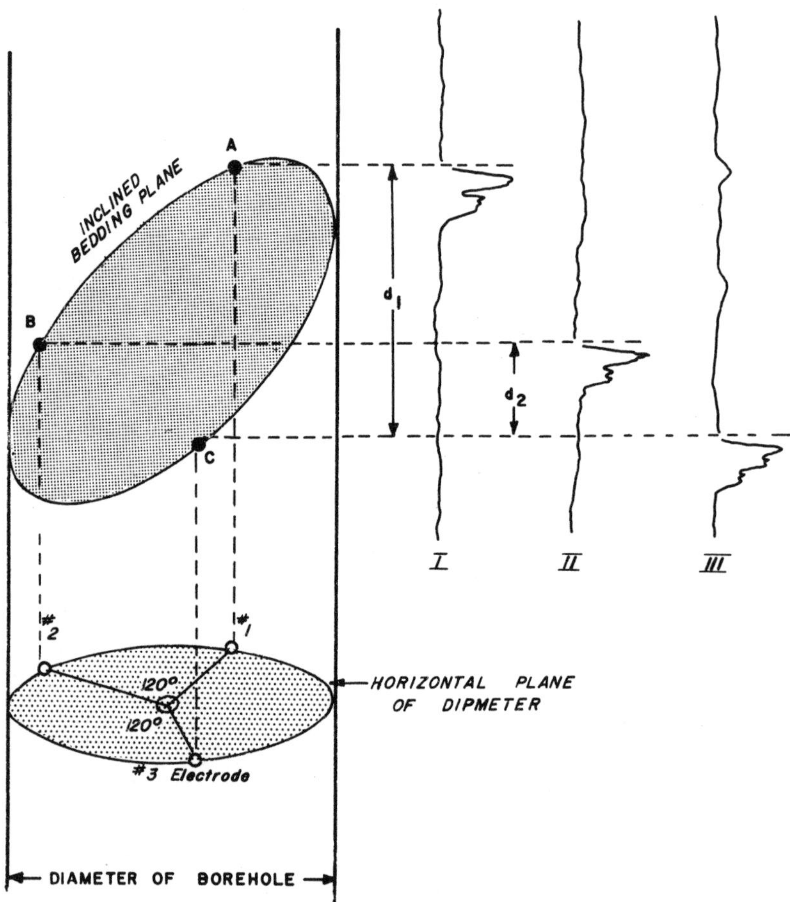

FIGURE 273. Shows electrodes 1, 2, and 3 traversing an inclined bedding plane. The registration of the three log curves I, II, and III is indicated on the right, together with the vertical elevation differences d_1 and d_2.

thus very similar to the three-point method described in Chapter 1. The three points *A, B, C* are obtained by means of a dipmeter, which is an instrument consisting of three electrodes spaced at 120° angles (Fig. 273). Each electrode records a separate curve (curves I, II, III). When electrode 1 passes the boundary of a bed, curve I will record a kick. Similarily electrodes 2 and 3 will record kicks on curves II and III when they pass the boundary of the same bed. From these curves, the vertical distances d_1 and d_2 may be obtained (Fig. 273). Thus all the information necessary for the standard three-point method is available except for the orientation of the core. This information is provided, however, by the azimuth curve of the dipmeter survey (Fig. 274).

The azimuth angle recorded is the angle measured clockwise from Magnetic North around to a vertical plane passing through the electrode 1. The azimuths for electrodes 2 and 3 may be determined by adding 120° and 240° to the azimuth for electrode 1, respectively. The diameter of the borehole is provided by the caliper curve on the right-hand side of Figure 274. The drift (angle of deviation from the vertical) of the borehole is described by the two drift curves on the left-hand side of Figure 274. One of these curves represents that component of the drift resolved into a north-south vertical plane, whereas the other curve represents the component in an east-west vertical plane (Fig. 282). The following example will illustrate the determination of strike and dip.

Data Provided: The vertical distances d_1 and d_2, the azimuth of electrode *A,* and the diameter of the borehole as obtained from a dipmeter survey (Fig. 275). Allowance for drift is omitted in this

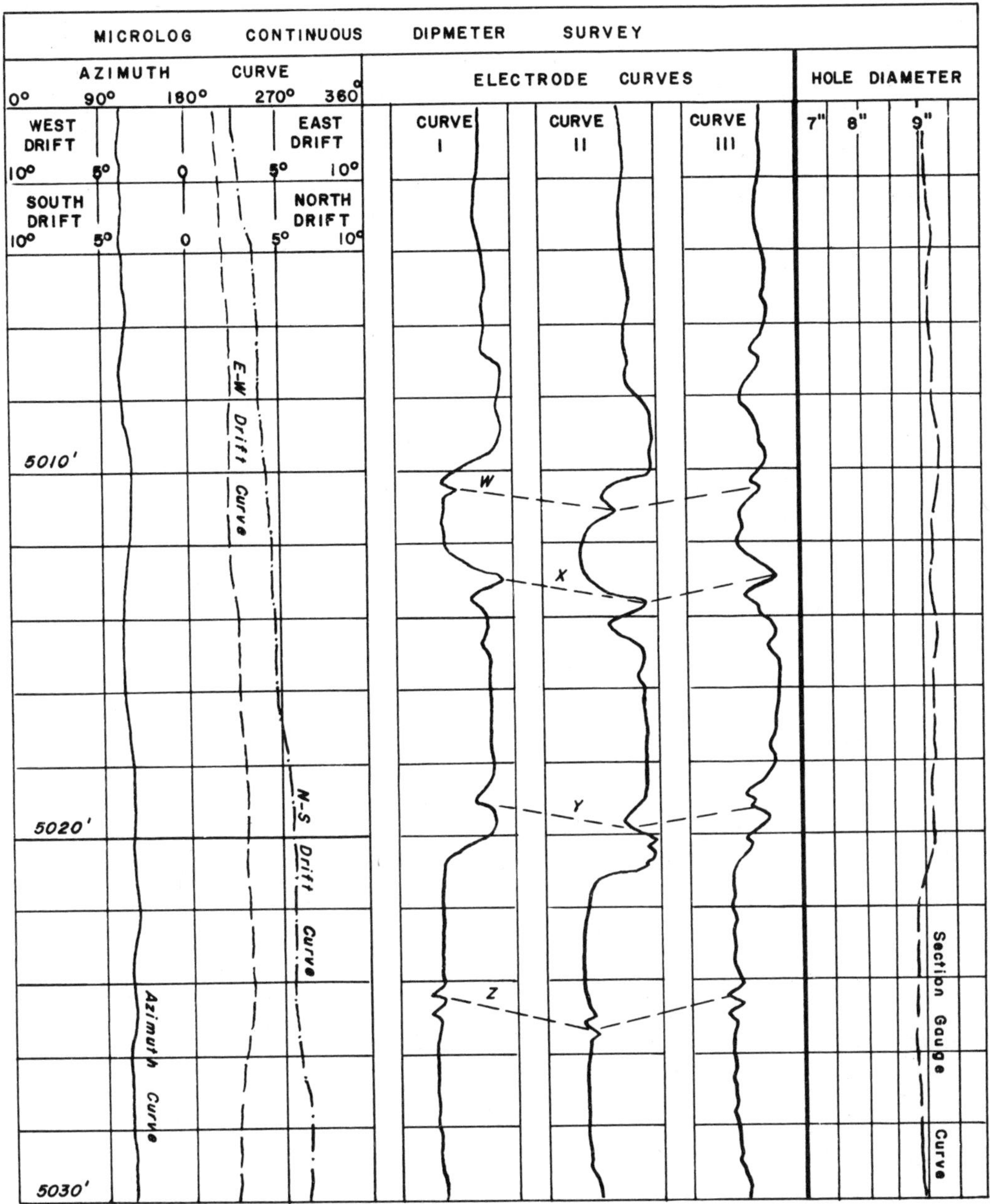

FIGURE 274.

diagram but will be allowed for later. Thus the axis of the borehole is considered as initially vertical.

Determine: The attitude of bedding plane *ABC*.

Method: The angular relations of bedding plane *ABC* to the horizontal electrode plane of the dipmeter 1 2 3 must be examined in more detail (Fig. 275). The length of each side of the equatorial triangle 1 2 3 equals $r\sqrt{3}$ or $\frac{1}{2}$ hole diameter $\times$ $\sqrt{3}$, from simple geometry, and $\sqrt{3} = 1.732$. The tangent of angle $\psi = \dfrac{d_1}{r \times 1.732}$, and the tangent $\phi = \dfrac{d_2}{r \times 1.732}$. The angles ψ and ϕ may be determined from tangent tables. Thus the slope (apparent dips) of *BA* and *CA* may be obtained by this simple equation.

The points B' and C' where lines *AB* and *AC*

would intersect the upper hemisphere of a spherical projection are then plotted on a tracing paper overlying a stereographic net (Fig. 276). In the case illustrated here, the azimuth of $A = 040°$, whereas $\psi = 29°$, and $\phi = 18°$. The tracing paper is then

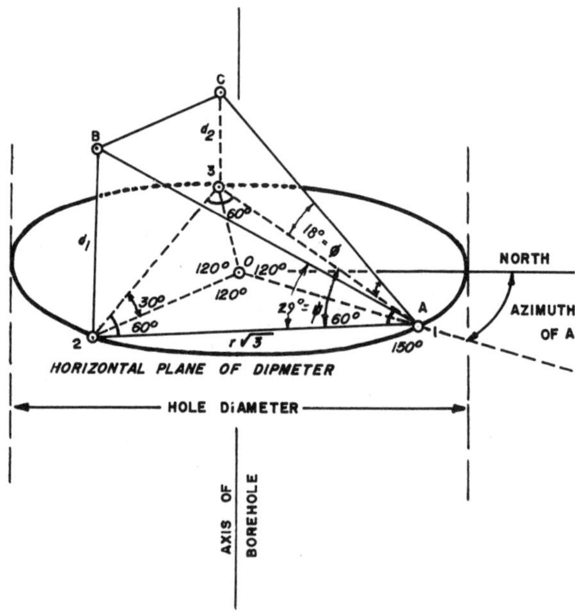

FIGURE 275. Geometric relations of bedding plane to the horizontal electrode plane. (Redrawn and modified from A. J. DeWitte [1956], *Am. Inst. Min. Met. Eng.*, Tech. Paper 4333, Petroleum Trans., vol. 207.)

rotated until both B' and C' lie on the same great circle (Fig. 277). The true dip, uncorrected for drift, is seen to be 30°. To find the strike and dip directions, uncorrected for drift, it is necessary to rotate the tracing paper until the north arrow (N) on the tracing paper overlays the north position on the underlying stereographic net. This gives a dip direction of 018° (N18°E) and a strike direction of 108° (S72°E), both uncorrected for drift, and measured from magnetic north rather than from true north (Fig. 278).

To allow for drift, the drift angles north and east (e.g., 8° and 5°, in this case) are plotted on a stereographic projection (Fig. 279). In this case the hade[2] angle is treated as dip because measurements at the center of the net are less accurate (smaller scale) than those near the circumference of the net. The procedure is similar to that used in determining true dip from two apparent dips (Fig. 282). The resultant drift is seen to be 9° on a bearing of 037° (N37°E).

[2] The *hade* angle is the complement of the dip angle; i.e., the hade angle = 90° − dip angle.

The next step is to plot the uncorrected attitude of the bedding and the drift direction on the same stereographic projection (Fig. 280).

The drift direction is then rotated around to the east position on the net (Fig. 280) and the resultant drift of 9° is applied to the uncorrected attitude of the bedding plane. This causes the stereogram for the bedding plane to shift leftwards (movement along small circles) through 9°. The corrected position of the bedding plane is then rotated until the north direction (N) on the tracing paper overlays the north position on the underlying net. The true attitude of the strike would then be 104° (magnetic) and the true dip would be 22° (Fig. 281).

Limitation: When a dipmeter sonde is pulled out of the hole, recording as it goes, it will normally rotate back and forth slowly in either a left-handed or right-handed spiral. Occasionally the sonde may spin so rapidly that the azimuth of electrode 1 changes between levels A and C or between A and B (Fig. 273). This would invalidate the method used. Fortunately this error generally occurs near the bottom of the borehole, and when this error is suspected, it is better not to compute attitudes for this portion of the hole. DeWitte (1956) has described a method to handle this error.

STATISTICAL ANALYSIS OF STRUCTURAL UNITS BY STEREOGRAPHIC AND RELATED PROJECTIONS

Principles Involved: In slightly deformed regions the location of fold axes can easily be determined by mapping bedding planes and formation contacts and by noting the arcuate patterns of the folded formations. In highly deformed metamorphic terrains these conventional means are not always possible as bedding planes and formation tops are frequently difficult to recognize, even though the distribution of formations may still be mapped.

There are several possible ways in which such complex regions may be analyzed structurally, but a brief review of lineation, cleavage, and jointing is needed before discussing these methods. The subjects of cleavage and lineation are complex ones and have been described in detail by G.

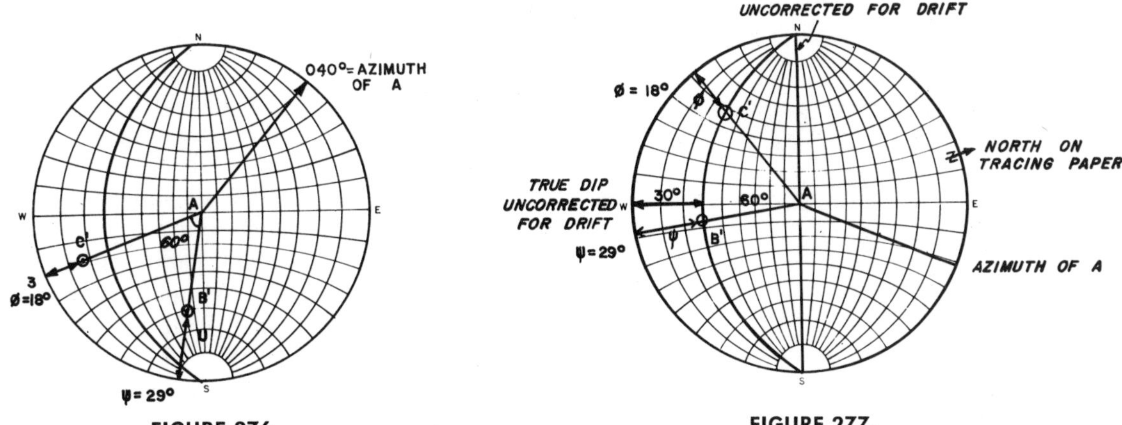

FIGURE 276.

FIGURE 277.

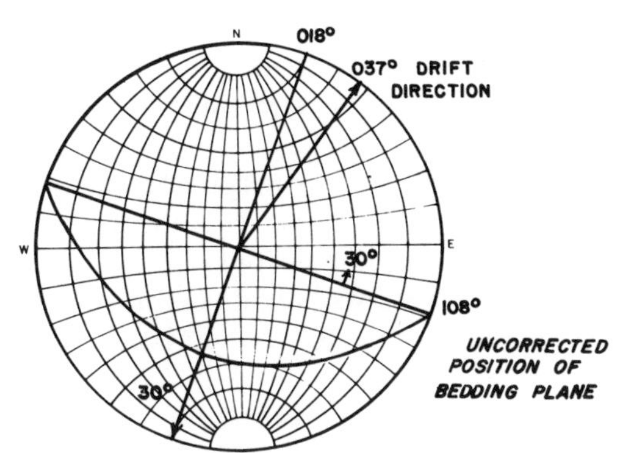

FIGURE 278.

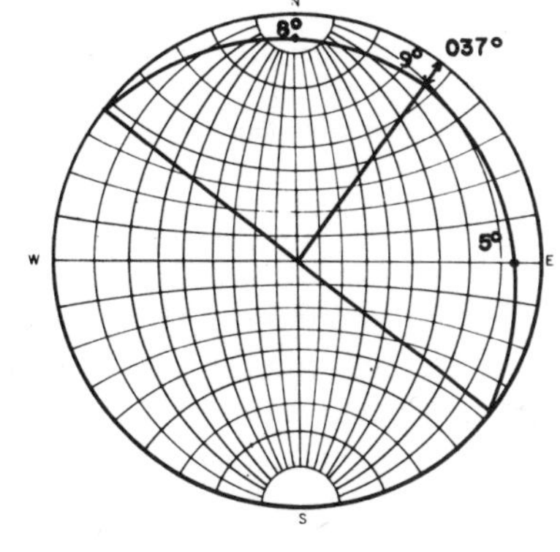

FIGURE 279.

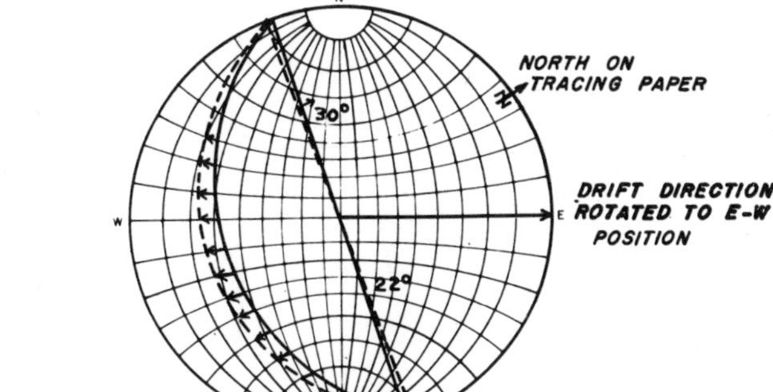

FIGURE 280.

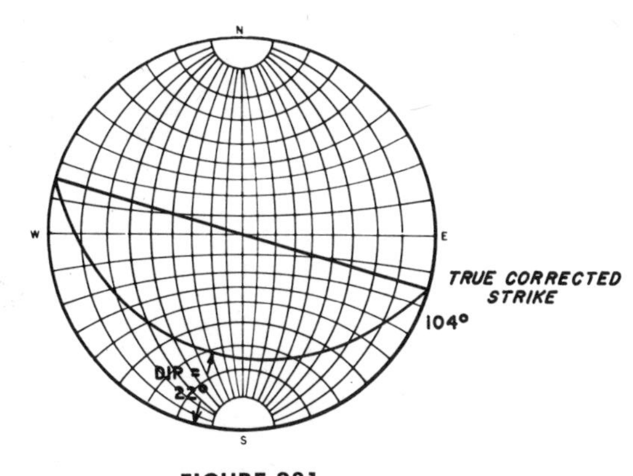

FIGURE 281.

Steps involved in determining strike and dip from dipmeter surveys, using the stereographic method. All diagrams are upper hemisphere stereographic projections.

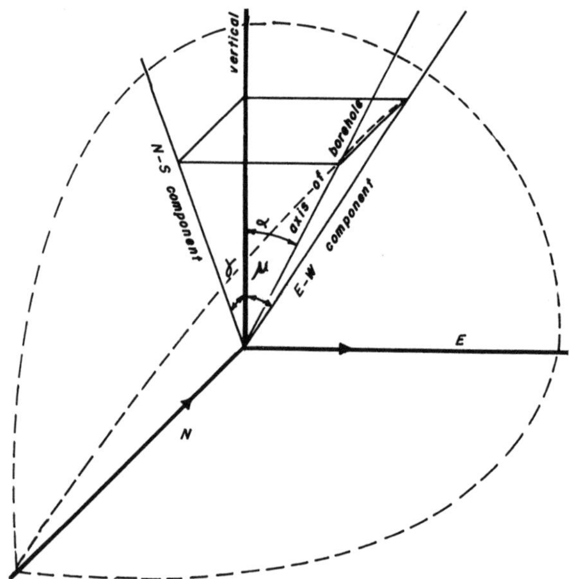

FIGURE 282. Relations between drift components and resulting drift. (Redrawn and modified from A. J. DeWitte [1956], *Am. Inst. Min. Met. Eng.*, vol. 207.)

Wilson (1946), E. Cloos (1946), and others. Figures 67, 68, and 283 show that the lineation usually occurs in one of two directions relative to fold axes. The *a* axis represents the direction of most intense stretching or flowage and maximum movement (direction of tectonic transport). It is represented usually by elongate fossils, oöids and pebbles, slickensides, mineral patches, mineral clots, porphyroblasts, and so forth. Most of these structures are visible in the flow cleavage plane. Minor folds sometimes develop parallel to the *a* lineation direction and give rise to lineations represented by warps, crinkles, and drag-fold axes. One of the best explanations of this phenomena is due to the lateral restriction, or squeezing in the *b* direction, of advancing folds (Fig. 284). Small cross folds due to a second period of deformation have been described by White and Jahns (1950), by Harrison and Wells (1956), and by Moench, Harrison, and Sims (1958).

The *b* lineation direction is approximately parallel to the fold axis and to the strike of dependent cleavage planes. It is normally the axis of least deformation or constant dimension, unless arcuation and flowage parallel to the fold axes occurs (Fig. 283). The *b* lineation is expressed in the form of cleavage-bedding intersections, crenulated cleavage, drag-fold axes, warps and crinkles, rodding or mullion structure, stretching of oöids and pebbles, and so forth.

The *c* direction lies perpendicular to cleavage planes and to the *a* axis. It is the axis of greatest shortening (thinning of fold limbs).

Figure 285 shows how lineation is measured in the field and indicates the symbols used on maps to express it.

Rock cleavage is measured in the same way as bedding. Joints related to folding are commonly of the shear diagonal type or of the vertical tensional type (Fig. 286). The tensional type are fre-

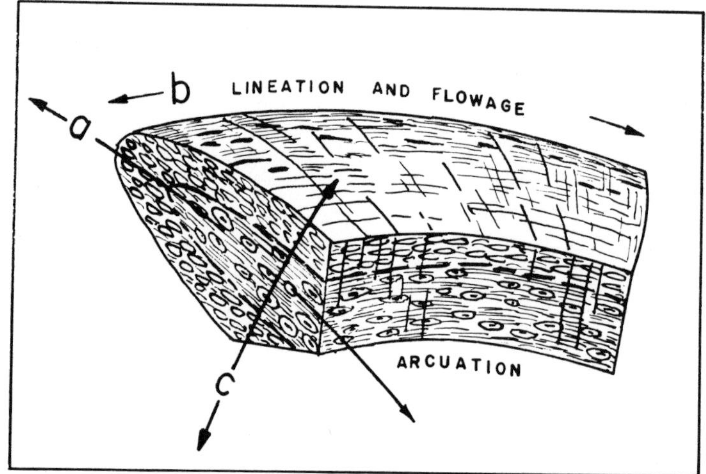

FIGURE 283. The relationship between lineation, cleavage, and folding in arcuate folds. (Modified from E. Cloos [1946], *Geol. Soc. Am.*, Mem. 18.)

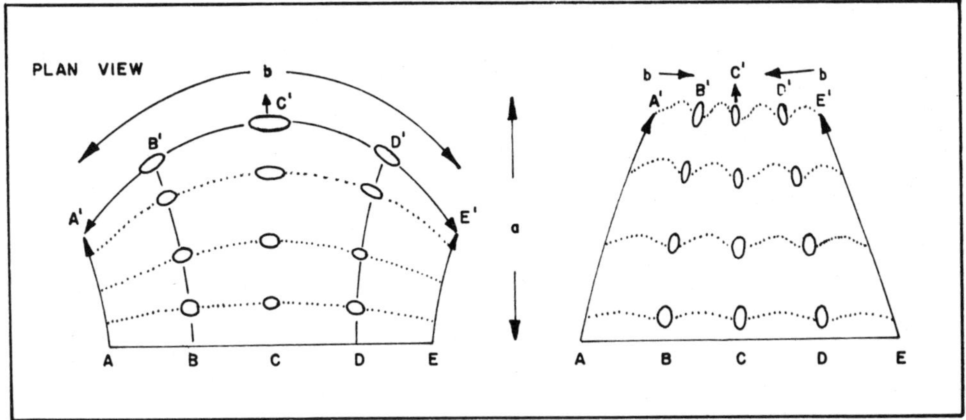

FIGURE 284. Cross folding may result when an advancing fold is confined (right diagram) laterally. The ellipses show the shapes assumed by oöids or pebbles as the result of diverging folds (left) and converging folds (right). (Modified from E. Cloos [1946], *Geol. Soc. Am., Mem.* 18.)

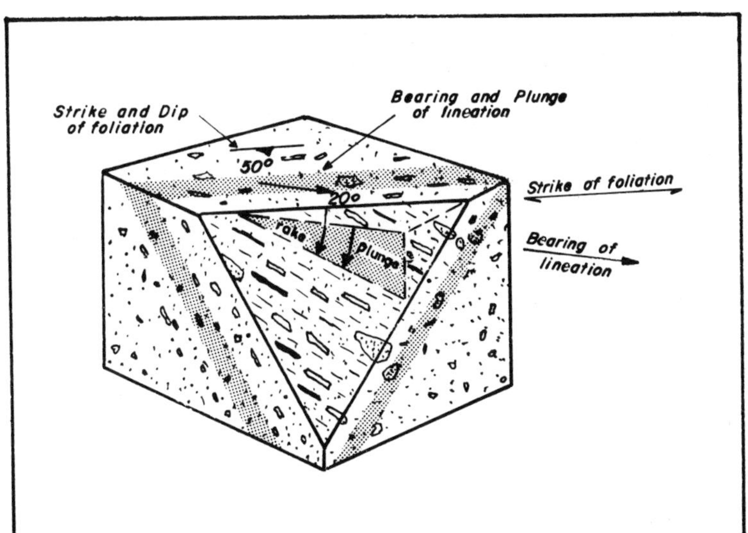

FIGURE 285. Illustrating how lineation may be measured in the field. The rake of the lineation is measured in the foliation plane, down from the horizontal. The plunge of the lineation is measured in a vertical plane. Note that the bearing of the lineation is different from the strike of the foliation.

quently either parallel (longitudinal) to the axial surface of the fold or perpendicular (cross) to this surface.

Two types of projection are used in the statistical analysis of megascopic structural units, the stereographic projection and the Lambert equal area projection (Schmidt net). The stereographic projection, as mentioned previously (Fig. 185–188), is constructed by joining points on the lower hemisphere of a spherical projection to the zenithal point of the sphere. The stereographic projection is thus a perspective projection, and it is this property which makes it useful for analyzing structural units in three dimensions. A stereographic projection is not area-true, however (Fig. 287), as areas bounded by four arcs of 10° near the center of the stereonet are much smaller than 10° areas near the circumference of the net. In statistical work it is necessary to bring a large number of scattered observations together about

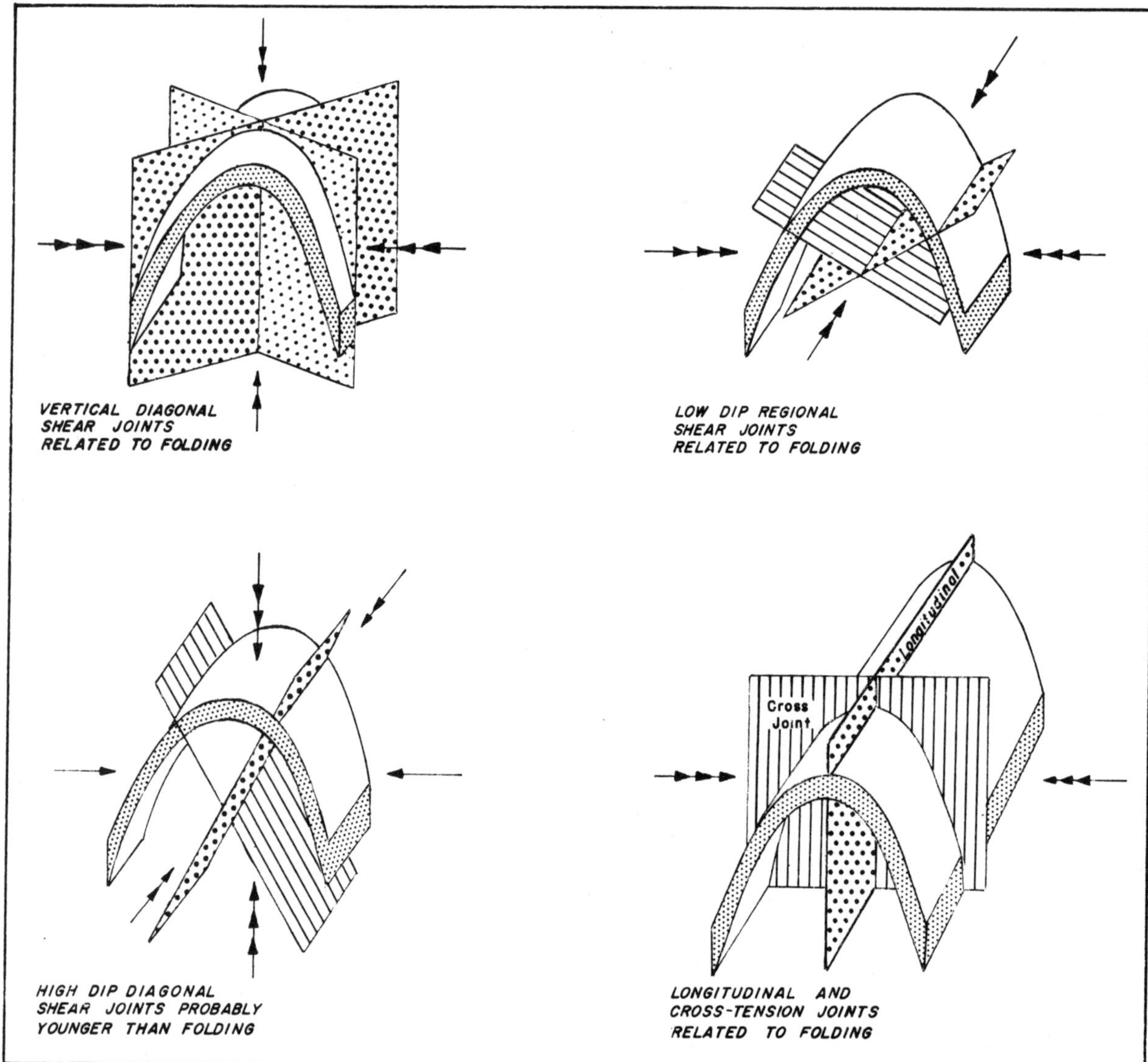

FIGURE 286. Illustrating the relationship between various types of joints and major folds.

a single origin in a composite diagram so that conclusions may be reached. The poles of joints or cleavage planes and lineation directions are the types of information which may be grouped in this manner. The relative spatial concentration of the measured data is important and the equal area projection (Fig. 287) accomplishes this with very little distortion. Pincus (1951) has suggested a rectangular co-ordinate diagram for statistical analysis, but Rodgers (1952) has objected to this type of diagram.

Method: The first step is to map the structures (lineation, cleavage, jointing, etc.) in the field. The next step is to plot the lineation directions, or poles to cleavage and joint planes on an equal area projection. Stereographic projection is occasionally used as described later. The equal area net is fastened to a table and is overlain with a sheet of transparent tracing paper. The bearing of the lineation is drawn outwards from the center of the net towards the circumference, and the tracing paper is then rotated about the center of the net, to the north-south or east-west position; the inclination angle is measured inward from the circumference and plotted as a point on the line. The line is then erased. In actuality the line need not be used if a mark is made on the circumference instead and used as a point of reference in rotating. To obtain a reliable structural picture of the area, one should plot a significant number of points (100 to 200 as a minimum). The points should come proportionately from all parts of a map area. Thus it may be advantageous to lay a grid system out on the map (see Fig. 306) and select several attitudes from each grid square. Figure 289 shows fold axes cleavage poles and lineations for the South Mountain Uplift in Maryland (Fig. 288).

Frequently it is desirable to contour such point diagrams in order to interpret the results of the structural survey, as there may be several types of lineation or jointing or several directions of folding in the same area. This is accomplished by means of a point counter (Fig. 290). Point counters are of two types: the center counter and the peripheral counter. The area within the counter circle is equal to 1 per cent of the area of the equal area net. Thus if the equal area net has a diameter of 20 centimeters, then a grid pattern is laid over the equal area net with each square being 1 centimeter square, and the diameter of the pointer circle is made equal to 2 centimeters. The peripheral counter is rotated about the center of the net and the number of points within the half circle at each end are totaled. If this total comes to 9 points (Fig. 290) and if a total of 300 points were plotted, then the value of 3 per cent is placed at the grid line intersection. The diagram could be contoured on the number of points instead of on per cent values however. The peripheral counter is then shifted over to the next grid line intersection and the new value is plotted. The center counter is moved across the diagram and values are determined wherever a grid line intersection falls at the center of the counter circle. This procedure is followed until a contour value has been determined for each grid line intersection on the net. These values are then contoured.

Applications: In structurally complex regions where fold patterns cannot be recognized by conventional mapping, statistical studies of small-scale structures are interpreted in order to shed light on the larger structural picture. The following examples will illustrate some of the possible applications.

Figure 291 shows a contour diagram of joints, representing an upper hemispheric equal area plot of 1680 joint poles in the Freeland-Lamartine district near Central City, Colorado. The upper hemisphere was used in this plot, as the poles plotted then fall into the same quadrant of the net as the true dip direction. Thus the pole of a joint

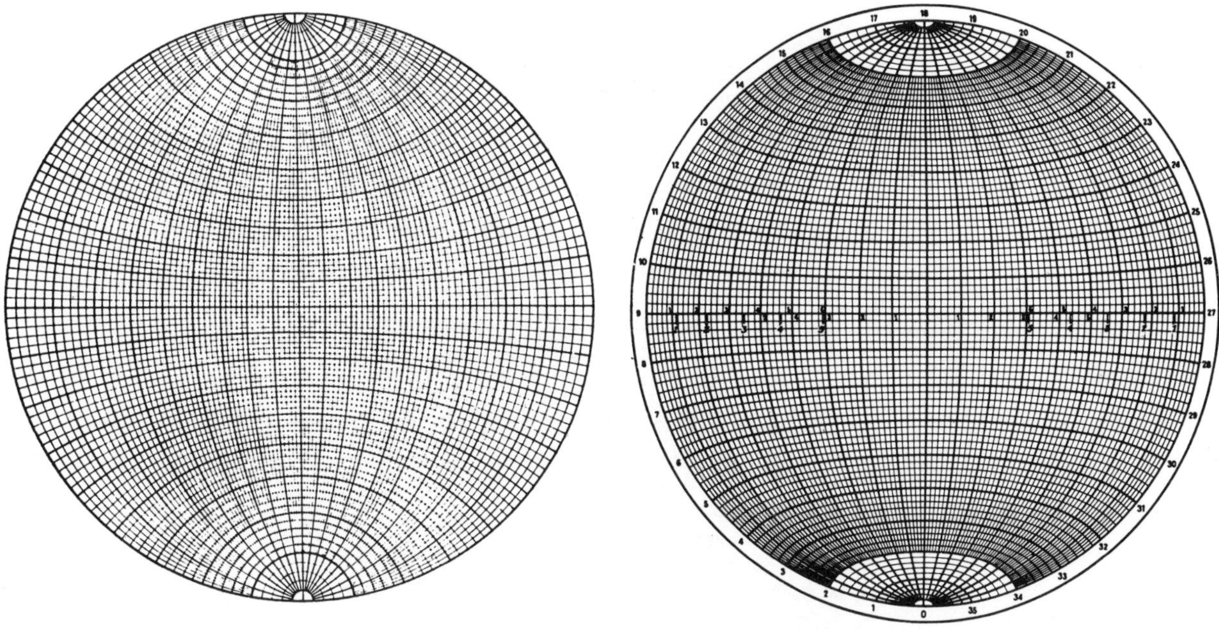

FIGURE 287. Illustrating the relationship between stereonets (left) and equal area nets (right). Note the greater distortion in the stereonet.

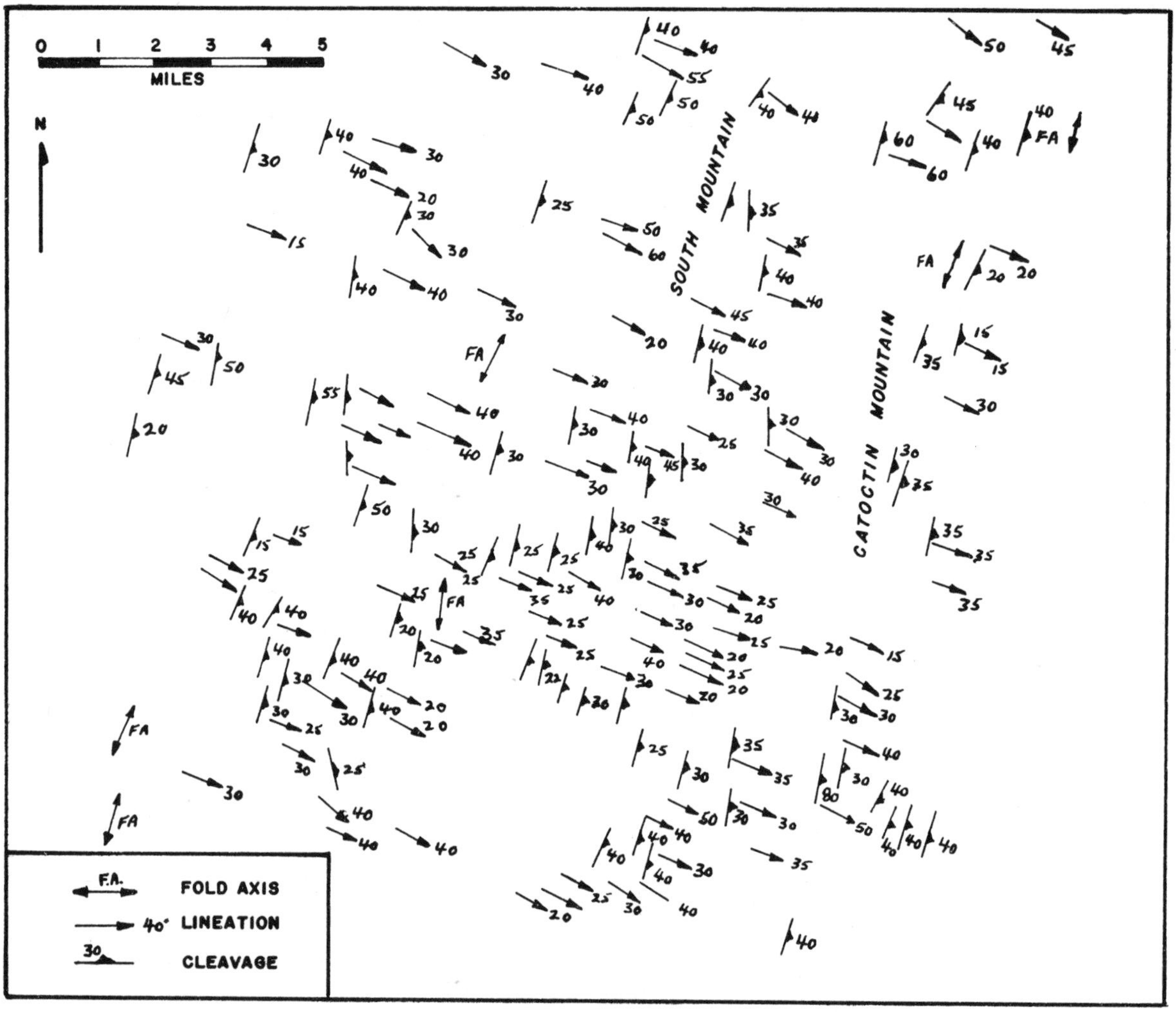

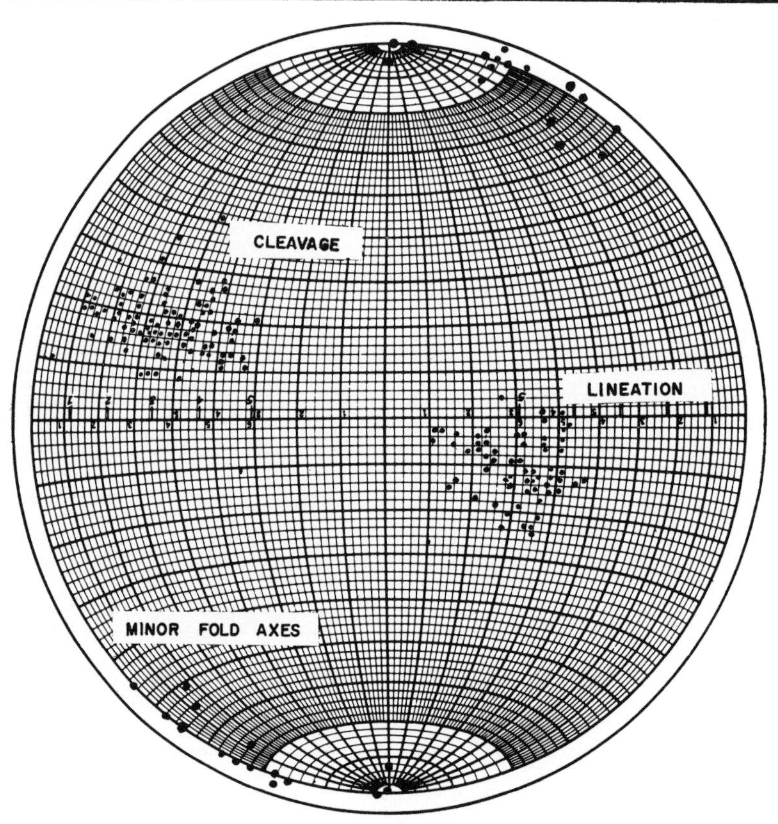

FIGURES 288 (*above*) **and 289** (*below*). Structural information mapped in the South Mountain-Catoctin Mountain area of Maryland. Figure 289 shows how the information obtained in the field (Fig. 288) is plotted on an equal area net. (Modified from E. Cloos and A. Hietanen [1941], *Geol. Soc. Am.,* Spec. Paper 35.)

plane dipping north-westward falls into the northwest quadrant of the net. This contour diagram discloses four joint sets:

N74°W (286°) Dipping 68°N
N82°E (082°) Dipping 62°N
N22°W (338°) Dipping 79°NE
N56°E (056°) Dipping 63°NW

These are arranged in order of prominence with the N74°W being strongest, and the N56°E set being weakest. The construction lines (Fig. 291) show how the joint patterns are derived from the contour picture. Each individual contour maximum is joined to the center of the net by a line, and a plane drawn perpendicular to this line represents the strike of the joint set.

The next step is to represent the four joint sets in stereoscopic projection (Fig. 292). It is noted that the joint planes intersect to form a very small triangle of intersection. This suggests that all four sets were formed in the same stress system. A comparison with Figure 286 suggests that the N74°W and 56°E directions are shear joints, that the N82°E direction is a cross joint, and that the N22°W direction is a longitudinal joint. This would require a maximum stress approximately parallel to the N82°E direction. The joint system is interpreted as being related to the Laramide uplift of the Colorado Front Range. The long axis of the uplift is interpreted as being approximately parallel to the longitudinal joints. Laramide (late

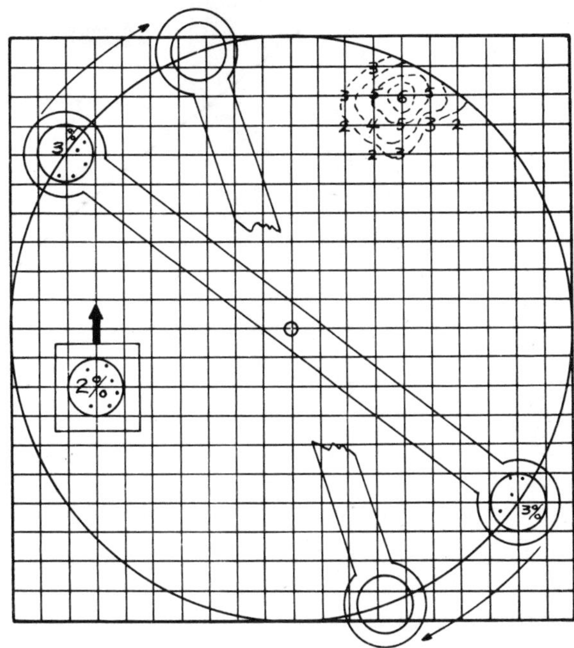

FIGURE 290. Showing the operation of a point counter. This diagram is contoured on per cent values. In this case 300 points were plotted. Thus 6 points represents 2 per cent.

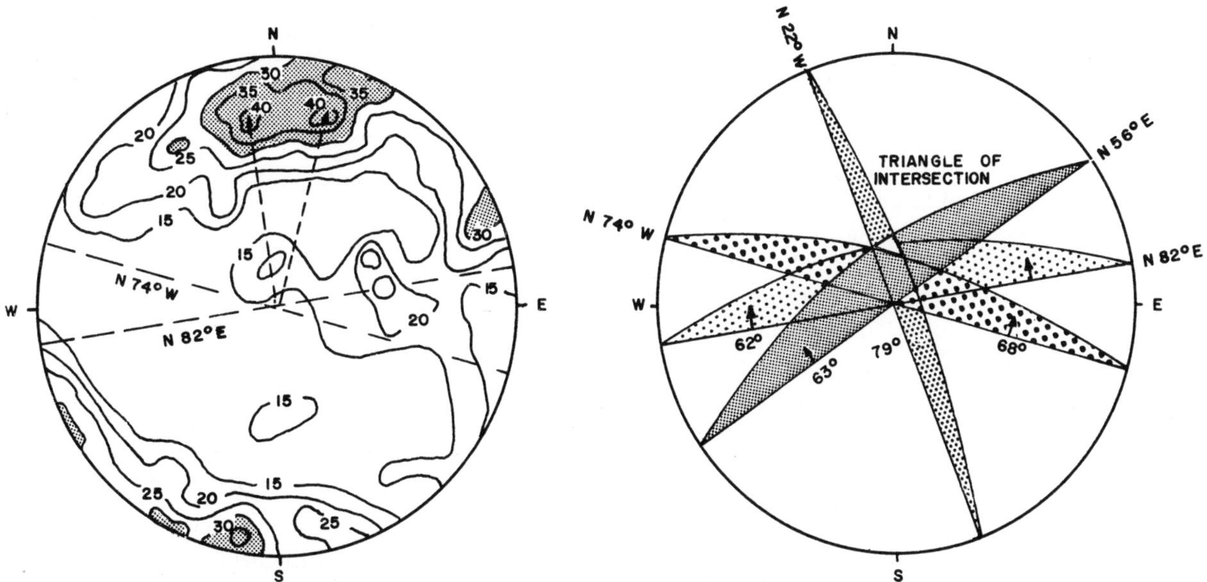

FIGURES 291 (*left*) and 292 (*right*). Contour diagram (upper hemispheric projection) of joints mapped in the Freeland-Lamartine area, near Central City, Colorado. (Redrawn from J. E. Harrison and J. D. Wells [1956], *U.S. Geol. Surv.*, Bull. 1032-B. Figure 292 shows stereographic projection (lower hemispheric) of the contour pattern appearing in Figure 291. (Redrawn from J. E. Harrison and J. D. Wells [1956], *U.S. Geol. Surv.*, Bull. 1032-B.)

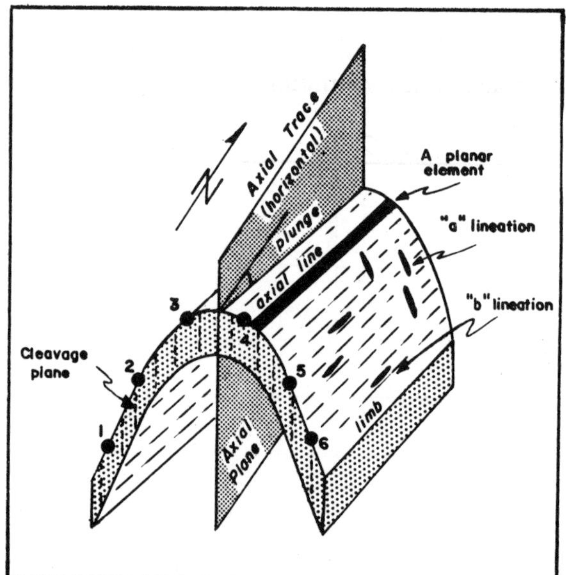

FIGURE 293. Orthographic projection of an open symmetrical cylindrical anticline plunging north at 20°.

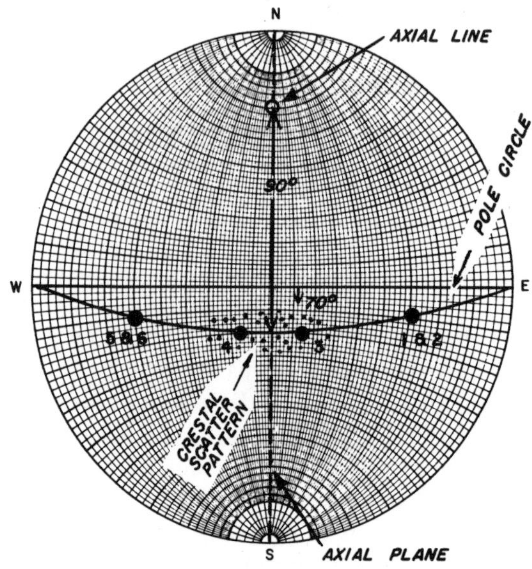

FIGURE 294. Stereographic projection (lower hemispheric) of fold elements appearing in Figure 293.

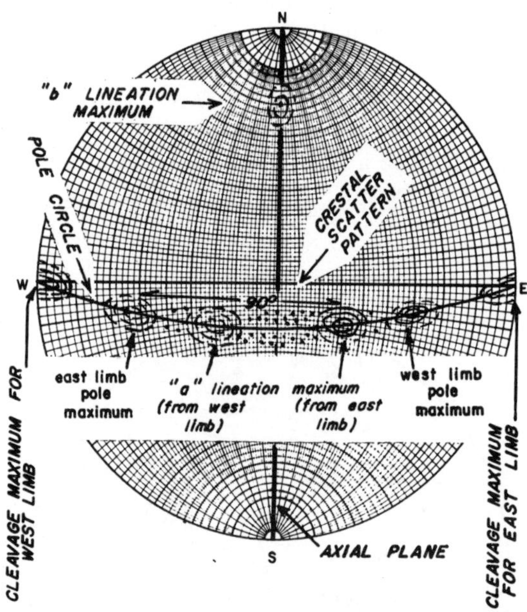

FIGURE 295. Stereographic projection (lower hemispheric) of lineations and poles to planar elements for the anticline appearing in Figure 293. The lineations and poles have been contoured to yield maxima. Note the 90° relationship between pole maxima and lineation maxima.

Cretaceous–early Tertiary) folds cannot be recognized in the Front Range area proper as the uplift has been eroded down to expose the Precambrian core, but Laramide folding on the flanks of the Front Range substantiates the Laramide age of the joint system in the Freeland-Lamartine area. The recognition of Laramide jointing superimposed on the earlier Precambrian deformation has important economic applications; this aspect will be discussed in the next chapter.

The subject of cylindrical folding was discussed in Chapter 3. A cylindrical fold consists of an infinite number of planar elements. Any planar (noncurving) portion of a fold limb is a planar element. In cylindrical folds, each planar element, and the intersection between any two elements, is parallel to the axial line of the fold. Most folds, even in highly deformed Precambrian areas, are cylindrical. Conical folds do occur occasionally, however, and thus it is important to be able to discern cylindrical or conical folds. The method of drawing right sections (sections perpendicular to the plunge) is not the same for both types of folds (Stockwell, 1951), nor is the relationship between cleavage, lineation, and axial lines the same for both types of folds. A *conical fold* is one in which all the planar elements pass through a fixed point or vertex and are not parallel to the axial line.

Figure 293 shows the relationship between dependent cleavage and lineation, axial plane, and fold limbs in a cylindrical fold. Each planar element has a pole, just as each joint in a joint system has a pole or line perpendicular to it. In cylindrical folds, each pole to a planar element is

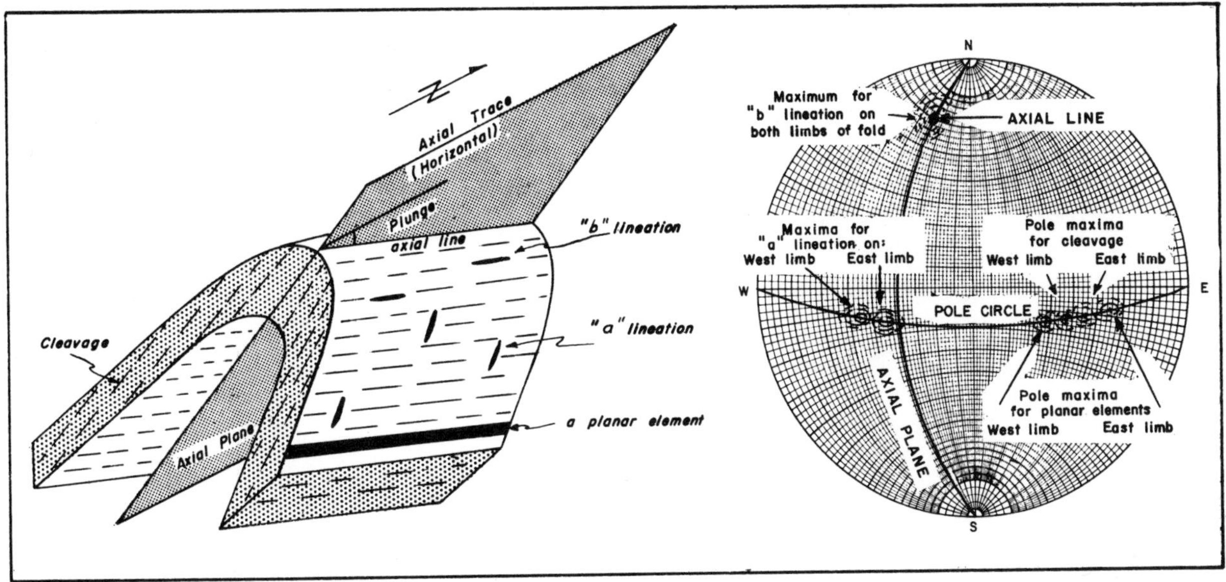

FIGURES 296 (*left*) and 297 (*right*). Orthographic projection of a tight, overturned, cylindrical anticline plunging north at 20°. Figure 297 shows stereographic projection (lower hemispheric) of lineations and poles to planar elements and cleavage planes for the anticline appearing in Figure 296. Note the 90° relationship between the cleavage and the *a* lineation maxima.

perpendicular to the axial line of the fold. All the possible poles for any cylindrical fold should lie within a plane which is perpendicular to the axial line.

On a stereonet, the axial line appears as a point, and the plane containing the poles appears as a great circle at right angles to it (Fig. 294). This great circle is referred to as the *pole circle* by Dahlstrom (1954). The poles for that portion of the fold limb which is planar will all appear at the same point on the pole circle. Thus points 1 and 2 (Fig. 293) both appear at the same point in stereographic projection (Fig. 294). A crestal scatter pattern results for the crestal portion of the fold which is not planar (Fig. 294). The axial plane appears as a great circle on the stereonet, being vertical in Figure 293. This great circle contains both the axial line and a point on the pole circle. For open symmetrical folds, the axial plane intersects the pole circle midway between the limb maxima (Fig. 294). Lineation parallel to the fold axis (i.e., *b* lineation, using the terminology of E. Cloos) will coincide with the axial line point in stereographic projection (Fig. 295). Lineation in the plane of the limbs (referred to as *a* lineation) is commonly almost perpendicular to the *b* lineation, and such is the case for the anticline in Figure 293. Thus this lineation occupies a position on the pole circle 90° removed from the respective pole maximum (Fig. 295). Poles to the cleavage planes shown in Figure 293 would appear at the ends of the pole circle in Figure 295, if the cleavage is related to folding. If the folding were intense enough to produce isoclinal folds, then the cleavage poles would almost coincide with the limb poles. Figures 296 and 297 show the relationship between planar elements, cleavage planes, lineation, axial planes, and axial lines in an overturned anticline, asymmetric to the east and plunging 20°N. Another type of structural feature which can be plotted on such diagrams is the axes of drag folds.

This method allows the geologist to bring all the structural elements of a fold onto one diagram. It will indicate whether the fold is cylindrical or not, and it will point to the position of axial planes and axial lines if these are not visible in the field. Further, this approach will test the dependency relationship between cleavage, lineation, and the major folding processes of the area. The cleavage and lineation may be related to different periods of deformation from the folding. Thus this type of study is useful in analyzing structural processes in highly deformed areas. Equal area nets could be used in lieu of stereonets. Dahlstrom (1954) discusses further applications of this approach.

PROBLEM 30

STEREOGRAPHIC EVALUATION OF A TILTED PETROLEUM STRUCTURAL TRAP

Data Provided: A reconnaissance surface mapping problem yielded the strike and dip information shown in Figure 298. The Mississippian formations are believed to contain numerous porous, oil-saturated beds. Migration and accumulation of petroleum is believed to have been more or less complete by the end of the Paleozoic. The constant attitude observed in the Cretaceous strata leads us to conclude that there has been a post-Cretaceous tilting of 16° ESE.

Determine: Estimate the oil possibilities for the Mississippian and locate a test well. Thus it is necessary to determine the pretilting attitude at each Mississippian outcrop and to draw a rough form line map for the area. Form lines are structure contours which represent the general form or shape of a structure without any absolute elevation values indicated, whereas structure contours are imaginary lines connecting points of equal elevation on a single horizon.

Method: In drawing the form line map bear in mind that contour spacing will be more closely packed in areas of steeper dip.

In allowing for the effect of tilt, by means of stereographic projection, remember that a bed can be tilted up through the horizontal, and then its dip will be reversed into the reciprocal direction. Thus, it may be necessary to apply part of the tilt correction on, for instance, the 060° small circle, and if this does not account for all of the necessary tilt correction, the remainder must be applied on the reciprocal small circle which happens to be the 240° small circle.

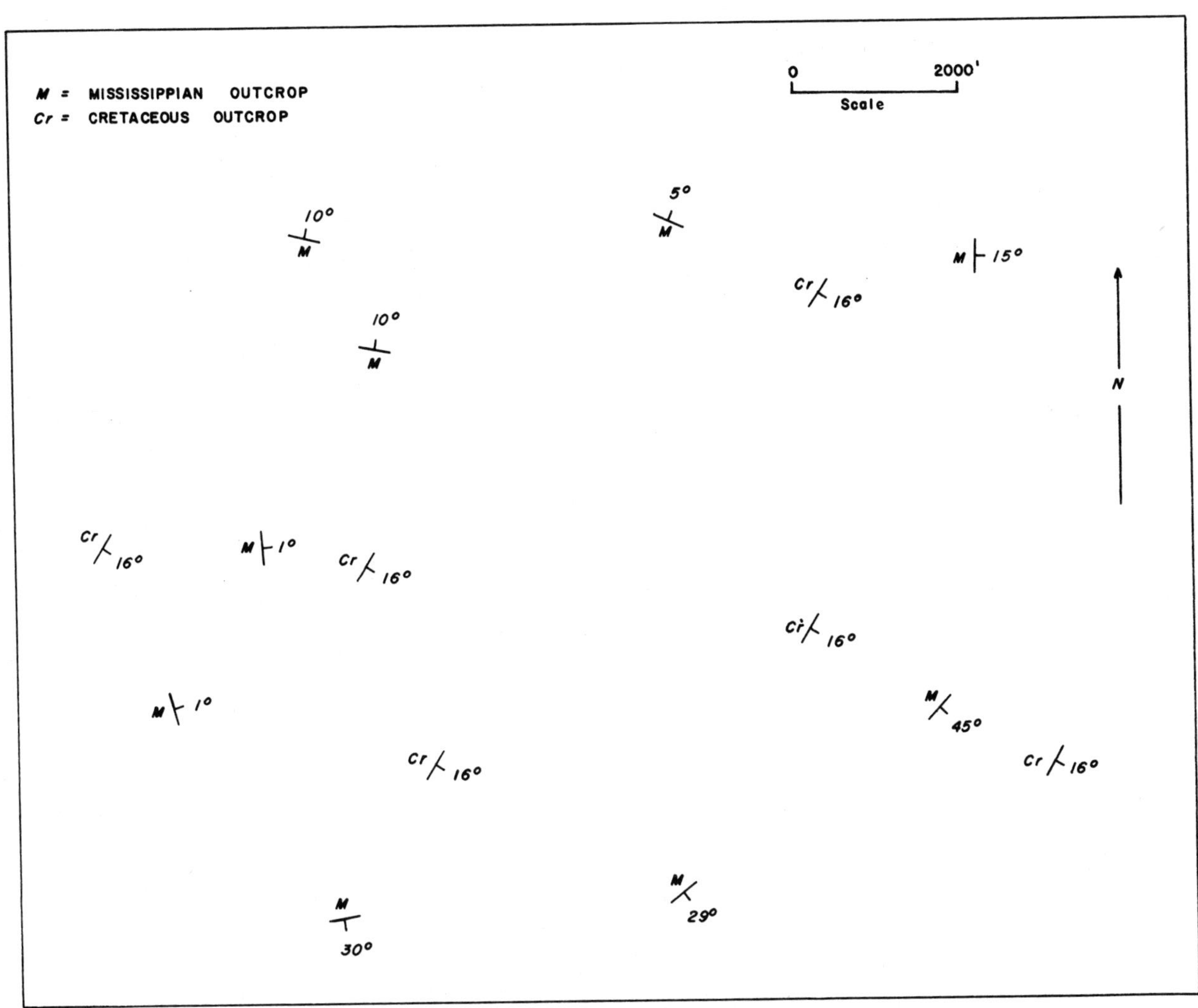

FIGURE 298. Map for use with Problem 30.

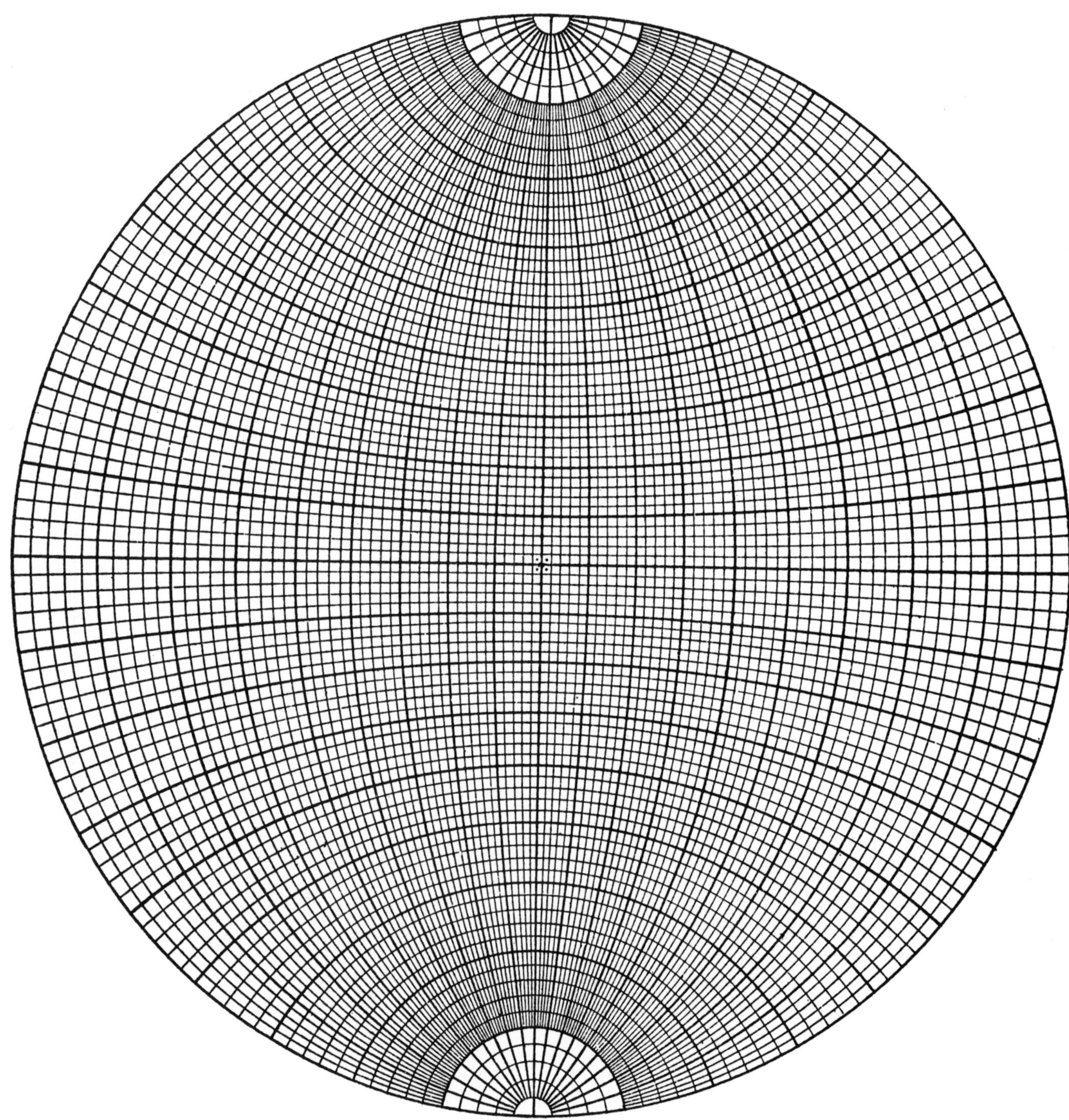

Stereonet for use with problems in Chapter 8. (Reprinted by permission of D. Jerome Fisher.)

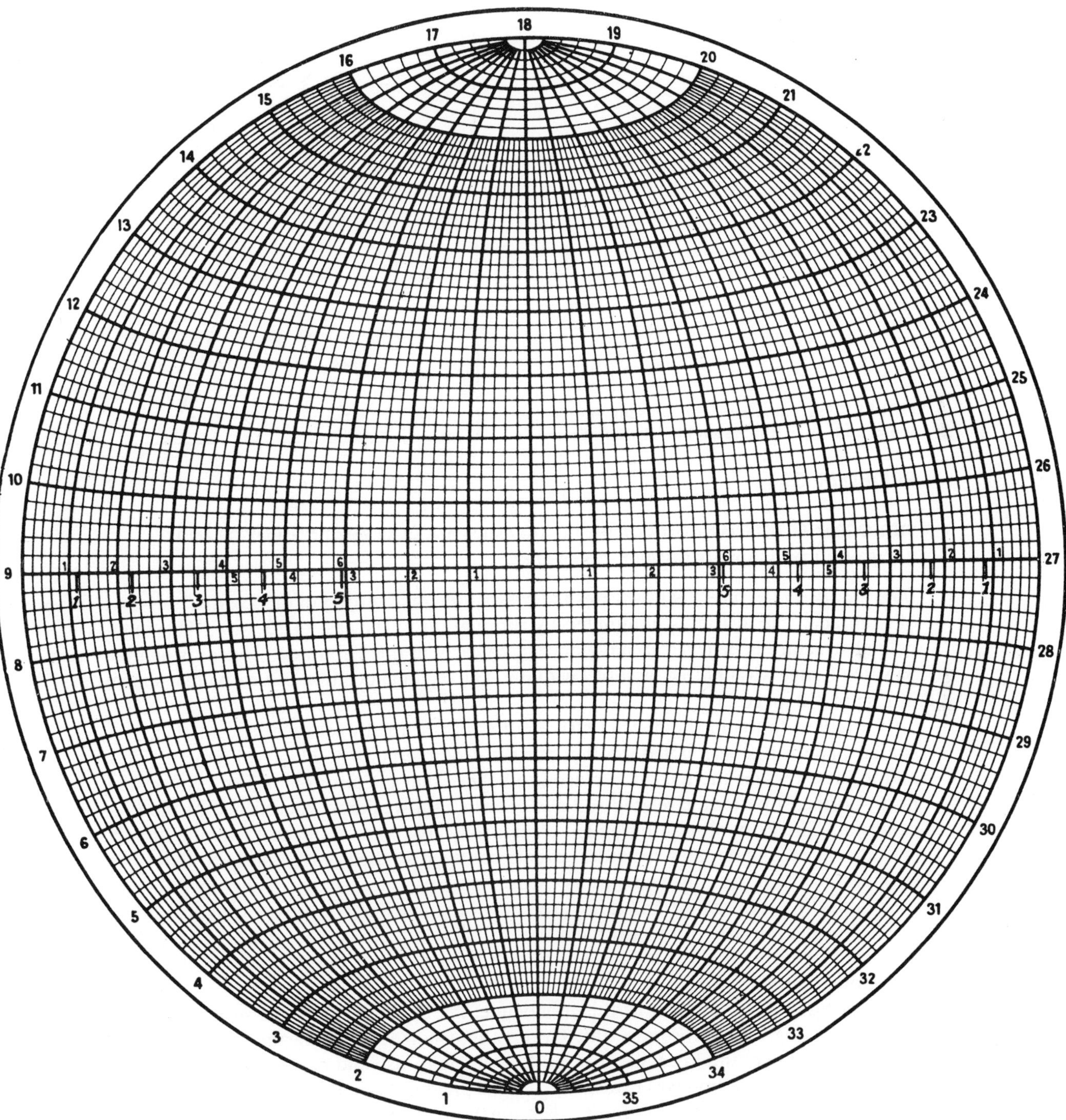

Equal area net for use with problems in Chapter 8.

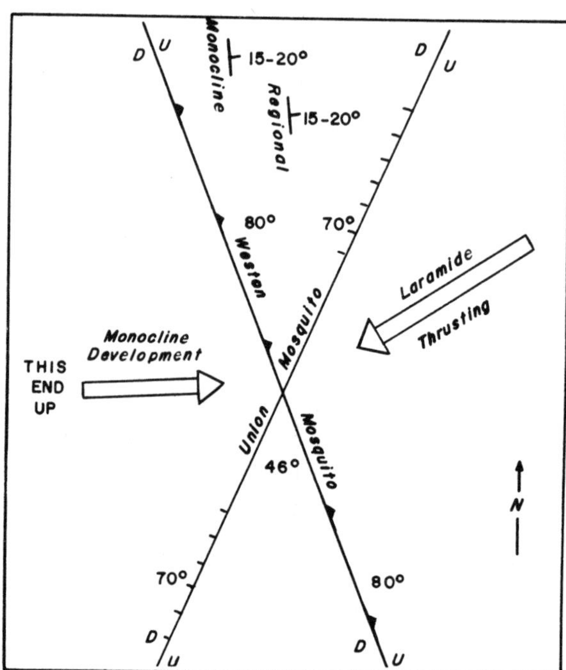

FIGURE 299. Summary of present major tectonic pattern in the Leadville district, Colorado.

PROBLEM 31

STEREOGRAPHIC DETERMINATION OF THE PRE-LARAMIDE ANGULAR RELATIONSHIPS OF FAULT PATTERNS IN THE LEADVILLE DISTRICT, COLORADO

Data Provided: Figure 299 illustrates the present tectonic setting in the Leadville district of Colorado. The district is dominated by regional tilt to the east of 15°–20°. This monoclinal structure is believed to have developed early in the Laramide orogeny when the Sawatch Range was uplifted west of Leadville. The regional position of Leadville is shown in Figure 312, page 245.

The largest faults in the district strike either north-northwest or north-northeast. A similar pattern has been noted in other parts of Colorado (see p. 249 and Figs. 312, 313), and in these regions there is good reason to believe that the strong north-northwest and north-northeast pattern is related to lines of structural weakness established in the Precambrian. The Precambrian basement structure is little known in the Leadville district and its influence upon later structural events has been studied only slightly to date. The strongest of the north-northeast faults (Mosquito-Union fault) and of the north-northwest faults (Weston and Mike faults) are known to have had composite movement histories. For the purpose of this problem these strongest faults are assumed to have been in existence prior to the doming of the Sawatch Range and the development of the Leadville monocline.

Following the development of this monocline, the Leadville area was subjected to regional thrusting. The Mosquito and Gore ranges northeast of Leadville were thrust southwestward over the Leadville district. Low-angle thrusts did not develop in the area. Instead, the thrust motion was transmitted to the previously established pattern of north-northwest and north-northeast faults. The north-northeast set was changed very little, being almost perpendicular to the thrusting. The north-northwest set became transformed to high-angle, steeply northeast-dipping reverse faults. To determine the Pre-Laramide attitude of the major fault pattern, it is necessary to remove both the effects of thrusting and of monocline development. Figure 300 is a summary of the presently existing fault pattern at Leadville.

Determine: The Pre-Laramide attitude of the major fault pattern in the Leadville district, assuming that thrusting did not affect the north-northeast fault pattern.

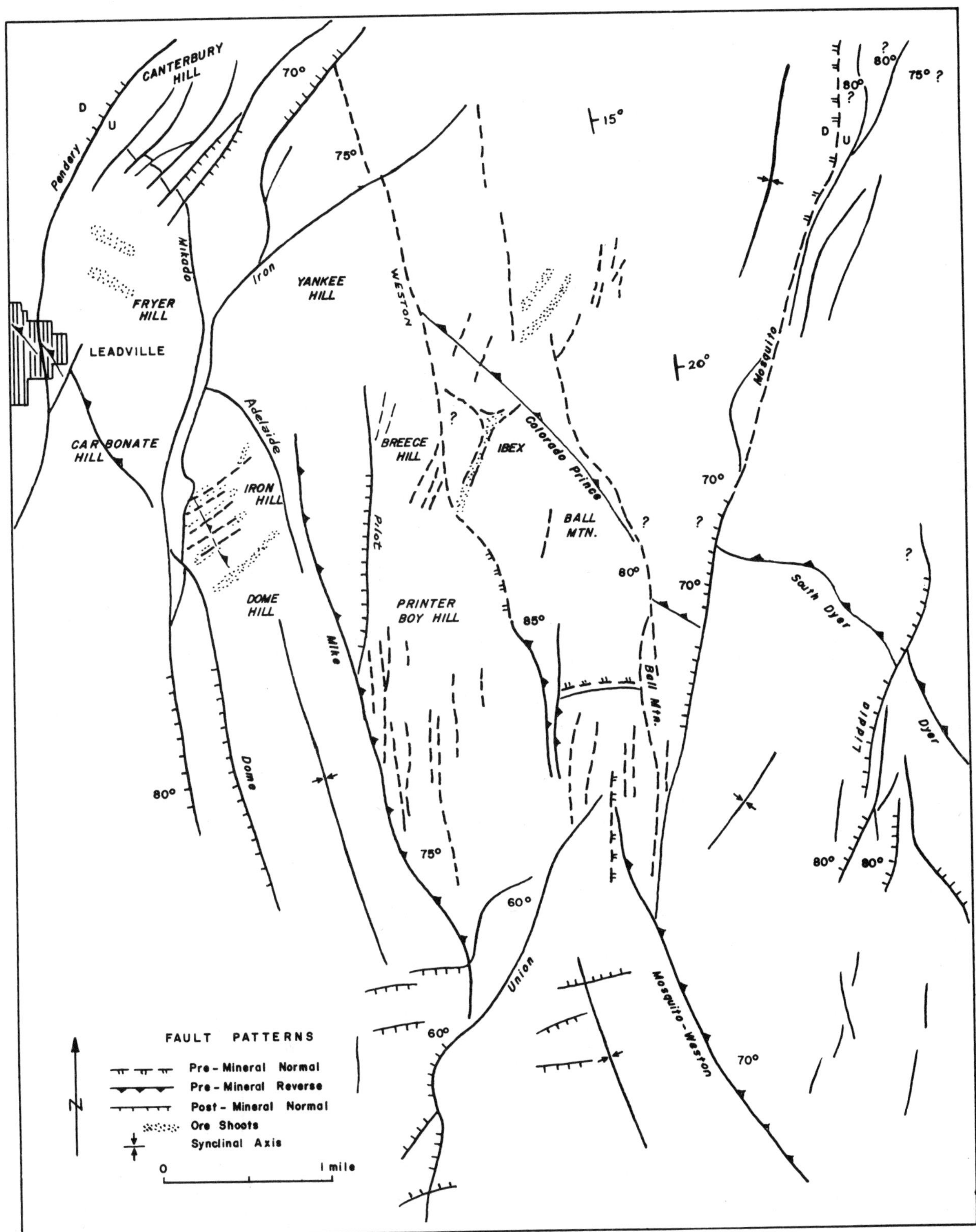

FIGURE 300. Present tectonic setting in the Leadville district, Colorado.

PROBLEM 32

DETERMINATION OF DIP AND STRIKE FROM AIR PHOTOGRAPHS, USING STEREOGRAPHIC METHODS

Data Provided: Plate 10 (at end of text). Figure 301 is provided for use with this problem.
Determine: The attitude of bedding at several outcrop localities on the photographs other than at location *D* (or *D′*). Briefly describe the steps used in determining these attitudes.

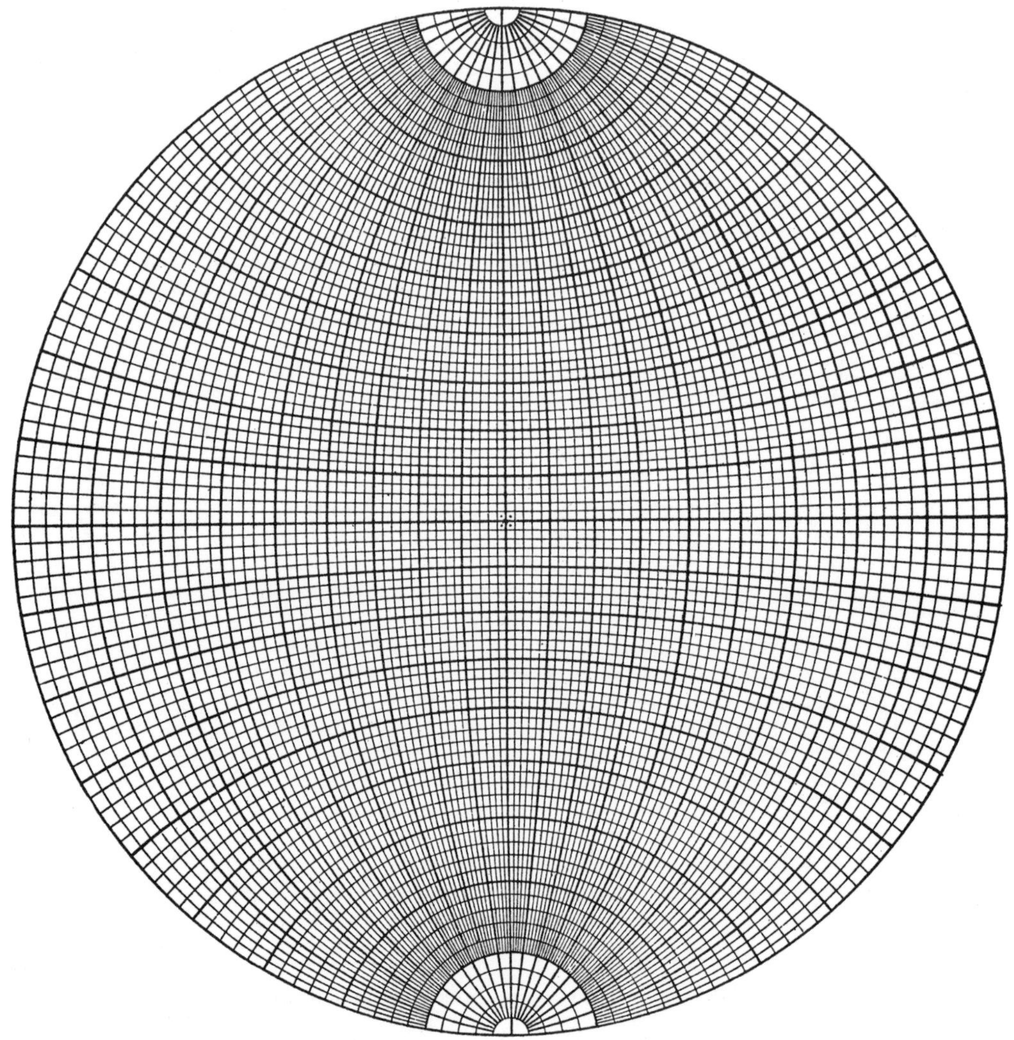

FIGURE 301. Stereonet for use with Problem 32.

PROBLEM 33

DETERMINATION OF STRESS ORIENTATION FOR A FAULT SYSTEM

Data Provided: A group of faults (Fig. 302) was observed in a mine tunnel. All of the faults are believed to have formed in the same stress system as they are all located within a single large tectonic unit. All of the faults occur in a relatively massive homogeneous formation. Bedding planes do not appear to have controlled the faulting.

Determine: Orientation of the stress system responsible for the faulting. Briefly describe the steps used in solving this problem.

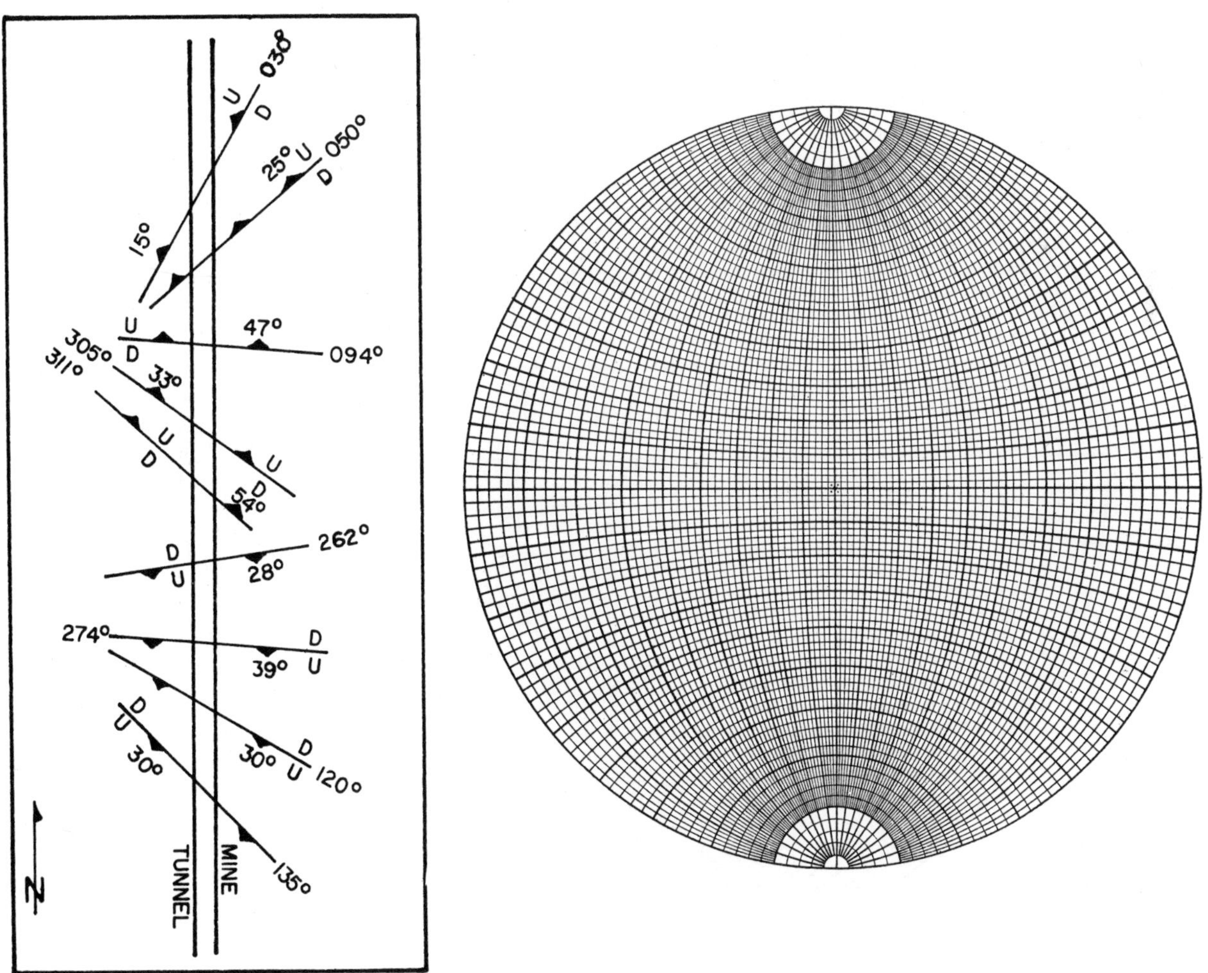

FIGURES 302 (*left*) and 303 (*right*). Diagrams for use with Problem 33.

PROBLEM 34

DETERMINATION OF ATTITUDE IN A BEDDED FORMATION LACKING KEY MARKER BEDS (FIG. 304)

Data Provided	*Bearing*	*Inclination*	*Angle Between Bedding-Normal and Core Axis*
Diamond drill hole *A*	200°	40°	50°
Diamond drill hole *B*	090°	50°	45°
Diamond drill hole *C*	298°	58°	85°

Determine: The attitude of the bedded series. Be sure to describe the steps used to solve this problem.

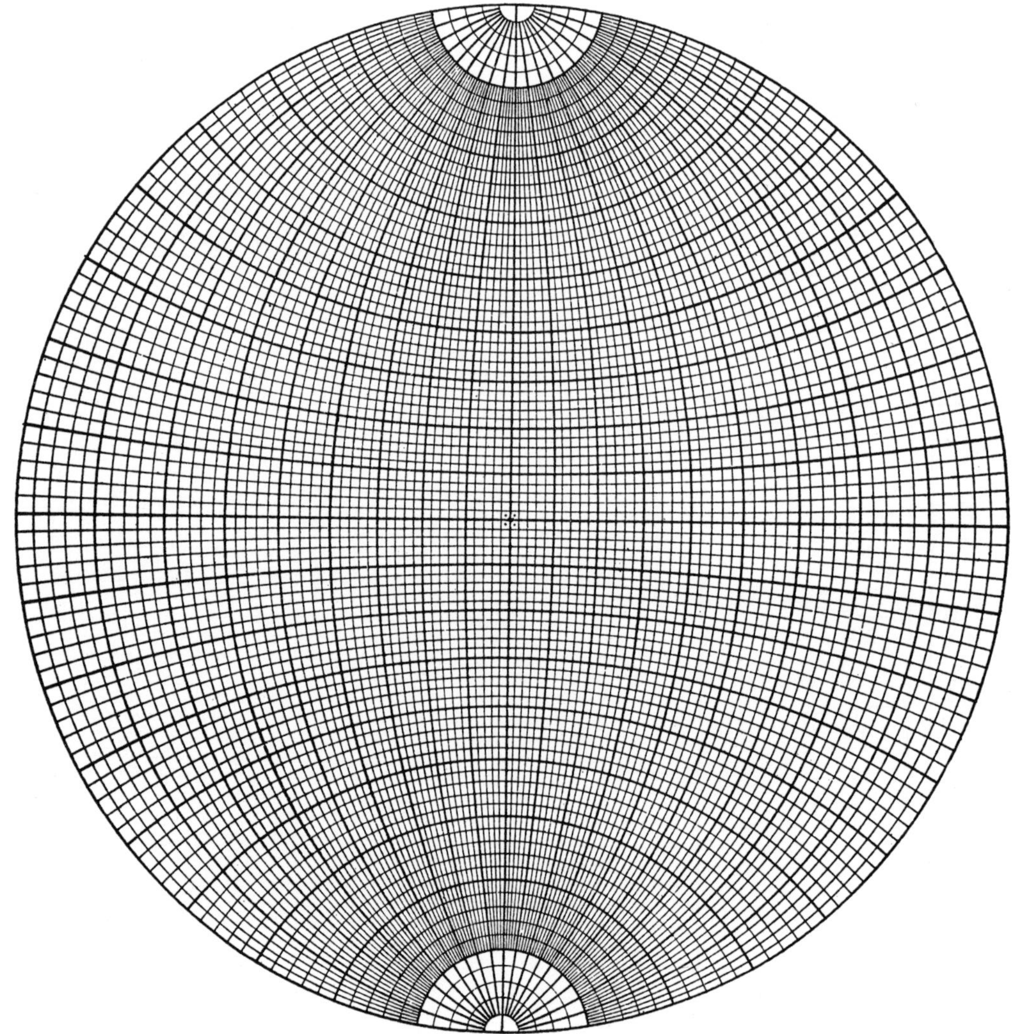

FIGURE 304. Stereonet for use with Problem 34.

PROBLEM 35

DETERMINATION OF THE AMOUNT OF DISPLACEMENT DURING ROTATIONAL FAULTING

Data Provided: The attitude, position and elevation of a thrust fault which disrupts veins *A* and *B* (Fig. 305). The positions and attitudes for veins *A* and *B* are known from outcrops on both sides of the thrust. The elevations for all outcrops are shown. Fractures *C* and *D* intersect on the south side of the thrust fault, and their intersection forms an ore shoot.

Determine: Net slip for intersection of veins *A* and *B* and for intersection of fractures *C* and *D*. Amount and direction of rotation angle. Position and attitude for the *C-D* intersection (= ore shoot) on both sides of the thrust fault. At what elevation does the ore shoot intersect each side of the thrust surface? Draw the map view on the 2000-foot level. Briefly describe all steps used to solve the problem and illustrate the solution with a section in the plane of the fault and with a vertical section through each segment of the displaced ore shoot.

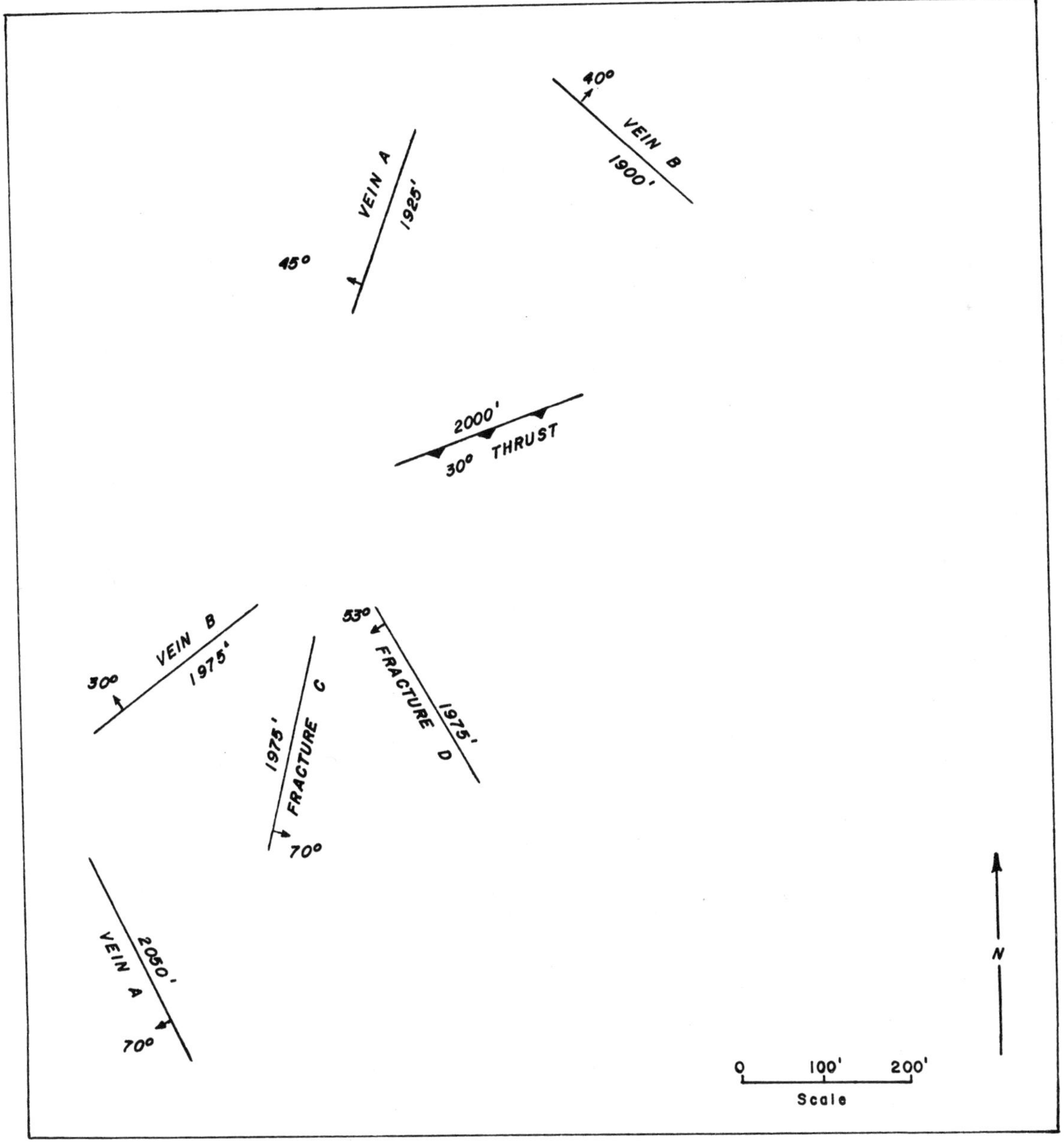

FIGURE 305. Map for use with Problem 35.

PROBLEM 36

DETERMINATION OF ATTITUDE IN A BOREHOLE BY DIPMETER SURVEYING AND STEREOGRAPHIC PROJECTION

Data Provided: The illustration on the facing page shows the results of a microlog continuous dipmeter survey in Oklahoma. Marker beds *W, X, Y, Z* can be recognized on all three electrode curves I, II, III. Table 15 is provided to facilitate the computations involved.
Determine: Attitude of bedding for all four marker beds.

TABLE 15. Strike and Dip Determination

Marker Bed		Distances		Hole Radius	Angles		Azimuth of Electrodes			Uncorrected		Drift Components		Resultant Drift		Corrected	
		d_1	d_2		ψ	ϕ	1	2	3	Strike	Dip	NS	EW	Azim.	Incl.	Strike	Dip
W																	
X																	
Y																	
Z																	

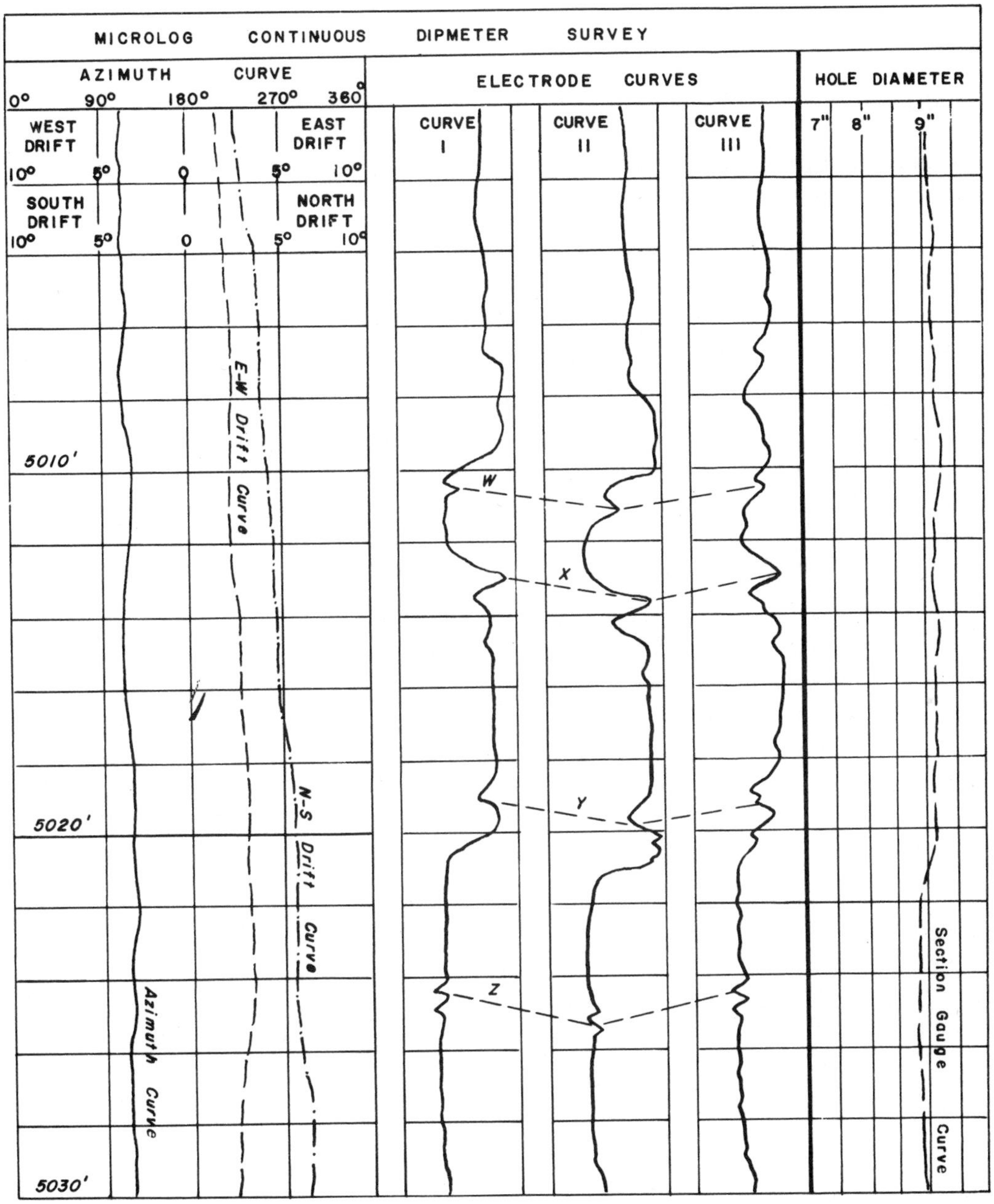

MICROLOG CONTINUOUS DIPMETER SURVEY

AZIMUTH CURVE

0° 90° 180° 270° 360°

WEST DRIFT 10° 5° 0 5° 10° EAST DRIFT

SOUTH DRIFT 10° 5° 0 5° 10° NORTH DRIFT

ELECTRODE CURVES

CURVE I

CURVE II

CURVE III

HOLE DIAMETER

7" 8" 9"

5010'

5020'

5030'

E-W Drift Curve

N-S Drift Curve

Azimuth Curve

W

X

Y

Z

Section Gauge Curve

PROBLEM 37

DETERMINATION OF LINEATION SIGNIFICANCE AND POSSIBLE RELATIONSHIP TO FOLDING IN THE CENTRAL CITY AREA, COLORADO

Data Provided: Figure 306 is a geologic map of the Freeland-Lamartine district near Central City, Colorado. The reader may refer to Figure 313, page 246, to see the regional setting of the area. The country rock of the map area consists dominantly of three units: (1) granite gneiss and pegmatite, (2) migmatite, (3) sillimanite-biotite-quartz gneiss and biotite quartz gneiss. There is some disagreement concerning the origin of these rocks, but the following summarization is probably as satisfactory as any interpretation. The oldest rocks (the biotite-quartz gneiss and the sillimanite-biotite-quartz gneiss) were originally sedimentary rocks of eugeosynclinal (?) facies. They have been referred to as the Idaho Springs formation by Lovering and Goddard (1950). These rocks were intruded by large masses of granodiorite (Boulder Creek granite of Lovering and Goddard) during a Precambrian orogeny. The main granodiorite unit outcrops south of the map area. This intrusion generated a wide metasomatic aureole. The most intensely metasomatized portion of the intruded Idaho Springs formation is the granite gneiss and the pegmatite of Figure 306 (Harrison and Wells, 1956). Lovering and Goddard (1950) feel that this portion of the aureole actually became mobile and acted as a part of the intruding Boulder Creek batholith. A slightly less metasomatized portion of the Idaho Springs formation has been shown as migmatite on Figure 306. Harrison and Wells (1956) classify that portion of the Idaho Springs formation which contains between 30 per cent and 70 per cent granitic material, and which has an interlayered injection-gneiss-like appearance, as migmatite. If the granite falls below 30 per cent, the rock is mapped as Idaho Springs formation; if it is greater than 70 per cent, the rock is mapped as granite gneiss and pegmatite. The entire sequence has been intruded by small phacolithic intrusions of biotite-muscovite granite (Silver Plume of Lovering and Goddard, 1950). These younger intrusions have sharp nonmetasomatised margins, for the most part, and are younger (posttectonic) than the northeast foliation (resulting from folding) which dominates the older rocks. The early intrusions (Boulder Creek) locally show primary flow structures of aligned xenoliths parallel to the contacts of the intrusion. These flow structures are intersected strongly by the later (?) regional foliation. This later (?) foliation is not apparent within the xenoliths themselves, however. The rocks of the region may have been affected by several periods of folding. Foliation and lineation are the main indicators of this folding.

Determine: Plot the lineations shown on Figure 306 on an equal area net and analyze the results statistically. Plot the foliation on a stereonet or on an equal area net.

Questions Based on Problem No. 37

1. How many lineations are apparent? Describe them briefly.
2. Is there more than one foliation?
3. Was the folding cylindrical or conical?
4. What are the directions of fold axes?
5. Discuss the relationship between folding, foliation, lineation, and intrusions in this area.

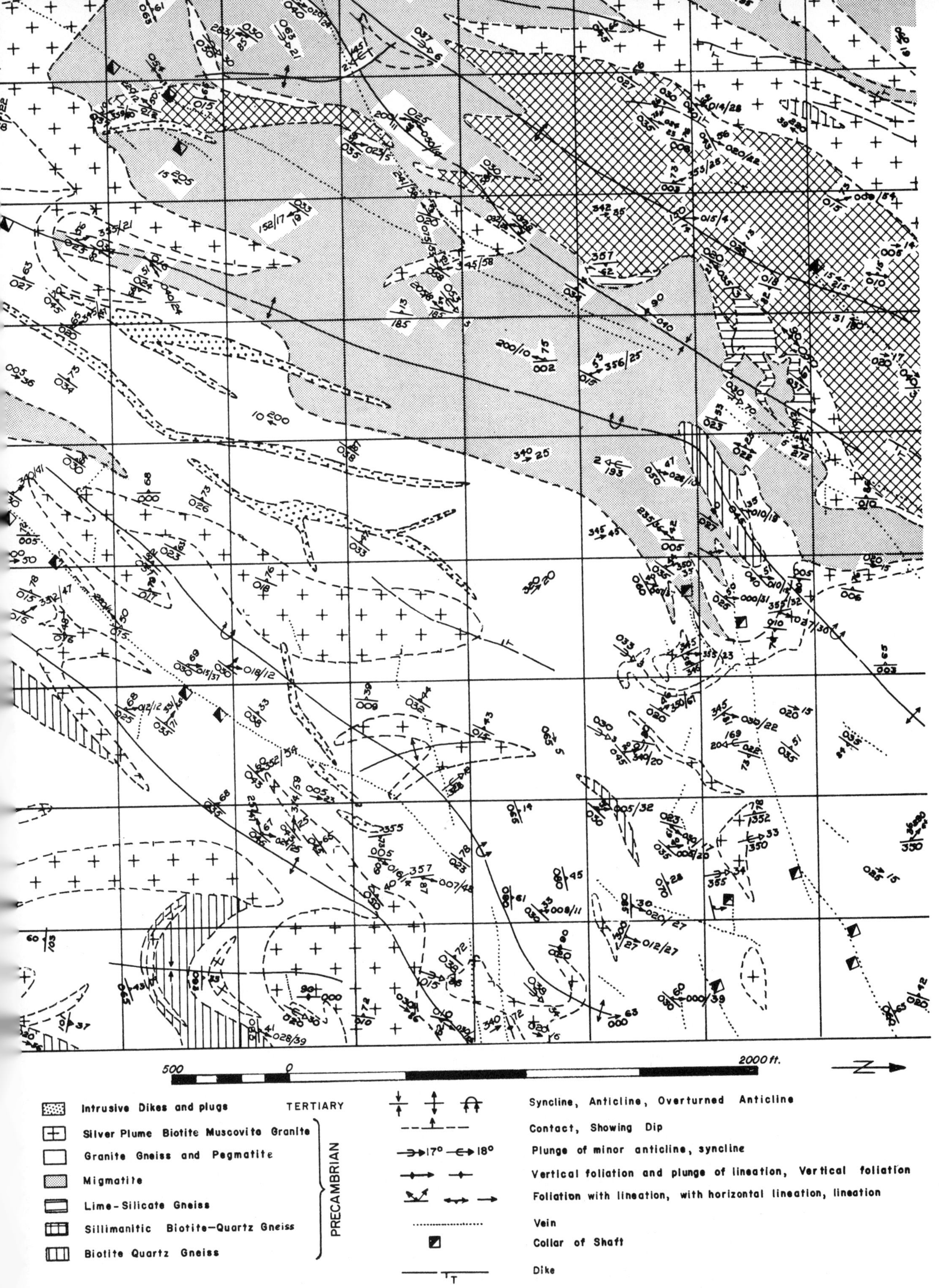

FIGURE 306. Geologic map of the Freeland-Lamartine district, near Central City, Colorado. For use with Problem 37.

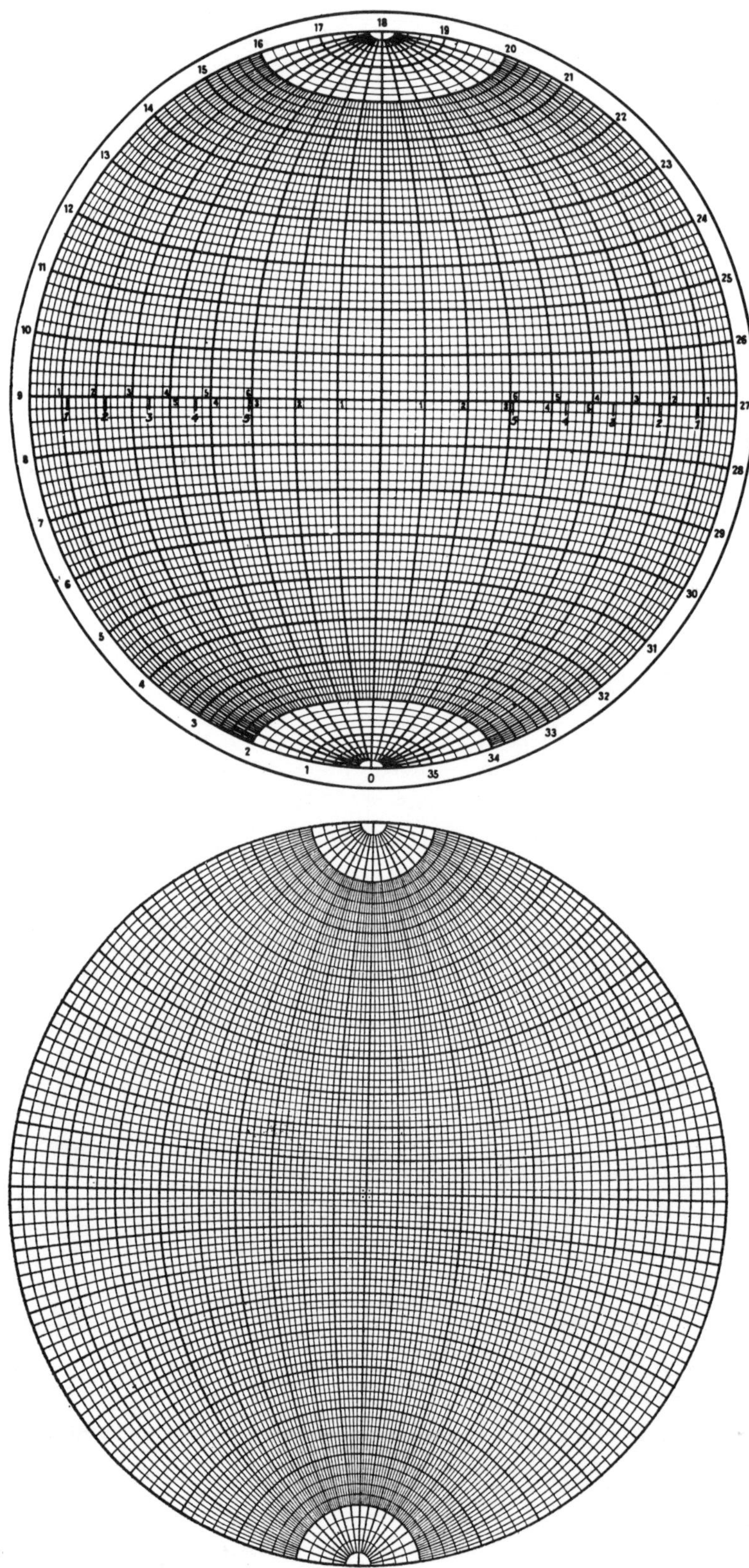

FIGURES 307 (*above*) and 308 (*below*). For use with Problem 37.

PROBLEM 38

DETERMINATION OF THE GEOMETRY OF COMPLEX FOLDS BY STATISTICAL ANALYSIS

Data Provided: Figure 66, page 52, shows a map of the folded Precambrian sequence near Sherridon, Manitoba, Canada.

Determine: Plot the poles of the planar elements (bedding) shown in Figure 66 on a stereographic projection and describe the geometry of the folds. How would one determine the average plunge of the folds? What it it?

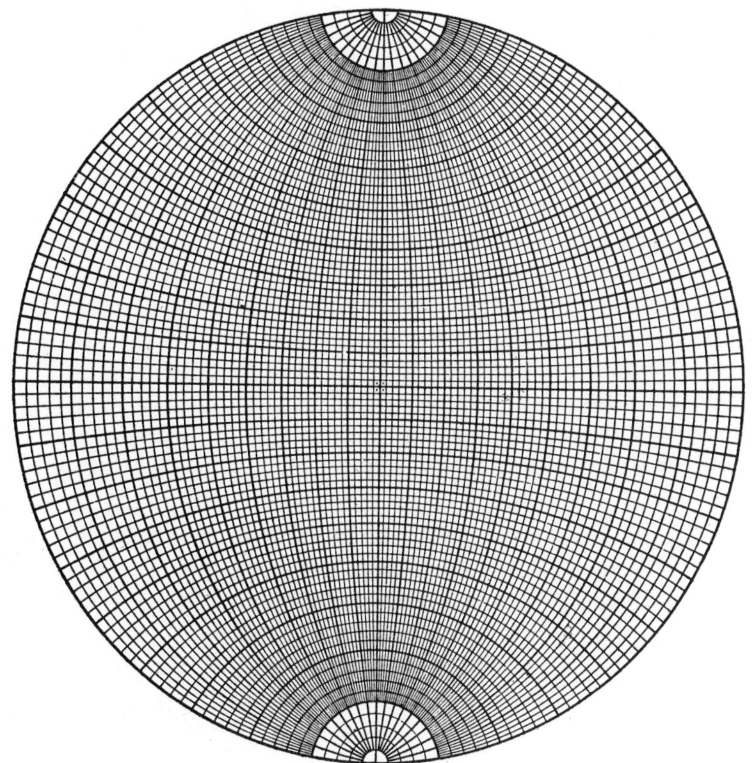

FIGURE 309. Stereonet for use with Problem 38.

PROBLEM 39

DETERMINATION OF THE RELATIONSHIP BETWEEN FOLDING AND JOINTING BY STATISTICAL ANALYSIS

Data Provided: Plate 11 is an uncontrolled mosaic (three air photographs) of a portion of the east flank of the Circle Cliffs anticlinal uplift in south central Utah. The anticlinal axis strikes approximately 335° (N25°W) and is situated about 2 miles west of the southwest portion of the mosaic. The Circle Cliffs uplift is located on the western edge of the Colorado Plateau.

Jurassic formations are exposed at the surface for most of the mosaic area. The light-colored formation trending southeastward from the northwest corner of Plate 11 is the Navajo sandstone. This formation is intersected by a very strongly developed joint system. Well-developed shorter joints may be observed in the Wingate sandstone in the southwest portion of Plate 11.

Plate 12 shows a series of three overlapping air photographs oriented and spaced for viewing stereoscopically. To study the air photographs stereoscopically, place a lens-type pocket stereoscope over and parallel to the dashed lines joining the small circles (principal points of the air photographs). Place the center of the stereoscope over the northern small circle, and while looking through the lenses, make small adjustments in orientation or lens spacing to obtain perfect fusion of the lines and circles. The stereoscope can then be moved east or west without losing the three-dimensional effect.

Determine: Make a statistical analysis of the joint system shown on Plates 11 and 12 by plotting the poles of individual joints on an equal area projection. Summarize the results of the analysis by means of stereographic projection similar to Figure 292, page 221. Discuss the possible relationship between jointing and folding which is demonstrated by the statistical analysis, and classify the joints.

Method: Place a sheet of acetate overlay on top of Plate 11 and lay out a ¼-mile north-south, east-west co-ordinate grid system on the acetate. Select a joint from each grid square and plot its pole on the equal area net.

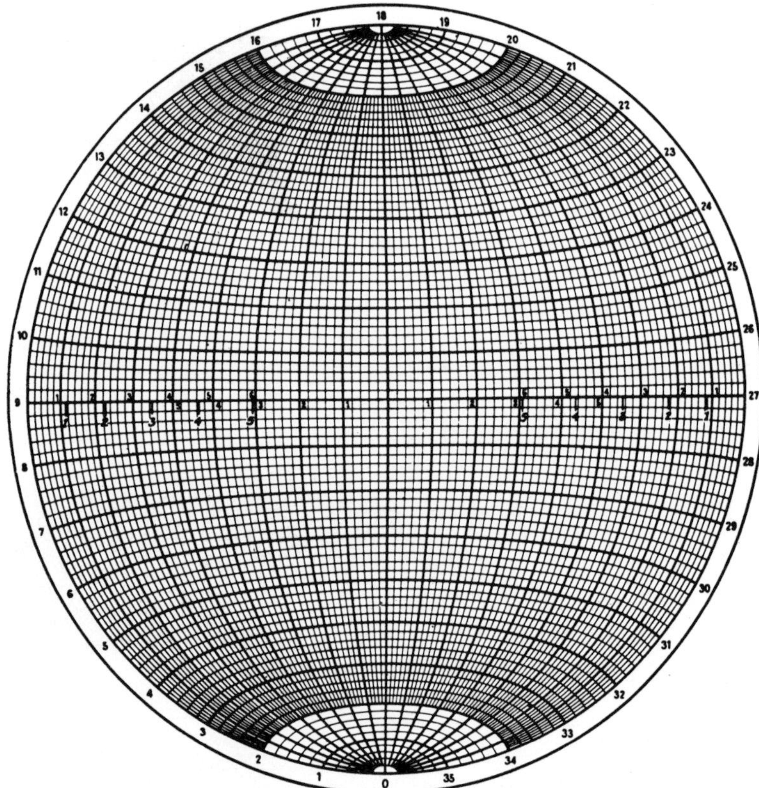

FIGURE 310. Equal area net for use with Problem 39.

References

Bateman, J. D., and Harrison, J. M. (1943), Geology of the Sherridon Map Area, Manitoba, *Geol. Surv. Can.,* Map 862A.

Beckwith, R. H. (1947), Fault Problems in Fault Planes, *Bull. Geol. Soc. Am.,* vol. 58, pp. 79–108.

Behre, C. H., Jr. (1953), Geology and Ore Deposits of the West Slope of the Mosquito Range, *U.S. Geol. Surv.,* Prof. Paper 235.

Bucher, W. H. (1943), Dip and Strike from Three Not Parallel Drill Cores Lacking Key Beds, *Econ. Geol.,* vol. 38, pp. 648–657.

Bucher, W. H. (1944), The Stereographic Projection, A Handy Tool for the Practical Geologist, *Jour. Geol.,* vol. 53, pp. 191–212.

Chambrier, Pierre (1953), The Microlog Continuous Dipmeter, *Geophysics,* vol. 18, pp. 929–950.

Clark, R. H., and McIntyre, D. R. (1951), A Microscopic Method of Fabric Analysis, *Am. Jour. Sci.,* vol. 249, pp. 755–768.

Cloos, E. (1946), Lineation, *Geol. Soc. Am.,* Mem. 18.

Cloos, E. (1947), Oölite Deformation in the South Mountain Fold, *Bull. Geol. Soc. Am.,* vol. 58, pp. 843–917.

Cloos, E., and Hietanen, A. (1941), Geology of the Martic Overthrust and the Glenarm Series in Pennsylvania and Maryland, *Geol. Soc Am.* Spec. Paper No. 35.

Cotton, L. A., and Garretty, M. D. (1945), Use of the Stereographic Projection in Solving Problems in Structural and Mining Geology, *Geol. Bull.* no. 2 (unpublished), North Broken Hill Mining Co., Ltd.

Dahlstrom, C. D. A. (1954), Statistical Analysis of Cylindrical Folds, *Can. Inst. Min. and Met.,* Trans., vol. 57, pp. 140–145.

DeWitte, A. J. (1956), A Graphic Method of Dipmeter Interpretation Using the Stereonet, *Am. Inst. Min. Met. Eng.,* Tech. Paper 4333, Petroleum Trans. 207, pp. 192–199.

Fairbairn, H. W. (1949), *Structural Petrology of Deformed Rocks,* Addison-Wesley Publishing Co., Inc., 344 pp.

Fisher, D. J. (1930), Problem of Two Tilts and the Stereographic Projection, *Bull. Amer. Assoc. Petrol. Geol.,* vol. 22, pp. 1261–1271.

Fisher, D. J. (1941), Drillhole Problems in the Stereographic Projection, *Econ. Geol.,* vol. 36, pp. 551–560.

Fisher, D. J. (1943), Measuring Linear Structures on Steep-dipping Surfaces, *Am. Miner.,* vol. 28, pp. 204–208.

Gilluly, J. (1944), Dip and Strike from Three Not Parallel Drill Cores Lacking Key Beds, *Econ. Geol.,* vol. 39, pp. 359–363.

Harrison, J. E., and Wells, J. D. (1956), Geology and Ore Deposits of the Freeland-Lamartine District, Clear Creek County, Colo., *U.S. Geol. Surv.,* Bull. 1032-B.

Hobson, G. D. (1943), A Graphical Solution of the Problem of Two Tilts, *Proc. Geol. Assoc.,* vol. 54, pp. 29–32.

Hobson, G. D. (1945), The Application of Tilt to a Fold, *Proc. Geol. Assoc.,* vol. 55, pp. 216–221.

Ingerson, E. (1942), Apparatus for Direct Measurement of Linear Structures, *Am. Miner.,* vol. 27, pp. 721–725.

Irwin, A. B. (1951), Mapping Complex Folds in the Slocan Series, British Columbia, *Can. Inst. Min. Met.,* Trans., vol. 54, pp. 494–501.

Johnson, C. H. (1939), New Mathematical and "Stereographic Net" Solutions to Problem of Two Tilts—with Applications to Core Orientation, *Bull. Am. Assoc. Petrol. Geol.,* vol. 23, pp. 663–685.

Kalliokoski, J. (1953), Interpretations of the Structural Geology of the Sherridon-Flin Flon Region, Manitoba, *Geol. Surv. Can.,* Bull. 25.

Knopf, E. B., and Ingerson, E. (1938), Structural Petrology, *Geol. Soc. Am.,* Mem. 6.

Livingston, C. W. (1939), Mechanics of Vein Formation in the Northern Half of the Baguio District (Philippines), *Eng. and Min. Jour.,* vol. 140, no. 9, pp. 38–42, and no. 10, pp. 49–51.

Lovering, T. S., and Goddard, E. N. (1950), Geology and Ore Deposits of the Front Range, Colorado, *U.S. Geol. Surv.,* Prof. Paper 223.

Lowe, K. E. (1946), A Graphic Solution for Certain Problems of Linear Structure, *Am. Miner.,* vol. 31, pp. 425–434.

McClellan, Hugh (1948), Core Orientation by Graphical and Mathematical Methods, *Bull. Am. Assoc. Petrol. Geol.,* vol. 32, pp. 262–282.

Mertie, J. B., Jr. (1943), Structural Determinations from Diamond Drilling, *Econ. Geol.,* vol. 38, pp. 298–312.

Moench, R. H., Harrison, J. E., and Sims, P. K. (1958), Pre-Cambrian Folding in the Central Part of the Front Range Mineral Belt, Colorado, Abstract for 1958 Annual Meeting, Rocky Mountain Section, Geol. Soc. Am., Golden, Colorado.

Morishita, M. (1938), On the Graphic Method of Representing Faults and Strata, *Jap. Jour. Geol. Geogr.,* vol. 15, pp. 207–239.

Phillips, F. C. (1954), *The Use of Stereographic Projection in Structural Geology,* Edward Arnold (publishers), 86 pp.

Pincus, H. J. (1951), Statistical Methods Applied to the Study of Rock Fractures, *Bull. Geol. Soc. Am.,* vol. 62, pp. 81–130.

Prescott, B. O. (1955), Graphical Method for Calculating Dip and Strike from Continuous Dipmeters, *Oil and Gas Jour.,* vol. 53, no. 44, pp. 118–125.

Rodgers, J. (1952), Use of Equal-Area or Other Projections in the Statistical Treatment of Joints, *Bull. Geol. Soc. Am.,* vol. 63, pp. 427–430.

Sims, P. K., and Harrison, J. E. (1958), Summary of Geology of Precambrian Rocks in the Central City—Idaho Springs Area, Front Range, Colorado, Field Guidebook for Rocky Mountain Section, Geol. Soc. Am., Golden Colo., 1958.

Stockwell, C. H. (1951), The Use of Plunge in the Construction of Folds, *Proc. Geol. Soc. Can.*, vol. 3, pp. 1–25.

Stratton, E. F., and Hamilton, R. G. (1947), Application of Dipmeter Surveys, *Am. Inst. Min. Eng.*, Paper, Tulsa Meeting (October 8–10).

Wallace, R. E. (1948), A Stereographic Calculator, *Jour. Geol.*, vol. 56, pp. 488–490.

Wallace, R. E. (1950), Determination of Dip and Strike by Indirect Observations in the Field and From Aerial Photographs: A Solution by Stereographic Projection, *Jour. Geol.*, vol. 58, pp. 269–280.

Wallace, R. E. (1951), Geometry of Shearing Stress and Relation to Faulting, *Jour. Geol.*, vol. 59, pp. 118–130.

Weiss, L. E. (1959), Geometry of Superposed Folding, *Bull. Geol. Soc. Amer.*, vol. 70, pp. 91–106.

White, S. W., and Jahns, R. H. (1950), Structure of Central and East-Central Vermont, *Jour. Geol.*, vol. 58, pp. 179–220.

Wilson, G. (1946), The Relationship of Slaty Cleavage and Kindred Structures to Tectonics, *Proc. Geol. Assoc.*, vol. LVII, pp. 263–302.

CHAPTER 9

Tectonic Analysis of Mining and Petroleum Districts as an Exploration Tool

Introduction

The localization of ore deposits and oil fields by structural control at the district level is fully appreciated by most geologists. The subject has been discussed thoroughly in the literature by Hulin (1929, 1948), McKinstry (1941, 1955), Newhouse *et al.* (1942), Wisser (1941, 1951), and many others. Systematic structural analysis of entire tectonic provinces, as an exploration tool, has been employed by relatively few geologists, notably Billingsley and Locke (1941), Blanchet (1951), Kaufmann (1951), Mayo (1958), Weeks, (1952), Klemme (1958), Hills (1947), Henson (1952), J. T. Wilson (1948, 1949). Specialized aspects of regional tectonic analysis, such as regional joint studies, have been used by Cizancourt (1947), Melton (1929), and Pincus (1951). Balk, Cloos, and others have applied systematic structural analysis to igneous and metamorphic terrains.

It should be apparent that regional systematic structure analysis of entire tectonic provinces can be extremely valuable in outlining favorable prospecting localities for both ore and oil. The following example taken from the Colorado Rockies will illustrate one approach to this problem.

Method: The first step is a thorough knowledge of tectonic history and framework at the continental level. Figure 311 shows the major structural features of the Cordilleran region of the United States and southern Canada. The close relationship between strike-slip faults (lineaments), arcuate fold-thrust zones, intrusive activity, and major mineral deposits is clearly apparent. The fact that arcuate junctions are nearly always associated with major lineaments is particularly interesting.

The next step is to select the most critical areas for more detailed study. The Colorado mineral belt and adjoining areas have been chosen for analysis in this case. A semidetailed tectonic map of the mineral belt is then constructed (Fig. 312). This is based on all available sources of information. Such sources include all geological maps and reports, topographic maps, and air photographs. Several strong structural alignments are apparent in Figure 312. East-northeast and northwest trends seem to be the most important. These two directions appear to have controlled both folding and faulting. The Tertiary intrusives and mining camps also follow these trends, notably the east-northeast trend. Studies at the district level substantiate these trend directions. A shaded relief map of the Colorado mineral belt (facing p. 244) shows the close relationship between known faults, dikes, and topographic lineaments. A study of shaded relief maps, topographic maps, and air photographs serves to point out many aspects of the structural fabric which are as yet unknown from detailed geological mapping on the ground. Topographic lineament areas which have not been mapped geologically are interesting for prospecting and exploration purposes. Special attention should be paid to the intersection of lineaments, particularly if intrusive activity is also present near the intersection. This aspect of the subject has been discussed recently by Mayo (1958).

The third step is to select one of these most promising intersection areas for intense geological study. Principles which evolve from such a study can then be applied to other promising intersection areas. The area selected in this case is the Central City district (Fig. 313).

At the district level, particular attention is paid to minor (second-order ?) faulting, folding and cross folding (second-order folding ?), foliation, lineation, jointing, intrusive activity, and mineralization. The relative time of origin and rejuvenation

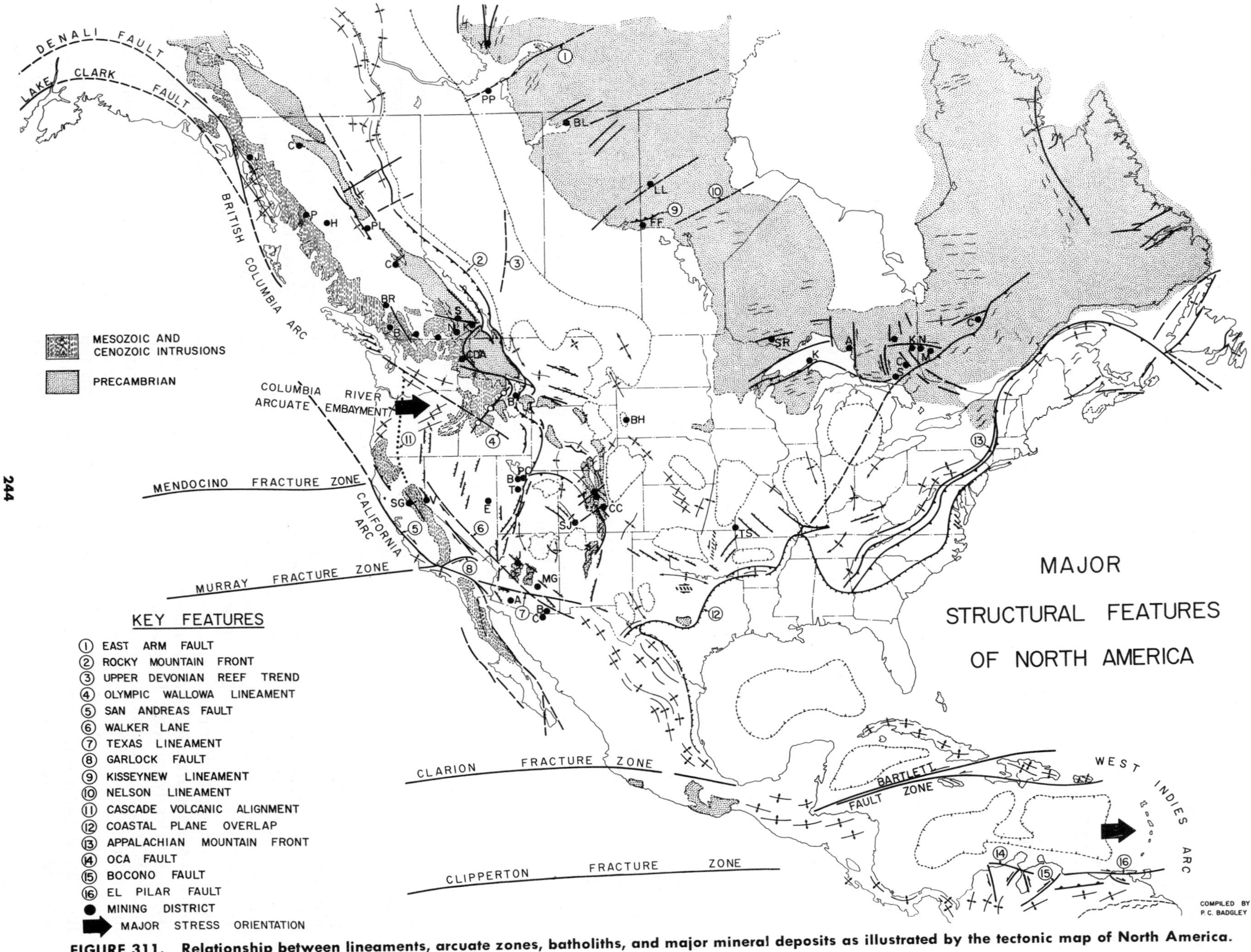

FIGURE 311. Relationship between lineaments, arcuate zones, batholiths, and major mineral deposits as illustrated by the tectonic map of North America.

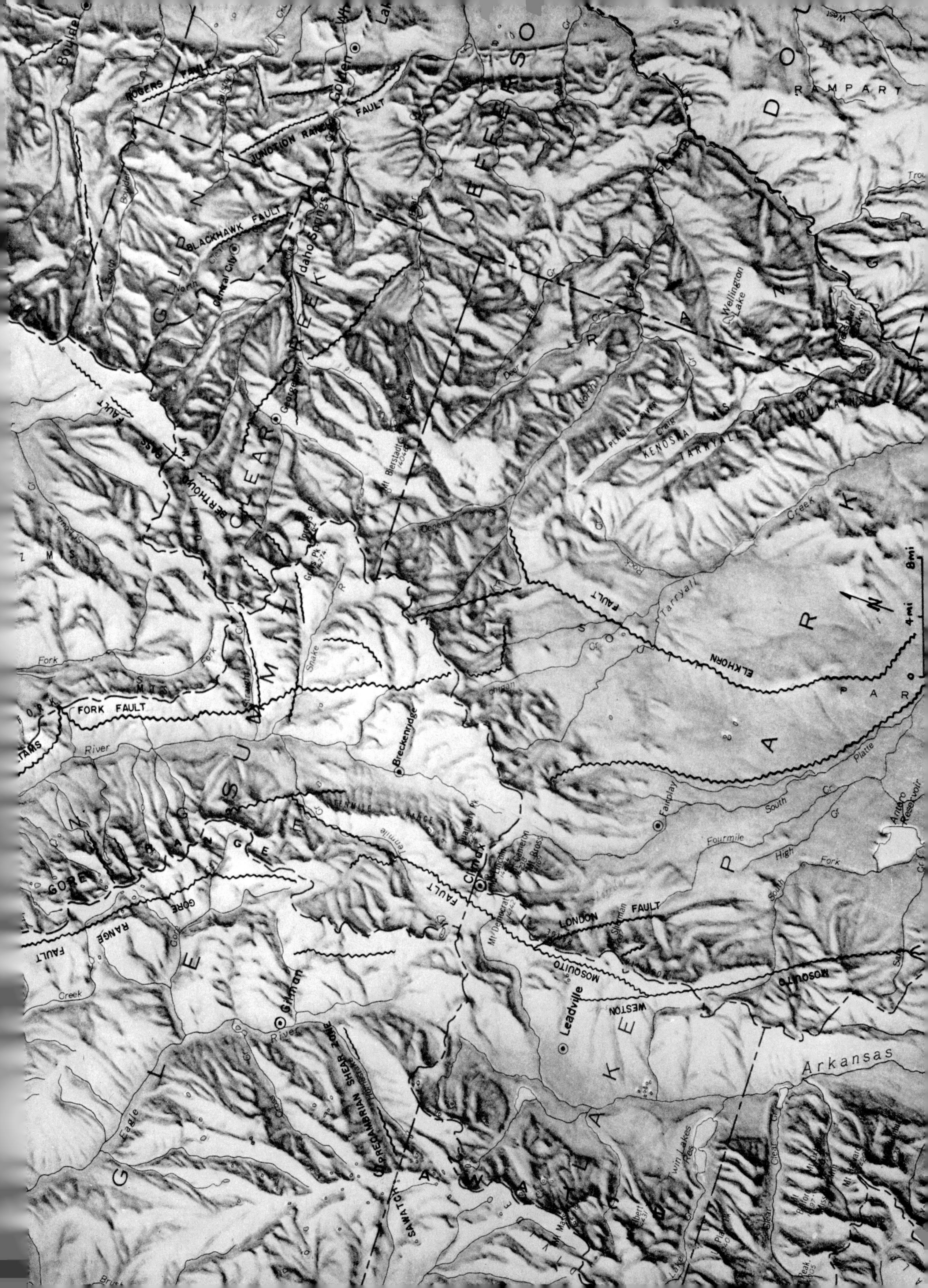

Boulder
ROGERS FAULT
Golden
JUNCTION RANCH FAULT
BLACKHAWK FAULT
Central City
Idaho Springs
Georgetown
Mt Bierstadt 14060
Grays Pk 14274
BERTHOUD PASS FAULT
FORK FAULT
Breckenridge
TENMILE RANGE
GORE RANGE
GORE FAULT
Climax
Mt Lincoln
Mt Bross
Mt Democrat
LONDON FAULT
MOSQUITO FAULT
WESTON
Leadville
Gilman
PRECAMBRIAN SHEAR ZONE
SAWATCH
Twin Lakes Res
Arkansas
Fairplay
Antero Reservoir
ELKHORN FAULT
Tarryall
Wellington Lake
KENOSHA
TARRYALL
MOUNTAINS
RAMPART
Fourmile
Eagle
Snake
Tenmile
0
4 mi
8 mi
N

Major faults superimposed on a shaded relief map of Central Colorado. Note the close relationship betwen topographic and structural lineaments. (The shaded relief map was prepared by the United States Geological Survey.)

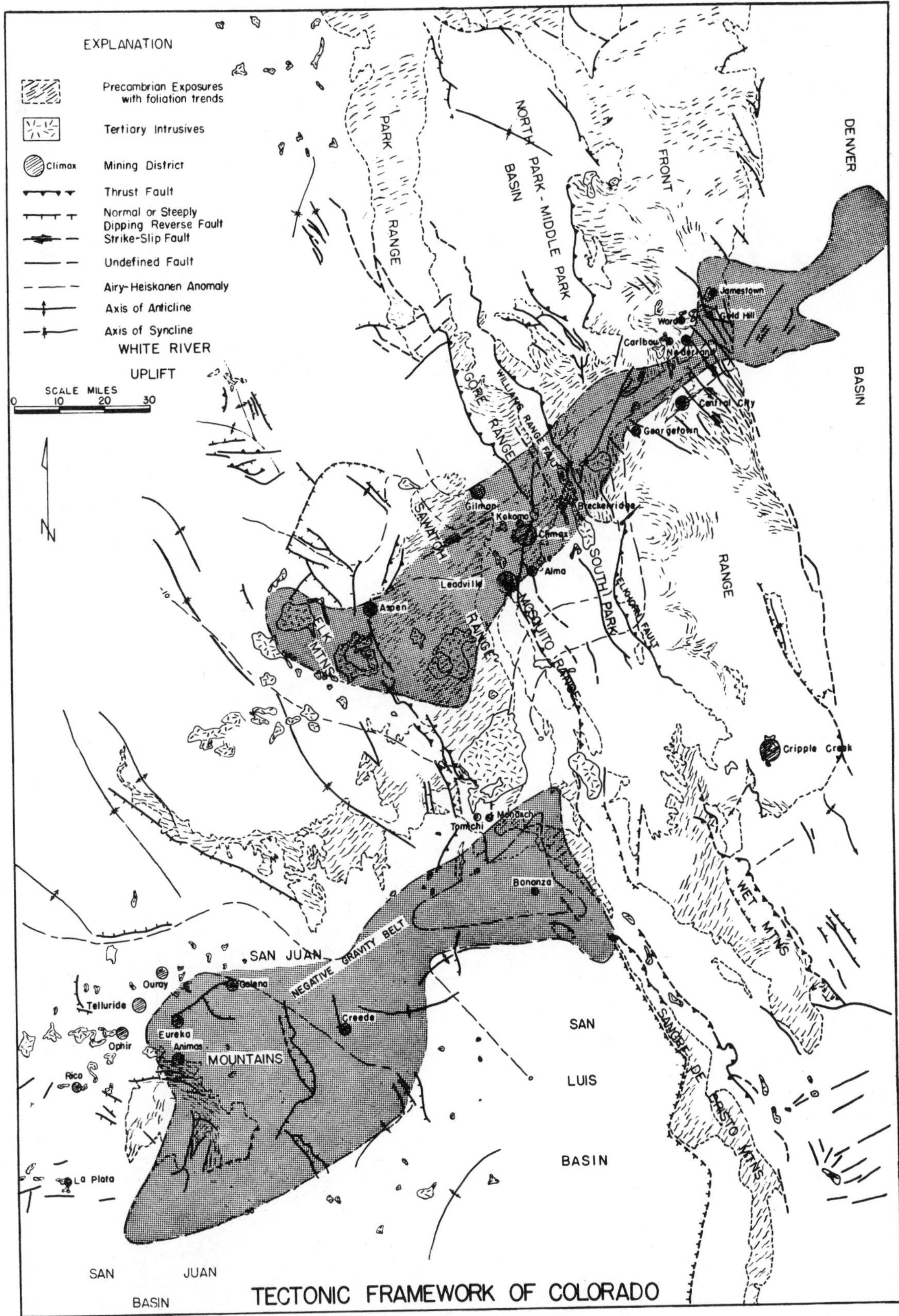

FIGURE 312. Tectonic framework of Colorado. Note the two northeast trending shaded zones. These are characterized by negative gravity, by alignment of Tertiary intrusives, and by alignment of mineral deposits, shear zones, and joint systems.

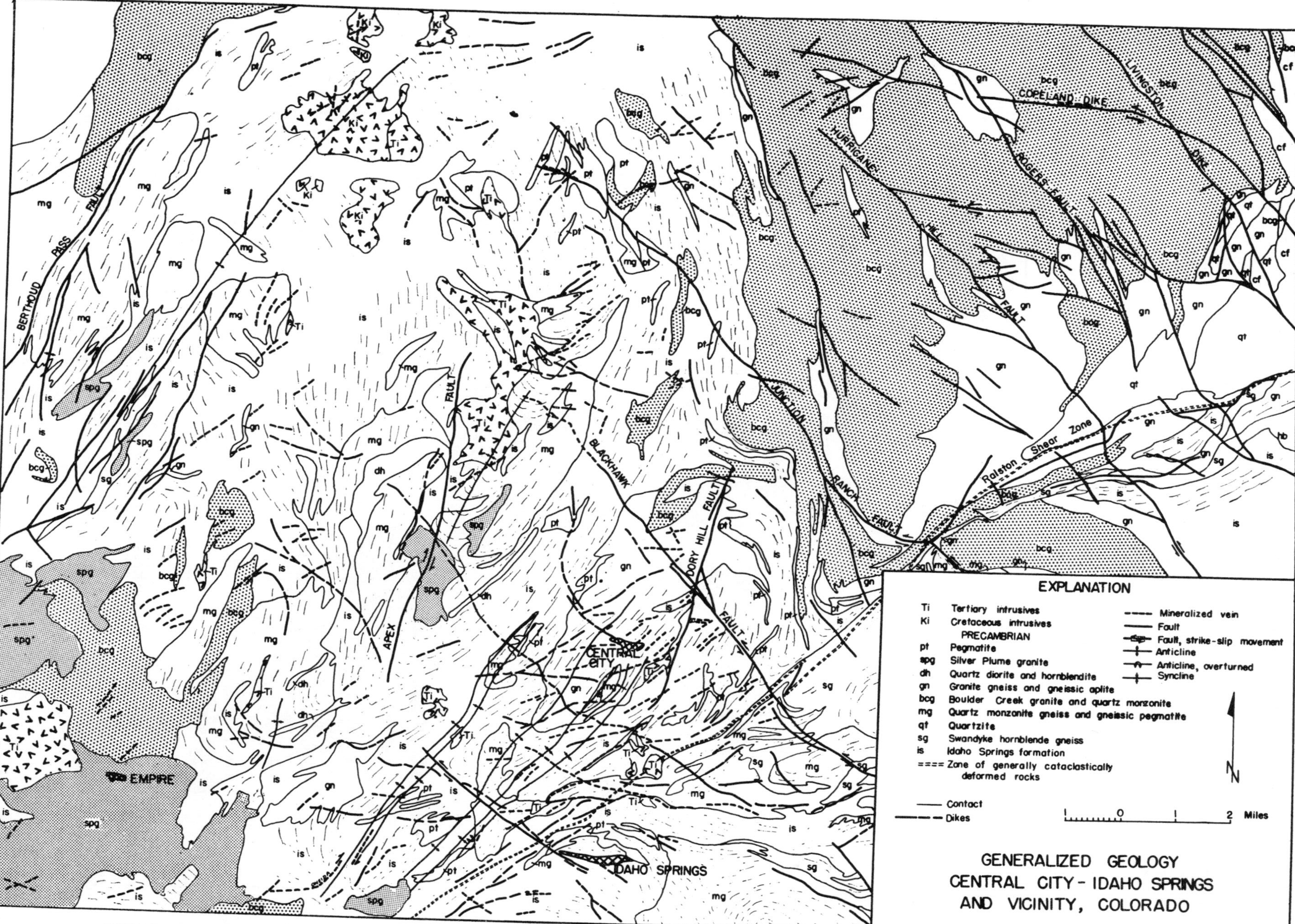

FIGURE 313. Note the *wedge area* which is outlined by the cataclastically deformed zone and the northwest fault system (breccia reef system).

of each type of structural feature is very important; also the angular relationship between the various elements of the structural fabric is significant. Statistical analyses, as described in Chapter 8, are frequently helpful. A thorough knowledge of stress principles is essential. The geologist should be acquainted with the stress theories of Anderson (1951), Bucher (1920–1921), Hafner (1951), Hubbert (1951), Livingston (1939), Lovering (1928), McKinstry (1953), Moody and Hill (1956), Seigel (1950), Swanson (1927), and Wallace (1951). Each of these geologists have presented ideas which are helpful.

The following tectonic interpretation for the Central City district is not final, as the region is still undergoing study by the writer and others. It will serve simply to demonstrate an approach which can be applied to other areas.

The oldest rocks in the Central City district were Archean eugeosynclinal sediments which were later metamorphosed and are now known as the Idaho Springs formation. The axis of the eugeosynclinal trough had an approximately northeast trend. The sediments of the trough were intruded, folded, faulted, and metamorphosed by the Boulder Creek granite or granodiorite. There is some disagreement in terminology and interpretation for the metasomatised border facies of this intrusion. Figure 313 is modified from Lovering and Goddard (1950). The quartz monzonite gneiss (mg) and granite gneiss (gn) of this map were considered as metamorphosed igneous rocks by Lovering and Goddard, but they have been mapped largely as microcline-bearing gneiss by Sims and Harrison (1958). This difference in opinion does not affect the present interpretation. The folding which accompanied the Boulder Creek batholithic intrusion imposed a well-developed foliation (rock cleavage and gneissic banding) and lineation, trending approximately 030° (N30°E), upon the entire rock complex (Figs. 313 and 314). The foliation consists mainly of gneissic layering and is the result of both compositional and textural differences. Sims and Harrison (1958) assume that this layering is parallel to the bedding

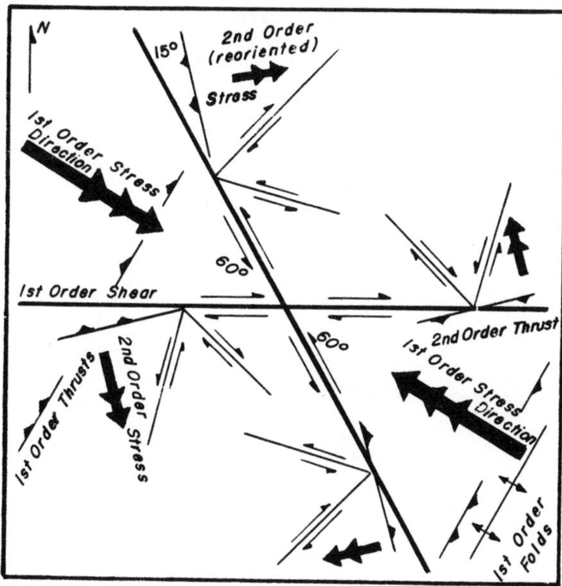

FIGURE 314. Theoretical pattern for conjugate shearing in a homogeneous medium under homogeneous stress. The stress system in this case is oriented to fit the earliest recorded period of folding in the Central City area. Both first- and second-order fold and fault directions are indicated. The first step in applying this type of analysis is to determine the age and orientation of the major folding.

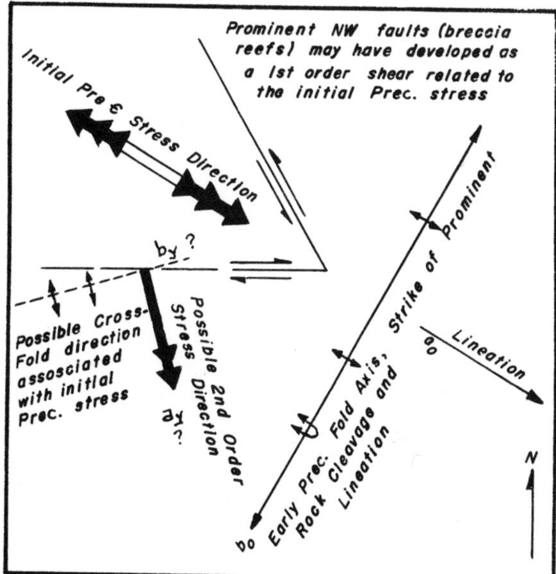

FIGURE 315. The cross folds (b_y lineation of Sims and Harrison, 1958) may have developed parallel to a second-order fold direction related to the initial Precambrian stress. The north-northwest-striking lineation (a_y lineation of Sims and Harrison, 1958) may have developed parallel to a second-order stress direction related to the initial Precambrian stress application. The northwest-striking breccia reefs, although active as late as the Tertiary, may be related to first-order shear directions established by the initial Precambrian stress application.

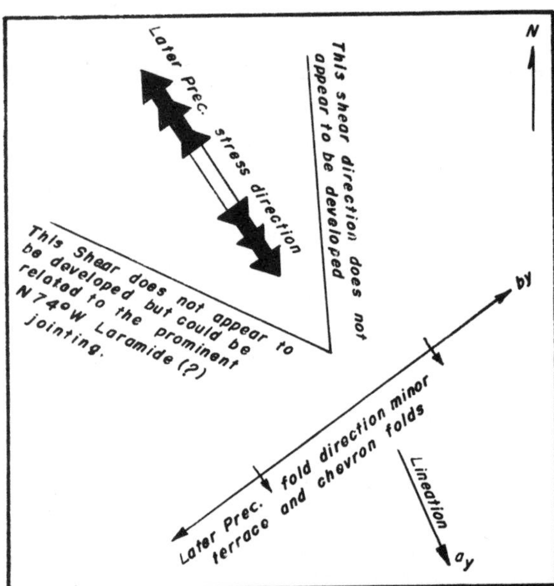

FIGURE 316. The small-scale b_y terrace and chevron folds of Sims and Harrison (1958) may have developed in response to a later and slightly reoriented Precambrian stress system. The a_y lineation would then probably have formed at this time also. The possibility of a reoriented later Precambrian stress system is an alternative to the explanation given in Figure 315.

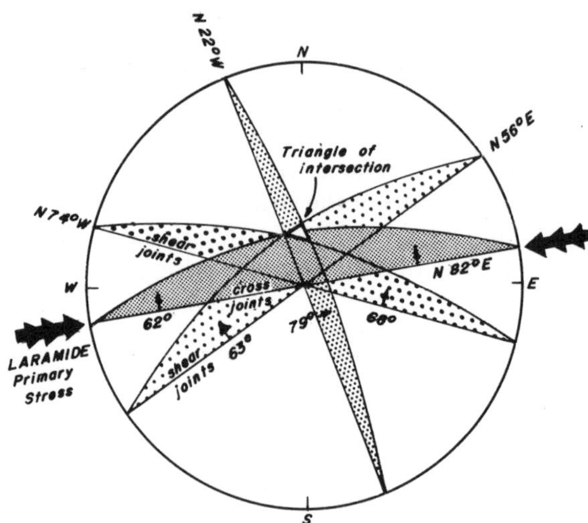

FIGURE 317. Lower hemisphere stereographic projection of the joint pattern observed in the Lamartine area by Harrison and Wells (1956). Quite similar patterns have been mapped by the present author at numerous localities in the Front Range. The longitudinal joint set frequently parallels the northwest fault (breccia reef) direction in many localities and thus may be guided by a previously existing Precambrian weakness direction. The joint system cuts rocks as young as Cretaceous on the flanks of the Front Range and is interpreted as early Laramide in age. The Laramide primary stress direction was probably parallel to the cross-joint set (N82°E in this figure). Note that the N56°E joint set is almost parallel to the b_y Precambrian lineation direction of Figure 316.

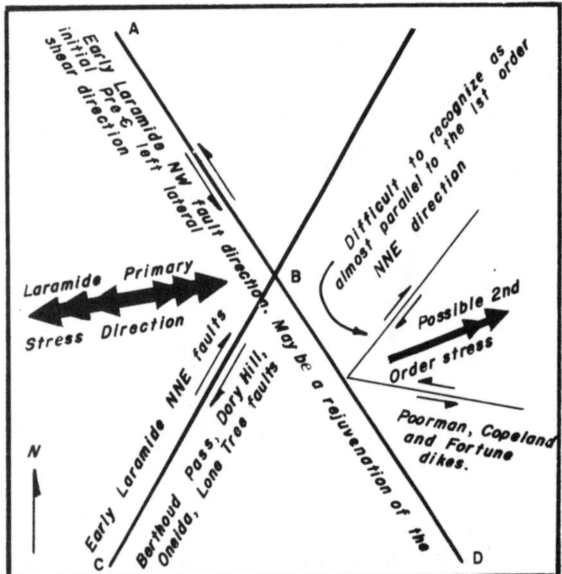

FIGURE 318. Initial Laramide shear faulting utilized the prominent north-northeast b_o foliation direction (established in the Precambrian) in the Central City area and the longitudinal joint-breccia reef direction (possibly established in the Precambrian), despite the unusually large conjugate shear angle *ABC*. This created an eastward-moving wedge (*ABC*). The second-order stress direction (of Laramide age) could have been initiated by the movement of this wedge. The second-order left lateral shear direction (Poorman, Fortune, and Copeland dikes) could be related to the already existing N74°W joint direction.

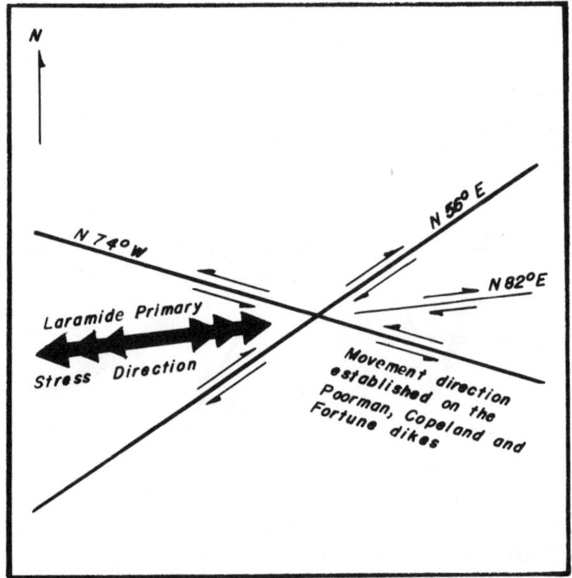

FIGURE 319. Later Laramide shearing utilized the N56°E jointing, but this joint and shear direction is not as apparent as it might be, because much of the movement utilized pre-existing foliation (b_y) lines of weakness. Still later Laramide shearing utilized the N82°E and N74°W joint directions. All of this later second-order faulting is expressed in terms of small veins, dikes, faults. The paragenesis of mineralization clearly establishes the sequence of faulting described.

of the original sediments. The layering could be related to axial plane cleavage, but the evidence is not clear-cut.

The Boulder Creek granite is considered to be syntectonic, as the regional folding stress (Fig. 315) caused platy minerals in the intruding magma to be arranged parallel to the regional foliation (030°) rather than parallel to the walls of the batholith. There are xenoliths in the batholith, however, which are aligned parallel to the walls of the batholith rather than parallel to the regional foliation. Apparently the regional stress was strong enough to orient the platy minerals in the magma but insufficient to orient the larger xenoliths, which range from a few inches to several feet in length.

At this point the reader should acquaint himself with the ideas of Moody and Hill (1956) and McKinstry (1953). They believe that a continuation of stress application in any region, after the initial development of major conjugate fractures or faults, will cause a reorientation of the stress in the adjoining blocks. Table 16 modified from Moody and Hill (1956) summarizes these ideas. In most regions only a portion of the theoretical fault system seems to develop, probably due to heterogeneity in stress application and heterogeneity of the rocks being deformed. This causes a departure from the theoretical angular relations shown in Table 16. These ideas are useful because they give a logical explanation for the time sequence of faulting and folding in many regions. Moody and Hill (1956) attempted to explain many of the major earth faults in terms of a consistent major north-south stress. In the writer's experience, a consistent north-south stress does not fit the detailed geological facts at the district level. Any regional interpretations must be based upon detailed knowledge from strategic district studies.

The next event seems to have been the development of second-order (?) b_y folds (Fig. 315). These appear in the field as small drag folds and terrace and chevron folds. They could have developed as a second-order effect of the initial stress application (Fig. 315) or as a result of reorientation of the Precambrian stress (Fig. 316). Sims and Harrison (1958) have recognized four lineation directions in the Central City district: b_o (N30°E), a_o (N60°W), b_y (N55°E), and a_y (N25°W). They believe that the b_o and b_y directions are parallel to fold axes and that the a_o and a_y directions are a lineation directions (see Chapter 8 for lineation terminology).

The next event was the injection of the Silver Plume batholith (Precambrian) and associated dikes, stocks, and phacoliths. The main batholith crops out southwest of the Central City district. The dikes, stocks, and phacoliths of this intrusive episode are dominantly concordant, being emplaced along lines of weakness (foliation and lineation) established during the earlier Precambrian orogeny. The Silver Plume rocks show a weak alignment of crystals and xenoliths parallel to the walls of the individual intrusions, but they show no evidence of the earlier regional foliation and lineation directions. Thus the Silver Plume intrusions could be classed as posttectonic.

The next development apparent in the structural fabric of the Central City district is the joint pattern (Fig. 317). This was discussed in detail in Chapter 8, pages 219, 221). The orientation of the joints suggests a west-southwest–east-northeast stress orientation, and the small triangle of intersection implies a similar (single ?) stress application. The joints appear to be younger than any of the Precambrian structural features already discussed, but two of the joint directions (N22°W, N56°E) are almost parallel to previously developed Precambrian lines of weakness. The jointing probably was developed in the early phases of the Laramide orogeny when the Front Range was domed upward, the long axis of the uplift being almost parallel to the longitudinal jointing.

Further Laramide compression initiated fault movement on those best developed pre-existing weakness planes (joints and foliation) which were most suitably oriented to accommodate the stress application. In Figure 318 it may be seen that the directions AB (the longitudinal joint direction) and CB (the b_o foliation-lineation direction) became shear faults at this time, and the "conjugate wedge" ABC appears to have dominated later Laramide structural events in the Central City district. The N56°E joint direction is also parallel to the b_o lineation direction. The angle ABC is much greater than the theoretical 60° discussed in Table 16, but this is due to the pre-existing fabric of the stressed complex. In other parts of the Front Range where the strongest foliation-lineation direction is east-northeast (frequently N56°E ± 10°) instead of north-northeast, this "conjugate wedge" is bounded by the longitudinal joint di-

TABLE 16. Theoretical Wrench Fault, Thrust Fault, and Fold Directions for a Homogeneous Media Under Simple North-South Compression

Wrench Fault Directions (Right or Left Lat.)	Anticline and Thrust Directions
RL N30 W	E-W
LL N30 E	E-W
RL N15 E	N45 E
RL N75 W	N45 E
LL N15 W	N45 W
LL N75 E	N45 W
RL N30 W	N-S
RL N30 W	N-S
RL N60 E	E-W
RL N60 E	E-W
LL N30 E	N-S
LL N30 E	N-S
LL N60 W	E-W
LL N60 W	E-W

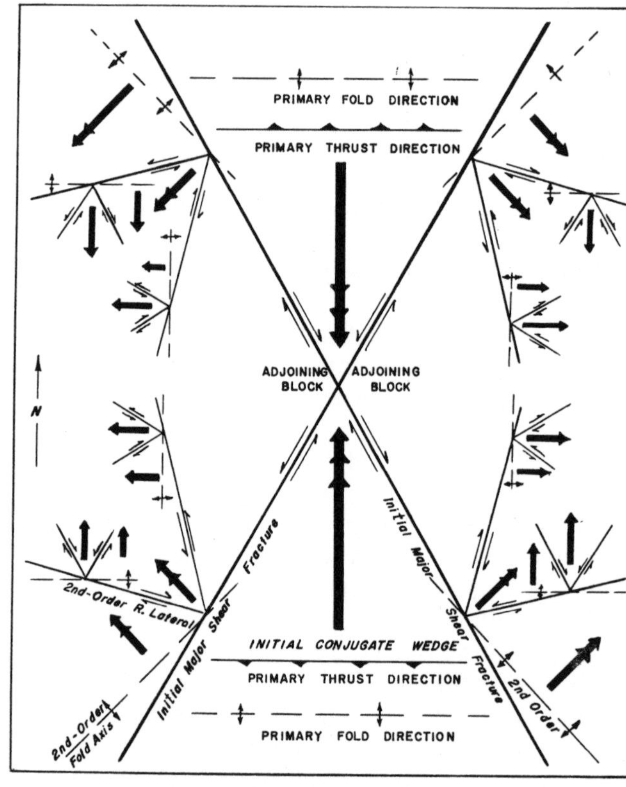

NOTE: A homogeneous isotropic material subjected to simple compression will shear at angles of 30° to the direction of maximum stress application even though the planes of maximum shearing stress are parallel to the intermediate stress axis and lie at 45° to the maximum compressive stress. The 15° angle between the 45° maximum shear planes and the 30° shear planes which actually form is believed to be due to internal friction.

A compressive stress applied to a uniform isotropic material commonly can be resolved into three stress directions (maximum, intermediate, and minimum stress axes). The air-earth interface is a surface of zero stress and thus is frequently normal to one of the principal stress directions. Consequently one of the three principal stress directions is often vertical.

If movement is in progress on a main fault or master shear, stresses in the "adjoining blocks" will have such orientations so as to cause failure on new pairs of mutually complementary planes (second-order shears). The new major stress direction is reoriented through 15° from the previous main stress direction. This 15° angle has been observed commonly in the field and is simply an empirical average. This angle has not been explained satisfactorily from a mathematical point of view as yet.

The shear and anticlinal directions shown in the above table indicate that the third-order directions start to duplicate the first-order directions. Thus it is impossible to distinguish fourth-order and lower directions from first-, second-, and third-order directions. Consequently an infinity of shear directions does not arise. The system is resolved into eight major shear directions and four major anticlinical and thrust directions for any tectonic province. In practice the first- and second-order features are distinguishable without difficulty whereas the third-order features commonly are difficult to find.

rection and the east-northeast foliation-lineation direction. Other "conjugate wedges" have been recognized by the writer in the Idaho Batholith-Butte region, in the Flin Flon-Sherridon area of northern Manitoba (see Chapter 6, Fig. 166), in the Sudbury-Porcupine-Malartic region of the Laurentian Shield (Fig. 320), in the Pachuca silver district of Mexico, in the Kimberley district of British Columbia, and elsewhere. In each case a wedge-shaped block or plate of the earth's crust, bounded by great tear faults, moves forward under compressive orogenic stress causing strike-slip movement on the boundary tears. Second-order effects have been noted in the adjoining blocks. Major mineral deposits are concentrated at strategic points along the boundary tear faults. In some tectonic provinces the boundary tear faults are so strongly developed that they extend outward from the mountain system into the adjoining sedimentary basins and have an important bearing on petroleum accumulations in the basins. The Montana lineament, the West Bay, and East Arm faults (Yellowknife area, N.W.T.) are good examples.

The final shearing movements in the Central City district were concentrated on many small faults (Fig. 319). Each of these faults could have been initiated as a second-order fault dependent upon the initial first-order Laramide faulting (Fig. 318). The following time sequence of Laramide faulting in the Central City area has been confirmed by the paragenetic studies of Harrison and Wells (1956):

1. North-northeast faulting (right lateral movement).
2. East-northeast faulting (right lateral movement).
3. Approximately east-west (right lateral movement).

Those faults which were open and moving at the

Local Name of the Structural Unit	Time of Origin	Orientation	Originated as	Rejuvenated as	Time of Rejuvenation	Type of Fault Movement
b_0 lineation direction	Early Precambrian	NNE (N30°E)	*b* lineation, Precambrian thrust faults, folds, and related foliation	First-order strike-slip faults (Berthoud Pass, Dory Hill, Oneida, etc., faults)	Early Laramide	Right lateral strike-slip
a_0 lineation direction	Early Precambrian	SE (S60°E)	*a* lineation, possible Precambrian cross joints	Shear joints	Early Laramide	——
b_y lineation direction	Early Precambrian or reoriented later Precambrian stress	NE (N55°E)	Secondary-fold axes, lineation and related foliation, thrust (?) faults	1. Shear joints 2. Second-order shear zones or faults	Early Laramide Later Laramide	—— Right lateral strike-slip
a_y lineation direction	Early Precambrian or later reoriented Precambrian stress	SSE (S25°E)	1. *a* lineation of secondary folds 2. Possible first-order shear direction 3. Possible Precambrian cross joints	1. Longitudinal joints 2. First-order shear faults (breccia reefs) 3. Thrust faults	Early Laramide Later Laramide	—— Left lateral strike-slip
	?	E (N82°E)	?	1. Cross joints (tensional)	Early Laramide	——
				2. Shear zones and minor faults	Later Laramide	Right lateral strike-slip
	?	WNW	?	1. Shear joints	Early Laramide	——
				2. Shear zones	Later Laramide	Right lateral strike-slip

time of ore solution migration became host fissures for ore localization. The table shown on page 251 summarizes the writer's current interpretation of the temporal, spatial, and genetic relationships for the various elements of the structural fabric in the Central City area.

A similar interpretation applies in other parts of the Colorado Rockies, although orientation changes somewhat from place to place. A Laramide joint set parallel to the Precambrian a_0 lineation has been observed in some areas. One other significant element of the fabric is the strong north-northeast (frequently N55° E) Precambrian shear direction. This is parallel to the foliation in some areas, and in others it cuts across the Precambrian foliation. The so-called Ralston shear zone, the Sawatch Range shear zone, and the Gore Range shear zone are examples of this type. They may represent Precambrian thrust zones or Precambrian strike-slip fault zones. If the later case is correct, then this would suggest some reorientation of the original Precambrian stress direction.

Conclusion: The tectonic analysis of mining and petroleum districts requires a close integration of continental, regional, and district structural events. Close attention should be paid to angular relationships and timing. Fundamental lines of weakness once generated are rejuvenated frequently. Systematic stress analysis provides a link between the various elements of the structural fabric.

References: Tectonic Analysis—General

Anderson, E. M. (1951), *The Dynamics of Faulting and Dyke Formation with Applications to Britain,* 2nd ed., Oliver & Boyd, Edinburgh, 206 pp.

Balk, R. (1948), Structural Behavior of Igneous Rocks, *Geol. Soc. Am.,* Mem. 5.

Billingsley, P., and Locke, A. (1941), Structure of Ore Districts in the Continental Framework, *Am. Inst. Min. Eng.,* Trans., vol. 144, pp. 9–59.

Blanchet, P. H. (1957), Development of Fracture Analysis as Exploration Method, *Bull. Am. Assoc. Petrol. Geol.,* vol. 41, pp. 1748–1759.

Bucher, W. H. (1920–1921), The Mechanical Interpretation of Joints, *Jour. Geol.,* vol. 28, pp. 707–730, vol. 29, pp. 1–28.

Chamberlain, R. T. (1945), Basement Control in Rocky Mountain Deformation, *Am. Jour. Sci.,* vol. 243A (Daly vol.) pp. 98–116.

Cizancourt, H. de (1947), Quelques Problemes de Tectonique Geometrique, Extrait de la Rev. de *L'Inst. Fr. de Petrole* et Ann. de Comb. liq., vol. II, no. 1, pp. 3–24, no. 2, pp. 81–98, no. 3, pp. 141–154, no. 5, pp. 252–254.

Cloos, E. (1946), Lineation, a Critical Review and Annotated Bibliography, *Geol. Soc. Am.,* Mem. 18.

Hafner, W. (1951), Stress Distributions and Faulting, *Bull. Geol. Soc. Am.,* vol. 62, pp. 373–398.

Henson, F. R. S. (1952), Observations on the Geology and Petroleum Ocurrences of the Middle East, *Proc. Third World* (Petrol.) *Cong.,* The Hague, Sect. I, pp. 118–140.

Hills, E. S. (1947), Tectonic Patterns in the Earth's Crust, *Australian and New Zealand Assoc. for Advancement of Science,* Pres. Address, Sect. P, vol. 26, pp. 290–302.

Hubbert, M. K. (1951), Mechanical Basis for Certain Familiar Geologic Structures, *Bull. Geol. Soc. Am.,* vol. 62, pp. 355–372.

Hulin, C. D. (1948), Factors in the Localization of Mineralized Districts, *Am. Inst. Min. Eng.,* Trans., vol. 178, pp. 36–57.

Kaufmann, G. F. (1951), The Tectonic Framework of the Far East and Its Influence on the Origin and Accumulation of Petroleum, *Proc. Third World Petrol. Cong.* (The Hague), Sect. I, pp. 86–117.

Klemme, H. D. (1958), Regional Geology of Circum-Mediterranean Region, *Bull. Am. Assoc. Petrol. Geol.,* vol. 42, pp. 477–512.

Knebel, G. M., and Rodriguez-Eraso, G. (1956), Habitat of Oil, *Bull. Am. Assoc. Petrol. Geol.,* vol. 40, pp. 547–561.

Livingston, C. W. (1939), Mechanics of Vein Formation in the Northern Half of the Baguio District (Philippines), *Eng. and Min. Jour.,* vol. 140, no. 9, pp. 38–42, no. 10, pp. 49–51.

Lovering, T. S. (1928), The Fracturing of Incompetent Beds, *Jour. Geol.,* vol. 36, pp. 709–717.

Mayo, E. B. (1958), Lineament Tectonics and Some Ore Deposits of the Southwest, *Am. Inst. Min. Eng.,* Preprint No. 5817P6, presented at the 1958 (New York) Annual Meeting, Am. Inst. Min. Eng.

McKinstry, H. E. (1941), Structural Control of Ore Deposits in Fissure Veins, *Am. Inst. Min. Eng.,* Trans., vol. 144, pp. 65–95.

McKinstry, H. E. (1953), Shears of the Second Order, *Am. Jour. Sci.,* vol. 251, pp. 401–414.

McKinstry, H. E. (1955), Structure of Hydrothermal Ore Deposits, *Econ. Geol.,* 50th Anniv. Vol. pp. 170–225.

Melton, F. A. (1929), A Reconnaissance of the Joint Systems in the Ouachita Mountains and Central Plains of Oklahoma, *Jour. Geol.,* vol. 37, pp. 733–738.

Moody, J. D., and Hill, M. J. (1956), Wrench-Fault Tectonics, *Bull. Geol. Soc. Am.,* vol. 67, pp. 1207–1246.

Newhouse, W. H. (ed.) (1942), *Ore Deposits as Related to Structural Features,* Princeton University Press, 280 pp.

Pincus, H. J. (1951), Statistical Methods Applied to the Study of Rock Fractures, *Bull. Geol. Soc. Am.,* vol. 62, pp. 81–130.

Seigel, H. O. (1950), A Theory of Fracture of Materials and Its Application to Geology, *Am. Geophy. Union,* Trans., vol. 31, pp. 611–619.

Swanson, C. O. (1927), Notes on Stress, Strain, and Joints, *Jour. Geol.,* vol. 35, pp. 193–223.

Wallace, R. E. (1951), Geometry of Shearing Stress and Relation to Faulting, *Jour. Geol.,* vol. 59, pp. 118–130.

Weeks, L. G. (1952), Factors of Sedimentary Basin Development that Control Oil Occurrence, *Bull. Am. Assoc. Petrol. Geol.,* vol. 40, pp. 457–561.

Wilson, E. (1941), The Environment of Ore Bodies, *Am. Inst. Min. Eng.,* Trans., vol. 144, pp. 96–110.

Wilson, J. T. (1948), Some Aspects of Geophysics in Canada with Special Reference to Structural Research in the Canadian Shield, *Am. Geophy. Union,* Trans., vol. 29, pp. 691–726.

Wilson, J. T. (1949), Some Major Structures of the Canadian Shield, *Bull. Can. Inst. Min.,* vol. 42, pp. 543–554.

Wisser, E. (1951), Tectonic Analysis of a Mining District, Pachuca, Mexico, *Econ. Geol.,* vol. 46, pp. 459–477.

References: Tectonic Analysis—Colorado Mineral Belt

Bastin, E. S., and Hill, J. M. (1917), Economic Geology of Gilpin County and Adjacent Parts of Clear Creek and Boulder Counties, Colorado, *U.S. Geol. Surv.,* Prof. Paper 94.

Behre, C. H., Jr. (1953), Geology and Ore Deposits of the West Slope of the Mosquito Range, *U.S. Geol. Surv.,* Prof. Paper 235.

Boos, M. F. (1954), Genesis of Pre-Cambrian Pegmatites in the Denver Mountain Parks Area, Colorado, *Bull. Geol. Soc. Am.* vol. 65, pp. 115–142.

Boos, C. M., and Boos, M. F. (1957), Tectonics of Eastern Flank and Foothills of Front Range, Colorado, *Bull. Am. Assoc. Petrol. Geol.,* vol. 41, pp. 2603–2676.

Burbank, W. S. (1932), Geology and Ore Deposits of the Bonanza Mining District, Colorado, *U.S. Geol. Surv.,* Prof. Paper 169.

Burbank, W. S. (1933), Relation of Paleozoic and Mesozoic Sedimentation to Cretaceous-Tertiary Igneous Activity and the Development of Tectonic Features in Colorado, *Ore Deposits of the Western States, 1933,* Am. Inst. Min. Eng.

Butler, B. S., and Vanderwilt, J. W. (1933), The Climax Molybdenum Deposit, Colorado, *U.S. Geol. Surv.,* Bull. 846-C.

Dings, M. G., and Robinson, C. S. (1957), Geology and Ore Deposits of the Garfield Quadrangle, Colorado, *U.S. Geol. Surv.,* Prof. Paper 289.

Eckel, E. B., Williams, J. S., and Galbraith, F. W. (1949), Geology and Ore Deposits of the La Plata District, Colorado, *U.S. Geol. Surv.,* Prof. Paper 219.

Emmons, S. F., Irving, J. D., and Loughlin, G. F. (1927), Geology and Ore Deposits of the Leadville Mining District, Colorado, *U.S. Geol. Surv.,* Prof. Paper 148.

Harrison, J. E. (1955), Relation Between Fracture Pattern and Hypogene Zoning in the Freeland-Lamartine District, Colorado, *Econ. Geol.,* vol. 50, pp. 311–320.

Harrison, J. E., and Wells, J. D. (1956), Geology and Ore Deposits of the Freeland-Lamartine District, Clear Creek County, Colorado, *U.S. Geol. Surv.,* Bull. 1932-B.

Harrison, J. E., and Wells, J. D. (1958), Geology and Ore Deposits of the Chicago Creek Area, Clear Creek County, Colorado, *U.S. Geol. Surv.,* Prof. Paper 319.

Johnson, R. B. (1958), Patterns of Radial Dike Swarms Associated with West Spanish Peak and Dike Mountain Stocks, South Central Colorado, 1958 Annual Meeting, Rocky Mountain Section, Geol. Soc. Am., Golden, Colorado.

Knopf, Adolph (1926), Recent Developments in the Aspen District, Colorado, *U.S. Geol. Surv.,* Bull. 785.

Koschmann, A. H. (1949), Structural Control of the Gold Deposits of the Cripple Creek District, Teller County, Colorado, *U.S. Geol. Surv.,* Bull. 955-B.

Kucera, R. E. (1958), Laramide and Late Cenozoic Deformation in the Yampa District, Northwest Colorado, 1958 Annual Meeting, Rocky Mountain Section, Geol. Soc. Am., Golden, Colorado.

Larsen, E. S. (1929), Recent Mining Developments in the Creede District, Colorado, *U.S. Geol. Surv.,* Bull. 811.

Larsen, E. S., Jr., and Cross, W. (1956), Geology and Petrology of the San Juan Region, Southwestern Colorado, *U.S. Geol. Surv.,* Prof. Paper 258.

Lovering, T. S. (1934), Geology and Ore Deposits of the Breckenridge Mining District, Colorado, *U.S. Geol. Surv.,* Prof. Paper 176.

Lovering, T. S. (1935), Geology and Ore Deposits of the Montezuma Quadrangle, *U.S. Geol. Surv.,* Prof. Paper 178.

Lovering, T. S., and Goddard, E. N. (1950), Geology and Ore Deposits of the Front Range, Colorado, *U.S. Geol. Surv.,* Prof. Paper 223.

Lovering, T. S., and Tweto, Ogden (1953), Geology and Ore Deposits of the Boulder County Tungsten District, Colorado, *U.S. Geol. Surv.,* Prof. Paper 245.

Moench, R. H., Harrison, J. E., and Sims, P. K. (1958), Precambrian Folding in the Central Part of the Front Range Mineral Belt, Colorado, 1958 Annual Meeting,

Rocky Mountain Section, Geol. Soc. Am., Golden, Colorado.

Sims, P. K. (1956), Paragenesis and Structure of Pitchblende-bearing Veins, Central City District, Gilpin County, Colorado, *Econ. Geol.,* vol. 51, pp. 539–576.

Sims, P. K., and Harrison, J. E. (1958), Summary of Geology of Precambrian Rocks in the Central City-Idaho Springs Area, Front Range, Colorado, Precambrian Field Trip Guidebook, 1958 Annual Meeting, Rocky Mountain Section, Geol. Soc. Am., Golden, Colorado.

Sims, P. K., Osterwald, F. W., and Tooker, E. W. (1955), Uranium Deposits in the Eureka Gulch Area, Central City District, Gilpin County, Colorado, *U.S. Geol. Surv.,* Bull. 1032-A.

Singewald, Q. D., and Butler, B. S. (1941), Ore Deposits in the Vicinity of the London Fault of Colorado, *U.S. Geol. Surv.,* Bull. 911.

Spurr, J. E., Garrey, G. H., and Ball, S. H. (1908), Economic Geology of the Georgetown Quadrangle, Colorado, *U.S. Geol. Surv.,* Prof. Paper 63.

Staatz, M. H., and Trites, A. F. (1955), Geology of the Quartz Creek Pegmatite District, Gunnison County, Colorado, *U.S. Geol. Surv.,* Prof. Paper 265.

Steven, T. A. (1957), Metamorphism and the Origin of Granitic Rocks, Northgate District, Colorado, *U.S. Geol. Surv.,* Prof. Paper 274-M.

Tweto, O., and Pearson, R. C. (1958), Great Precambrian Shear Zone, Sawatch Range, Colorado, 1958 Annual Meeting, Rocky Mountain Section, Geol. Soc. Am., Golden, Colorado.

Warner, L. A. (1956), Tectonics of the Colorado Front Range, 1956, *Geol. Rec.* of the Rocky Mountain Section of the Am. Assoc. Petrol. Geol., pp. 129–144.

PROBLEM 40

TECTONIC ANALYSIS OF THE SOUTHEASTERN PORTION OF THE LAURENTIAN SHIELD

Data Provided: Figure 320 is a regional tectonic map of the southeastern portion of the Laurentian shield. Fold axes and foliation are generalized in some regions. Figure 321 is an enlargement of the key area from Larder Lake (McFadden township) to Malartic. Figures 322 and 323 are detailed tectonic maps of the Kirkland Lake-Larder Lake and Porcupine areas. Table 17 is a generalized summary of the major Precambrian events. The sequence of events would be treated differently by some geologists because of the many correlation problems which exist. The main tectonic trends, their sequence of development, and their angular relationships are open to less argument. Nearly every large ore deposit in this region shows a close relationship to pre-existing lines of structural weakness. There is good reason to believe that many of the major structural directions (Porcupine-Destor, Kirkland Lake-Cadillac, Timiskaming, Onaping, Grenville) were initiated early in Precambrian history and were rejuvenated by each orogenic pulse. The movement directions, however, probably were different in different orogenies.

Determine: Study the accompanying material and work out a generalized tectonic interpretation along the lines of that evolved for the Colorado Front Range area (Figs. 314 to 319, pp. 247–252). Then select several areas in the southeast Laurentian shield for detailed study and see if they support the original working hypotheses evolved. The length of this problem can be adjusted to fit the time available to the student. It can be extended into a term project by having the student examine all the regional references as well as many detailed reports. A comprehensive review with exploration recommendations might then be drawn up in report form. Detailed studies from the literature may be supplemented by air photo groups ordered from the National Air Photo Library of the Department of Mines and Technical Surveys, Ottawa, Canada. It may be necessary for the student to look beyond the confines of Figure 320 to see if structures of continental dimensions (see tectonic maps of the United States and of Canada) have a bearing on the structural features of the southeastern Laurentian shield. The references which follow are broad regional papers with extensive bibliographies in most cases. There are many excellent detailed papers at the quadrangle level which could not be included in this bibliography without making it excessively long. These detailed reports will be referred to in the bibliographies accompanying the regional papers.

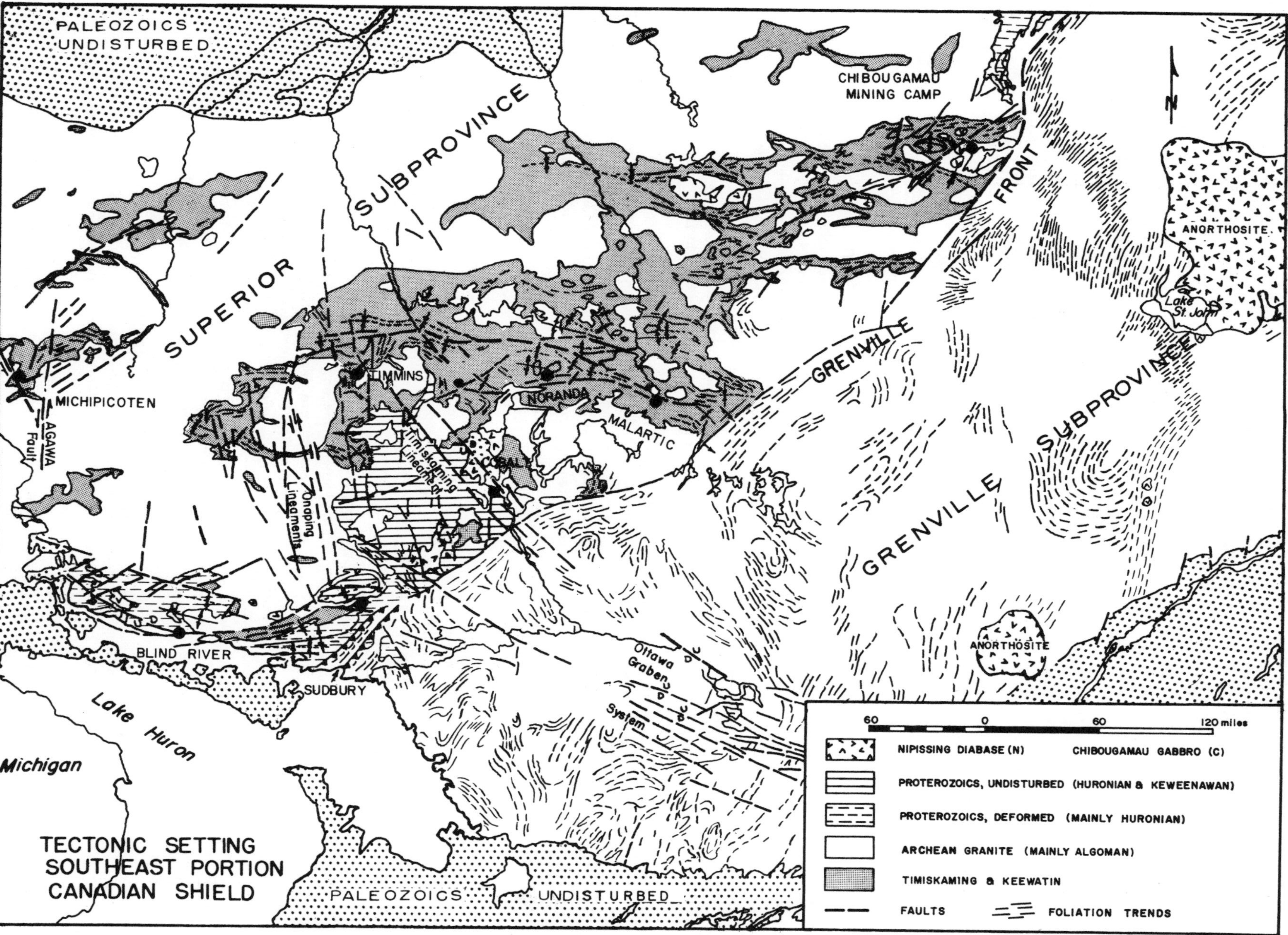

FIGURE 320. (Modified from the Tectonic Map of Canada [1950], Geol. Assoc. Can.)

TABLE 17. Precambrian History

Location		Rock Units	Comments of Lithological and Tectonic Nature
Superior Subprovince	Proterozoic	Keeweenawan Series (550 M.Y.)	Consists dominantly of arkoses (often conglomeratic) and amygdaloidal basalts (copper bearing in Michigan, epigenetic). Part of the series is intruded by gabbros (Duluth lopolith) and norites (nickle bearing at Sudbury). The intrusions were injected into a "down-warping tectonic environment" (post-tectonic ?) associated with the development of the Lake Superior syncline. These basic intrusions are cut by the Murray and Creighton granites (correlative with the Killarney granite ?) at Sudbury. The Killarney granite is believed to be associated with the Penokean orogeny which folded the Huronian rocks (NE-SW folds) and parts of the Keeweenawan series and probably thrust the Grenville rocks over the Huronian. The final event in Keeweenawan time was the injection of large olivine Diabase Dikes.
			UNCONFORMITY
		Upper Huronian (Animikie series)	Graywackes and slates overlying iron formations.
			UNCONFORMITY
		Middle Huronian (Cobalt series)	Graywackes, slates, and boulder conglomerate (glacial). These rocks were intruded by the Nipissing diabase. Some folding occurred before deposition of the overlying rocks.
			UNCONFORMITY
		Lower Huronian (Bruce series)	Dolomite, limestone, quartzose sandstone, and conglomerate. The conglomerate thickens and coarsens to the south like many of the other clastic units of the Huronian. The Huronian rocks were probably derived through erosion of the uplifted Grenville mountain range to the southeast.
			FAULT CONTACT
Grenville Subprovince	Archean or Proterozoic		The Grenville and Huronian rocks are separated by a fault contact, by mylonitized zones, or by different degrees of metamorphism in most places.
		Granites and Anorthosites of The Grenville Subprovince (800–1100 M.Y.)	The granites become more abundant than the anorthosites as the Grenville Front is approached. At least two groups of granite are younger than the anorthosite. The younger granites are unsheared, like the Silver Plume granites (600–900 M.Y., Phair, 1958) in Colorado. Folding with NE-SW fold axes (Grenville orogeny) accompanied the earlier intrusions.
		Hastings series	Shales, graywackes, and conglomerates locally unconformable over the Grenville series.
		Grenville series (Could be as old as the Timiskaming series)	Marbles, quartzites, gneisses, and schists. The Grenville rocks in Quebec may be older than those in the Adirondacks. The Grenville and Hastings series may have been derived from the Algoman mountains to the northwest.
Superior Subprovince	Archean	Algoman granites (1750 M.Y.)	Was accompanied by strong folding, some thrust faulting, and some strike-slip faulting toward the end of the orogeny (E-W fold axes). Most of the gold and base metal ore deposits in the Superior province are associated with this orogeny. The Porcupine-Destor and Kirkland-Larder Lake-Cadillac "breaks" were active at this time.
		Timiskaming series	The Timiskaming sediments are mainly graywackes but some slates, conglomerates, and volcanic tuffs are present. The Timiskaming and Keewatin rocks were folded (E-W fold axes) by an orogeny older than the Algoman orogeny.
			UNCONFORMITY
		Laurentian Granites (2100–2200 M.Y. (?))	Its existence and correlation is open to discussion. The Timiskaming sediments contain considerable granite detrital material however.
		Keewatin volcanics (Abitibi series) Coutchiching graywackes (2100–2550 M.Y. (?))	The relative age of the Keewatin and Coutchiching is open to discussion. There is little evidence to support the idea of an original granitic crust. The oldest rocks are probably basic intermediate volcanics.

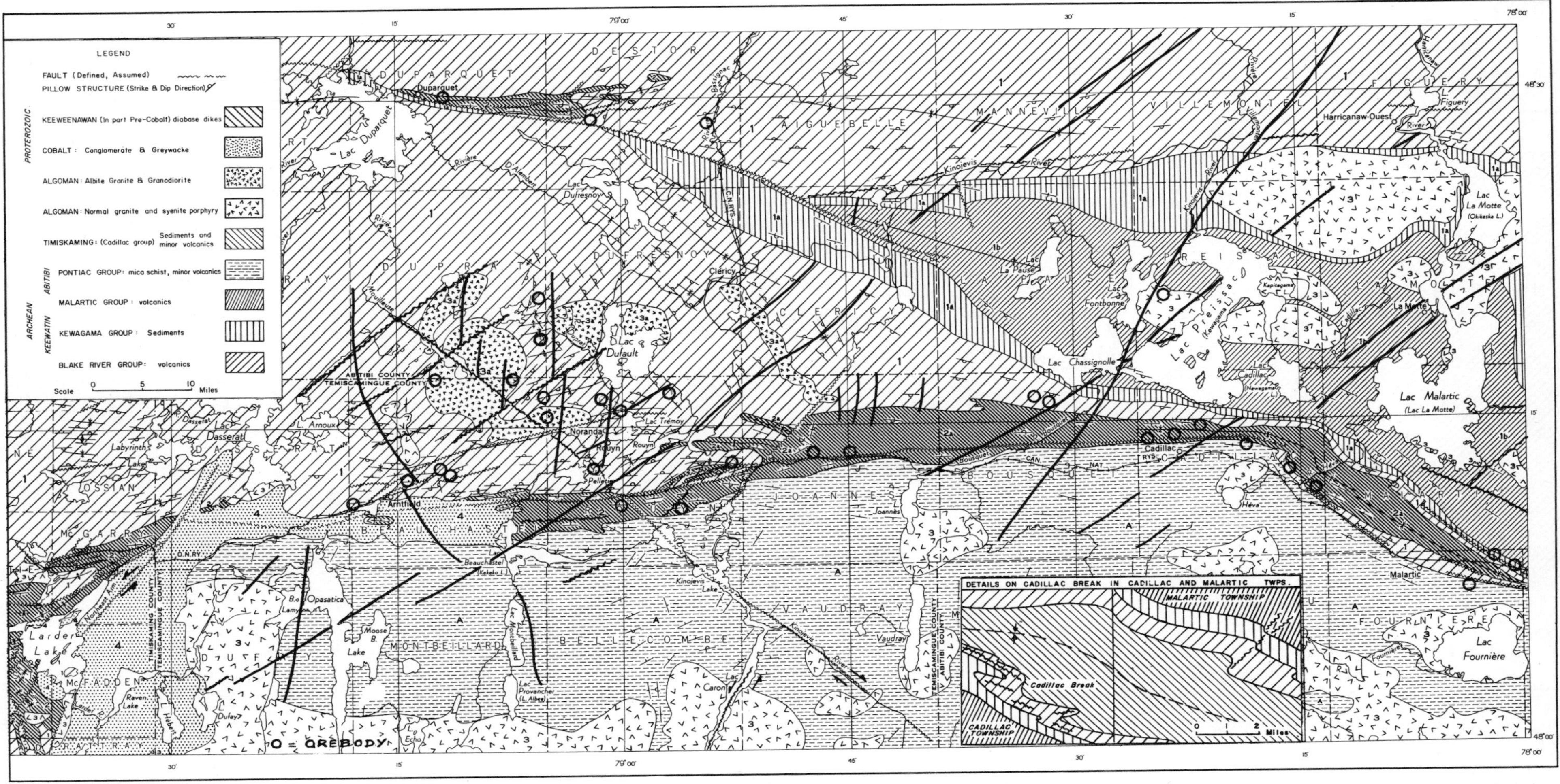

FIGURE 321. Tectonic setting for the area from Larder Lake, Ontario to Malartic, Quebec. Note the well-developed conjugate wedge which is outlined by the Malartic-Cadillac-Larder Lake fault system. (Modified from M. E. Wilson [1956], *Geol. Soc. Am.*, vol. 67.)

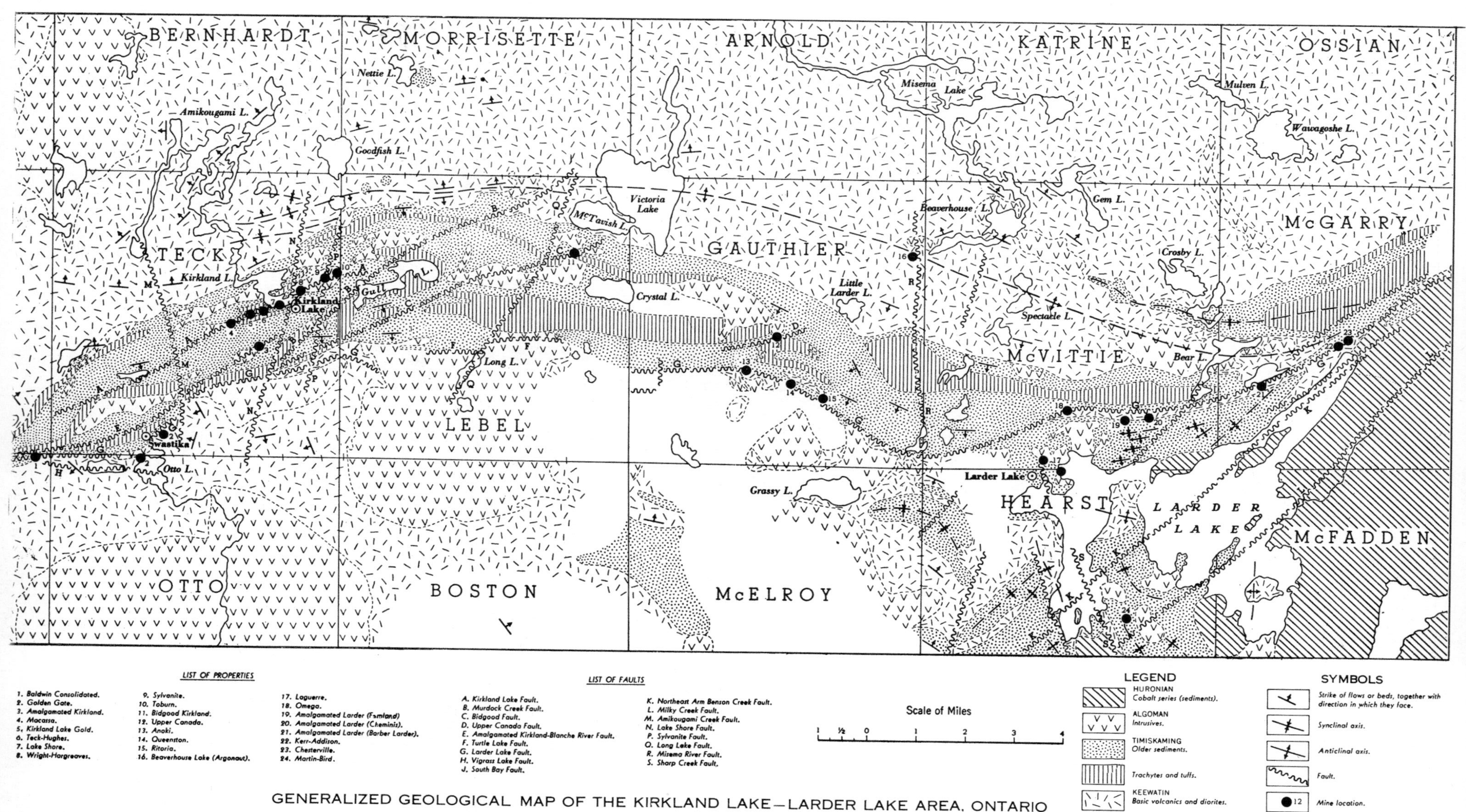

GENERALIZED GEOLOGICAL MAP OF THE KIRKLAND LAKE—LARDER LAKE AREA, ONTARIO

FIGURE 322. (Modified from J. E. Thomson [1948], *Structural Geology of Canadian Ore Deposits*, Can. Inst. Min. Met.)

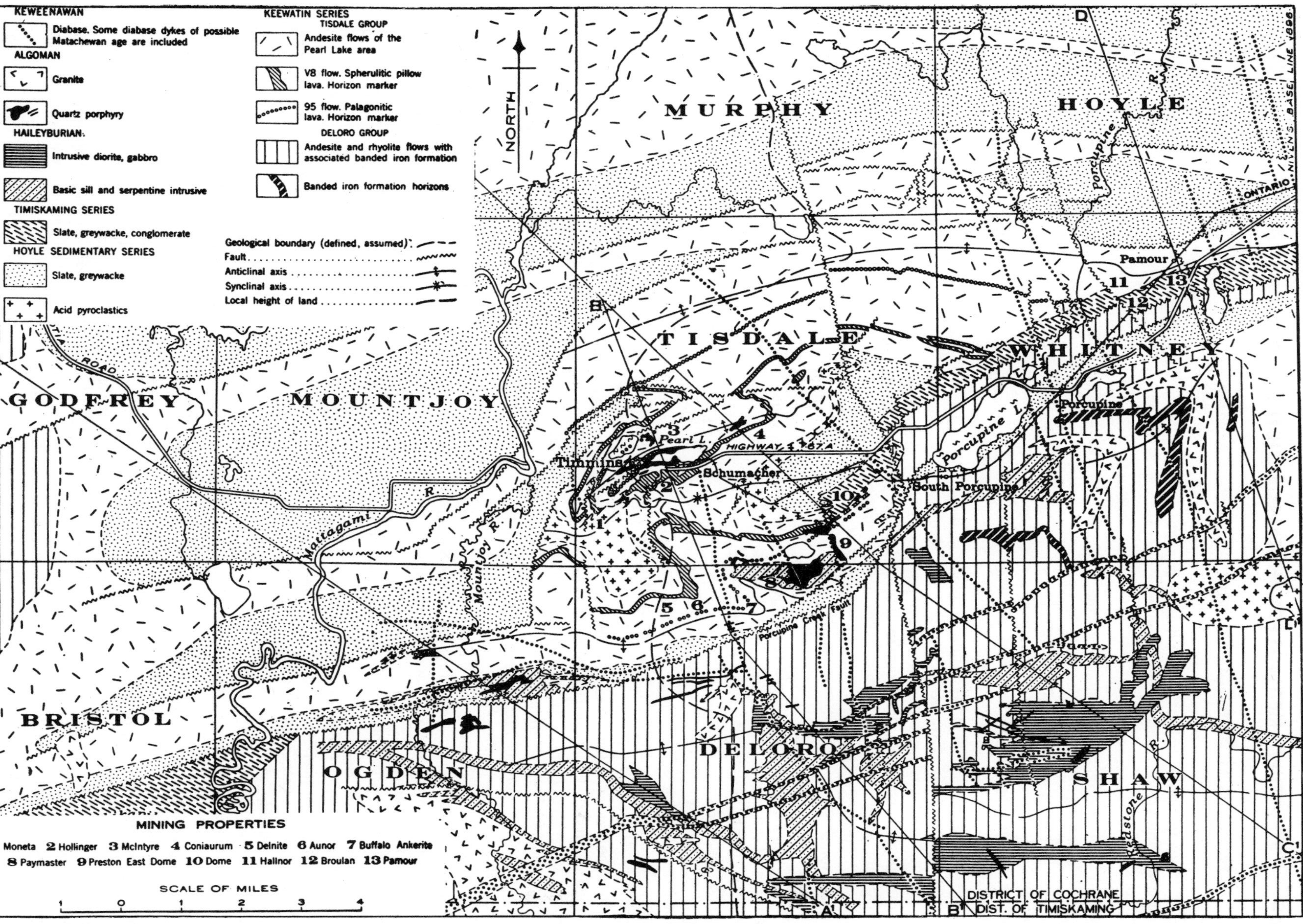

FIGURE 323. Geological map of the Porcupine mining camp, Timmins, Ontario. The Matachewan dikes are of Huronian age, the Haileyburian rocks are of Pre-Algoman age, and the Hoyle sediments are of Pre-Laurentian age. (From W. R. Dunbar [1948], *Structural Geology of Canadian Ore Deposits*, Can. Inst. Min. Met.)

Selected List of References

The following annotated list will be helpful in analyzing the tectonics of the southeastern portion of the Laurentian shield.

Buddington, A. F. (1939), Adirondack Igneous Rocks and Their Metamorphism, *Geol. Soc. Am.,* Mem. 7.
Detailed study of petrological aspects.

Can. Inst. Min. Met. Jubilee Volume on *Structural Geology of Canadian Ore Deposits,* vol. I, 1948, vol. II, 1958.
Structural aspects of many mining regions in the Laurentian shield. Extensive bibliographies. Probably the best single reference work. See particularly the papers by G. W. H. Norman (Major Faults, Abitibi Region), W. R. Dunbar (Structural Relations of the Porcupine Ore Deposits), J. E. Thomson (Regional Structure of the Kirkland Lake-Larder Lake Area).

Collins, C. B., Farquhar, R. M., and Russell, R. D. (1954), Isotopic Constitution of Radiogenic Leads and the Measurement of Geological Time, *Bull. Geol. Soc. Am.,* vol. 65, pp. 1–22.

Engel, A. E., and Engel, C. G. (1953), Grenville Series in the Northwest Adirondack Mountains, New York, *Bull. Geol. Soc. Am.,* vol. 64, Pt. I, pp. 1013–1048, Pt. II, pp. 1049– 1097.
Regional review, extensive bibliography.

Geological Survey of Canada (1947), *Geology and Economic Minerals of Canada,* 3rd ed., Chap. II, "The Canadian Shield." See also 4th ed. (1958).
Excellent summary of Precambrian events and mineral deposits. No bibliography.

Gilbert, J. E. (1953), Geology and Mineral Deposits of Northwestern Quebec Guidebook for Field Trip No. 10 of the Annual Meeting, Geol. Soc. Amer. and Geol. Assoc. Can. (Toronto).
Contains a good compilation map of northwestern Quebec.

Gill, J. E. (1952), Early History of the Canadian Precambrian Shield, *Proc. Geol. Assoc. Can.,* vol. 5, pp. 57–68.

Gill, J. E. (1952), Mountain Building in the Canadian Precambrian Shield, *Internat. Geol. Cong.,* 18th Session (Great Britain), Rept., pt. 13, pp. 97–104.
Summary of some of the tectonic problems.

Gill, J. E. (1952), Original Crust in the Canadian Shield (Abstract), *Am. Miner.,* vol. 37, p. 292.

Gill, J. E., and L'Espérance, R. L. (1952), Diabase Dykes in the Canadian Shield, *Royal Soc. Can.,* Trans., 3rd ser., vol. 46, sect. 4, pp. 25–36.

Gunning, H. C., and Ambrose, J. W. (1940), Malartic Area, Quebec, *Geol. Serv. Can.,* Mem. 222.
Detailed mapping along the Cadillac break is shown. Drag folding along this fault zone is a good indicator of strike-slip movement.

Johnston, W. G. Q. (1954), Geology of the Timiskaming-Grenville Contact Southeast of Lake Temaganic, Northern Ontario, Canada, *Bull. Geol. Soc. Am.,* vol. 65, pp. 1047–1074.
Review of the Grenville fault problem. Extensive bibliography.

Kay, G. M. (1952), Ottawa-Bonnechère Graben and Lake Ontario Homocline, *Bull. Geol. Soc. Am.,* vol. 53, pp. 585–646.

King, P. B. (1951), *The Tectonics of Middle North America East of the Cordilleran System,* Princeton University Press, 203 pp.
Excellent summary of Precambrian history. Extensive bibliography.

McLaughlin, D. B. (1954), Suggested Extension of the Grenville Orogenic Belt and the Grenville Front, *Sci.,* vol. 120, pp. 287–289.
Discusses the possibility of the Grenville line of weakness extending west-southwest toward the Mississippi embayment active seismic zone.

Pettijohn, F. J. (1937), Early Precambrian Geology and Correlational Problems of the Northern Subprovince of the Lake Superior Region, *Bull. Geol. Soc. Am.,* vol. 48, pp. 153–202.
Detailed review of Precambrian correlation problems. Extensive bibliography.

Pettijohn, F. J. (1943), Archean Sedimentation, *Bull. Geol. Soc. Am.,* vol. 54, pp. 925–972.
Detailed review and extensive bibliography.

Savage, W. S. (1953), Geology and Mineral Deposits of the Kirkland-Larder Mining District, Ontario, Guidebook for Field Trip, No. 8, Annual Meeting, Geol. Soc. Am. and Geol. Assoc. Can. (Toronto).

Snelgrove, A. K. (ed.) (1957), Geological Exploration.
A collection of 12 papers dealing with the geology of the Lake Superior region. Published by the Lake Superior Geol. Soc. Available at the College of Mining & Technology, Houghton, Mich.

Symposium on the Grenville Subprovince (1955), *Royal Soc. Can.,* Trans., 3rd ser., vol. 49.
Good review of Grenville problems.

Symposium on Precambrian Correlation and Dating (1955), *Proc. Geol. Assoc. Can.,* vol. 7, pt. II, pp. 5–135.
Comprehensive review of age determination aspects.

Tectonic Map of Canada (1950), Prepared by the Geol. Assoc. Can., available from the Geol. Soc. Am. (New York).
Excellent compilation map.

Tectonic Map of the United States, 2nd ed. (1958), Available from the Am. Assoc. Petrol. Geol., Tulsa, Okla.
Excellent compilation map.

Wilson, M. E. (1956), Early Precambrian Rocks of the Timiskaming Region, Quebec and Ontario, Canada, *Geol. Soc. Am.,* vol. 67, pp. 1397–1430.
Detailed discussion of Precambrian correlation problems in the southeastern portion of the Laurentian

shield. Discusses possible existence of the Grenville fault zone. Extensive bibliography. Contains a good compilation map of northwestern Quebec.

Wilson, J. T. (1948), Some Aspects of Geophysics in Canada with Special Reference to Structural Research in the Canadian Shield, pt. 2, An Approach to the Structure of the Canadian Shield, *Am. Geophy. Union,* Trans., vol. 29, pp. 691–762.

Comprehensive review of structural aspects.

Wilson, J. T. (1949), Some Major Structures of the Canadian Shield, *Bull. Can. Inst. Min. Met.,* pp. 543–554.

Stimulating discussion of tectonic problems, extensive bibliography.

Wilson, J. T. (1954), The Development and Structure of the Earth's Crust, chap. 4 in G. P. Kuiper (ed.), *The Earth as a Planet,* University of Chicago Press.

Comprehensive review of major structural aspects. Extensive bibliography.

PROBLEM 41

TECTONIC ANALYSIS OF THE YELLOWKNIFE DISTRICT, N. W. T., CANADA

Data Provided: The Yellowknife district, located in the Northwest Territories of Canada, on the north shore of Great Slave Lake, is one of the most interesting structural regions in North America. The broad tectonic setting for the Northwest Territories is shown in Figure 324. Note the large faults. The relationship of these lineaments to other major faults of North America is shown in Figure 311, page 244. Figure 325 is a regional map of the Yellowknife district, whereas Figure 326 is a semidetailed map of the Yellowknife Greenstone belt. Finally, Figures 327 and 328 are very detailed maps of the area near and south of the Con mine. Thus it is possible to see the structural geology at all scales of magnitude. This is very important, as some structures become apparent only at the appropriate scale. This "focusing-down" process allows the geologist to see both the forest and the trees at the same time.

The oldest rocks in the region are Archean volcanic flows and sediments of the Archean Yellowknife group (Keewatin? equivalent). The volcanic flows in general underlie the more widespread sediments. In the Yellowknife Bay area an erosional unconformity separates the sediments from the volcanics. In other areas the contact is gradational in some cases.

The rocks of the Yellowknife group have undergone at least two periods of folding. Each period of folding was accompanied by intrusive activity. The older intrusions are granodioritic and larger in size than the younger pegmatitic muscovite granite (Fig. 325). Early Proterozoic rocks of the Snare group (other names used away from the Yellowknife district) unconformably overlie the Yellowknife group and Archean granodiorite and are intruded by the younger Proterozoic pegmatitic muscovite granite. The Snare group is not shown on Figures 325–328.

The sedimentary rocks of the Yellowknife group lie in tight isoclinal folds and have been altered to knotted quartz mica schist over large areas by the intrusive activity. The volcanic rocks of the Yellowknife group are not as tightly folded as the sedimentary portion of the group. The axial trend of the folds is generally northeast but diverges considerably in some areas. This primary fold trend is apparent on all scales of magnitude (Figs. 324, 325, 326, 327). The younger pegmatitic muscovite granites were accompanied by cross-folding and a younger cleavage development (Fig. 325). Note the alignment of the younger intrusions. Both the cross-folding direction and the alignment of the intrusions may be related to faulting as indicated later.

There have been at least two periods of major faulting in the area and several periods of minor faulting. The minor faults appear to be closely related to the major faulting, and each period of minor faulting probably followed the major fault movement to which it is related. Most writers describe the major faults as prediabase or postdiabase. The diabase dikes cut both the Snare group and younger pegmatitic muscovite granites, and they may be of the same age as the Keeweenawan diabase dikes of the Larder Lake-Malartic area (Fig. 321, p. 257). Plate 13 shows several large diabase dikes (dark gray) cutting the younger granite (light gray). The younger granite in turn is intrusive into quartz mica schist (dark gray) in this area. The diabase dikes form two sets, one striking northwest, the other striking northeast. Both dip steeply. The northwest set is more common. A few of the diabase dikes follow the fractures of the late faulting. In these cases the late faults are not postdiabase. The largest faults of this region may have acted as lines of weakness from early Precambrian time and this possibility should be considered in analyzing the area.

Most of the early prediabase faults are of the shear-zone type, with chlorite schist or chlorite-sericite schist developed along them in widths ranging from a few inches to sev-

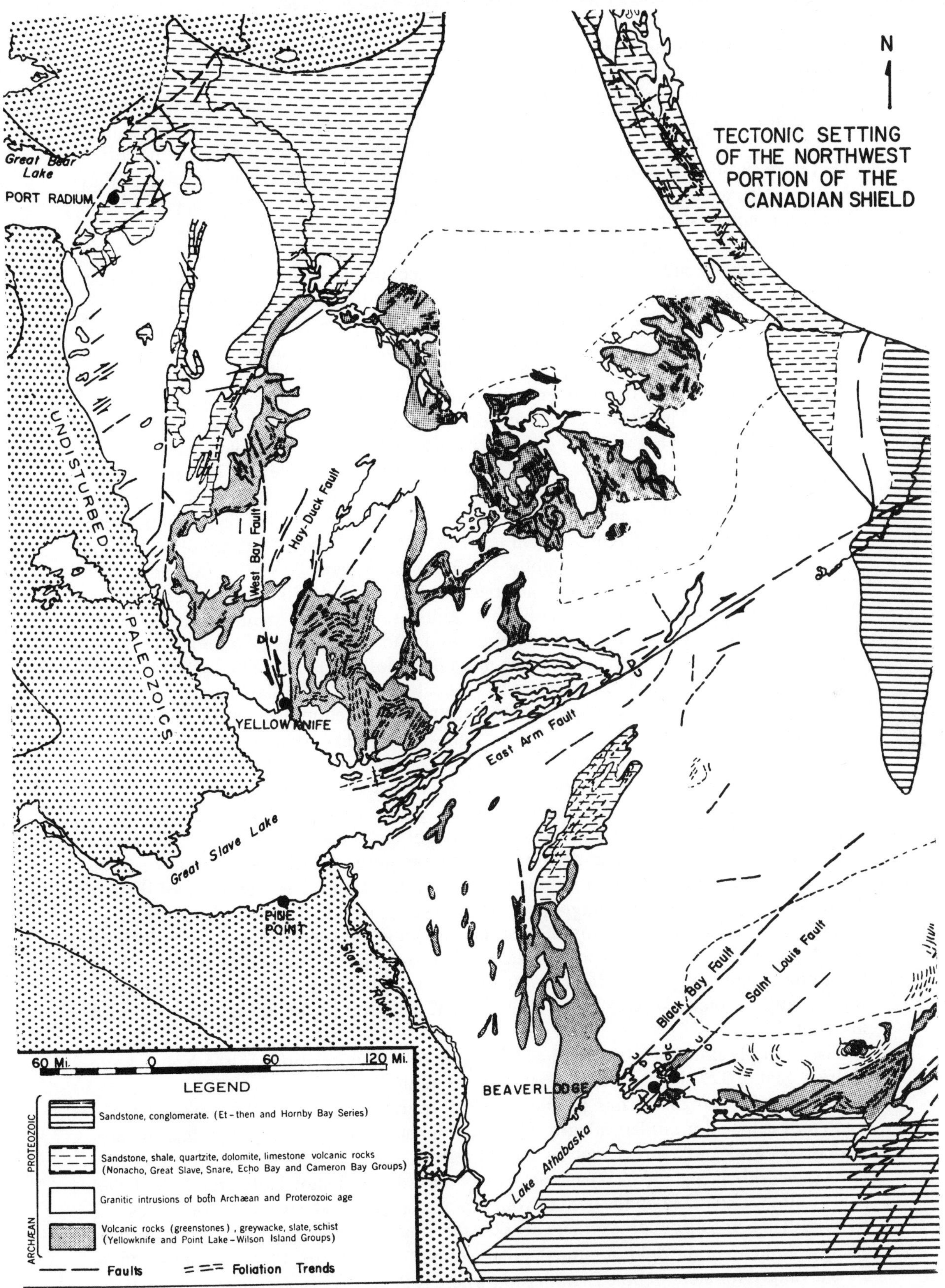

N
TECTONIC SETTING
OF THE NORTHWEST
PORTION OF THE
CANADIAN SHIELD
Great Bear Lake
PORT RADIUM
UNDISTURBED
PALEOZOICS
West Bay Fault
Hay-Duck Fault
YELLOWKNIFE
East Arm Fault
Great Slave Lake
PINE POINT
Slave River
Black Bay Fault
Saint Louis Fault
BEAVERLODGE
Lake Athabaska
60 Mi. 0 60 120 Mi.
LEGEND
PROTEOZOIC
Sandstone, conglomerate. (Et-then and Hornby Bay Series)
Sandstone, shale, quartzite, dolomite, limestone volcanic rocks (Nonacho, Great Slave, Snare, Echo Bay and Cameron Bay Groups)
Granitic intrusions of both Archæan and Proterozoic age
ARCHÆAN
Volcanic rocks (greenstones), greywacke, slate, schist (Yellowknife and Point Lake-Wilson Island Groups)
Faults
Foliation Trends

FIGURE 324. (Modified from the Tectonic Map of Canada [1950], Geol. Assoc. Can.)

eral hundred feet. Some of the early shear-zone type of faults parallel the regional strike (i.e., parallel to bedding and fold axes). These may be seen on Figures 327 and 328. These are suggestive of an original thrust-fault nature. Other prediabase shear zones trend north-northeast for the most part (Figs. 326, 327, and 328), and some of these are left-handed strike-slip faults. They appear to be younger than the shears parallel to the regional strike. There are thousands of metagabbro dikes older than the north-northeast shears (Figs. 327 and 328) which also trend generally north-northeast. This direction appears to have been a pronounced line of weakness for some time before faulting occurred.

The most important mineral deposits in the area are gold deposits associated with the north-northeast trending shear zones which transect the flows of the Yellowknife group. The gold deposits occur either in well-defined quartz veins introduced along narrow shear zones, such as on the Negus and Rycon properties, or in large lenticular masses of highly mineralized sericite schist and vein quartz that occur along large shear zones or systems of shear zones up to several hundred feet wide. The large Con and Giant ore deposits are of this type. Small gold deposits occur in shear zones parallel to the regional trend of the volcanics. The Thompson-Lundmark deposit (Fig. 325) is of this type. Gold-bearing quartz bodies associated with the crests, troughs, or axial planes of folds occur in some places, as at the Camlaren mine (Fig. 325) where there is a saddle reef occurrence.

The postdiabase faults are of several orders of magnitude. The largest of these faults are the Kam, West Bay, and Hay-Duck faults which have had left-handed strike-slip movement measured in the order of miles (Fig. 326). Associated with these faults, and dependent upon them, are the slightly smaller Pud, Martin, Townsite, Akaitcho, and Madeline faults. These are also characterized by left-handed strike-slip movement (Fig. 326). Subsidiary to these larger postdiabase faults are numerous small strike-slip faults, which are best developed between the Kam and Pud faults (Figs. 326 and 327). These smaller faults are concentrated in three main directions: (1) 330°–340°, (2) 280°–290°, (3) 050°–060°. All of the faults are nearly vertical. Most of them have strike-slip movement. The 050°–060° set have quite consistent right-handed movement (Fig. 327). The movement on the 280°–290° set is usually right-handed also, whereas the 330°–340° set is left-handed mainly. The latter set is almost parallel to the strike direction of the Akaitcho and Pud faults. The 280°–290° set is more open than the other two sets, and was probably tensional in origin originally, although showing some later strike-slip movement. The postdiabase faults are commonly straight narrow fissures. The rock within the fault zones is brecciated and gouged but schistose material is lacking. Rusty ferruginous carbonate and hematite commonly occur in the fault zones. The wallrocks of the late fault zones rarely show any dragging. The late faults are seldom mineralized, although giant quartz veins occur in many of postdiabase faults between Great Slave and Great Bear Lake. Strike-slip movement has occurred on some of the faults now filled by these giant quartz veins (Fig. 324). Right-handed strike-slip movement has also been suggested for the faults of the East Arm Trend (Jolliffe, 1952), but this region has not been mapped in detail.

The multiple faulting has caused complicated offsetting relations in the Yellowknife district. Figure 329 shows a simplification of the faulting.

Determine: The length of this problem is flexible depending upon the time available. Each part can be done independently. (1) Study the maps and geological information presented and work out a stress analysis for the region along the lines evolved for the Colorado mineral belt (pp. 247–252). (2) Select key areas in the Yellowknife area for detailed study and examine them in the light of your regional analysis. The list of references should be helpful in pointing out areas where detailed information is available. Does your regional analysis hold up in the light of more detailed studies? (3) Examine Plates 13 and 14. Plate 14 is arranged for stereoscopic examination whereas Plate 13 is an air photo mosaic of the

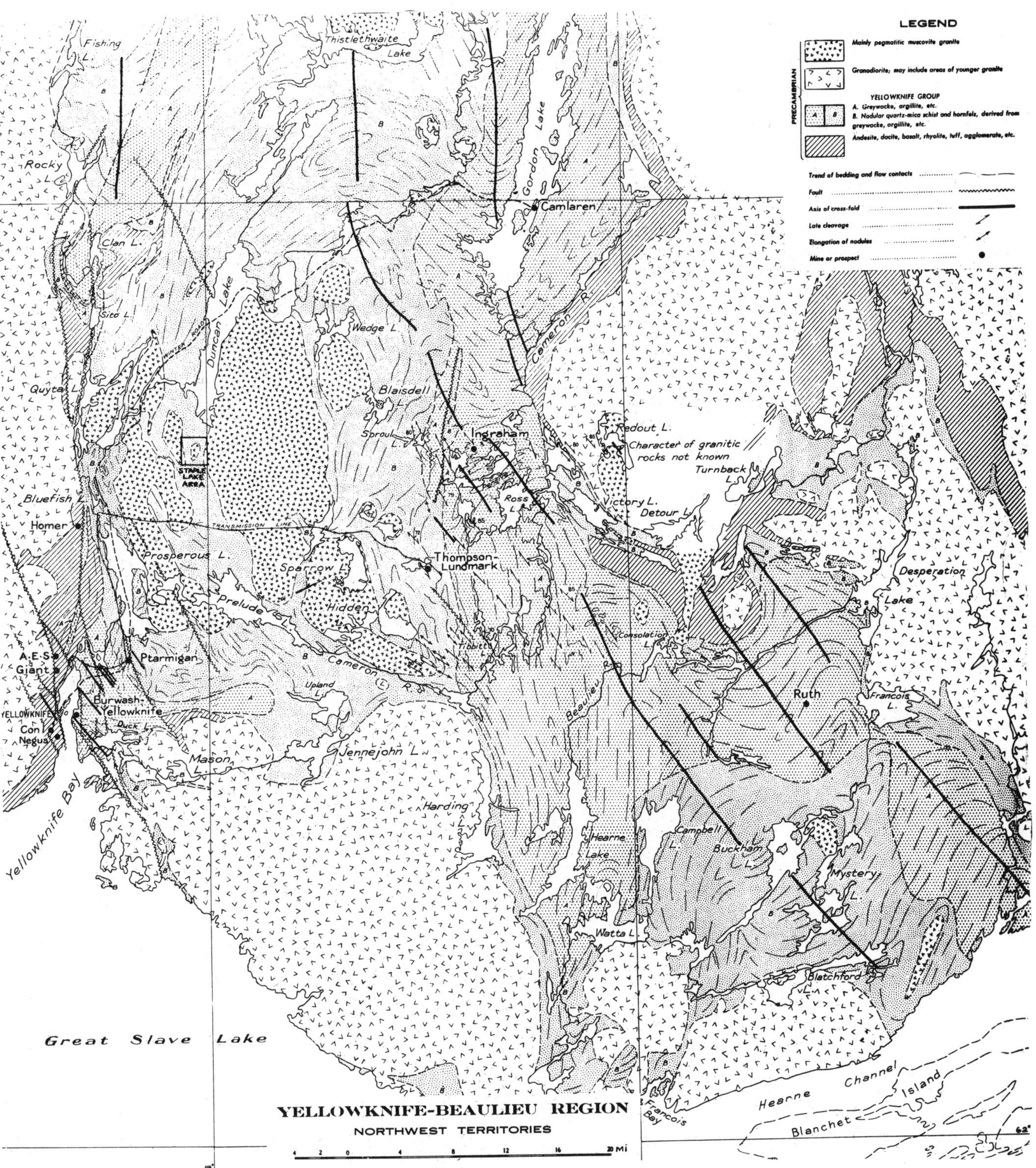

FIGURE 325. Note the relationship between intrusions, cross folds, and late cleavage. (From Y. O. Forteir [1946], *Geol. Surv. Can.*, Prel. Map 46–23.)

area. The location of these air photographs is shown on Figure 325. The area covered by the photographs is the Staple Lake area which lies 2 to 3 miles northeast of the main Prosperous Lake late intrusion of pegmatitic muscovite granite. A small stock (light gray) of this granite is intrusive into quartz mica schist of the Yellowknife group (medium gray). Both the stock and country rock are cut by diabase dikes (dark gray) and faults. Study the photos stereoscopically (Plate 14) and map all aspects of the structural fabric, recording your findings on a sheet of acetate overlay placed over Plate 13. What are the relations between the stock and the country rock (discordant or concordant)? Do the dikes follow pre-existing lines of weakness? Is there any relationship between the pegmatitic dikes (light gray) and the regional foliation? This is the type of thing to look for. Integrate all of your findings in a concise report. (4) Plates 15 and 16 are air photographs showing some of the structural features on the west side of Yellowknife Bay. Map as many of the structural features as you can on these photos, recording your results on acetate or tracing paper overlays. Analyze the results and review them by means of a concise report.

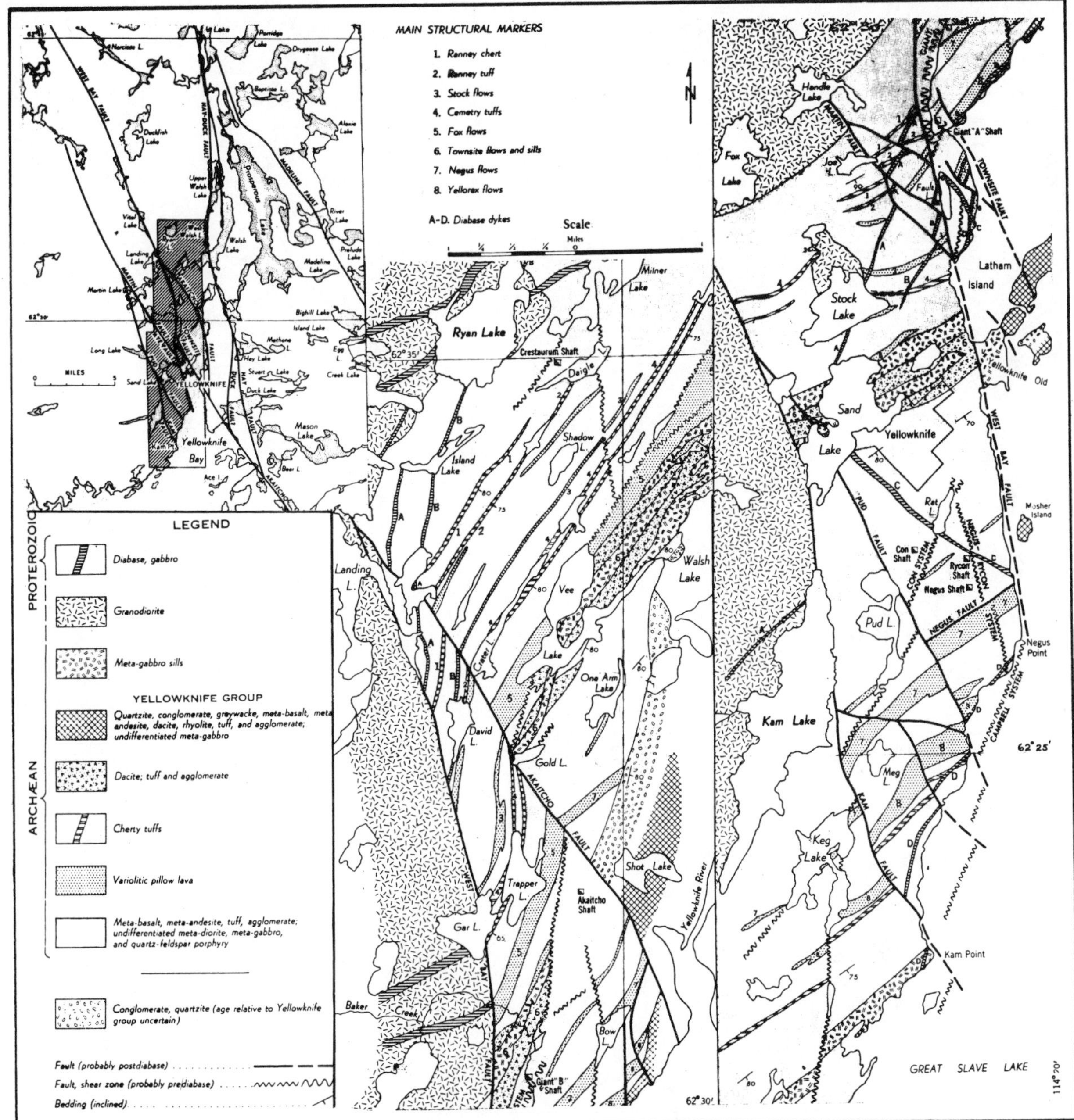

FIGURE 326. Tectonic setting of the Yellowknife Greenstone belt. The map at the right is situated south of the map in the center of the diagram. The relations of the two maps are shown on the index map at the left. (From J. F. Henderson and I. C. Brown [1950], *Geol. Surv. Can.*, Prel. Paper 52-28.)

FIGURE 327 (p. 268). Detailed geologic map of the area near the Con mine, west side of Yellowknife Bay, N.W.T., Canada. (From J. F. Henderson and I. C. Brown [1948], *Geol. Surv. Can.*)

FIGURE 328 (p. 269). Detailed geologic map of the area south of Figure 327. On west side of Yellowknife Bay. The position of Kam Point is indicated on Figure 326 also. (From J. F. Henderson and I. C. Brown [1948], *Geol. Surv., Can.*)

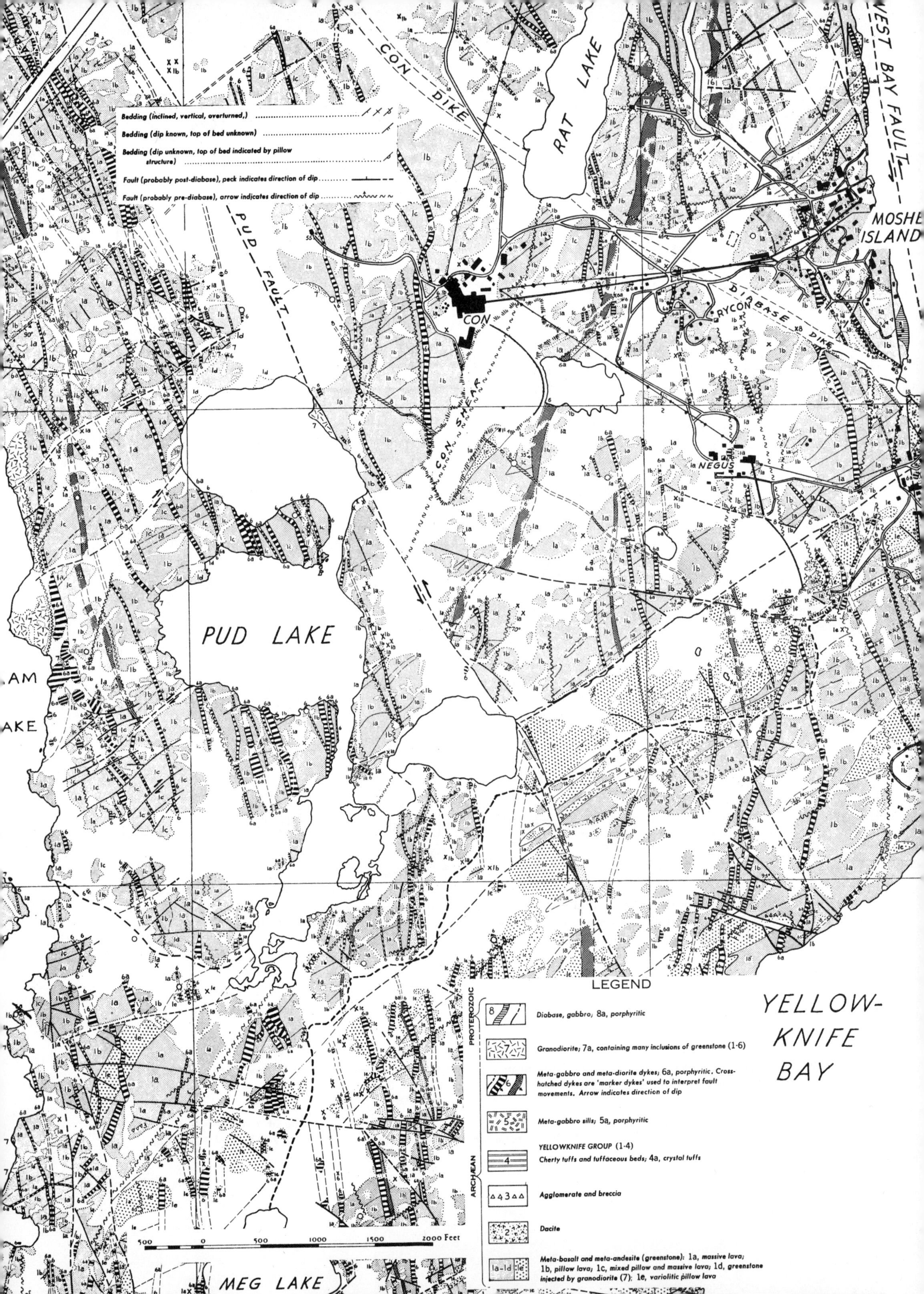

Bedding (inclined, vertical, overturned,)
Bedding (dip known, top of bed unknown)
Bedding (dip unknown, top of bed indicated by pillow structure)
Fault (probably post-diabase), peck indicates direction of dip
Fault (probably pre-diabase), arrow indicates direction of dip
CON DIKE
RAT LAKE
WEST BAY FAULT
MOSHER ISLAND
PUD FAULT
CON
RYCON
DIABASE DIKE
CON SHEAR
NEGUS
PUD LAKE
AM
AKE
LEGEND
PROTEROZOIC
Diabase, gabbro; 8a, porphyritic
Granodiorite; 7a, containing many inclusions of greenstone (1-6)
Meta-gabbro and meta-diorite dykes; 6a, porphyritic. Cross-hatched dykes are 'marker dykes' used to interpret fault movements. Arrow indicates direction of dip
Meta-gabbro sills; 5a, porphyritic
ARCHEAN
YELLOWKNIFE GROUP (1-4)
Cherty tuffs and tuffaceous beds; 4a, crystal tuffs
Agglomerate and breccia
Dacite
Meta-basalt and meta-andesite (greenstone): 1a, massive lava; 1b, pillow lava; 1c, mixed pillow and massive lava; 1d, greenstone injected by granodiorite (7); 1e, variolitic pillow lava
YELLOW-KNIFE BAY
500 0 500 1000 1500 2000 Feet
MEG LAKE

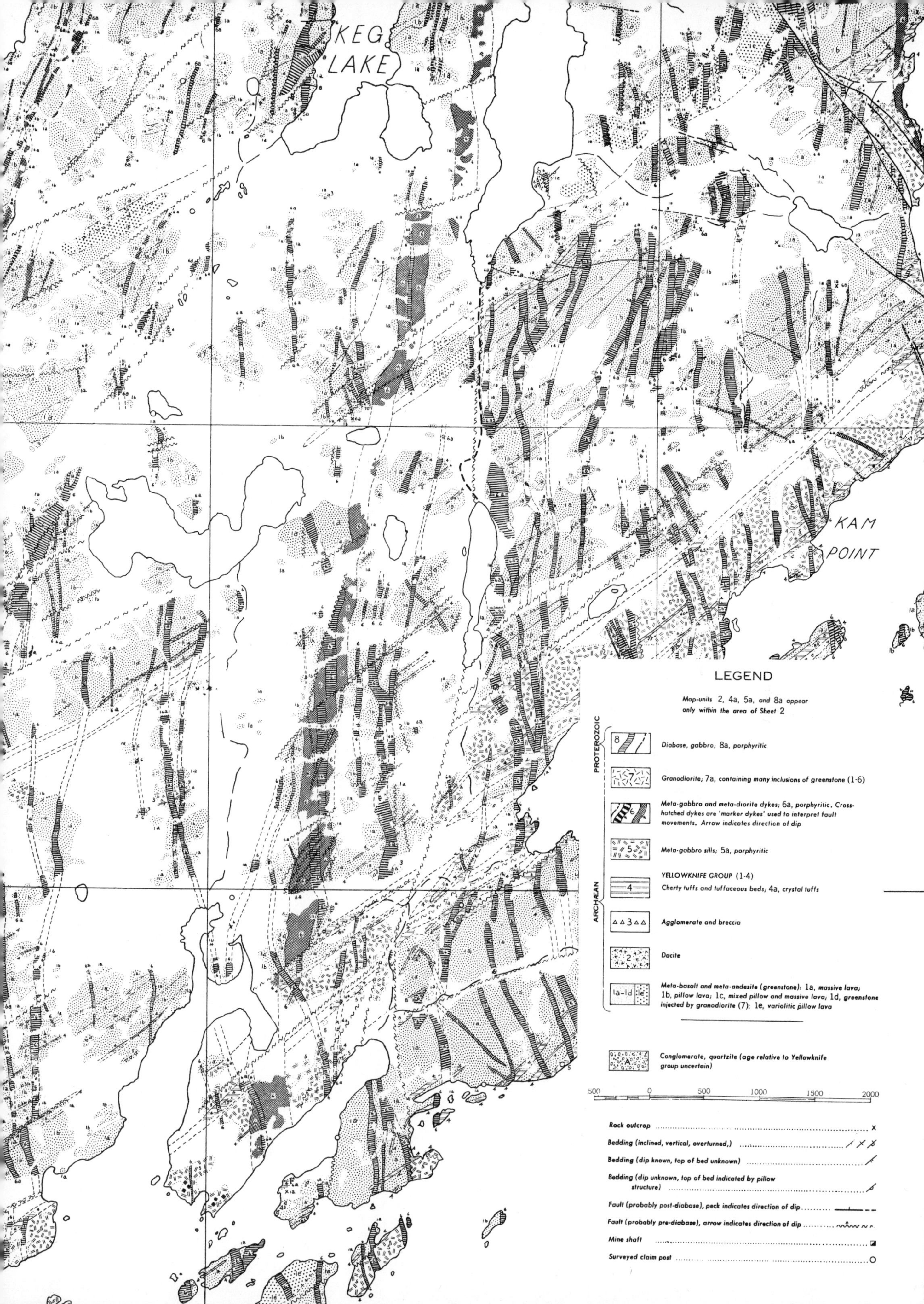
KEG
LAKE
KAM
POINT
LEGEND
Map-units 2, 4a, 5a, and 8a appear only within the area of Sheet 2
PROTEROZOIC
8 Diabase, gabbro, 8a, porphyritic
7 Granodiorite; 7a, containing many inclusions of greenstone (1-6)
6 Meta-gabbro and meta-diorite dykes; 6a, porphyritic. Cross-hatched dykes are 'marker dykes' used to interpret fault movements. Arrow indicates direction of dip
5 Meta-gabbro sills; 5a, porphyritic
ARCHÆAN
YELLOWKNIFE GROUP (1-4)
4 Cherty tuffs and tuffaceous beds; 4a, crystal tuffs
3 Agglomerate and breccia
2 Dacite
1a-1d 1e Meta-basalt and meta-andesite (greenstone): 1a, massive lava; 1b, pillow lava; 1c, mixed pillow and massive lava; 1d, greenstone injected by granodiorite (7); 1e, variolitic pillow lava
A Conglomerate, quartzite (age relative to Yellowknife group uncertain)
500 0 500 1000 1500 2000
Rock outcrop
Bedding (inclined, vertical, overturned,)
Bedding (dip known, top of bed unknown)
Bedding (dip unknown, top of bed indicated by pillow structure)
Fault (probably post-diabase), peck indicates direction of dip
Fault (probably pre-diabase), arrow indicates direction of dip
Mine shaft
Surveyed claim post

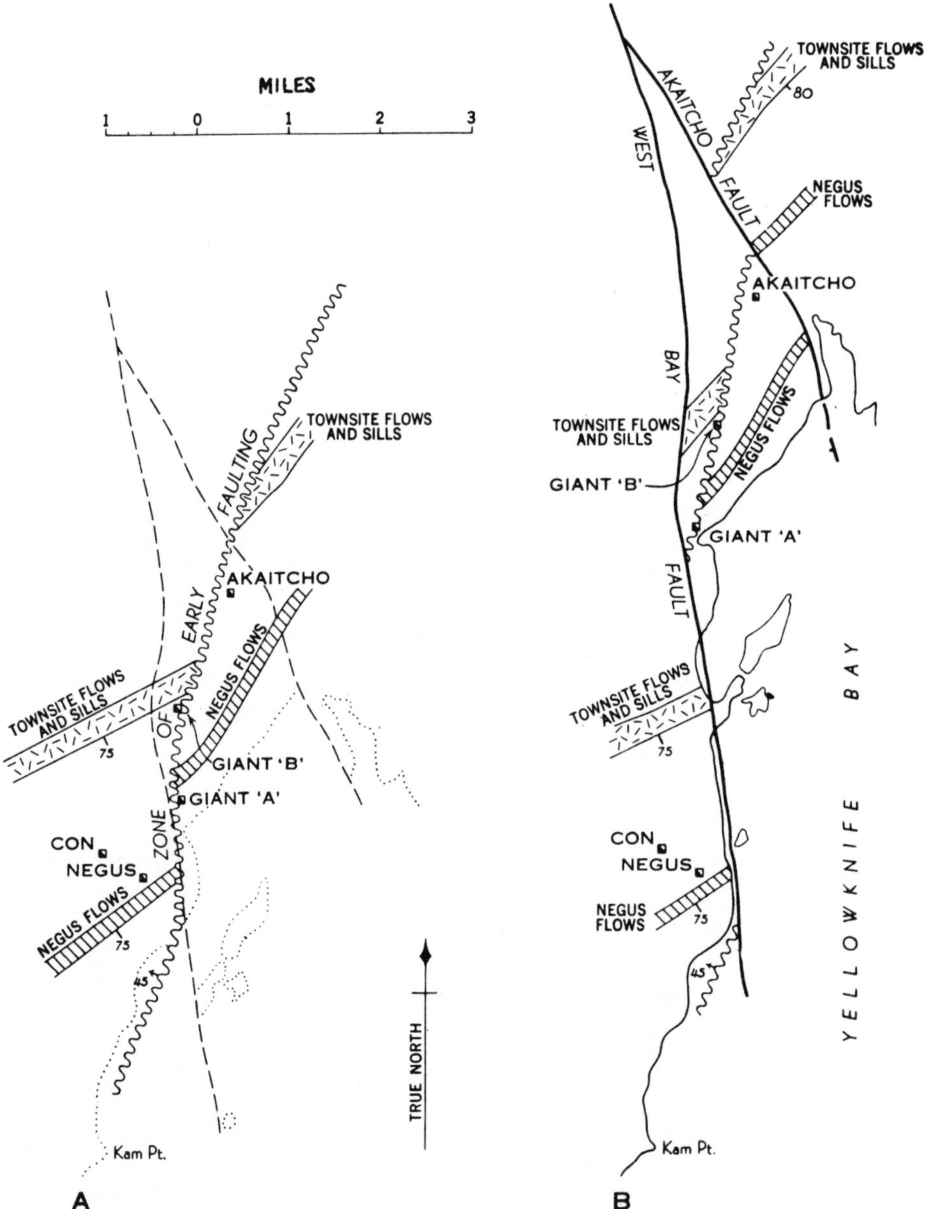

FIGURE 329. Illustrating the relationship between early and late faulting in the Yellowknife area, N.W.T., Canada. (From J. F. Henderson and I. C. Brown [1952], *Geol. Surv. Can.*, Prel. Paper 52–28.)

References for the Yellowknife Area, N.W.T.

Brown, I. C. (1953), Late Faults in the Yellowknife area, Canada (Abstract), *Bull. Geol. Soc. Am.*, vol. 64, p. 1401.

Brown, I. C. (1955), Late Faults in the Yellowknife area, *Proc. Geol. Assoc. Can.*, vol. 7, pp. 123–138.

Campbell, N. (1948), West Bay Fault, *Structural Geology of Canadian Ore Deposits,* Can. Inst. Min. Met. Symposium Volume, pp. 244–259.

Can. Inst. Min. Met. Jubilee Volume, *Structural Geology of Canadian Ore Deposits* (1948), pp. 238–283.

Dadson, A. S., and Bateman, J. D. (1948), Giant Yellowknife Mine, *Structural Geology of Canadian Ore Deposits,* Can. Inst. Min. Met., Symposium Volume, pp. 273–283.

Fortier, Y. O. (1946), Yellowknife-Beaulieu Region, Northwest Territories, *Geol. Surv. Can.*, Prel. Map No. 46–23

Fortier, Y. O. (1947), Ross Lake, Northwest Territories, *Geol. Surv. Can.,* Paper 47–16.

Fortier, Y. O. (1949), Indin Lake Map-area (East Half), *Geol. Surv. Can.,* Paper 49–10.

Henderson, J. F. (1943), Structure and Metamorphism of Early Precambrian rocks between Gordon and Great Slave Lakes, N.W.T., *Am. Jour. Sci.,* vol. 241, pp. 430–446.

Henderson, J. F. (1950), Structure of the Yellowknife Greenstone Belt, N.W.T., *Can. Inst. Min. Met.,* Trans., vol. 53, pp. 427–434.

Henderson, J. F., and Brown, I. C. (1948), Yellowknife, Northwest Territories, *Geol. Surv. Can.,* Paper 48–17 (Sheets 1 and 2), Paper 49–26 (Sheet 3), Paper 50–34 (Sheet 4), Paper 52–24 (Sheet 5).

Henderson, J. F., and Brown, I. C. (1952), The Yellowknife Greenstone Belt, *Geol. Surv. Can.,* Prel. Paper 52–28.

Henderson, J. F., and Jolliffe, A. W. (1939), Relation of Gold Deposits to Structure, Yellowknife and Gordon Lake areas, N.W.T., *Can. Inst. Min. Met.,* Trans., vol. 42, pp. 314–336.

Jolliffe, A. W. (1942), Structures in the Canadian Shield, *Am. Geophy. Union,* Trans., 23rd Annual Meeting, Pt. II, pp. 699–707.

Jolliffe, A. W. (1942), Yellowknife Bay area, *Geol. Surv. Can.,* Map 709A.

Jolliffe, A. W. (1945), Yellowknife Faults and Orebodies, *The Precambrian,* vol. 18, no. 5, pp. 6–11.

Jolliffe, A. W. (1946), Prosperous Lake area, *Geol. Surv. Can.,* Map 868A.

Jolliffe, A. W. (1952), The Northwestern Part of the Canadian Shield, *Internat. Geol. Cong.,* 18th Session (Great Britain), Rept., Pt. 13, pp. 141–149.

Lord, C. S. (1951), Mineral Industry of District of Mackenzie, N.W.T., *Geol. Surv. Can.,* Mem. 261.

Lord, C. S. (1953), Geological Notes on Southern District of Keewatin, Northwest Territories, *Geol. Surv. Can.,* Paper 53–22.

McKinstry, H. E. (1953), Shears of the Second Order, *Am. Jour. Sci.,* vol. 251, pp. 401–414.

Moody, J. D., and Hill, M. J. (1956), Wrench Fault Tectonics, *Bull. Geol. Soc. Am.,* vol. 67, pp. 1207–1246.

Rowe, R. B. (1952), Pegmatitic Mineral Deposits of the Yellowknife-Beaulieu Region, District of Mackenzie, N.W.T., *Geol. Surv. Can.,* Paper 52–8.

Stanton, M. S., Tremblay, L. P., and Yardley, D. H. (1948), Chalco Lake, Northwest Territories, *Geol. Surv. Can.,* Paper 48–20.

Tremblay, L. P. (1948), Ranji Lake Map-area, Northwest Territories, *Geol. Surv. Can.,* Paper 48–10.

Wilson, J. T. (1941), Structural Features in the Northwest Territories, *Am. Jour. Sci.,* vol. 239, pp. 493–502.

Wilson, J. T. (1948), Some Aspects of Geophysics in Canada with Special Reference to Structural Research in the Canadian Shield, *Am. Geophy. Union,* Trans., vol. 29, pp. 691–726.

Wilson, J. T. (1949), Some Major Structures of the Canadian Shield, *Can. Inst. Min. Met.,* Trans., vol. 52, pp. 231–242.

Wright, G. M. (1950), Ghost Lake map-area, Northwest Territories, *Geol. Surv. Can.,* Paper 50–13.

Yardley, D. H. (1949), Wecho River (East Half), Northwest Territories, *Geol. Surv. Can.,* Paper 49–14.

MOSAIC AND OVERLAPPING AIR PHOTOGRAPHS

PLATE 1. Air photograph mosaic (uncontrolled) of the Sherridon area, Northern Manitoba, Canada. (Air photographs of the Royal Canadian Air Force.)

PLATE 2. Air photograph mosaic (uncontrolled) of the Circle Ridge anticline, Fremont County, Wyoming. (Air photographs of the United States Geological Survey.)

PLATE 3. Overlapping air photographs arranged for viewing stereoscopically. Circle Ridge anticline, Fremont County, Wyoming. (Air photographs of the United States Geological Survey.)

PLATE 4. Overlapping air photographs arranged for viewing stereoscopically. Circle Ridge anticline, Fremont County, Wyoming. (Air photographs of the United States Geological Survey.)

PLATE 5. Overlapping air photographs arranged for viewing stereoscopically. The Grenville dome, Carbon County, Wyoming. (Air photographs of the United States Geological Survey.)

PLATE 6. Overlapping air photographs arranged for viewing stereoscopically. West end of the Grenville dome, Carbon County, Wyoming. (Air photographs of Jack Ammann Photogrammetric Engineers, Inc.)

PLATE 7. Overlapping air photographs arranged for viewing stereoscopically. East end of the Grenville dome, Carbon County, Wyoming. (Air photographs of Jack Ammann Photogrammetric Engineers, Inc.)

PLATE 8. Overlapping air photographs arranged for viewing stereoscopically. Flin Flon area, Manitoba, Canada. (Air photographs of the Royal Canadian Air Force.)

PLATE 9. Air photograph mosaic (uncontrolled) of the Flin Flon mining area, Manitoba, Canada. (Air photographs of the Royal Canadian Air Force.)

PLATE 10. Overlapping air photographs arranged for viewing stereoscopically. An area north of the Circle Ridge anticline, Fremont County, Wyoming. To be used in determining attitude of bedding from air photograph observations. (Air photographs of the United States Geological Survey.)

PLATE 1

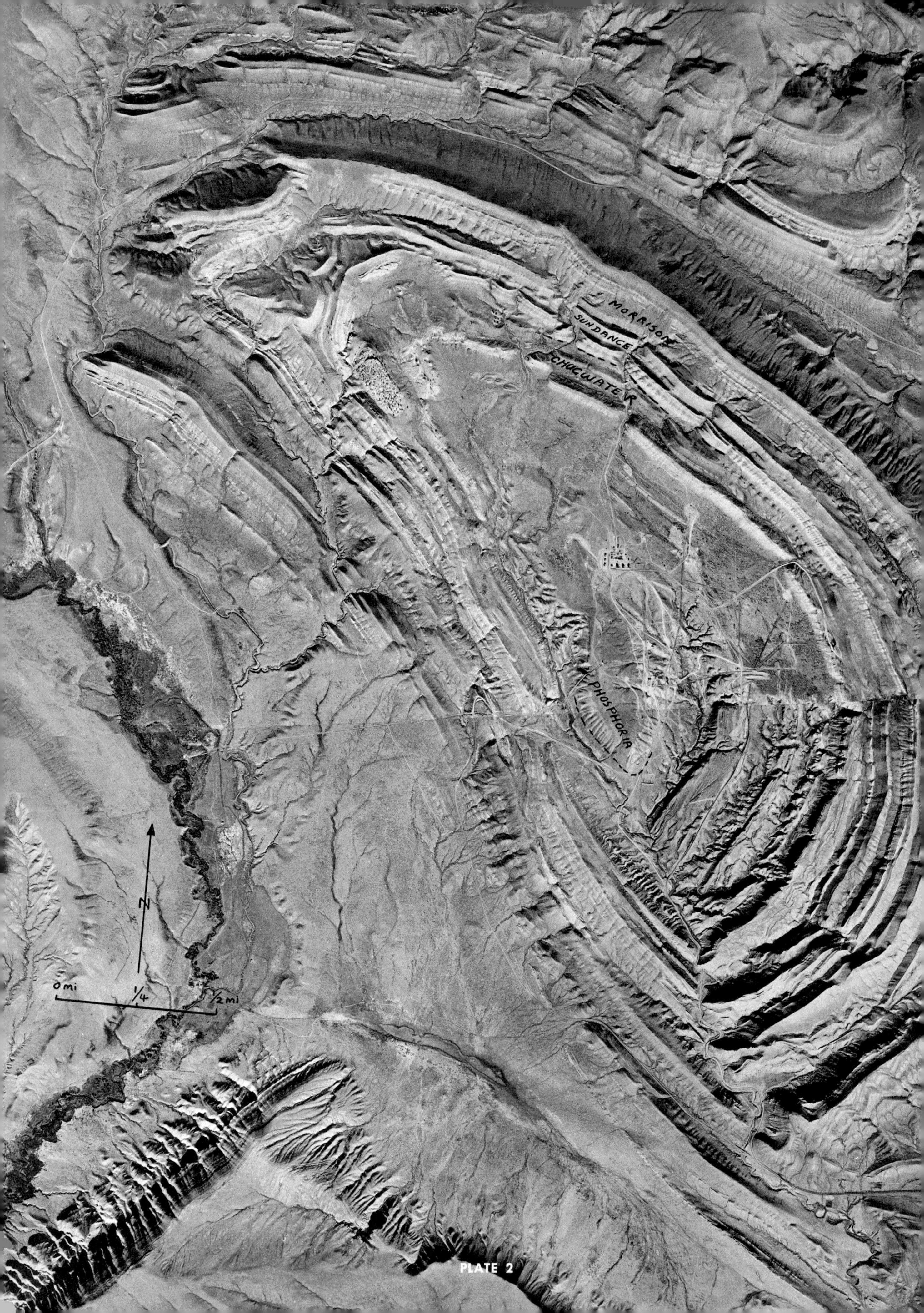

PLATE 2

PLATE 3

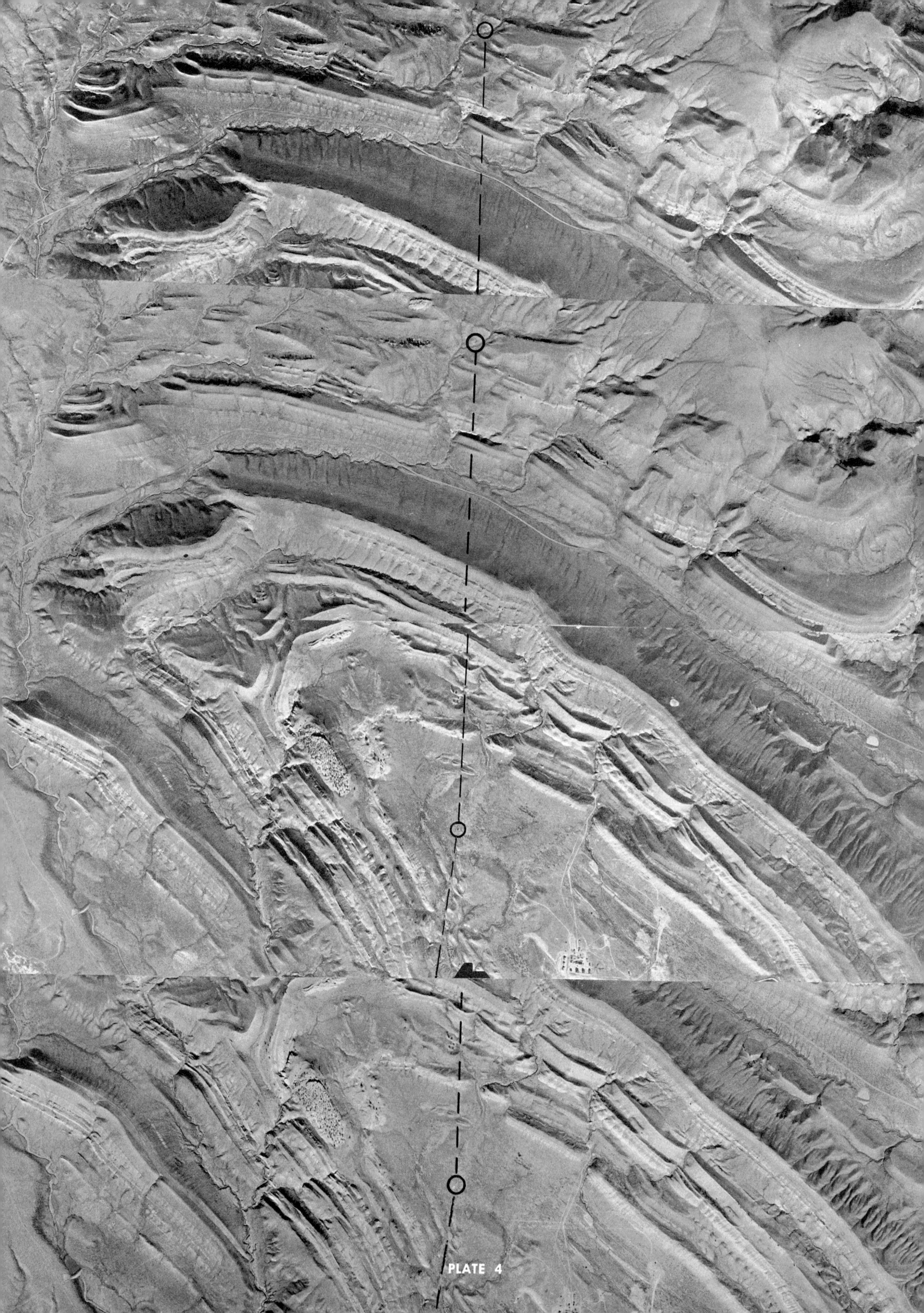

PLATE 4

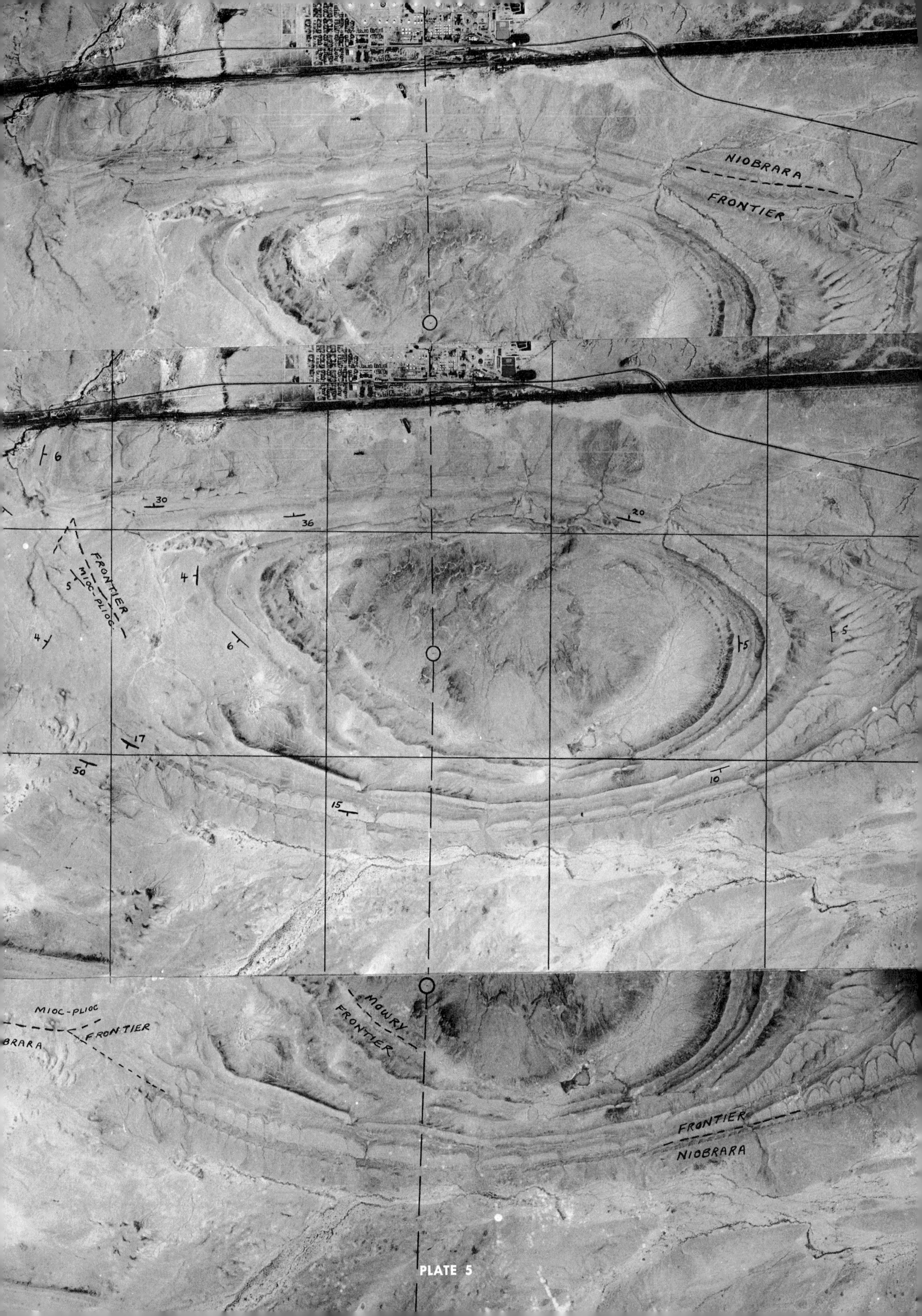
NIOBRARA
FRONTIER
6
30
36
20
FRONTIER
MIOC-PLIOC.
5
4
4
6
5
5
17
50
10
15
MIOC-PLIOC
FRONTIER
BRARA
MOWRY
FRONTIER
FRONTIER
NIOBRARA

PLATE 5

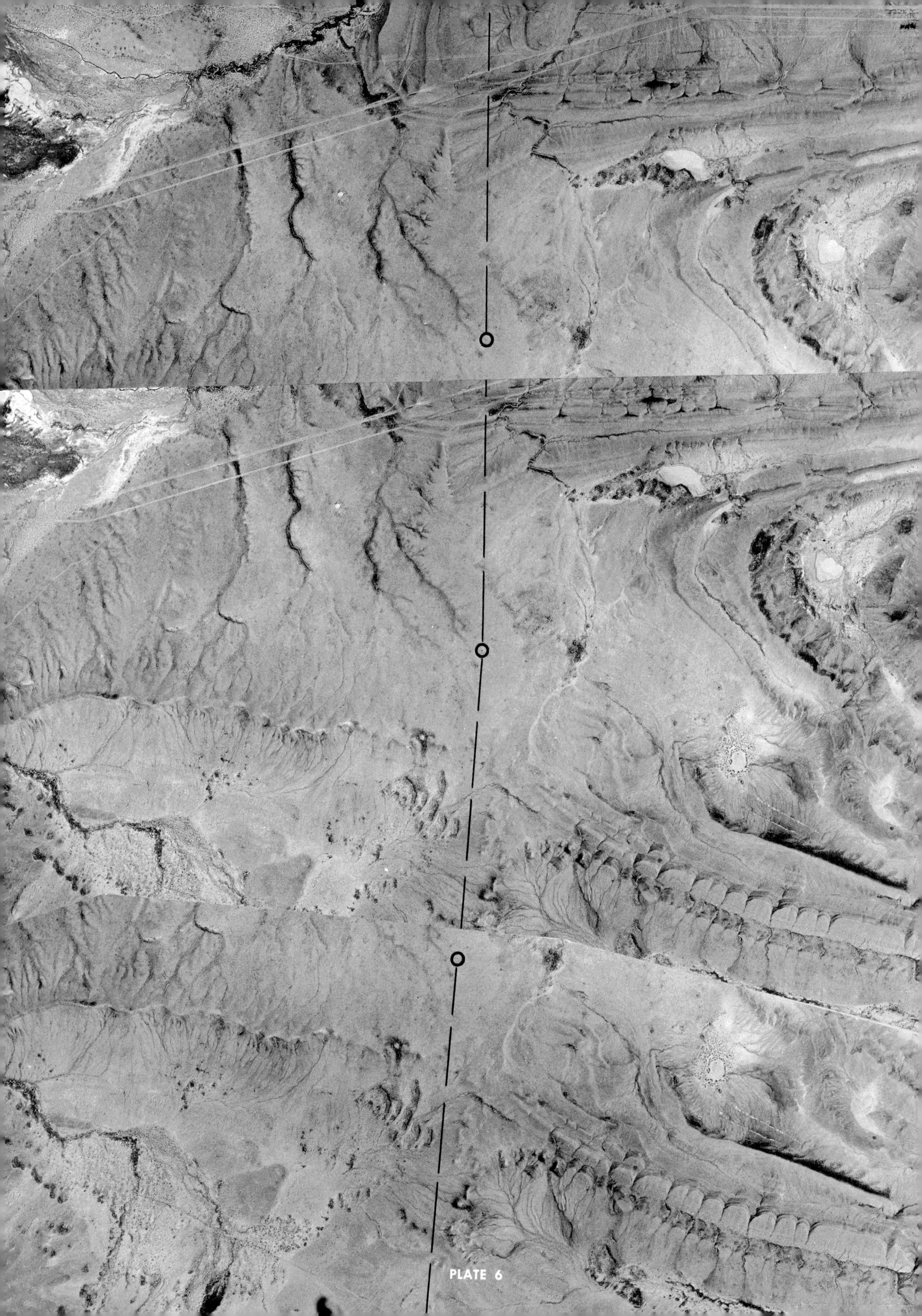

PLATE 6

PLATE 7

PLATE 8

PLATE 9

PLATE 10

MOSAIC AND OVERLAPPING AIR PHOTOGRAPHS *(Continued)*

PLATE 11. Air photograph mosaic (uncontrolled) of an area on the east flank of the Circle Cliffs uplift, Garfield County, Utah. The stream trending north-northwest on the right side of the mosaic is Halls Creek. (Air photographs of Jack Ammann Photogrammetric Engineers, Inc.)

PLATE 12. Overlapping air photographs arranged for viewing stereoscopically, covering a portion of the area shown in Plate 11. (Air photographs of Jack Ammann Photogrammetric Engineers, Inc.)

PLATE 13. Air photograph mosaic (uncontrolled) of the Staple Lake area, north of Yellowknife, N.W.T., Canada. For location see Figure 325. (Air photographs of the Royal Canadian Air Force.)

PLATE 14. Overlapping air photographs arranged for viewing stereoscopically. Staple Lake area, N.W.T., Canada. For location see Figure 325. (Air photographs of the Royal Canadian Air Force.)

PLATE 15. Air photograph mosaic (uncontrolled) of the Yellowknife area, N.W.T., Canada. (Air photographs of the Royal Canadian Air Force.)

PLATE 16. Overlapping air photographs arranged for viewing stereoscopically. The left-hand stereo pair covers the West Bay fault, north of the Giant A shaft area; the right-hand pair covers the area around the Con and Negus mines. (Air photographs of the Royal Canadian Air Force.)

PLATE 11

PLATE 12

PLATE 13

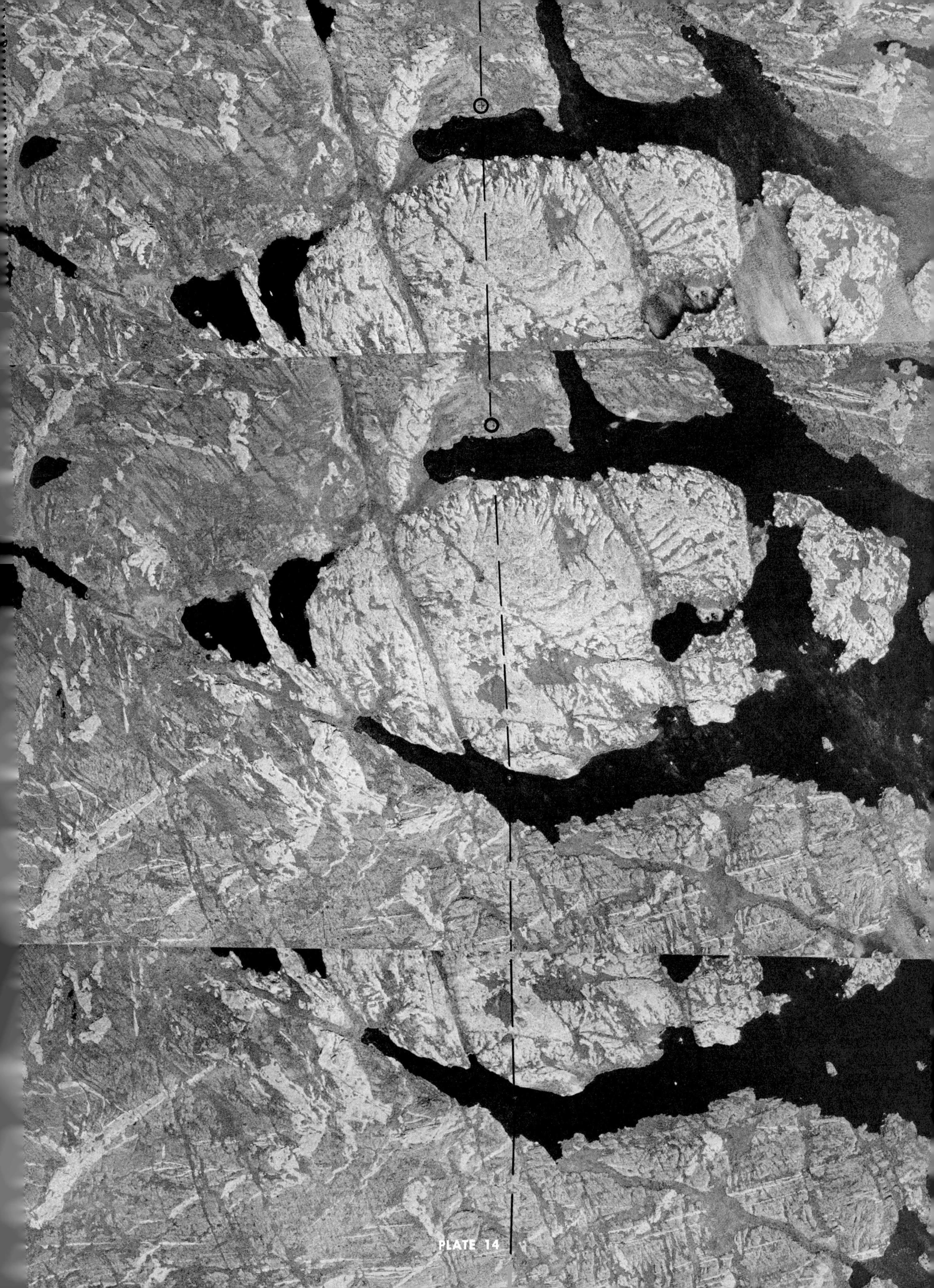

PLATE 14

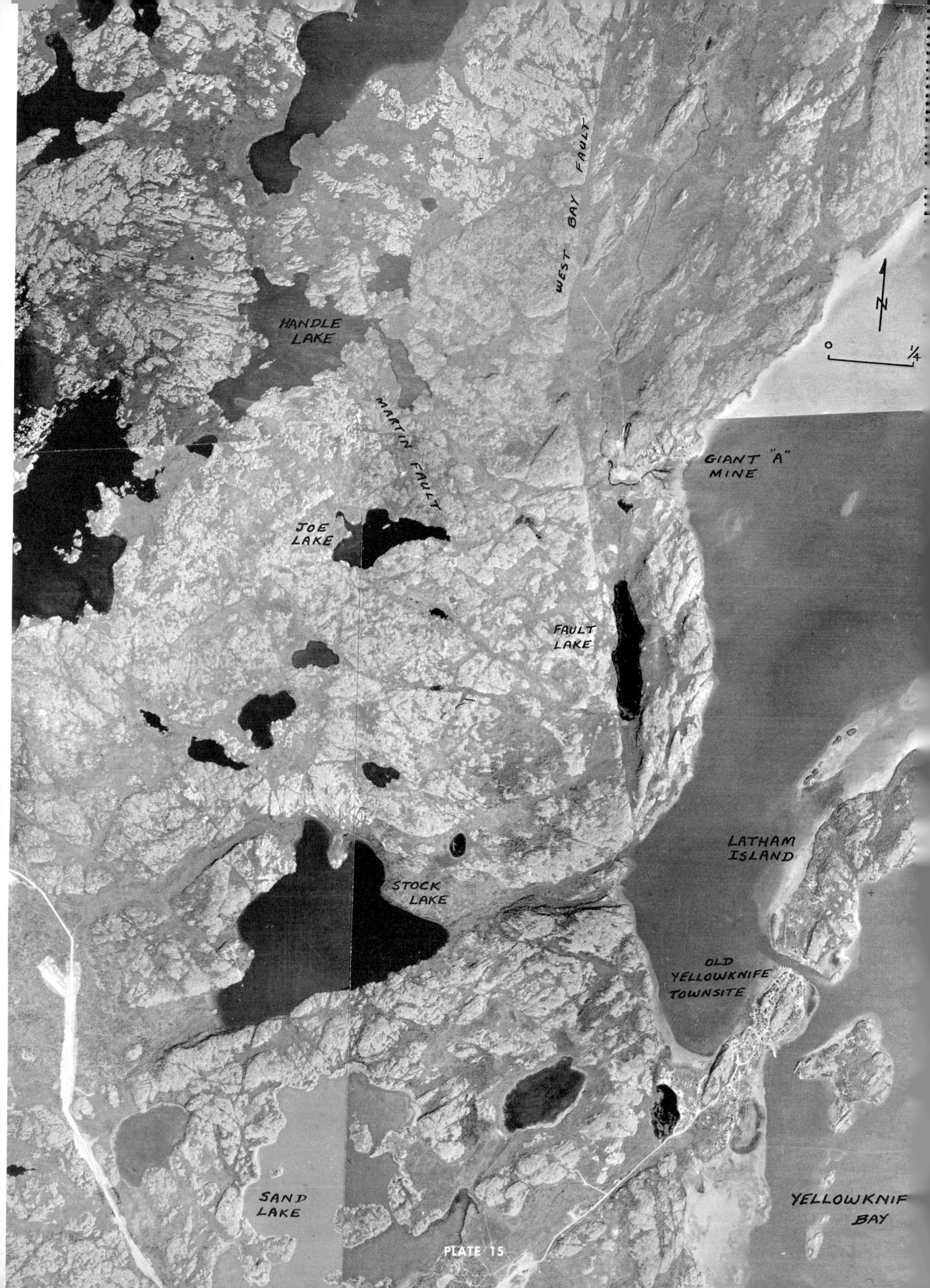
WEST BAY FAULT
HANDLE LAKE
MARTIN FAULT
GIANT "A" MINE
JOE LAKE
FAULT LAKE
LATHAM ISLAND
STOCK LAKE
OLD YELLOWKNIFE TOWNSITE
SAND LAKE
YELLOWKNIF BAY
0
1/4
N

PLATE 15

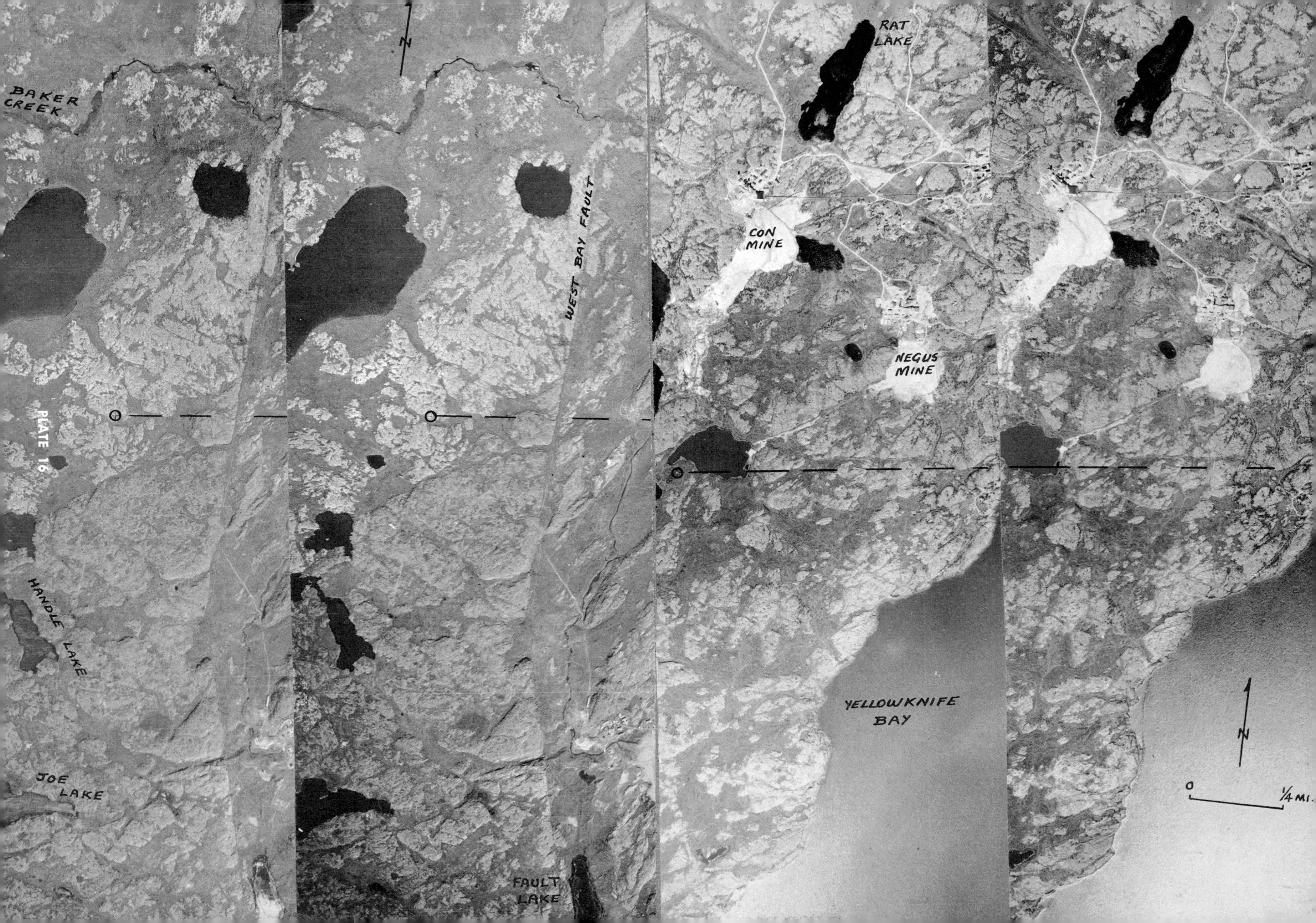

BAKER CREEK
N
WEST BAY FAULT
RAT LAKE
CON MINE
NEGUS MINE
HANDLE LAKE
JOE LAKE
FAULT LAKE
YELLOWKNIFE BAY
N
0
1/4 MI.

PLATE 16

Appendix

TABLE 18. Trigonometric Functions

Angle	Sin	Cos	Tan	Cot	Sec	Csc
0°00	0.000	1.0000	0.000	∞	1.000	∞
15	0.004	1.0000	0.004	229.18	1.000	229.18
30	0.009	0.9999	0.009	145.59	1.000	114.59
45	0.013	0.9999	0.013	76.39	1.0001	76.40
1 00	0.017	0.9998	0.017	57.29	1.0001	57.30
15	0.022	0.9997	0.022	45.83	1.0002	45.84
30	0.026	0.9996	0.026	38.19	1.0003	38.20
45	0.031	0.9995	0.031	32.73	1.0005	32.75
2 00	0.035	0.9994	0.035	28.64	1.0006	28.65
15	0.039	0.9992	0.039	25.45	1.0006	25.47
30	0.044	0.9990	0.044	22.90	1.0008	22.93
45	0.048	0.9988	0.048	20.82	1.0009	20.84
3 00	0.052	0.9986	0.052	19.08	1.0014	19.11
15	0.057	0.9984	0.057	17.61	1.0016	17.64
30	0.061	0.9981	0.061	16.35	1.0019	16.38
45	0.065	0.9979	0.066	15.26	1.0021	15.29
4 00	0.070	0.9976	0.070	14.30	1.0024	14.34
15	0.074	0.9972	0.074	13.46	1.0028	13.49
30	0.078	0.9969	0.079	12.71	1.0031	12.74
45	0.083	0.9966	0.083	12.03	1.0034	12.08
5°	0.087	0.996	0.087	11.43	1.004	11.47
6	0.105	0.995	0.105	9.514	1.006	9.567
7	0.122	0.993	0.123	8.144	1.008	8.206
8	0.139	0.990	0.141	7.115	1.010	7.185
9	0.156	0.988	0.158	6.314	1.012	6.392
10°	0.174	0.985	0.176	5.671	1.015	5.759
11	0.191	0.982	0.194	5.145	1.019	5.241
12	0.208	0.978	0.213	4.705	1.022	4.810
13	0.225	0.974	0.231	4.331	1.026	4.445
14	0.242	0.970	0.249	4.011	1.031	4.134
15°	0.259	0.966	0.268	3.732	1.035	3.864
16	0.276	0.961	0.287	3.487	1.040	3.628
17	0.292	0.956	0.306	3.271	1.046	3.420
18	0.309	0.951	0.325	3.078	1.051	3.236
19	0.326	0.946	0.344	2.904	1.058	3.072
20°	0.342	0.940	0.364	2.747	1.064	2.924
21	0.358	0.934	0.384	2.605	1.071	2.790
22	0.375	0.927	0.404	2.475	1.079	2.669
23	0.391	0.921	0.424	2.356	1.086	2.559
24	0.407	0.914	0.445	2.246	1.095	2.459
25°	0.423	0.906	0.466	2.145	1.103	2.366
26	0.438	0.899	0.488	2.050	1.113	2.281
27	0.454	0.891	0.510	1.963	1.122	2.203

TABLE 18 (*Continued*).

Angle	Sin	Cos	Tan	Cot	Sec	Csc
28	0.469	0.883	0.532	1.881	1.133	2.130
29	0.485	0.875	0.554	1.804	1.143	2.063
30°	0.500	0.866	0.577	1.732	1.155	2.000
31	0.515	0.857	0.601	1.664	1.167	1.942
32	0.530	0.848	0.625	1.600	1.179	1.887
33	0.545	0.839	0.649	1.540	1.192	1.836
34	0.559	0.829	0.675	1.483	1.206	1.788
35°	0.574	0.819	0.700	1.428	1.221	1.743
36	0.588	0.809	0.727	1.376	1.236	1.701
37	0.602	0.799	0.754	1.327	1.252	1.662
38	0.616	0.788	0.781	1.280	1.269	1.624
39	0.629	0.777	0.810	1.235	1.287	1.589
40°	0.643	0.766	0.839	1.192	1.305	1.556
41	0.656	0.755	0.869	1.150	1.325	1.524
42	0.669	0.743	0.900	1.111	1.346	1.494
43	0.682	0.731	0.933	1.072	1.367	1.466
44	0.695	0.719	0.966	1.036	1.390	1.440
45	0.707	0.707	1.000	1.000	1.414	1.414
46	0.719	0.695	1.036	0.966	1.440	1.390
47	0.731	0.682	1.072	0.933	1.466	1.367
48	0.743	0.669	1.111	0.900	1.494	1.346
49	0.755	0.656	1.150	0.869	1.524	1.325
50	0.766	0.643	1.192	0.839	1.556	1.305
51	0.777	0.629	1.235	0.810	1.589	1.287
52	0.788	0.616	1.280	0.781	1.624	1.269
53	0.799	0.602	1.357	0.754	1.662	1.252
54	0.809	0.588	1.376	0.727	1.701	1.236
55	0.819	0.574	1.428	0.700	1.743	1.221
56	0.829	0.559	1.483	0.675	1.788	1.206
57	0.839	0.545	1.540	0.649	1.836	1.192
58	0.848	0.530	1.600	0.625	1.887	1.179
59	0.857	0.515	1.664	0.601	1.942	1.167
60	0.866	0.500	1.732	0.577	2.000	1.155
61	0.875	0.485	1.804	0.554	2.063	1.143
62	0.883	0.469	1.881	0.532	2.130	1.133
63	0.891	0.454	1.963	0.510	2.203	1.122
64	0.899	0.438	2.050	0.488	2.281	1.113
65	0.906	0.423	2.145	0.466	2.366	1.103
66	0.914	0.407	2.246	0.445	2.459	1.095
67	0.921	0.391	2.356	0.424	2.559	1.086
68	0.927	0.375	2.475	0.404	2.669	1.079
69	0.934	0.358	2.605	0.384	2.790	1.071
70	0.940	0.342	2.747	0.364	2.924	1.064
71	0.946	0.326	2.904	0.344	3.072	1.058
72	0.951	0.309	3.078	0.325	3.236	1.051
73	0.956	0.292	3.271	0.306	3.420	1.046
74	0.961	0.276	3.487	0.287	3.628	1.040
75	0.966	0.259	3.732	0.268	3.864	1.035
76	0.970	0.242	4.011	0.249	4.134	1.031
77	0.974	0.225	4.331	0.231	4.445	1.026
78	0.978	0.208	4.705	0.213	4.810	1.022
79	0.982	0.191	5.145	0.194	5.241	1.019

TABLE 18 (*Continued*).

Angle	Sin	Cos	Tan	Cot	Sec	Csc
80	0.985	0.174	5.671	0.176	5.759	1.015
81	0.988	0.156	6.314	0.158	6.392	1.012
82	0.990	0.139	7.115	0.141	7.185	1.010
83	0.993	0.122	8.144	0.123	8.206	1.008
84	0.995	0.105	9.514	0.105	9.567	1.006
85°00′	0.9962	0.0872	11.420	0.0875	11.474	1.0038
15	0.9964	0.0828	12.035	0.0831	12.076	1.0034
30	0.9969	0.0785	12.706	0.0787	12.475	1.0031
45	0.9972	0.0741	13.457	0.0743	13.494	1.0028
86 00	0.9976	0.0698	14.301	0.0699	14.356	1.0024
15	0.9979	0.0654	15.257	0.0655	15.290	1.0021
30	0.9981	0.0610	16.350	0.0612	16.380	1.0019
45	0.9984	0.0567	17.611	0.0568	17.638	1.0016
87 00	0.9986	0.0523	19.081	0.0524	19.107	1.0014
15	0.9989	0.0480	20.819	0.0480	20.843	1.0011
30	0.9990	0.0436	22.904	0.0437	22.926	1.0009
45	0.9992	0.0393	25.452	0.0393	25.471	1.0008
88 00	0.9994	0.0349	28.636	0.0349	28.654	1.0006
15	0.9995	0.0305	32.730	0.0306	32.746	1.0005
30	0.9997	0.0262	38.188	0.0262	38.202	1.0003
45	0.9998	0.0218	45.829	0.0218	45.480	1.0002
89 00	0.9999	0.0174	57.290	0.0175	57.299	1.0001
15	0.9999	0.0131	76.390	0.0131	76.397	1.0001
30	1.0000	0.0087	114.59	0.0087	114.59	1.0000
45	1.0000	0.0004	229.18	0.0044	229.18	1.0000
90 00	1.0000	0.0000	∞	0.0000	∞	1.0000

Index

Italic numbers refer to pages with illustrations.

Set in Intertype Fotosetter Times Roman
Format by James T. Parker
Manufactured by The Haddon Craftsmen, Inc,
Published by HARPER & BROTHERS, *New York*